Wayne Tomasi

Advanced Electronic Communications Systems

Custom Sixth Edition

Taken from:
Advanced Electronic Communications Systems,
Sixth Edition by Wayne Tomasi

000200010271266836

RG

ISBN 10: 1-256-41394-1
ISBN 13: 978-1-256-41394-3

In loving memory of my father, Harry Tomasi

Preface

The purpose of this book is to extend and update the knowledge of the reader to the basic concepts of modern digital and data communications systems and networks, optical fiber communications systems, terrestrial and satellite radio systems, and both wireline and wireless telephone communications systems. The book was written so that a reader with knowledge in basic electronics and electronic communications principles and an understanding of mathematics through the fundamental concepts of calculus will be able to grasp the topics presented. Numerous examples emphasize the most important concepts. Questions and problems are included at the end of each chapter, and answers to selected problems are provided at the end of the book.

This edition of *Advanced Electronic Communications Systems* provides a modern, comprehensive coverage of the field of electronic communications. Although nothing has been omitted from the previous edition, there are significant additions, such as three new chapters on telephone circuits and systems, two new chapters on cellular and PCS telephone systems, and three new chapters on the fundamental concepts of data communications and networking. In addition, numerous figures have been added and many figures have been updated.

Chapter 1 introduces the reader to the basic concept of optical fiber transmission lines and lightwave propagation. Chapter 2 describes the fundamental concepts of digital modulation, including comprehensive descriptions of amplitude-shift keying (ASK), frequency-shift keying (FSK), phase-shift keying (PSK), quadrature amplitude modulation (QAM), and differential phase-shift keying (DPSK). Chapter 2 also introduces the student to trellis code modulation and gives a comprehensive description of probability of error, bit error rate, and error performance.

Chapters 3 through 5 cover the fundamental concepts of data communications circuits and describe basic networking fundamentals, such as topologies, error control, protocols, hardware, assessing techniques, and network architectures.

Chapters 6 and 7 describe the basic concepts of digital transmission and multiplexing. Chapter 6 describes pulse code modulation, while Chapter 7 describes time-division multiplexing of PCM-encoded signals and explains the North American Digital Hierarchy and the North American FDM hierarchy. Wavelength division multiplexing of light waves is also introduced in Chapter 7.

Chapters 8 through 10 give a comprehensive description of telephone instruments, signals, and wireline systems used in the public telephone network. Chapters 11 and 12 describe the basic concepts of wireless telephone systems, including cellular and PCS.

Chapters 13 through 15 describe the fundamental concepts of terrestrial and satellite microwave-radio communications. Chapter 13 describes analog terrestrial microwave systems; Chapters 14 and 15 describe digital satellite systems.

ACKNOWLEDGMENTS

I would like to thank the following reviewers for their valuable feedback: Jeffrey L. Rankinen, Pennsylvania College of Technology; Walter Hedges, Fox Valley Technical College; Samuel A. Guccione, Eastern Illinois University; Costas Vassiliadis, Ohio University; and Siben Dasgupta, Wentworth Institute of Technology. I would also like to thank my project editor, Kelli Jauron, for her sincere efforts in producing the past two editions of this book and for being my friend for the past four years. I would also like to thank my assistant editor, Mayda Bosco, for all her efforts. The contributions from these people helped make this book possible.

Wayne Tomasi

Brief Contents

Contents

Appendix is original material. All other content is taken from *Advanced Electronic Communications Systems*, Sixth Edition, by Wayne Tomasi.

C H A P T E R   1

Optical Fiber Transmission Media

OBJECTIVES

- Define *optical communications*
- Present an overview of the history of optical fibers and optical fiber communications
- Compare the advantages and disadvantages of optical fibers over metallic cables
- Define *electromagnetic frequency* and *wavelength spectrum*
- Describe several types of optical fiber construction
- Explain the physics of light and the following terms: velocity of propagation, refraction, refractive index, critical angle, acceptance angle, acceptance cone, and numerical aperture
- Describe how light waves propagate through an optical fiber cable
- Define *modes of propagation* and *index profile*
- Describe the three types of optical fiber configurations: single-mode step index, multimode step index, and multimode graded index
- Describe the various losses incurred in optical fiber cables
- Define *light source* and *optical power*
- Describe the following light sources: light-emitting diodes and injection diodes
- Describe the following light detectors: PIN diodes and avalanche photodiodes
- Describe the operation of a laser
- Explain how to calculate a link budget for an optical fiber system

Optical fiber cables are the newest and probably the most promising type of guided transmission medium for virtually all forms of digital and data communications applications, including local, metropolitan, and wide area networks. With optical fibers, electromagnetic waves are guided through a media composed of a transparent material without using electrical current flow. With optical fibers, electromagnetic light waves propagate through the media in much the same way that radio signals propagate through Earth's atmosphere.

In essence, an *optical communications system* is one that uses light as the carrier of information. Propagating light waves through Earth's atmosphere is difficult and often impractical. Consequently, optical fiber communications systems use glass or plastic fiber cables to "*contain*" the light waves and guide them in a manner similar to the way electromagnetic waves are guided through a metallic transmission medium.

The *information-carrying capacity* of any electronic communications system is directly proportional to bandwidth. Optical fiber cables have, for all practical purposes, an infinite bandwidth. Therefore, they have the capacity to carry much more information than their metallic counterparts or, for that matter, even the most sophisticated wireless communications systems.

For comparison purposes, it is common to express the bandwidth of an analog communications system as a percentage of its carrier frequency. This is sometimes called the *bandwidth utilization ratio*. For instance, a VHF radio communications system operating at a carrier frequency of 100 MHz with 10-MHz bandwidth has a bandwidth utilization ratio of 10%. A microwave radio system operating at a carrier frequency of 10 GHz with a 10% bandwidth utilization ratio would have 1 GHz of bandwidth available. Obviously, the higher the carrier frequency, the more bandwidth available, and the greater the information-carrying capacity. Light frequencies used in optical fiber communications systems are between 1×10^{14} Hz and 4×10^{14} Hz (100,000 GHz to 400,000 GHz). A bandwidth utilization ratio of 10% would be a bandwidth between 10,000 GHz and 40,000 GHz.

1-2   HISTORY OF OPTICAL FIBER COMMUNICATIONS

In 1880, Alexander Graham Bell experimented with an apparatus he called a *photophone.* The photophone was a device constructed from mirrors and selenium detectors that transmitted sound waves over a beam of light. The photophone was awkward and unreliable and had no real practical application. Actually, visual light was a primary means of communicating long before electronic communications came about. Smoke signals and mirrors were used ages ago to convey short, simple messages. Bell's contraption, however, was the first attempt at using a beam of light for carrying information.

Transmission of light waves for any useful distance through Earth's atmosphere is impractical because water vapor, oxygen, and particulates in the air absorb and attenuate the signals at light frequencies. Consequently, the only practical type of optical communications system is one that uses a fiber guide. In 1930, J. L. Baird, an English scientist, and C. W. Hansell, a scientist from the United States, were granted patents for scanning and transmitting television images through uncoated fiber cables. A few years later, a German scientist named H. Lamm successfully transmitted images through a single glass fiber. At that time, most people considered fiber optics more of a toy or a laboratory stunt and, consequently, it was not until the early 1950s that any substantial breakthrough was made in the field of fiber optics.

In 1951, A. C. S. van Heel of Holland and H. H. Hopkins and N. S. Kapany of England experimented with light transmission through *bundles* of fibers. Their studies led to the development of the *flexible fiberscope,* which is used extensively in the medical field. It was Kapany who coined the term "fiber optics" in 1956.

In 1958, Charles H. Townes, an American, and Arthur L. Schawlow, a Canadian, wrote a paper describing how it was possible to use stimulated emission for amplifying light waves (laser) as well as microwaves (maser). Two years later, Theodore H. Maiman, a scientist with Hughes Aircraft Company, built the first optical maser.

The *laser* (*l*ight *a*mplification by *s*timulated *e*mission of *r*adiation) was invented in 1960. The laser's relatively high output power, high frequency of operation, and capability of carrying an extremely wide bandwidth signal make it ideally suited for high-capacity communications systems. The invention of the laser greatly accelerated research efforts in fiber-optic communications, although it was not until 1967 that K. C. Kao and G. A. Bockham of the Standard Telecommunications Laboratory in England proposed a new communications medium using *cladded* fiber cables.

The fiber cables available in the 1960s were extremely *lossy* (more than 1000 dB/km), which limited optical transmissions to short distances. In 1970, Kapron, Keck, and Maurer of Corning Glass Works in Corning, New York, developed an optical fiber with losses less than 2 dB/km. That was the "big" breakthrough needed to permit practical fiber optics communications systems. Since 1970, fiber optics technology has grown exponentially. Recently, Bell Laboratories successfully transmitted 1 billion bps through a fiber cable for 600 miles without a regenerator.

In the late 1970s and early 1980s, the refinement of optical cables and the development of high-quality, affordable light sources and detectors opened the door to the development of high-quality, high-capacity, efficient, and affordable optical fiber communications systems. By the late 1980s, losses in optical fibers were reduced to as low as 0.16 dB/km, and in 1988 NEC Corporation set a new long-haul transmission record by transmitting 10 gigabytes per second over 80.1 kilometers of optical fiber. Also in 1988, the American National Standards Institute (ANSI) published the *Synchronous Optical Network* (*SONET*). By the mid-1990s, optical voice and data networks were commonplace throughout the United States and much of the world.

1-3 OPTICAL FIBERS VERSUS METALLIC CABLE FACILITIES

Communications through glass or plastic fibers has several advantages over conventional metallic transmission media for both telecommunication and computer networking applications.

1-3-1 Advantages of Optical Fiber Cables

The advantages of using optical fibers include the following:

1. *Wider bandwidth and greater information capacity*. Optical fibers have greater information capacity than metallic cables because of the inherently wider bandwidths available with optical frequencies. Optical fibers are available with bandwidths up to several thousand gigahertz. The *primary electrical constants* (resistance, inductance, and capacitance) in metallic cables cause them to act like low-pass filters, which limit their transmission frequencies, bandwidth, bit rate, and information-carrying capacity. Modern optical fiber communications systems are capable of transmitting several gigabits per second over hundreds of miles, allowing literally millions of individual voice and data channels to be combined and propagated over one optical fiber cable.

2. *Immunity to crosstalk*. Optical fiber cables are immune to crosstalk because glass and plastic fibers are nonconductors of electrical current. Therefore, fiber cables are not surrounded by a changing magnetic field, which is the primary cause of crosstalk between metallic conductors located physically close to each other.

3. *Immunity to static interference*. Because optical fiber cables are nonconductors of electrical current, they are immune to static noise due to electromagnetic interference (EMI) caused by lightning, electric motors, relays, fluorescent lights, and other electrical noise sources (most of which are man-made). For the same reason, fiber cables do not radiate electromagnetic energy.

4. *Environmental immunity.* Optical fiber cables are more resistant to environmental extremes (including weather variations) than metallic cables. Optical cables also operate over a wider temperature range and are less affected by corrosive liquids and gases.

5. *Safety and convenience.* Optical fiber cables are safer and easier to install and maintain than metallic cables. Because glass and plastic fibers are nonconductors, there are no electrical currents or voltages associated with them. Optical fibers can be used around volatile liquids and gasses without worrying about their causing explosions or fires. Optical fibers are also smaller and much more lightweight and compact than metallic cables. Consequently, they are more flexible, easier to work with, require less storage space, cheaper to transport, and easier to install and maintain.

6. *Lower transmission loss.* Optical fibers have considerably less signal loss than their metallic counterparts. Optical fibers are currently being manufactured with as little as a few-tenths-of-a-decibel loss per kilometer. Consequently, optical regenerators and amplifiers can be spaced considerably farther apart than with metallic transmission lines.

7. *Security.* Optical fiber cables are more secure than metallic cables. It is virtually impossible to tap into a fiber cable without the user's knowledge, and optical cables cannot be detected with metal detectors unless they are reinforced with steel for strength.

8. *Durability and reliability.* Optical fiber cables last longer and are more reliable than metallic facilities because fiber cables have a higher tolerance to changes in environmental conditions and are immune to corrosive materials.

9. *Economics.* The cost of optical fiber cables is approximately the same as metallic cables. Fiber cables have less loss and require fewer repeaters, which equates to lower installation and overall system costs and improved reliability.

1-3-2 Disadvantages of Optical Fiber Cables

Although the advantages of optical fiber cables far exceed the disadvantages, it is important to know the limitations of the fiber. The disadvantages of optical fibers include the following:

1. *Interfacing costs.* Optical fiber cable systems are virtually useless by themselves. To be practical and useful, they must be connected to standard electronic facilities, which often require expensive interfaces.

2. *Strength.* Optical fibers by themselves have a significantly lower tensile strength than coaxial cable. This can be improved by coating the fiber with standard *Kevlar* and a protective jacket of PVC. In addition, glass fiber is much more fragile than copper wire, making fiber less attractive where hardware portability is required.

3. *Remote electrical power.* Occasionally, it is necessary to provide electrical power to remote interface or regenerating equipment. This cannot be accomplished with the optical cable, so additional metallic cables must be included in the cable assembly.

4. *Optical fiber cables are more susceptible to losses introduced by bending the cable.* Electromagnetic waves propagate through an optical cable by either refraction or reflection. Therefore, bending the cable causes irregularities in the cable dimensions, resulting in a loss of signal power. Optical fibers are also more prone to manufacturing defects, as even the most minor defect can cause excessive loss of signal power.

5. *Specialized tools, equipment, and training.* Optical fiber cables require special tools to splice and repair cables and special test equipment to make routine measurements. Not only is repairing fiber cables difficult and expensive, but technicians working on optical cables also require special skills and training. In addition, sometimes it is difficult to locate faults in optical cables because there is no electrical continuity.

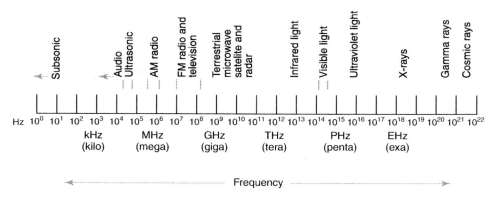

FIGURE 1-1 Electromagnetic frequency spectrum

1-4 ELECTROMAGNETIC SPECTRUM

The total electromagnetic frequency spectrum is shown in Figure 1-1. From the figure, it can be seen that the frequency spectrum extends from the subsonic frequencies (a few hertz) to cosmic rays (10^{22} Hz). The light frequency spectrum can be divided into three general bands:

1. *Infrared.* The band of light frequencies that is too high to be seen by the human eye with wavelengths ranging between 770 nm and 10^6 nm. Optical fiber systems generally operate in the infrared band.
2. *Visible.* The band of light frequencies to which the human eye will respond with wavelengths ranging between 390 nm and 770 nm. This band is visible to the human eye.
3. *Ultraviolet.* The band of light frequencies that are too low to be seen by the human eye with wavelengths ranging between 10 nm and 390 nm.

When dealing with ultra-high-frequency electromagnetic waves, such as light, it is common to use units of wavelength rather than frequency. Wavelength is the length that one cycle of an electromagnetic wave occupies in space. The length of a wavelength depends on the frequency of the wave and the velocity of light. Mathematically, wavelength is

$$\lambda = \frac{c}{f} \tag{1-1}$$

where λ = wavelength (meters/cycle)
   c = velocity of light (300,000,000 meters per second)
   f = frequency (hertz)

With light frequencies, wavelength is often stated in microns, where 1 micron = 10^{-6} meter (1 μm), or in nanometers (nm), where 1 nm = 10^{-9} meter. However, when describing the optical spectrum, the unit angstrom is sometimes used to express wavelength, where 1 angstrom = 10^{-10} meter, or 0.0001 micron. Figure 1-2 shows the total electromagnetic wavelength spectrum.

1-5 BLOCK DIAGRAM OF AN OPTICAL FIBER COMMUNICATIONS SYSTEM

Figure 1-3 shows a simplified block diagram of a simplex optical fiber communications link. The three primary building blocks are the transmitter, the receiver, and the optical fiber cable. The transmitter is comprised of a voltage-to-current converter, a light source, and a source-to-fiber interface (light coupler). The fiber guide is the transmission medium, which

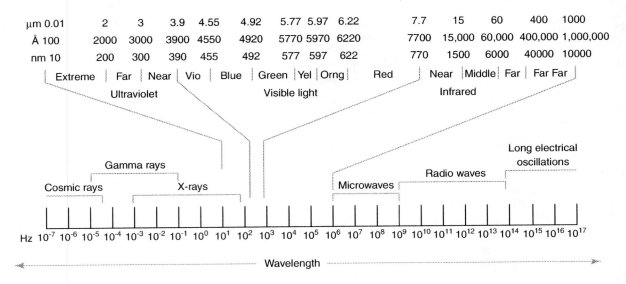

FIGURE 1-2   Electromagnetic wavelength spectrum

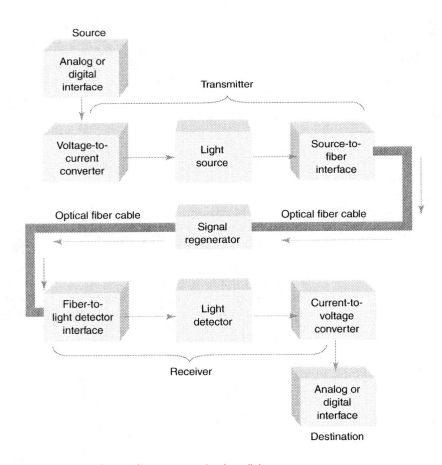

FIGURE 1-3   Optical fiber communications link

is either an ultrapure glass or a plastic cable. It may be necessary to add one or more regenerators to the transmission medium, depending on the distance between the transmitter and receiver. Functionally, the regenerator performs light amplification. However, in reality the signal is not actually amplified; it is reconstructed. The receiver includes a fiber-to-interface (light coupler), a photo detector, and a current-to-voltage converter.

In the transmitter, the light source can be modulated by a digital or an analog signal. The voltage-to-current converter serves as an electrical interface between the input circuitry and the light source. The light source is either an *infrared light-emitting diode* (LED) or an *injection laser diode* (ILD). The amount of light emitted by either an LED or ILD is proportional to the amount of drive current. Thus, the voltage-to-current converter converts an input signal voltage to a current that is used to drive the light source. The light outputted by the light source is directly proportional to the magnitude of the input voltage. In essence, the light intensity is modulated by the input signal.

The source-to-fiber coupler (such as an optical lens) is a mechanical interface. Its function is to couple light emitted by the light source into the optical fiber cable. The optical fiber consists of a glass or plastic fiber core surrounded by a cladding and then encapsulated in a protective jacket. The fiber-to-light detector-coupling device is also a mechanical coupler. Its function is to couple as much light as possible from the fiber cable into the light detector.

The light detector is generally a PIN (*p*-type-*intrinsic*-*n*-type) diode, an APD (avalanche photodiode), or a *phototransistor*. All three of these devices convert light energy to current. Consequently, a current-to-voltage converter is required to produce an output voltage proportional to the original source information. The current-to-voltage converter transforms changes in detector current to changes in voltage.

The analog or digital interfaces are electrical interfaces that match impedances and signal levels between the information source and destination to the input and output circuitry of the optical system.

1-6 OPTICAL FIBER TYPES

1-6-1 Optical Fiber Construction

The actual fiber portion of an optical cable is generally considered to include both the fiber *core* and its *cladding* (see Figure 1-4). A special lacquer, silicone, or acrylate coating is generally applied to the outside of the cladding to seal and preserve the fiber's strength, help-

Polyurethane outer jacket

Strength members

Buffer jacket

Protective coating

Fiber core and cladding

FIGURE 1-4 Optical fiber cable construction

ing maintain the cables attenuation characteristics. The coating also helps protect the fiber from moisture, which reduces the possibility of the occurrence of a detrimental phenomenon called *stress corrosion* (sometimes called *static fatigue*) caused by high humidity. Moisture causes silicon dioxide crystals to interact, causing bonds to break down and spontaneous fractures to form over a prolonged period of time. The protective coating is surrounded by a *buffer jacket,* which provides the cable additional protection against abrasion and shock. Materials commonly used for the buffer jacket include steel, fiberglass, plastic, flame-retardant polyvinyl chloride (FR-PVC), Kevlar yarn, and paper. The buffer jacket is encapsulated in a *strength member,* which increases the tensile strength of the overall cable assembly. Finally, the entire cable assembly is contained in an outer polyurethane jacket.

There are three essential types of optical fibers commonly used today. All three varieties are constructed of either glass, plastic, or a combination of glass and plastic:

Plastic core and cladding
Glass core with plastic cladding (called PCS fiber [plastic-clad silica])
Glass core and glass cladding (called SCS [silica-clad silica])

Plastic fibers are more flexible and, consequently, more rugged than glass. Therefore, plastic cables are easier to install, can better withstand stress, are less expensive, and weigh approximately 60% less than glass. However, plastic fibers have higher attenuation characteristics and do not propagate light as efficiently as glass. Therefore, plastic fibers are limited to relatively short cable runs, such as within a single building.

Fibers with glass cores have less attenuation than plastic fibers, with PCS being slightly better than SCS. PCS fibers are also less affected by radiation and, therefore, are more immune to external interference. SCS fibers have the best propagation characteristics and are easier to terminate than PCS fibers. Unfortunately, SCS fibers are the least rugged, and they are more susceptible to increases in attenuation when exposed to radiation.

The selection of a fiber for a given application is a function of the specific system requirements. There are always trade-offs based on the economics and logistics of a particular application.

1-6-1-1 Cable configurations.   There are many different cable designs available today. Figure 1-5 shows examples of several optical fiber cable configurations. With loose tube construction (Figure 1-5a), each fiber is contained in a protective tube. Inside the tube, a polyurethane compound encapsules the fiber and prevents the intrusion of water. A phenomenon called *stress corrosion* or *static fatigue* can result if the glass fiber is exposed to long periods of high humidity. Silicon dioxide crystals interact with the moisture and cause bonds to break down, causing spontaneous fractures to form over a prolonged period. Some fiber cables have more than one protective coating to ensure that the fiber's characteristics do not alter if the fiber is exposed to extreme temperature changes. Surrounding the fiber's cladding is usually a coating of either lacquer, silicon, or acrylate that is typically applied to seal and preserve the fiber's strength and attenuation characteristics.

Figure 1-5b shows the construction of a constrained optical fiber cable. Surrounding the fiber are a primary and a secondary buffer comprised of Kevlar yarn, which increases the tensile strength of the cable and provides protection from external mechanical influences that could cause fiber breakage or excessive optical attenuation. Again, an outer protective tube is filled with polyurethane, which prevents moisture from coming into contact with the fiber core.

Figure 1-5c shows a *multiple-strand* cable configuration, which includes a steel central member and a layer of Mylar tape wrap to increase the cable's tensile strength. Figure 1-5d shows a ribbon configuration for a telephone cable, and Figure 1-5e shows both end and side views of a PCS cable.

FIGURE 1-5 Fiber optic cable configurations: (a) loose tube construction; (b) constrained fiber; (c) multiple strands; (d) telephone cable; (e) plastic-silica cable

As mentioned, one disadvantage of optical fiber cables is their lack of tensile (pulling) strength, which can be as low as a pound. For this reason, the fiber must be reinforced with strengthening material so that it can withstand mechanical stresses it will typically undergo when being pulled and jerked through underground and overhead ducts and hung on poles. Materials commonly used to strengthen and protect fibers from abrasion and environmental stress are steel, fiberglass, plastic, FR-PVC (flame-retardant polyvinyl chloride), Kevlar yarn, and paper. The type of cable construction used depends on the performance requirements of the system and both economic and environmental constraints.

1-7 LIGHT PROPAGATION

1-7-1 The Physics of Light

Although the performance of optical fibers can be analyzed completely by application of Maxwell's equations, this is necessarily complex. For most practical applications, geometric wave tracing may be used instead.

In 1860, James Clerk Maxwell theorized that electromagnetic radiation contained a series of oscillating waves comprised of an electric and a magnetic field in quadrature (at 90° angles). However, in 1905, Albert Einstein and Max Planck showed that when light is emitted or absorbed, it behaves like an electromagnetic wave and also like a particle, called a *photon,* which possesses energy proportional to its frequency. This theory is known as *Planck's law.* Planck's law describes the photoelectric effect, which states, "When visible light or high-frequency electromagnetic radiation illuminates a metallic surface, electrons are emitted." The emitted electrons produce an electric current. Planck's law is expressed mathematically as

$$E_p = hf \tag{1-2}$$

where E_p = energy of the photon (joules)
       h = Planck's constant = $6.625 \times 10^{-34} J - s$
       f = frequency of light (photon) emitted (hertz)

Photon energy may also be expressed in terms of wavelength. Substituting Equation 1-1 into Equation 1-2 yields

$$E_p = hf \tag{1-3a}$$

or

$$E_p = \frac{hc}{\lambda} \tag{1-3b}$$

An atom has several energy levels or states, the lowest of which is the ground state. Any energy level above the ground state is called an *excited state.* If an atom in one energy level decays to a lower energy level, the loss of energy (in electron volts) is emitted as a photon of light. The energy of the photon is equal to the difference between the energy of the two energy levels. The process of decaying from one energy level to another energy level is called *spontaneous decay* or *spontaneous emission.*

Atoms can be irradiated by a light source whose energy is equal to the difference between ground level and an energy level. This can cause an electron to change from one energy level to another by absorbing light energy. The process of moving from one energy level to another is called *absorption.* When making the transition from one energy level to another, the atom absorbs a packet of energy (a photon). This process is similar to that of emission.

The energy absorbed or emitted (photon) is equal to the difference between the two energy levels. Mathematically,

$$E_p = E_2 - E_1 \tag{1-4}$$

where E_p is the energy of the photon (joules).

1-7-2 Optical Power

Light intensity is a rather complex concept that can be expressed in either *photometric* or *radiometric* terms. *Photometry* is the science of measuring only light waves that are visible to the human eye. Radiometry, on the other hand, measures light throughout the entire electromagnetic spectrum. In photometric terms, light intensity is generally described in terms of luminous *flux density* and measured in lumens per unit area. Radiometric terms, however, are often more useful to engineers and technologists. In radiometric terms, *optical power* measures the rate at which electromagnetic waves transfer light energy. In simple terms, optical power is described as the flow of light energy past a given point in a specified time. Optical power is expressed mathematically as

$$P = \frac{d(\text{energy})}{d(\text{time})} \tag{1-5a}$$

or
$$= \frac{dQ}{dt} \qquad (1\text{-}5b)$$

where P = optical power (watts)

  dQ = instantaneous charge (joules)

  dt = instantaneous change in time (seconds)

Optical power is sometimes called *radiant flux* (ϕ), which is equivalent to joules per second and is the same power that is measured electrically or thermally in watts. Radiometric terms are generally used with light sources with output powers ranging from tens of microwatts to more than 100 milliwatts. Optical power is generally stated in decibels relative to a defined power level, such as 1 mW (dBm) or 1 μW (dBμ). Mathematically stated,

$$dBm = 10 \log\left[\frac{P\,(\text{watts})}{0.001\,(\text{watts})}\right] \qquad (1\text{-}6)$$

and

$$db\mu = 10 \log\left[\frac{P\,(\text{watts})}{0.000001\,(\text{watts})}\right] \qquad (1\text{-}7)$$

Example 1-1

Determine the optical power in dBm and dBμ for power levels of

a. 10 mW

b. 20 μW

Solution

a. Substituting into Equations 1-6 and 1-7 gives

$$dBm = 10 \log\frac{10\ mW}{1\ mW} = 10\ dBm$$

$$dB\mu = 10 \log\frac{10\ mW}{1\ \mu W} = 40\ dB\mu$$

b. Substituting into Equations 1-6 and 1-7 gives

$$dBm = 10 \log\frac{20\ \mu W}{1\ mW} = -17\ dBm$$

$$dB\mu = 10 \log\frac{20\ \mu W}{1 \mu W} = 13\ dB\mu$$

1-7-3 Velocity of Propagation

In free space (a vacuum), electromagnetic energy, such as light waves, travels at approximately 300,000,000 meters per second (186,000 mi/s). Also, in free space the velocity of propagation is the same for all light frequencies. However, it has been demonstrated that electromagnetic waves travel slower in materials more dense than free space and that all light frequencies do not propagate at the same velocity. When the velocity of an electromagnetic wave is reduced as it passes from one medium to another medium of denser material, the light ray changes direction or refracts (bends) toward the normal. When an electromagnetic wave passes from a more dense material into a less dense material, the light ray is refracted away from the normal. The *normal* is simply an imaginary line drawn perpendicular to the interface of the two materials at the point of incidence.

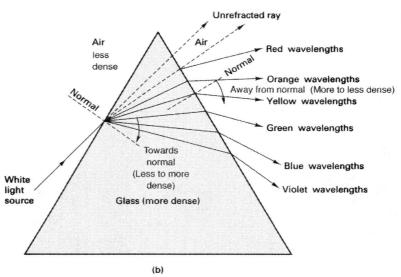

FIGURE 1-6   Refraction of light: (a) light refraction; (b) prismatic refraction

1-7-3-1 Refraction.   For light-wave frequencies, electromagnetic waves travel through Earth's atmosphere (air) at approximately the same velocity as through a vacuum (i.e., the speed of light). Figure 1-6a shows how a light ray is refracted (bent) as it passes from a less dense material into a more dense material. (Actually, the light ray is not bent; rather, it changes direction at the interface.) Figure 1-6b shows how sunlight, which contains all light frequencies (*white light*), is affected as it passes through a material that is more dense than air. Refraction occurs at both air/glass interfaces. The violet wavelengths are refracted the most, whereas the red wavelengths are refracted the least. The spectral separation of white light in this manner is called *prismatic refraction*. It is this phenomenon that causes rainbows, where water droplets in the atmosphere act as small prisms that split the white sunlight into the various wavelengths, creating a visible spectrum of color.

1-7-3-2 Refractive Index.   The amount of bending or refraction that occurs at the interface of two materials of different densities is quite predictable and depends on the *refractive indexes* of the two materials. Refractive index is simply the ratio of the velocity of propagation of a light ray in free space to the velocity of propagation of a light ray in a given material. Mathematically, refractive index is

$$n = \frac{c}{v}$$

(1-8)

where n = refractive index (unitless)
   c = speed of light in free space (3×10^8 meters per second)
   v = speed of light in a given material (meters per second)

Although the refractive index is also a function of frequency, the variation in most light wave applications is insignificant and, thus, omitted from this discussion. The indexes of refraction of several common materials are given in Table 1-1.

1-7-3-3 Snell's law.   How a light ray reacts when it meets the interface of two transmissive materials that have different indexes of refraction can be explained with *Snell's law*. A refractive index model for Snell's law is shown in Figure 1-7. The *angle of incidence* is the angle at which the propagating ray strikes the interface with respect to the normal, and the *angle of refraction* is the angle formed between the propagating ray and the normal after the ray has entered the second medium. At the interface of medium 1 and medium 2, the incident ray may be refracted toward the normal or away from it, depending on whether n_1 is greater than or less than n_2. Hence, the angle of refraction can be larger or

Table 1-1   Typical Indexes of Refraction

Material	Index of Refraction[a]
Vacuum	1.0
Air	1.0003 ($\approx$1)
Water	1.33
Ethyl alcohol	1.36
Fused quartz	1.46
Glass fiber	1.5–1.9
Diamond	2.0–2.42
Silicon	3.4
Gallium-arsenide	2.6

[a]Index of refraction is based on a wavelength of light emitted from a sodium flame (589 nm).

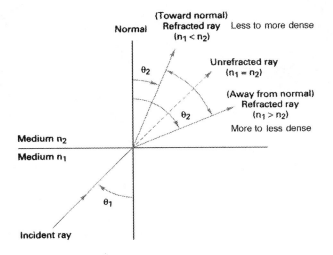

FIGURE 1-7   Refractive model for Snell's law

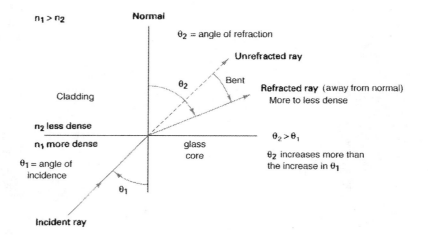

FIGURE 1-8 Light ray refracted away from the normal

smaller than the angle of incidence, depending on the refractive indexes of the two materials. Snell's law stated mathematically is

$$n_1 \sin \theta_1 = n_2 \sin \theta_2 \qquad (1\text{-}9)$$

where
n_1 = refractive index of material 1 (unitless)
n_2 = refractive index of material 2 (unitless)
θ_1 = angle of incidence (degrees)
θ_2 = angle of refraction (degrees)

Figure 1-8 shows how a light ray is refracted as it travels from a more dense (higher refractive index) material into a less dense (lower refractive index) material. It can be seen that the light ray changes direction at the interface, and the angle of refraction is greater than the angle of incidence. Consequently, when a light ray enters a less dense material, the ray bends away from the normal. The normal is simply a line drawn perpendicular to the interface at the point where the incident ray strikes the interface. Similarly, when a light ray enters a more dense material, the ray bends toward the normal.

Example 1-2

In Figure 1-8, let medium 1 be glass and medium 2 be ethyl alcohol. For an angle of incidence of 30°, determine the angle of refraction.

Solution From Table 1-1,

$$n_1 \text{ (glass)} = 1.5$$
$$n_2 \text{ (ethyl alcohol)} = 1.36$$

Rearranging Equation 1-9 and substituting for n_1, n_2, and θ_1 gives us

$$\frac{n_1}{n_2} \sin \theta_1 = \sin \theta_2$$

$$\frac{1.5}{1.36} \sin 30 = 0.5514 = \sin \theta_2$$

$$\theta_2 = \sin^{-1} 0.5514 = 33.47°$$

The result indicates that the light ray refracted (bent) or changed direction by 33.47° at the interface. Because the light was traveling from a more dense material into a less dense material, the ray bent away from the normal.

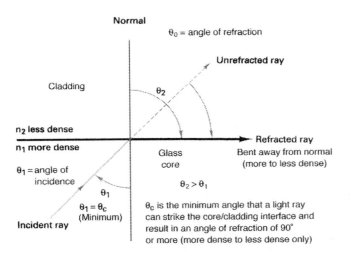

FIGURE 1-9 Critical angle refraction

1-7-3-4 Critical angle. Figure 1-9 shows a condition in which an incident ray is striking the glass/cladding interface at an angle ($_1$) such that the angle of refraction (θ_2) is 90° and the refracted ray is along the interface. This angle of incidence is called the *critical angle* (θ_c), which is defined as the minimum angle of incidence at which a light ray may strike the interface of two media and result in an angle of refraction of 90° or greater. It is important to note that the light ray must be traveling from a medium of higher refractive index to a medium with a lower refractive index (i.e., glass into cladding). If the angle of refraction is 90° or greater, the light ray is not allowed to penetrate the less dense material. Consequently, total reflection takes place at the interface, and the angle of reflection is equal to the angle of incidence. Critical angle can be represented mathematically by rearranging Equation 1-9 as

$$\sin \theta_1 = \frac{n_2}{n_1} \sin \theta_2$$

With $\theta_2 = 90°$, θ_1 becomes the critical angle (θ_c), and

$$\sin \theta_c = \frac{n_2}{n_1}(1) = \qquad \sin \theta_c = \frac{n_2}{n_1}$$

and
$$\theta_c = \sin^{-1} \frac{n_2}{n_1} \qquad\qquad (1\text{-}10)$$

where θ_c is the critical angle.

From Equation 1-10, it can be seen that the critical angle is dependent on the ratio of the refractive indexes of the core and cladding. For example a ratio $n_2/n_1 = 0.77$ produces a critical angle of 50.4°, whereas a ratio $n_2/n_1 = 0.625$ yields a critical angle of 38.7°.

Figure 1-10 shows a comparison of the angle of refraction and the angle of reflection when the angle of incidence is less than or more than the critical angle.

1-7-3-5 Acceptance angle, acceptance cone, and numerical aperture. In previous discussions, the source-to-fiber aperture was mentioned several times, and the critical and acceptance angles at the point where a light ray strikes the core/cladding interface were explained. The following discussion addresses the light-gathering ability of a fiber, which is the ability to couple light from the source into the fiber.

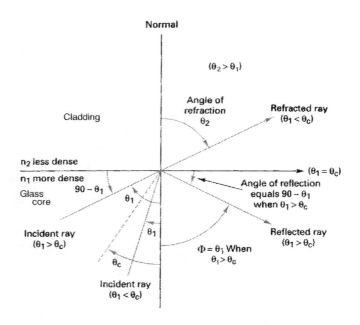

FIGURE 1-10   Angle of reflection and refraction

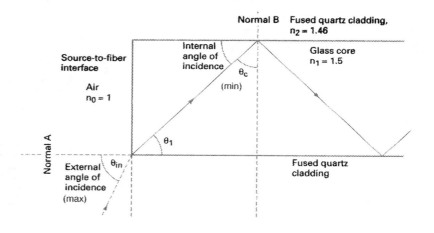

FIGURE 1-11   Ray propagation into and down an optical fiber cable

Figure 1-11 shows the source end of a fiber cable and a light ray propagating into and then down the fiber. When light rays enter the core of the fiber, they strike the air/glass interface at normal A. The refractive index of air is approximately 1, and the refractive index of the glass core is 1.5. Consequently, the light enters the cable traveling from a less dense to a more dense medium, causing the ray to refract toward the normal. This causes the light rays to change direction and propagate diagonally down the core at an angle that is less than the external angle of incidence (θ_{in}). For a ray of light to propagate down the cable, it must strike the internal core/cladding interface at an angle that is greater than the critical angle (θ_c). Using Figure 1-12 and Snell's law, it can be shown that the maximum angle that external light rays may strike the air/glass interface and still enter the core and propagate down the fiber is

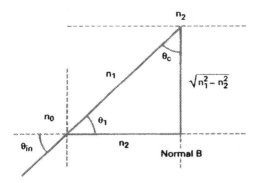

FIGURE 1-12 Geometric relationship of Equations 1-11a and b

$$\theta_{in(max)} = \sin^{-1}\frac{\sqrt{n_1^2 - n_2^2}}{n_o} \qquad (1\text{-}11\text{a})$$

where $\theta_{in(max)}$ = acceptance angle (degrees)
        n_o = refractive index of air (1)
        n_1 = refractive index of glass fiber core (1.5)
        n_2 = refractive index of quartz fiber cladding (1.46)

Since the refractive index of air is 1, Equation 1-11a reduces to

$$\theta_{in(max)} = \sin^{-1}\sqrt{n_1^2 - n_2^2} \qquad (1\text{-}11\text{b})$$

$\theta_{in(max)}$ is called the *acceptance angle* or *acceptance cone half-angle*. $\theta_{in(max)}$ defines the maximum angle in which external light rays may strike the air/glass interface and still propagate down the fiber. Rotating the acceptance angle around the fiber core axis describes the acceptance cone of the fiber input. Acceptance cone is shown in Figure 1-13a, and the relationship between acceptance angle and critical angle is shown in Figure 1-13b. Note that the critical angle is defined as a minimum value and that the acceptance angle is defined as a maximum value. Light rays striking the air/glass interface at an angle greater than the acceptance angle will enter the cladding and, therefore, will not propagate down the cable.

Numerical aperture (NA) is closely related to acceptance angle and is the figure of merit commonly used to measure the magnitude of the acceptance angle. In essence, numerical aperture is used to describe the light-gathering or light-collecting ability of an optical fiber (i.e., the ability to couple light into the cable from an external source). The larger the magnitude of the numerical aperture, the greater the amount of external light the fiber will accept. The numerical aperture for light entering the glass fiber from an air medium is described mathematically as

$$NA = \sin \theta_{in} \qquad (1\text{-}12\text{a})$$

and

$$NA = \sqrt{n_1^2 - n_2^2} \qquad (1\text{-}12\text{b})$$

Therefore

$$\theta_{in} = \sin^{-1} NA \qquad (1\text{-}12\text{c})$$

where θ_{in} = acceptance angle (degrees)
        NA = numerical aperture (unitless)
        n_1 = refractive index of glass fiber core (unitless)
        n_2 = refractive index of quartz fiber cladding (unitless)

(a)

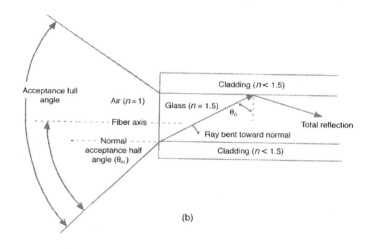

(b)

FIGURE 1-13 (a) Acceptance angle; (b) acceptance cone

A larger-diameter core does not necessarily produce a larger numerical aperture, although in practice larger-core fibers tend to have larger numerical apertures. Numerical aperture can be calculated using Equations 1-12a or b, but in practice it is generally measured by looking at the output of a fiber because the light-guiding properties of a fiber cable are symmetrical. Therefore, light leaves a cable and spreads out over an angle equal to the acceptance angle.

1-8 OPTICAL FIBER CONFIGURATIONS

Light can be propagated down an optical fiber cable using either reflection or refraction. How the light propagates depends on the *mode of propagation* and the *index profile* of the fiber.

1-8-1 Mode of Propagation

In fiber optics terminology, the word *mode* simply means path. If there is only one path for light rays to take down a cable, it is called *single mode.* If there is more than one path, it is called *multimode.* Figure 1-14 shows single and multimode propagation of light rays down an optical fiber. As shown in Figure 1-14a, with single-mode propagation, there is only one

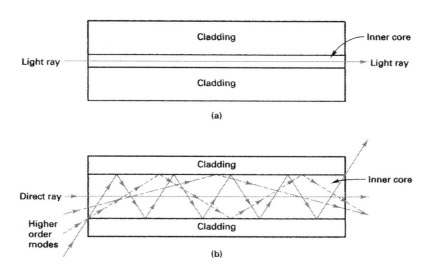

FIGURE 1-14   Modes of propagation: (a) single mode; (b) multimode

path for light rays to take, which is directly down the center of the cable. However, as Figure 1-14b shows, with multimode propagation there are many higher-order modes possible, and light rays propagate down the cable in a zigzag fashion following several paths.

The number of paths (modes) possible for a multimode fiber cable depends on the frequency (wavelength) of the light signal, the refractive indexes of the core and cladding, and the core diameter. Mathematically, the number of modes possible for a given cable can be approximated by the following formula:

$$N \approx \left(\frac{\pi d}{\lambda} \sqrt{n_1^2 - n_2^2} \right)^2 \tag{1-13}$$

where N = number of propagating modes
         d = core diameter (meters)
         λ = wavelength (meters)
         n_1 = refractive index of core
         n_2 = refractive index of cladding

A multimode step-index fiber with a core diameter of 50 μm, a core refractive index of 1.6, a cladding refractive index of 1.584, and a wavelength of 1300 nm has approximately 372 possible modes.

1-8-2   Index Profile

The index profile of an optical fiber is a graphical representation of the magnitude of the refractive index across the fiber. The refractive index is plotted on the horizontal axis, and the radial distance from the core axis is plotted on the vertical axis. Figure 1-15 shows the core index profiles for the three types of optical fiber cables.

There are two basic types of index profiles: step and graded. A *step-index* fiber has a central core with a uniform refractive index (i.e., constant density throughout). An outside cladding that also has a uniform refractive index surrounds the core; however, the refractive index of the cladding is less than that of the central core. From Figures 1-15a and b, it can be seen that in step-index fibers, there is an abrupt change in the refractive index at the core/cladding interface. This is true for both single and multimode step-index fibers.

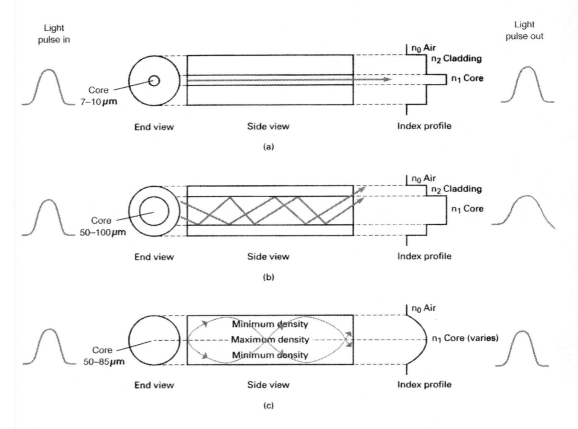

FIGURE 1-15 Core index profiles: (a) single-mode step index; (b) multimode step index; (c) multimode graded index

In the *graded-index* fiber, shown in Figure 1-15c, it can be see that there is no cladding, and the refractive index of the core is nonuniform; it is highest in the center of the core and decreases gradually with distance toward the outer edge. The index profile shows a core density that is maximum in the center and decreases symmetrically with distance from the center.

1-9 OPTICAL FIBER CLASSIFICATIONS

Propagation modes can be categorized as either multimode or single mode, and then multimode can be further subdivided into step index or graded index. Although there are a wide variety of combinations of modes and indexes, there are only three practical types of optical fiber configurations: *single-mode step-index, multimode step index,* and *multimode graded index.*

1-9-1 Single-Mode Step-Index Optical Fiber

Single-mode step-index fibers are the dominant fibers used in today's telecommunications and data networking industries. A single-mode step-index fiber has a central core that is significantly smaller in diameter than any of the multimode cables. In fact, the diameter is sufficiently small that there is essentially only one path that light may take as it propagates down the cable. This type of fiber is shown in Figure 1-16a. In the simplest form of single-mode step-index fiber, the outside cladding is simply air. The refractive index of the glass core (n_1) is approximately 1.5, and the refractive index of the air cladding (n_2) is 1. The large

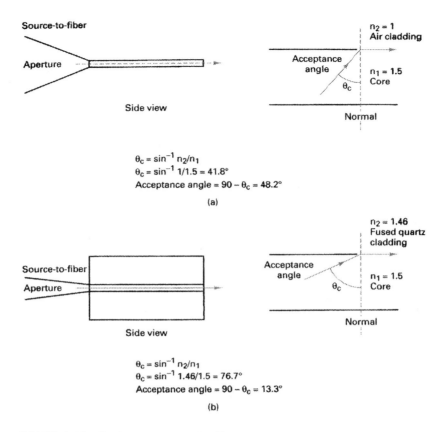

$$\theta_c = \sin^{-1} n_2/n_1$$
$$\theta_c = \sin^{-1} 1/1.5 = 41.8°$$
$$\text{Acceptance angle} = 90 - \theta_c = 48.2°$$

(a)

$$\theta_c = \sin^{-1} n_2/n_1$$
$$\theta_c = \sin^{-1} 1.46/1.5 = 76.7°$$
$$\text{Acceptance angle} = 90 - \theta_c = 13.3°$$

(b)

FIGURE 1-16   Single-mode step-index fibers: (a) air cladding; (b) glass cladding

difference in the refractive indexes results in a small critical angle (approximately 42°) at the glass/air interface. Consequently, a single-mode step-index fiber has a wide external acceptance angle, which makes it relatively easy to couple light into the cable from an external source. However, this type of fiber is very weak and difficult to splice or terminate.

A more practical type of single-mode step-index fiber is one that has a cladding other than air, such as the cable shown in Figure 1-16b. The refractive index of the cladding (n_2) is slightly less than that of the central core (n_1) and is uniform throughout the cladding. This type of cable is physically stronger than the air-clad fiber, but the critical angle is also much higher (approximately 77°). This results in a small acceptance angle and a narrow source-to-fiber aperture, making it much more difficult to couple light into the fiber from a light source.

With both types of single-mode step-index fibers, light is propagated down the fiber through reflection. Light rays that enter the fiber either propagate straight down the core or, perhaps, are reflected only a few times. Consequently, all light rays follow approximately the same path down the cable and take approximately the same amount of time to travel the length of the cable. This is one overwhelming advantage of single-mode step-index fibers, as explained in more detail in a later section of this chapter.

1-9-2   Multimode Step-Index Optical Fiber

A *multimode step-index* optical fiber is shown in Figure 1-17. Multimode step-index fibers are similar to the single-mode step-index fibers except the center core is much larger with the multimode configuration. This type of fiber has a large light-to-fiber aperture and, consequently, allows more external light to enter the cable. The light rays that strike the core/cladding interface at an angle greater than the critical angle (ray A) are propagated down the core in a zigzag fashion, continuously reflecting off the interface boundary. Light

FIGURE 1-17   Multimode step-index fiber

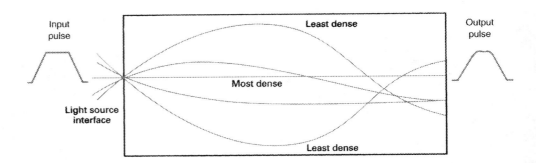

FIGURE 1-18   Multimode graded-index fiber

rays that strike the core/cladding interface at an angle less than the critical angle (ray B) enter the cladding and are lost. It can be seen that there are many paths that a light ray may follow as it propagates down the fiber. As a result, all light rays do not follow the same path and, consequently, do not take the same amount of time to travel the length of the cable.

1-9-3   Multimode Graded-Index Optical Fiber

A multimode graded-index optical fiber is shown in Figure 1-18. Graded-index fibers are characterized by a central core with a nonuniform refractive index. Thus, the cable's density is maximum at the center and decreases gradually toward the outer edge. Light rays propagate down this type of fiber through refraction rather than reflection. As a light ray propagates diagonally across the core toward the center, it is continually intersecting a less dense to more dense interface. Consequently, the light rays are constantly being refracted, which results in a continuous bending of the light rays. Light enters the fiber at many different angles. As the light rays propagate down the fiber, the rays traveling in the outermost area of the fiber travel a greater distance than the rays traveling near the center. Because the refractive index decreases with distance from the center and the velocity is inversely proportional to refractive index, the light rays traveling farthest from the center propagate at a higher velocity. Consequently, they take approximately the same amount of time to travel the length of the fiber.

1-9-4   Optical Fiber Comparison

1-9-4-1 Single-mode step-index fiber.   Advantages include the following:

1. Minimum dispersion: All rays propagating down the fiber take approximately the same path; thus, they take approximately the same length of time to travel down the cable. Consequently, a pulse of light entering the cable can be reproduced at the receiving end very accurately.

2. Because of the high accuracy in reproducing transmitted pulses at the receive end, wider bandwidths and higher information transmission rates (bps) are possible with single-mode step-index fibers than with the other types of fibers.

Disadvantages include the following:

1. Because the central core is very small, it is difficult to couple light into and out of this type of fiber. The source-to-fiber aperture is the smallest of all the fiber types.
2. Again, because of the small central core, a highly directive light source, such as a laser, is required to couple light into a single-mode step-index fiber.
3. Single-mode step-index fibers are expensive and difficult to manufacture.

1-9-4-2 Multimode step-index fiber. Advantages include the following:

1. Multimode step-index fibers are relatively inexpensive and simple to manufacture.
2. It is easier to couple light into and out of multimode step-index fibers because they have a relatively large source-to-fiber aperture.

Disadvantages include the following:

1. Light rays take many different paths down the fiber, which results in large differences in propagation times. Because of this, rays traveling down this type of fiber have a tendency to spread out. Consequently, a pulse of light propagating down a multimode step-index fiber is distorted more than with the other types of fibers.
2. The bandwidths and rate of information transfer rates possible with this type of cable are less than that possible with the other types of fiber cables.

1-9-4-3 Multimode graded-index fiber. Essentially, there are no outstanding advantages or disadvantages of this type of fiber. Multimode graded-index fibers are easier to couple light into and out of than single-mode step-index fibers but are more difficult than multimode step-index fibers. Distortion due to multiple propagation paths is greater than in single-mode step-index fibers but less than in multimode step-index fibers. This multimode graded-index fiber is considered an intermediate fiber compared to the other fiber types.

1-10 LOSSES IN OPTICAL FIBER CABLES

Power loss in an optical fiber cable is probably the most important characteristic of the cable. Power loss is often called *attenuation* and results in a reduction in the power of the light wave as it travels down the cable. Attenuation has several adverse effects on performance, including reducing the system's bandwidth, information transmission rate, efficiency, and overall system capacity.

The standard formula for expressing the total power loss in an optical fiber cable is

$$A_{(dB)} = 10 \log\left(\frac{P_{out}}{P_{in}}\right) \qquad (1\text{-}14)$$

where $A_{(dB)}$ = total reduction in power level, attenuation (unitless)
  P_{out} = cable output power (watts)
  P_{in} = cable input power (watts)

In general, multimode fibers tend to have more attenuation than single-mode cables, primarily because of the increased scattering of the light wave produced from the dopants in the glass. Table 1-2 shows output power as a percentage of input power for an optical

Table 1-2   % Output Power versus Loss in dB

Loss (dB)	Output Power (%)
1	79
3	50
6	25
9	12.5
10	10
13	5
20	1
30	0.1
40	0.01
50	0.001

Table 1-3   Fiber Cable Attenuation

Cable Type	Core Diameter (μm)	Cladding Diameter (μm)	NA (unitless)	Attenuation (dB/km)
Single mode	8	125	—	0.5 at 1300 nm
	5	125	—	0.4 at 1300 nm
Graded index	50	125	0.2	4 at 850 nm
	100	140	0.3	5 at 850 nm
Step index	200	380	0.27	6 at 850 nm
	300	440	0.27	6 at 850 nm
PCS	200	350	0.3	10 at 790 nm
	400	550	0.3	10 at 790 nm
Plastic	—	750	0.5	400 at 650 nm
	—	1000	0.5	400 at 650 nm

fiber cable with several values of decibel loss. A 1-dB cable loss reduces the output power to 50% of the input power.

Attenuation of light propagating through glass depends on wavelength. The three wavelength bands typically used for optical fiber communications systems are centered around 0.85 microns, 1.30 microns, and 1.55 microns. For the kind of glass typically used for optical communications systems, the 1.30-micron and 1.55-micron bands have less than 5% loss per kilometer, while the 0.85-micron band experiences almost 20% loss per kilometer.

Although total power loss is of primary importance in an optical fiber cable, attenuation is generally expressed in decibels of loss per unit length. Attenuation is expressed as a positive dB value because by definition it is a loss. Table 1-3 lists attenuation in dB/km for several types of optical fiber cables.

The optical power in watts measured at a given distance from a power source can be determined mathematically as

$$P = P_t \times 10^{-Al/10} \tag{1-15}$$

where P = measured power level (watts)
   P_t = transmitted power level (watts)
   A = cable power loss (dB/km)
   l = cable length (km)

Likewise, the optical power in decibel units is

$$P(\text{dBm}) = P_{\text{in}}(\text{dBm}) - Al(\text{dB}) \tag{1-16}$$

where P = measured power level (dBm)
   P_{in} = transmit power (dBm)
   Al = cable power loss, attenuation (dB)

Example 1-3

For a single-mode optical cable with 0.25-dB/km loss, determine the optical power 100 km from a 0.1-mW light source.

Solution Substituting into Equation 1-15 gives

$$P = 0.1\text{mW} \times 10^{-\{[(0.25)(100)]/(10)\}}$$
$$= 1 \times 10^{-4} \times 10^{\{[(0.25)(100)]/(10)\}}$$
$$= (1 \times 10^{-4})(1 \times 10^{-2.5})$$
$$= 0.316\ \mu\text{W}$$

and

$$P(\text{dBm}) = 10 \log\left(\frac{0.316\ \mu\text{W}}{0.001}\right)$$
$$= -35\ \text{dBm}$$

or by substituting into Equation 1-16

$$P(\text{dBm}) = 10 \log\left(\frac{0.1\ \text{mW}}{0.001\ \text{W}}\right) - [(100\ \text{km})(0.25\ \text{dB/km})]$$
$$= -10\ \text{dBm} - 25\ \text{dB}$$
$$= -35\ \text{dBm}$$

Transmission losses in optical fiber cables are one of the most important characteristics of the fibers. Losses in the fiber result in a reduction in the light power, thus reducing the system bandwidth, information transmission rate, efficiency, and overall system capacity. The predominant losses in optical fiber cables are the following:

Absorption loss

Material, or Rayleigh, scattering losses

Chromatic, or wavelength, dispersion

Radiation losses

Modal dispersion

Coupling losses

1-10-1 Absorption Losses

Absorption losses in optical fibers is analogous to power dissipation in copper cables; impurities in the fiber absorb the light and convert it to heat. The ultrapure glass used to manufacture optical fibers is approximately 99.9999% pure. Still, absorption losses between 1 dB/km and 1000 dB/km are typical. Essentially, there are three factors that contribute to the absorption losses in optical fibers: *ultraviolet absorption, infrared absorption,* and *ion resonance absorption.*

1-10-1-1 Ultraviolet absorption. Ultraviolet absorption is caused by valence electrons in the silica material from which fibers are manufactured. Light ionizes the valence electrons into conduction. The ionization is equivalent to a loss in the total light field and, consequently, contributes to the transmission losses of the fiber.

1-10-1-2 Infrared absorption. Infrared absorption is a result of photons of light that are absorbed by the atoms of the glass core molecules. The absorbed photons are converted to random mechanical vibrations typical of heating.

1-10-1-3 Ion resonance absorption. Ion resonance absorption is caused by OH^- ions in the material. The source of the OH^- ions is water molecules that have been trapped in the glass during the manufacturing process. Iron, copper, and chromium molecules also cause ion absorption.

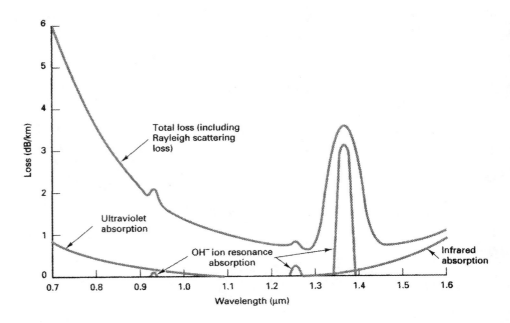

FIGURE 1-19   Absorption losses in optical fibers

Figure 1-19 shows typical losses in optical fiber cables due to ultraviolet, infrared, and ion resonance absorption.

1-10-2   Material, or Rayleigh, Scattering Losses

During manufacturing, glass is drawn into long fibers of very small diameter. During this process, the glass is in a plastic state (not liquid and not solid). The tension applied to the glass causes the cooling glass to develop permanent submicroscopic irregularities. When light rays propagating down a fiber strike one of these impurities, they are diffracted. Diffraction causes the light to disperse or spread out in many directions. Some of the diffracted light continues down the fiber, and some of it escapes through the cladding. The light rays that escape represent a loss in light power. This is called *Rayleigh scattering loss*. Figure 1-20 graphically shows the relationship between wavelength and Rayleigh scattering loss.

1-10-3   Chromatic, or Wavelength, Dispersion

Light-emitting diodes (LEDs) emit light containing many wavelengths. Each wavelength within the composite light signal travels at a different velocity when propagating through glass. Consequently, light rays that are simultaneously emitted from an LED and propagated down an optical fiber do not arrive at the far end of the fiber at the same time, resulting in an impairment called *chromatic distortion* (sometimes called *wavelength dispersion*). Chromatic distortion can be eliminated by using a monochromatic light source such as an injection laser diode (ILD). Chromatic distortion occurs only in fibers with a single mode of transmission.

1-10-4   Radiation Losses

Radiation losses are caused mainly by small bends and kinks in the fiber. Essentially, there are two types of bends: microbends and constant-radius bends. *Microbending* occurs as a result of differences in the thermal contraction rates between the core and the cladding material. A microbend is a miniature bend or geometric imperfection along the axis of the fiber and represents a discontinuity in the fiber where Rayleigh scattering can occur. Microbending losses generally contribute less than 20% of the total attenuation in a fiber.

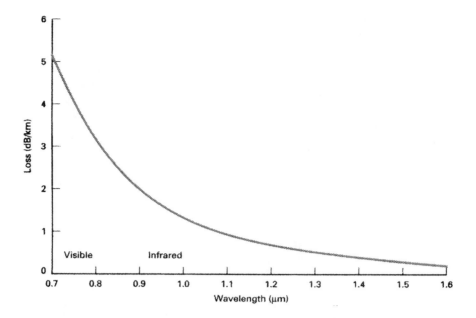

FIGURE 1-20   Rayleigh scattering loss as a function of wavelength

Constant-radius bends are caused by excessive pressure and tension and generally occur when fibers are bent during handling or installation.

1-10-5   Modal Dispersion

Modal dispersion (sometimes called *pulse spreading*) is caused by the difference in the propagation times of light rays that take different paths down a fiber. Obviously, modal dispersion can occur only in multimode fibers. It can be reduced considerably by using graded-index fibers and almost entirely eliminated by using single-mode step-index fibers.

Modal dispersion can cause a pulse of light energy to spread out in time as it propagates down a fiber. If the pulse spreading is sufficiently severe, one pulse may interfere with another. In multimode step-index fibers, a light ray propagating straight down the axis of the fiber takes the least amount of time to travel the length of the fiber. A light ray that strikes the core/cladding interface at the critical angle will undergo the largest number of internal reflections and, consequently, take the longest time to travel the length of the cable.

For multimode propagation, dispersion is often expressed as a *bandwidth length product* (BLP) or *bandwidth distance product* (BDP). BLP indicates what signal frequencies can be propagated through a given distance of fiber cable and is expressed mathematically as the product of distance and bandwidth (sometimes called *linewidth*). Bandwidth length products are often expressed in MHz − km units. As the length of an optical cable increases, the bandwidth (and thus the bit rate) decreases in proportion.

Example 1-4

For a 300-meter optical fiber cable with a BLP of 600 MHz−km, determine the bandwidth.

Solution $B = \dfrac{600 \text{ MHz} - \text{km}}{0.3 \text{ km}}$

$B = 2 \text{ GHz}$

Figure 1-21 shows three light rays propagating down a multimode step-index optical fiber. The lowest-order mode (ray 1) travels in a path parallel to the axis of the fiber. The middle-order mode (ray 2) bounces several times at the interface before traveling the length

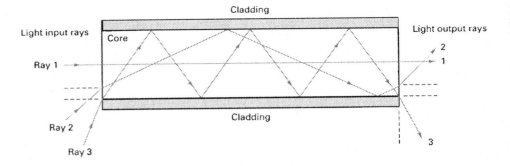

FIGURE 1-21 Light propagation down a multimode step-index fiber

FIGURE 1-22 Light propagation down a single-mode step-index fiber

FIGURE 1-23 Light propagation down a multimode graded-index fiber

of the fiber. The highest-order mode (ray 3) makes many trips back and forth across the fiber as it propagates the entire length. It can be seen that ray 3 travels a considerably longer distance than ray 1 over the length of the cable. Consequently, if the three rays of light were emitted into the fiber at the same time, each ray would reach the far end at a different time, resulting in a spreading out of the light energy with respect to time. This is called modal dispersion and results in a stretched pulse that is also reduced in amplitude at the output of the fiber.

Figure 1-22 shows light rays propagating down a single-mode step-index cable. Because the radial dimension of the fiber is sufficiently small, there is only a single transmission path that all rays must follow as they propagate down the length of the fiber. Consequently, each ray of light travels the same distance in a given period of time, and modal dispersion is virtually eliminated.

Figure 1-23 shows light propagating down a multimode graded-index fiber. Three rays are shown traveling in three different modes. Although the three rays travel different paths, they all take approximately the same amount of time to propagate the length of the fiber. This is because the refractive index decreases with distance from the center, and the velocity at which a ray travels is inversely proportional to the refractive in-

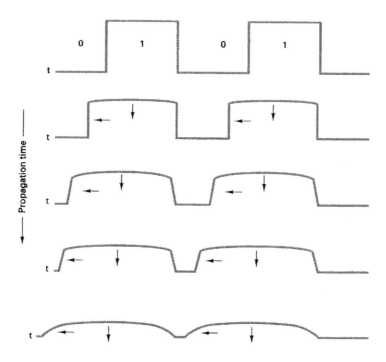

FIGURE 1-24 Pulse-width dispersion in an optical fiber cable

dex. Consequently, the farther rays 2 and 3 travel from the center of the cable, the faster they propagate.

Figure 1-24 shows the relative time/energy relationship of a pulse of light as it propagates down an optical fiber cable. From the figure, it can be seen that as the pulse propagates down the cable, the light rays that make up the pulse spread out in time, causing a corresponding reduction in the pulse amplitude and stretching of the pulse width. This is called *pulse spreading* or *pulse-width dispersion* and causes errors in digital transmission. It can also be seen that as light energy from one pulse falls back in time, it will interfere with the next pulse, causing intersymbol interference.

Figure 1-25a shows a unipolar return-to-zero (UPRZ) digital transmission. With UPRZ transmission (assuming a very narrow pulse), if light energy from pulse A were to fall back (*spread*) one bit time (t_b), it would interfere with pulse B and change what was a logic 0 to a logic 1. Figure 1-25b shows a unipolar nonreturn-to-zero (UPNRZ) digital transmission where each pulse is equal to the bit time. With UPNRZ transmission, if energy from pulse A were to fall back one-half of a bit time, it would interfere with pulse B. Consequently, UPRZ transmissions can tolerate twice as much delay or spread as UPNRZ transmissions.

The difference between the absolute delay times of the fastest and slowest rays of light propagating down a fiber of unit length is called the *pulse-spreading constant* (Δt) and is generally expressed in nanoseconds per kilometer (ns/km). The total pulse spread (ΔT) is then equal to the pulse-spreading constant (Δt) times the total fiber length (L). Mathematically, ΔT is

$$\Delta T_{(ns)} = \Delta t_{(ns/km)} \times L_{(km)} \qquad (1\text{-}17)$$

For UPRZ transmissions, the maximum data transmission rate in bits per second (bps) is expressed as

$$f_{b(bps)} = \frac{1}{\Delta t \times L} \qquad (1\text{-}18)$$

FIGURE 1-25 Pulse spreading of digital transmissions: (a) UPRZ; (b) UPNRZ

and for UPNRZ transmissions, the maximum transmission rate is

$$f_{b(bps)} = \frac{1}{2\Delta t \times L} \qquad (1\text{-}19)$$

Example 1-5

For an optical fiber 10 km long with a pulse-spreading constant of 5 ns/km, determine the maximum digital transmission rates for

a. Return-to-zero.
b. Nonreturn-to-zero transmissions.

Solution

a. Substituting into Equation 1-18 yields

$$f_b = \frac{1}{5 \text{ ns/km} \times 10 \text{ km}} = 20 \text{ Mbps}$$

b. Substituting into Equation 1-19 yields

$$f_b = \frac{1}{(2 \times 5 \text{ ns/km}) \times 10 \text{ km}} = 10 \text{ Mbps}$$

The results indicate that the digital transmission rate possible for this optical fiber is twice as high (20 Mbps versus 10 Mbps) for UPRZ as for UPNRZ transmission.

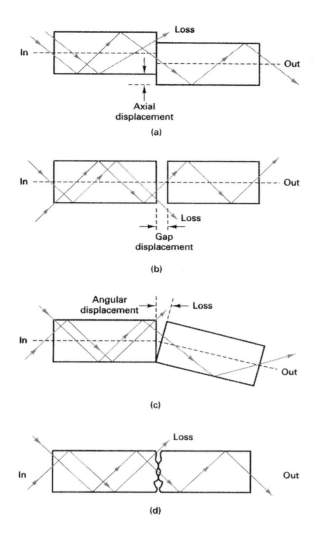

FIGURE 1-26 Fiber alignment impairments: (a) lateral misalignment; (b) gap displacement; (c) angular misalignment; (d) surface finish

1-10-6 Coupling Losses

Coupling losses are caused by imperfect physical connections. In fiber cables, coupling losses can occur at any of the following three types of optical junctions: light source-to-fiber connections, fiber-to-fiber connections, and fiber-to-photodetector connections. Junction losses are most often caused by one of the following alignment problems: lateral misalignment, gap misalignment, angular misalignment, and imperfect surface finishes.

1-10-6-1 Lateral displacement. *Lateral displacement* (*misalignment*) is shown in Figure 1-26a and is the lateral or axial displacement between two pieces of adjoining fiber cables. The amount of loss can be from a couple tenths of a decibel to several decibels. This loss is generally negligible if the fiber axes are aligned to within 5% of the smaller fiber's diameter.

1-10-6-2 Gap displacement (misalignment). *Gap displacement* (*misalignment*) is shown in Figure 1-26b and is sometimes called *end separation.* When splices are made in optical fibers, the fibers should actually touch. The farther apart the fibers, the greater the loss of light. If two fibers are joined with a connector, the ends should not touch because the two ends rubbing against each other in the connector could cause damage to either or both fibers.

1-10-6-3 Angular displacement (misalignment). Angular displacement (misalignment) is shown in Figure 1-26c and is sometimes called *angular displacement*. If the angular displacement is less than 2°, the loss will typically be less than 0.5 dB.

1-10-6-4 Imperfect surface finish. *Imperfect surface finish* is shown in Figure 1-26d. The ends of the two adjoining fibers should be highly polished and fit together squarely. If the fiber ends are less than 3° off from perpendicular, the losses will typically be less than 0.5 dB.

1-11 LIGHT SOURCES

The range of light frequencies detectable by the human eye occupies a very narrow segment of the total electromagnetic frequency spectrum. For example, blue light occupies the higher frequencies (shorter wavelengths) of visible light, and red hues occupy the lower frequencies (longer wavelengths). Figure 1-27 shows the light wavelength distribution produced from a tungsten lamp and the range of wavelengths perceivable by the human eye. As the figure shows, the human eye can detect only those lightwaves between approximately 380 nm and 780 nm. Furthermore, light consists of many shades of colors that are directly related to the heat of the energy being radiated. Figure 1-27 also shows that more visible light is produced as the temperature of the lamp is increased.

Light sources used for optical fiber systems must be at wavelengths efficiently propagated by the optical fiber. In addition, the range of wavelengths must be considered because the wider the range, the more likely the chance that chromatic dispersion will occur. Light

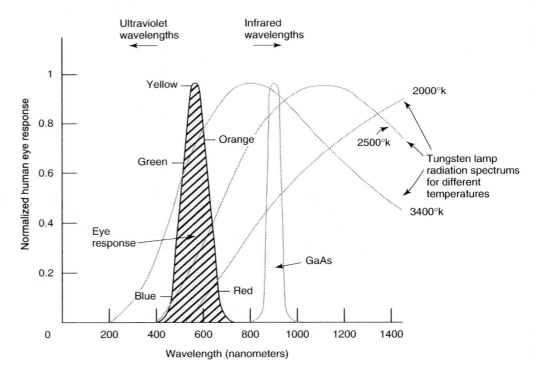

FIGURE 1-27 Tungsten lamp radiation and human eye response

sources must also produce sufficient power to allow the light to propagate through the fiber without causing distortion in the cable itself or in the receiver. Lastly, light sources must be constructed so that their outputs can be efficiently coupled into and out of the optical cable.

1-12 OPTICAL SOURCES

There are essentially only two types of practical light sources used to generate light for optical fiber communications systems: LEDs and ILDs. Both devices are constructed from semiconductor materials and have advantages and disadvantages. Standard LEDs have spectral widths of 30 nm to 50 nm, while injection lasers have spectral widths of only 1 nm to 3 nm (1 nm corresponds to a frequency of about 178 GHz). Therefore, a 1320-nm light source with a spectral linewidth of 0.0056 nm has a frequency bandwidth of approximately 1 GHz. Linewidth is the wavelength equivalent of bandwidth.

Selection of one light-emitting device over the other is determined by system economic and performance requirements. The higher cost of laser diodes is offset by higher performance. LEDs typically have a lower cost and a corresponding lower performance. However, LEDs are typically more reliable.

1-12-1 LEDs

An LED is a *p-n* junction diode, usually made from a semiconductor material such as aluminum-gallium-arsenide (AlGaAs) or gallium-arsenide-phosphide (GaAsP). LEDs emit light by spontaneous emission—light is emitted as a result of the recombination of electrons and holes.

When forward biased, minority carriers are injected across the *p-n* junction. Once across the junction, these minority carriers recombine with majority carriers and give up energy in the form of light. This process is essentially the same as in a conventional semiconductor diode except that in LEDs certain semiconductor materials and dopants are chosen such that the process is radiative; that is, a photon is produced. A photon is a quantum of electromagnetic wave energy. Photons are particles that travel at the speed of light but at rest have no mass. In conventional semiconductor diodes (germanium and silicon, for example), the process is primarily nonradiative, and no photons are generated. The energy gap of the material used to construct an LED determines the color of light it emits and whether the light emitted by it is visible to the human eye.

To produce LEDs, semiconductors are formed from materials with atoms having either three or five valence electrons (known as Group III and Group IV atoms, respectively, because of their location in the periodic table of elements). To produce light wavelengths in the 800-nm range, LEDs are constructed from Group III atoms, such as gallium (Ga) and aluminum (Al), and a Group IV atom, such as arsenide (As). The junction formed is commonly abbreviated GaAlAs for gallium-aluminum-arsenide. For longer wavelengths, gallium is combined with the Group III atom indium (In), and arsenide is combined with the Group V atom phosphate (P), which forms a gallium-indium-arsenide-phosphate (GaInAsP) junction. Table 1-4 lists some of the common semiconductor materials used in LED construction and their respective output wavelengths.

Table 1-4   Semiconductor Material Wavelengths

Material	Wavelength (nm)
AlGaInP	630–680
GaInP	670
GaAlAs	620–895
GaAs	904
InGaAs	980
InGaAsP	1100–1650
InGaAsSb	1700–4400

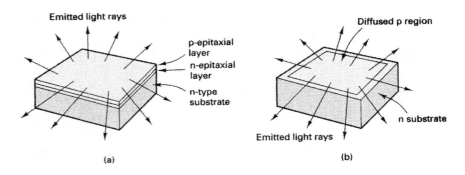

FIGURE 1-28 Homojunction LED structures: (a) silicon-doped gallium arsenide; (b) planar diffused

1-12-2 Homojunction LEDs

A *p-n* junction made from two different mixtures of the same types of atoms is called a homojunction structure. The simplest LED structures are homojunction and epitaxially grown, or they are single-diffused semiconductor devices, such as the two shown in Figure 1-28. *Epitaxially grown* LEDs are generally constructed of silicon-doped gallium-arsenide (Figure 1-28a). A typical wavelength of light emitted from this construction is 940 nm, and a typical output power is approximately 2 mW (3 dBm) at 100 mA of forward current. Light waves from homojunction sources do not produce a very useful light for an optical fiber. Light is emitted in all directions equally; therefore, only a small amount of the total light produced is coupled into the fiber. In addition, the ratio of electricity converted to light is very low. Homojunction devices are often called *surface emitters.*

Planar diffused homojunction LEDs (Figure 1-28b) output approximately 500 μW at a wavelength of 900 nm. The primary disadvantage of homojunction LEDs is the nondirectionality of their light emission, which makes them a poor choice as a light source for optical fiber systems.

1-12-3 Heterojunction LEDs

Heterojunction LEDs are made from a *p*-type semiconductor material of one set of atoms and an *n*-type semiconductor material from another set. Heterojunction devices are layered (usually two) such that the concentration effect is enhanced. This produces a device that confines the electron and hole carriers and the light to a much smaller area. The junction is generally manufactured on a substrate backing material and then sandwiched between metal contacts that are used to connect the device to a source of electricity.

With heterojunction devices, light is emitted from the edge of the material and are therefore often called *edge emitters.* A *planar heterojunction LED* (Figure 1-29) is quite similar to the epitaxially grown LED except that the geometry is designed such that the forward current is concentrated to a very small area of the active layer.

Heterojunction devices have the following advantages over homojunction devices:

The increase in current density generates a more brilliant light spot.

The smaller emitting area makes it easier to couple its emitted light into a fiber.

The small effective area has a smaller capacitance, which allows the planar heterojunction LED to be used at higher speeds.

Figure 1-30 shows the typical electrical characteristics for a low-cost infrared light-emitting diode. Figure 1-30a shows the output power versus forward current. From the figure, it can be seen that the output power varies linearly over a wide range of input current

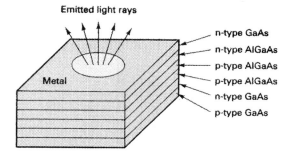

Emitted light rays

n-type GaAs
n-type AlGaAs
p-type AlGaAs
p-type AlGaAs
n-type GaAs
p-type GaAs

Metal

FIGURE 1-29   Planar heterojunction LED

(0.5 mW [−3 dBm] at 20 mA to 3.4 mW [5.3 dBm] at 140 mA). Figure 1-30b shows output power versus temperature. It can be seen that the output power varies inversely with temperature between a temperature range of −40°C to 80°C. Figure 1-30c shows relative output power in respect to output wavelength. For this particular example, the maximum output power is achieved at an output wavelength of 825 nm.

1-12-4   Burrus Etched-Well Surface-Emitting LED

For the more practical applications, such as telecommunications, data rates in excess of 100 Mbps are required. For these applications, the etched-well LED was developed. Burrus and Dawson of Bell Laboratories developed the etched-well LED. It is a surface-emitting LED and is shown in Figure 1-31. The Burrus etched-well LED emits light in many directions. The etched well helps concentrate the emitted light to a very small area. Also, domed lenses can be placed over the emitting surface to direct the light into a smaller area. These devices are more efficient than the standard surface emitters, and they allow more power to be coupled into the optical fiber, but they are also more difficult and expensive to manufacture.

1-12-5   Edge-Emitting LED

The edge-emitting LED, which was developed by RCA, is shown in Figure 1-32. These LEDs emit a more directional light pattern than do the surface-emitting LEDs. The construction is similar to the planar and Burrus diodes except that the emitting surface is a stripe rather than a confined circular area. The light is emitted from an active stripe and forms an elliptical beam. Surface-emitting LEDs are more commonly used than edge emitters because they emit more light. However, the coupling losses with surface emitters are greater, and they have narrower bandwidths.

The *radiant* light power emitted from an LED is a linear function of the forward current passing through the device (Figure 1-33). It can also be seen that the optical output power of an LED is, in part, a function of the operating temperature.

1-12-6   ILD

Lasers are constructed from many different materials, including gases, liquids, and solids, although the type of laser used most often for fiber-optic communications is the semiconductor laser.

The ILD is similar to the LED. In fact, below a certain threshold current, an ILD acts similarly to an LED. Above the threshold current, an ILD oscillates; lasing occurs. As current passes through a forward-biased *p-n* junction diode, light is emitted by spontaneous emission at a frequency determined by the energy gap of the semiconductor material. When a particular current level is reached, the number of minority carriers and photons produced on either side of the *p-n* junction reaches a level where they begin to collide with already excited minority carriers. This causes an increase in the ionization energy level and makes the carriers unstable. When this happens, a typical carrier recombines with an opposite type

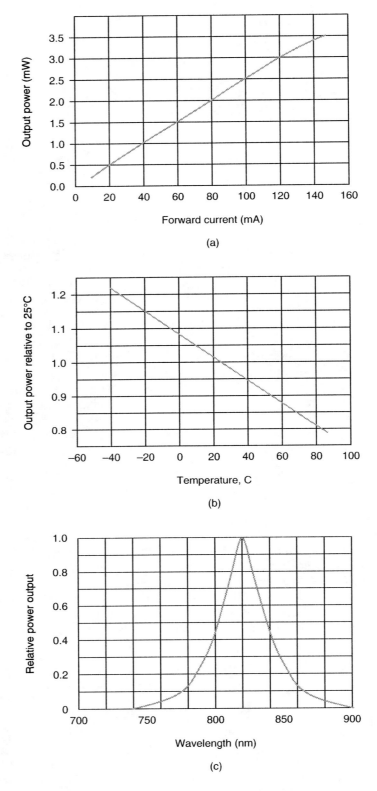

FIGURE 1-30 Typical LED electrical characteristics: (a) output power-versus-forward current; (b) output power-versus-temperature; and (c) output power-versus-output wavelength

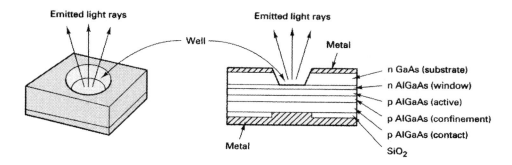

FIGURE 1-31 Burrus etched-well surface-emitting LED

FIGURE 1-32 Edge-emitting LED

FIGURE 1-33 Output power versus forward current and operating temperature for an LED

of carrier at an energy level that is above its normal before-collision value. In the process, two photons are created; one is stimulated by another. Essentially, a gain in the number of photons is realized. For this to happen, a large forward current that can provide many carriers (holes and electrons) is required.

The construction of an ILD is similar to that of an LED (Figure 1-34) except that the ends are highly polished. The mirrorlike ends trap the photons in the active region and, as they reflect back and forth, stimulate free electrons to recombine with holes at a higher-than-normal energy level. This process is called *lasing*.

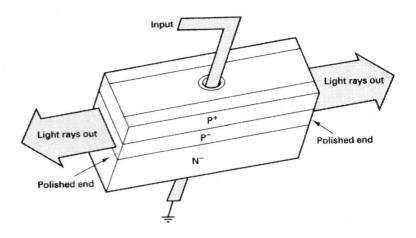

FIGURE 1-34   Injection laser diode construction

FIGURE 1-35   Output power versus forward current and
temperature for an ILD

The radiant output light power of a typical ILD is shown in Figure 1-35. It can
be seen that very little output power is realized until the threshold current is reached;
then lasing occurs. After lasing begins, the optical output power increases dramatically, with small increases in drive current. It can also be seen that the magnitude of
the optical output power of the ILD is more dependent on operating temperature than
is the LED.

Figure 1-36 shows the light radiation patterns typical of an LED and an ILD. Because
light is radiated out the end of an ILD in a narrow concentrated beam, it has a more direct
radiation pattern.

ILDs have several advantages over LEDs and some disadvantages. Advantages include the following:

ILDs emit coherent (orderly) light, whereas LEDs emit incoherent (disorderly) light.
Therefore, ILDs have a more direct radian pattern, making it easier to couple light
emitted by the ILD into an optical fiber cable. This reduces the coupling losses and
allows smaller fibers to be used.

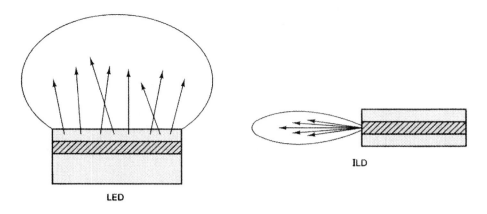

FIGURE 1-36 LED and ILD radiation patterns

The radiant output power from an ILD is greater than that for an LED. A typical output power for an ILD is 5 mW (7 dBm) and only 0.5 mW (−3 dBm) for LEDs. This allows ILDs to provide a higher drive power and to be used for systems that operate over longer distances.

ILDs can be used at higher bit rates than LEDs.

ILDs generate monochromatic light, which reduces chromatic or wavelength dispersion.

Disadvantages include the following:

ILDs are typically 10 times more expensive than LEDs.

Because ILDs operate at higher powers, they typically have a much shorter lifetime than LEDs.

ILDs are more temperature dependent than LEDs.

1-13 LIGHT DETECTORS

There are two devices commonly used to detect light energy in fiber-optic communications receivers: PIN diodes and APDs.

1-13-1 PIN Diodes

A *PIN diode* is a *depletion-layer photodiode* and is probably the most common device used as a light detector in fiber-optic communications systems. Figure 1-37 shows the basic construction of a PIN diode. A very lightly doped (almost pure or intrinsic) layer of *n*-type semiconductor material is sandwiched between the junction of the two heavily doped *n*- and *p*-type contact areas. Light enters the device through a very small window and falls on the carrier-void intrinsic material. The intrinsic material is made thick enough so that most of the photons that enter the device are absorbed by this layer. Essentially, the PIN photodiode operates just the opposite of an LED. Most of the photons are absorbed by electrons in the valence band of the intrinsic material. When the photons are absorbed, they add sufficient energy to generate carriers in the depletion region and allow current to flow through the device.

1-13-1-1 Photoelectric effect. Light entering through the window of a PIN diode is absorbed by the intrinsic material and adds enough energy to cause electronics to move from the valence band into the conduction band. The increase in the number of electrons that move into the conduction band is matched by an increase in the number of holes in the

FIGURE 1-37   PIN photodiode construction

valence band. To cause current to flow in a photodiode, light of sufficient energy must be absorbed to give valence electrons enough energy to jump the energy gap. The energy gap for silicon is 1.12 eV (electron volts). Mathematically, the operation is as follows:

For silicon, the energy gap (E_g) equals 1.12 eV:

$$1 \text{ eV} = 1.6 \times 10^{-19} \text{ J}$$

Thus, the energy gap for silicon is

$$E_g = (1.12 \text{ eV})\left(1.6 \times 10^{-19} \frac{\text{J}}{\text{eV}}\right) = 1.792 \times 10^{-19} \text{ J}$$

and   energy (E) = hf (1-20)

where h = Planck's constant = 6.6256×10^{-34} J/Hz
           f = frequency (hertz)

Rearranging and solving for f yields

$$f = \frac{E}{h} \qquad (1\text{-}21)$$

For a silicon photodiode,

$$f = \frac{1.792 \times 10^{-19} \text{ J}}{6.6256 \times 10^{-34} \text{ J/Hz}} = 2.705 \times 10^{14} \text{ Hz}$$

Converting to wavelength yields

$$\lambda = \frac{c}{f} = \frac{3 \times 10^8 \text{ m/s}}{2.705 \times 10^{14} \text{ Hz}} = 1109 \text{ nm/cycle}$$

1-13-2   APDs

Figure 1-38 shows the basic construction of an APD. An APD is a *pipn* structure. Light enters the diode and is absorbed by the thin, heavily doped *n*-layer. A high electric field intensity developed across the *i-p-n* junction by reverse bias causes impact ionization to occur. During impact ionization, a carrier can gain sufficient energy to ionize other bound electrons. These ionized carriers, in turn, cause more ionizations to occur. The process continues as in an avalanche and is, effectively, equivalent to an internal gain or carrier multiplication. Consequently, APDs are more sensitive than PIN diodes and require less additional amplification. The disadvantages of APDs are relatively long transit times and additional internally generated noise due to the avalanche multiplication factor.

FIGURE 1-38   Avalanche photo-diode construction

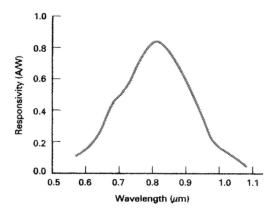

FIGURE 1-39   Spectral response curve

1-13-3   Characteristics of Light Detectors

The most important characteristics of light detectors are the following:

1. *Responsivity.* A measure of the conversion efficiency of a photodetector. It is the ratio of the output current of a photodiode to the input optical power and has the unit of amperes per watt. Responsivity is generally given for a particular wavelength or frequency.
2. *Dark current.* The leakage current that flows through a photodiode with no light input. Thermally generated carriers in the diode cause dark current.
3. *Transit time.* The time it takes a light-induced carrier to travel across the depletion region of a semiconductor. This parameter determines the maximum bit rate possible with a particular photodiode.
4. *Spectral response.* The range of wavelength values that a given photodiode will respond. Generally, relative spectral response is graphed as a function of wavelength or frequency, as shown in Figure 1-39.
5. *Light sensitivity.* The minimum optical power a light detector can receive and still produce a usable electrical output signal. Light sensitivity is generally given for a particular wavelength in either dBm or dBμ.

1-14   LASERS

Laser is an acronym for *l*ight *a*mplification *s*timulated by the *e*mission of *r*adiation. Laser technology deals with the concentration of light into a very small, powerful beam. The acronym was chosen when technology shifted from microwaves to light waves. Basically, there are four types of lasers: gas, liquid, solid, and semiconductor.

The first laser was developed by Theodore H. Maiman, a scientist who worked for Hughes Aircraft Company in California. Maiman directed a beam of light into ruby crystals with a xenon flashlamp and measured emitted radiation from the ruby. He discovered that when the emitted radiation increased beyond threshold, it caused emitted radiation to become extremely intense and highly directional. Uranium lasers were developed in 1960 along with other rare-earth materials. Also in 1960, A. Javin of Bell Laboratories developed the helium laser. Semiconductor lasers (injection laser diodes) were manufactured in 1962 by General Electric, IBM, and Lincoln Laboratories.

1-14-1   Laser Types

Basically, there are four types of lasers: gas, liquid, solid, and semiconductor.

1. *Gas lasers.* Gas lasers use a mixture of helium and neon enclosed in a glass tube. A flow of coherent (one frequency) light waves is emitted through the output coupler when an electric current is discharged into the gas. The continuous light-wave output is monochromatic (one color).
2. *Liquid lasers.* Liquid lasers use organic dyes enclosed in a glass tube for an active medium. Dye is circulated into the tube with a pump. A powerful pulse of light excites the organic dye.
3. *Solid lasers.* Solid lasers use a solid, cylindrical crystal, such as ruby, for the active medium. Each end of the ruby is polished and parallel. The ruby is excited by a tungsten lamp tied to an ac power supply. The output from the laser is a continuous wave.
4. *Semiconductor lasers.* Semiconductor lasers are made from semiconductor *p-n* junctions and are commonly called ILDs. The excitation mechanism is a dc power supply that controls the amount of current to the active medium. The output light from an ILD is easily modulated, making it very useful in many electronic communications applications.

1-14-2   Laser Characteristics

All types of lasers have several common characteristics. They all use (1) an active material to convert energy into laser light, (2) a pumping source to provide power or energy, (3) optics to direct the beam through the active material to be amplified, (4) optics to direct the beam into a narrow powerful cone of divergence, (5) a feedback mechanism to provide continuous operation, and (6) an output coupler to transmit power out of the laser.

The radiation of a laser is extremely intense and directional. When focused into a fine hairlike beam, it can concentrate all its power into the narrow beam. If the beam of light were allowed to diverge, it would lose most of its power.

1-14-3   Laser Construction

Figure 1-40 shows the construction of a basic laser. A power source is connected to a flashtube that is coiled around a glass tube that holds the active medium. One end of the glass tube is a polished mirror face for 100% internal reflection. The flashtube is energized by a trigger pulse and produces a high-level burst of light (similar to a flashbulb). The flash causes the chromium atoms within the active crystalline structure to become excited. The process of pumping raises the level of the chromium atoms from ground state to an excited energy state. The ions then decay, falling to an intermediate energy level. When the population of ions in the intermediate level is greater than the ground state, a population inversion occurs. The population inversion causes laser action (lasing) to occur. After a period of time, the excited chromium atoms will fall to the ground energy level. At this time, photons are emitted. A photon is a packet of radiant energy. The emitted photons strike atoms and two other photons are emitted (hence the term "stimulated emission"). The frequency of the energy determines the strength of the photons; higher frequencies cause greater-strength photons.

FIGURE 1-40   Laser construction

1-15   OPTICAL FIBER SYSTEM LINK BUDGET

As with any communications system, optical fiber systems consist of a source and a destination that are separated by numerous components and devices that introduce various amounts of loss or gain to the signal as it propagates through the system. Figure 1-41 shows two typical optical fiber communications system configurations. Figure 1-41a shows a repeaterless system where the source and destination are interconnected through one or more sections of optical cable. With a repeaterless system, there are no amplifiers or regenerators between the source and destination.

Figure 1-41b shows an optical fiber system that includes a repeater that either amplifies or regenerates the signal. Repeatered systems are obviously used when the source and destination are separated by great distances.

Link budgets are generally calculated between a light source and a light detector; therefore, for our example, we look at a link budget for a repeaterless system. A repeaterless system consists of a light source, such as an LED or ILD, and a light detector, such as an APD connected by optical fiber and connectors. Therefore, the link budget consists of a light power source, a light detector, and various cable and connector losses. Losses typical to optical fiber links include the following:

1. *Cable losses.* Cable losses depend on cable length, material, and material purity. They are generally given in dB/km and can vary between a few tenths of a dB to several dB per kilometer.
2. *Connector losses.* Mechanical connectors are sometimes used to connect two sections of cable. If the mechanical connection is not perfect, light energy can escape, resulting in a reduction in optical power. Connector losses typically vary between a few tenths of a dB to as much as 2 dB for each connector.
3. *Source-to-cable interface loss.* The mechanical interface used to house the light source and attach it to the cable is seldom perfect. Therefore, a small percentage of optical power is not coupled into the cable, representing a power loss to the system of several tenths of a dB.
4. *Cable-to-light detector interface loss.* The mechanical interface used to house the light detector and attach it to the cable is also not perfect and, therefore, prevents a small percentage of the power leaving the cable from entering the light detector. This, of course, represents a loss to the system usually of a few tenths of a dB.
5. *Splicing loss.* If more than one continuous section of cable is required, cable sections can be fused together (spliced). Because the splices are not perfect, losses ranging from a couple tenths of a dB to several dB can be introduced to the signal.

(a)

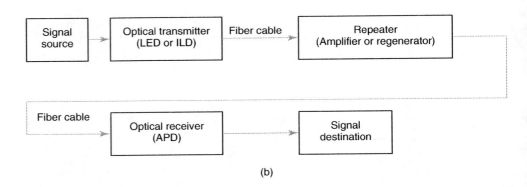

(b)

FIGURE 1-41   Optical fiber communications systems: (a) without repeaters; (b) with repeaters

6. *Cable bends.* When an optical cable is bent at too large an angle, the internal characteristics of the cable can change dramatically. If the changes are severe, total reflections for some of the light rays may no longer be achieved, resulting in refraction. Light refracted at the core/cladding interface enters the cladding, resulting in a net loss to the signal of a few tenths of a dB to several dB.

As with any link or system budget, the useful power available in the receiver depends on transmit power and link losses. Mathematically, receive power is represented as

$$P_r = P_t - \text{losses} \tag{1-22}$$

where P_r = power received (dBm)
             P_t = power transmitted (dBm)
          losses = sum of all losses (dB)

Example 1-6

Determine the optical power received in dBm and watts for a 20-km optical fiber link with the following parameters:

LED output power of 30 mW

Four 5-km sections of optical cable each with a loss of 0.5 dB/km

Three cable-to-cable connectors with a loss of 2 dB each

No cable splices

Light source-to-fiber interface loss of 1.9 dB

Fiber-to-light detector loss of 2.1 dB

No losses due to cable bends

Solution   The LED output power is converted to dBm using Equation 1-6:

$$P_{\text{out}} = 10 \log \frac{30 \text{ mW}}{1 \text{ mW}}$$

$$= 14.8 \text{ dBm}$$

The cable loss is simply the product of the total cable length in km and the loss in dB/km. Four 5-km sections of cable is a total cable length of 20 km; therefore,

$$\text{total cable loss} = 20 \text{ km} \times 0.5 \text{ dB/km}$$

$$= 10 \text{ dB}$$

Cable connector loss is simply the product of the loss in dB per connector and the number of connectors. The maximum number of connectors is always one less than the number of sections of cable. Four sections of cable would then require three connectors; therefore,

$$\text{total connector loss} = 3 \text{ connectors} \times 2 \text{ dB/connector}$$

$$= 6 \text{ dB}$$

The light source-to-cable and cable-to-light detector losses were given as 1.9 dB and 2.1 dB, respectively. Therefore,

$$\text{total loss} = \text{cable loss} + \text{connector loss} + \text{light source-to-cable loss} + \text{cable-to-light detector loss}$$

$$= 10 \text{ dB} + 6 \text{ dB} + 1.9 \text{ dB} + 2.1 \text{ dB}$$

$$= 20 \text{ dB}$$

The receive power is determined by substituting into Equation 1-22:

$$P_r = 14.8 \text{ dBm} - 20 \text{ dB}$$

$$= -5.2 \text{ dBm}$$

$$= 0.302 \text{ mW}$$

QUESTIONS

1-1. Define a fiber-optic system.

1-2. What is the relationship between information capacity and bandwidth?

1-3. What development in 1951 was a substantial breakthrough in the field of fiber optics? In 1960? In 1970?

1-4. Contrast the advantages and disadvantages of fiber-optic cables and metallic cables.

1-5. Outline the primary building blocks of a fiber-optic system.

1-6. Contrast glass and plastic fiber cables.

1-7. Briefly describe the construction of a fiber-optic cable.

1-8. Define the following terms: *velocity of propagation, refraction,* and *refractive index.*

1-9. State Snell's law for refraction and outline its significance in fiber-optic cables.

1-10. Define *critical angle.*

1-11. Describe what is meant by *mode of operation;* by *index profile.*

1-12. Describe a step-index fiber cable; a graded-index cable.

1-13. Contrast the advantages and disadvantages of step-index, graded-index, single-mode, and multimode propagation.

1-14. Why is single-mode propagation impossible with graded-index fibers?

1-15. Describe the source-to-fiber aperture.

1-16. What are the *acceptance angle* and the *acceptance cone* for a fiber cable?

1-17. Define *numerical aperture.*

1-18. List and briefly describe the losses associated with fiber cables.

1-19. What is *pulse spreading?*

1-20. Define *pulse spreading constant.*

1-21. List and briefly describe the various coupling losses.

1-22. Briefly describe the operation of a light-emitting diode.

1-23. What are the two primary types of LEDs?

1-24. Briefly describe the operation of an injection laser diode.

1-25. What is lasing?

1-26. Contrast the advantages and disadvantages of ILDs and LEDs.

1-27. Briefly describe the function of a photodiode.

1-28. Describe the photoelectric effect.

1-29. Explain the difference between a PIN diode and an APD.

1-30. List and describe the primary characteristics of light detectors.

PROBLEMS

1-1. Determine the wavelengths in nanometers and angstroms for the following light frequencies:

    a. 3.45×10^{14} Hz

    b. 3.62×10^{14} Hz

    c. 3.21×10^{14} Hz

1-2. Determine the light frequency for the following wavelengths:

    a. 670 nm

    b. 7800 Å

    c. 710 nm

1-3. For a glass ($n = 1.5$)/quartz ($n = 1.38$) interface and an angle of incidence of 35°, determine the angle of refraction.

1-4. Determine the critical angle for the fiber described in problem 1-3.

1-5. Determine the acceptance angle for the cable described in problem 1-3.

1-6. Determine the numerical aperture for the cable described in problem 1-3.

1-7. Determine the maximum bit rate for RZ and NRZ encoding for the following pulse-spreading constants and cable lengths:

    a. $\Delta t = 10$ ns/m, $L = 100$ m

    b. $\Delta t = 20$ ns/m, $L = 1000$ m

    c. $\Delta t = 2000$ ns/km, $L = 2$ km

1-8. Determine the lowest light frequency that can be detected by a photodiode with an energy gap = 1.2 eV.

1-9. Determine the wavelengths in nanometers and angstroms for the following light frequencies:

    a. 3.8×10^{14} Hz

    b. 3.2×10^{14} Hz

    c. 3.5×10^{14} Hz

1-10. Determine the light frequencies for the following wavelengths:

    a. 650 nm

    b. 7200 Å

    c. 690 nm

1-11. For a glass ($n = 1.5$)/quartz ($n = 1.41$) interface and an angle of incidence of 38°, determine the angle of refraction.

1-12. Determine the critical angle for the fiber described in problem 1-11.

1-13. Determine the acceptance angle for the cable described in problem 1-11.

1-14. Determine the numerical aperture for the cable described in problem 1-11.

1-15. Determine the maximum bit rate for RZ and NRZ encoding for the following pulse-spreading constants and cable lengths:

    a. $\Delta t = 14$ ns/m, $L = 200$ m

    b. $\Delta t = 10$ ns/m, $L = 50$ m

    c. $\Delta t = 20$ ns/m, $L = 200$ m

1-16. Determine the lowest light frequency that can be detected by a photodiode with an energy gap = 1.25 eV.

1-17. Determine the optical power received in dBm and watts for a 24-km optical fiber link with the following parameters:

    LED output power of 20 mW

    Six 4-km sections of optical cable each with a loss of 0.6 dB/km

    Three cable-to-cable connectors with a loss of 2.1 dB each

    No cable splices

    Light source-to-fiber interface loss of 2.2 dB

    Fiber-to-light detector loss of 1.8 dB

    No losses due to cable bends

CHAPTER 2

Digital Modulation

OBJECTIVES

- Define *electronic communications*
- Define *digital modulation* and *digital radio*
- Define *digital communications*
- Define *information capacity*
- Define *bit, bit rate, baud,* and *minimum bandwidth*
- Explain Shannon's limit for information capacity
- Explain *M*-ary encoding
- Define and describe digital amplitude modulation
- Define and describe frequency-shift keying
- Describe continuous-phase frequency-shift keying
- Define *phase-shift keying*
- Explain binary phase-shift keying
- Explain quaternary phase-shift keying

- Describe 8- and 16-PSK
- Describe quadrature-amplitude modulation
- Explain 8-QAM
- Explain 16-QAM
- Define *bandwidth efficiency*
- Explain carrier recovery
- Explain clock recovery
- Define and describe differential phase-shift keying
- Define and explain trellis-code modulation
- Define *probability of error* and *bit error rate*
- Develop error performance equations for FSK, PSK, and QAM

In essence, *electronic communications* is the transmission, reception, and processing of information with the use of electronic circuits. *Information* is defined as knowledge or intelligence that is communicated (i.e., transmitted or received) between two or more points. *Digital modulation* is the transmittal of digitally modulated analog signals (carriers) between two or more points in a communications system. Digital modulation is sometimes called *digital radio* because digitally modulated signals can be propagated through Earth's atmosphere and used in wireless communications systems. Traditional electronic communications systems that use conventional analog modulation, such as *amplitude modulation* (AM), *frequency modulation* (FM), and *phase modulation* (PM), are rapidly being replaced with more modern digital moduluation systems that offer several outstanding advantages over traditional analog systems, such as ease of processing, ease of multiplexing, and noise immunity.

Digital communications is a rather ambiguous term that could have entirely different meanings to different people. In the context of this book, digital communications include systems where relatively high-frequency analog carriers are modulated by relatively low-frequency digital information signals (*digital radio*) and systems involving the transmission of digital pulses (*digital transmission*). Digital transmission systems transport information in digital form and, therefore, require a physical facility between the transmitter and receiver, such as a metallic wire pair, a coaxial cable, or an optical fiber cable. Digital transmission is covered in Chapters 10 and 11. In digital radio systems, the carrier facility could be a physical cable, or it could be free space.

The property that distinguishes digital radio systems from conventional analog-modulation communications systems is the nature of the modulating signal. Both analog and digital modulation systems use analog carriers to transport the information through the system. However, with analog modulation systems, the information signal is also analog, whereas with digital modulation, the information signal is digital, which could be computer-generated data or digitally encoded analog signals.

Referring to Equation 2-1, if the information signal is digital and the amplitude (V) of the carrier is varied proportional to the information signal, a digitally modulated signal called *amplitude shift keying* (ASK) is produced. If the frequency (f) is varied proportional to the information signal, *frequency shift keying* (FSK) is produced, and if the phase of the carrier (θ) is varied proportional to the information signal, *phase shift keying* (PSK) is produced. If both the amplitude and the phase are varied proportional to the information signal, *quadrature amplitude modulation* (QAM) results. ASK, FSK, PSK, and QAM are all forms of digital modulation:

$$v(t) = V \sin (2\pi \cdot ft + \boldsymbol{\theta})$$

$$\underset{\text{ASK}}{|} \quad \underset{\text{FSK}}{|} \quad \underset{\text{PSK}}{|}$$

$$\searrow \text{QAM} \swarrow \tag{2-1}$$

Digital modulation is ideally suited to a multitude of communications applications, including both cable and wireless systems. Applications include the following: (1) relatively low-speed voice-band data communications modems, such as those found in most personal computers; (2) high-speed data transmission systems, such as broadband *digital subscriber lines* (DSL); (3) digital microwave and satellite communications systems; and (4) cellular telephone *Personal Communications Systems* (PCS).

Figure 2-1 shows a simplified block diagram for a digital modulation system. In the transmitter, the precoder performs level conversion and then encodes the incoming data into groups of bits that modulate an analog carrier. The modulated carrier is shaped (fil-

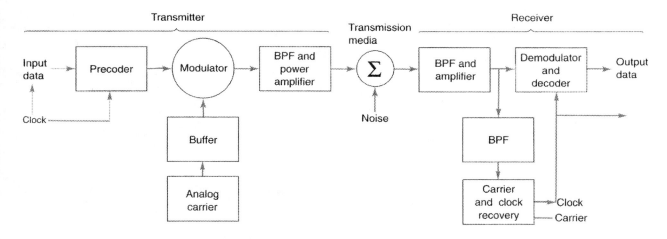

FIGURE 2-1 Simplified block diagram of a digital radio system

tered), amplified, and then transmitted through the transmission medium to the receiver. The transmission medium can be a metallic cable, optical fiber cable, Earth's atmosphere, or a combination of two or more types of transmission systems. In the receiver, the incoming signals are filtered, amplified, and then applied to the demodulator and decoder circuits, which extracts the original source information from the modulated carrier. The clock and carrier recovery circuits recover the analog carrier and digital timing (clock) signals from the incoming modulated wave since they are necessary to perform the demodulation process.

2-2 INFORMATION CAPACITY, BITS, BIT RATE, BAUD, AND M-ARY ENCODING

2-2-1 Information Capacity, Bits, and Bit Rate

Information theory is a highly theoretical study of the efficient use of bandwidth to propagate information through electronic communications systems. Information theory can be used to determine the *information capacity* of a data communications system. Information capacity is a measure of how much information can be propagated through a communications system and is a function of bandwidth and transmission time.

Information capacity represents the number of independent symbols that can be carried through a system in a given unit of time. The most basic digital symbol used to represent information is the *binary digit,* or *bit.* Therefore, it is often convenient to express the information capacity of a system as a *bit rate.* Bit rate is simply the number of bits transmitted during one second and is expressed in *bits per second* (bps).

In 1928, R. Hartley of Bell Telephone Laboratories developed a useful relationship among bandwidth, transmission time, and information capacity. Simply stated, Hartley's law is

$$I \propto B \times t \qquad (2\text{-}2)$$

where I = information capacity (bits per second)
  B = bandwidth (hertz)
  t = transmission time (seconds)

From Equation 2-2, it can be seen that information capacity is a linear function of bandwidth and transmission time and is directly proportional to both. If either the bandwidth or the transmission time changes, a directly proportional change occurs in the information capacity.

In 1948, mathematician Claude E. Shannon (also of Bell Telephone Laboratories) published a paper in the *Bell System Technical Journal* relating the information capacity of a communications channel to bandwidth and *signal-to-noise ratio*. The higher the signal-to-noise ratio, the better the performance and the higher the information capacity. Mathematically stated, *the Shannon limit for information capacity* is

$$I = B \log_2\left(1 + \frac{S}{N}\right) \tag{2-3}$$

or

$$I = 3.32B \log_{10}\left(1 + \frac{S}{N}\right) \tag{2-4}$$

where
I = information capacity (bps)
B = bandwidth (hertz)
$\dfrac{S}{N}$ = signal-to-noise power ratio (unitless)

For a standard telephone circuit with a signal-to-noise power ratio of 1000 (30 dB) and a bandwidth of 2.7 kHz, the Shannon limit for information capacity is

$$I = (3.32)(2700) \log_{10}(1 + 1000)$$
$$= 26.9 \text{ kbps}$$

Shannon's formula is often misunderstood. The results of the preceding example indicate that 26.9 kbps can be propagated through a 2.7-kHz communications channel. This may be true, but it cannot be done with a binary system. To achieve an information transmission rate of 26.9 kbps through a 2.7-kHz channel, each symbol transmitted must contain more than one bit.

2-2-2 M-ary Encoding

M-ary is a term derived from the word *binary*. *M* simply represents a digit that corresponds to the number of conditions, levels, or combinations possible for a given number of binary variables. It is often advantageous to encode at a level higher than binary (sometimes referred to as *beyond binary* or *higher-than-binary encoding*) where there are more than two conditions possible. For example, a digital signal with four possible conditions (voltage levels, frequencies, phases, and so on) is an *M*-ary system where $M = 4$. If there are eight possible conditions, $M = 8$ and so forth. The number of bits necessary to produce a given number of conditions is expressed mathematically as

$$N = \log_2 M \tag{2-5}$$

where
N = number of bits necessary
M = number of conditions, levels, or combinations possible with N bits

Equation 2-5 can be simplified and rearranged to express the number of conditions possible with N bits as

$$2^N = M \tag{2-6}$$

For example, with one bit, only $2^1 = 2$ conditions are possible. With two bits, $2^2 = 4$ conditions are possible, with three bits, $2^3 = 8$ conditions are possible, and so on.

Baud is a term that is often misunderstood and commonly confused with bit rate (bps). Bit rate refers to the rate of change of a digital information signal, which is usually binary. Baud, like bit rate, is also a rate of change; however, baud refers to the rate of change of a signal on the transmission medium after encoding and modulation have occurred. Hence, baud is a unit of transmission rate, modulation rate, or symbol rate and, therefore, the terms *symbols per second* and *baud* are often used interchangeably. Mathematically, baud is the reciprocal of the time of one output *signaling element,* and a signaling element may represent several information bits. Baud is expressed as

$$\text{baud} = \frac{1}{t_s} \qquad (2\text{-}7)$$

where   baud = symbol rate (baud per second)
t_s = time of one signaling element (seconds)

A signaling element is sometimes called a *symbol* and could be encoded as a change in the amplitude, frequency, or phase. For example, binary signals are generally encoded and transmitted one bit at a time in the form of discrete voltage levels representing logic 1s (highs) and logic 0s (lows). A baud is also transmitted one at a time; however, a baud may represent more than one information bit. Thus, the baud of a data communications system may be considerably less than the bit rate. In binary systems (such as binary FSK and binary PSK), *baud* and *bits per second* are equal. However, in higher-level systems (such as QPSK and 8-PSK), bps is always greater than baud.

According to H. Nyquist, binary digital signals can be propagated through an ideal noiseless transmission medium at a rate equal to two times the bandwidth of the medium. The minimum theoretical bandwidth necessary to propagate a signal is called the minimum *Nyquist bandwidth* or sometimes the minimum *Nyquist frequency.* Thus, $f_b = 2B$, where f_b is the bit rate in bps and B is the *ideal Nyquist bandwidth.* The actual bandwidth necessary to propagate a given bit rate depends on several factors, including the type of encoding and modulation used, the types of filters used, system noise, and desired error performance. The ideal bandwidth is generally used for comparison purposes only.

The relationship between bandwidth and bit rate also applies to the opposite situation. For a given bandwidth (B), the highest theoretical bit rate is $2B$. For example, a standard telephone circuit has a bandwidth of approximately 2700 Hz, which has the capacity to propagate 5400 bps through it. However, if more than two levels are used for signaling (higher-than-binary encoding), more than one bit may be transmitted at a time, and it is possible to propagate a bit rate that exceeds $2B$. Using multilevel signaling, the Nyquist formulation for channel capacity is

$$f_b = 2B \log_2 M \qquad (2\text{-}8)$$

where f_b = channel capacity (bps)
B = minimum Nyquist bandwidth (hertz)
M = number of discrete signal or voltage levels

Equation 2-8 can be rearranged to solve for the minimum bandwidth necessary to pass *M*-ary digitally modulated carriers

$$B = \left(\frac{f_b}{\log_2 M} \right) \qquad (2\text{-}9)$$

If N is substituted for $\log_2 M$, Equation 2-9 reduces to

$$B = \frac{f_b}{N} \qquad (2\text{-}10)$$

where N is the number of bits encoded into each signaling element.

If information bits are encoded (grouped) and then converted to signals with more than two levels, transmission rates in excess of $2B$ are possible, as will be seen in subsequent sections of this chapter. In addition, since baud is the encoded rate of change, it also equals the bit rate divided by the number of bits encoded into one signaling element. Thus,

$$\text{baud} = \frac{f_b}{N} \qquad (2\text{-}11)$$

By comparing Equation 2-10 with Equation 2-11, it can be seen that with digital modulation, the baud and the ideal minimum Nyquist bandwidth have the same value and are equal to the bit rate divided by the number of bits encoded. This statement holds true for all forms of digital modulation except frequency-shift keying.

2-3 AMPLITUDE-SHIFT KEYING

The simplest digital modulation technique is *amplitude-shift keying* (ASK), where a binary information signal directly modulates the amplitude of an analog carrier. ASK is similar to standard amplitude modulation except there are only two output amplitudes possible. Amplitude-shift keying is sometimes called *digital amplitude modulation* (DAM). Mathematically, amplitude-shift keying is

$$v_{(ask)}(t) = [1 + v_m(t)]\left[\frac{A}{2}\cos(\omega_c t)\right] \qquad (2\text{-}12)$$

where $v_{ask}(t)$ = amplitude-shift keying wave
$v_m(t)$ = digital information (modulating) signal (volts)
$A/2$ = unmodulated carrier amplitude (volts)
ω_c = analog carrier radian frequency (radians per second, $2\pi f_c t$)

In Equation 2-12, the modulating signal ($v_m[t]$) is a normalized binary waveform, where $+1$ V = logic 1 and -1 V = logic 0. Therefore, for a logic 1 input, $v_m(t) = +1$ V, Equation 2-12 reduces to

$$v_{(ask)}(t) = [1 + 1]\left[\frac{A}{2}\cos(\omega_c t)\right]$$

$$= A\cos(\omega_c t)$$

and for a logic 0 input, $v_m(t) = -1$ V, Equation 2-12 reduces to

$$v_{(ask)}(t) = [1 - 1]\left[\frac{A}{2}\cos(\omega_c t)\right]$$

$$= 0$$

Thus, the modulated wave $v_{ask}(t)$, is either $A\cos(\omega_c t)$ or 0. Hence, the carrier is either "*on*" or "*off*," which is why amplitude-shift keying is sometimes referred to as *on-off keying* (OOK).

Figure 2-2 shows the input and output waveforms from an ASK modulator. From the figure, it can be seen that for every change in the input binary data stream, there is one change in the ASK waveform, and the time of one bit (t_b) equals the time of one analog signaling element (t_s). It is also important to note that for the entire time the binary input is high, the output is a constant-amplitude, constant-frequency signal, and for the entire time the binary input is low, the carrier is off. The bit time is the reciprocal of the bit rate and the time of one signaling element is the reciprocal of the baud. Therefore, the rate of change of the

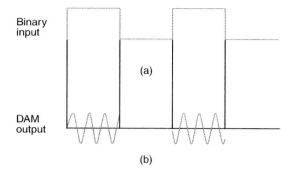

FIGURE 2-2 Digital amplitude modulation: (a) input binary; (b) output DAM waveform

ASK waveform (baud) is the same as the rate of change of the binary input (bps); thus, the bit rate equals the baud. With ASK, the bit rate is also equal to the minimum Nyquist bandwidth. This can be verified by substituting into Equations 2-10 and 2-11 and setting N to 1:

$$B = \frac{f_b}{1} = f_b \qquad \text{baud} = \frac{f_b}{1} = f_b$$

Example 2-1

Determine the baud and minimum bandwidth necessary to pass a 10 kbps binary signal using amplitude shift keying.

Solution   For ASK, $N = 1$, and the baud and minimum bandwidth are determined from Equations 2-11 and 2-10, respectively:

$$B = \frac{10{,}000}{1} = 10{,}000$$

$$\text{baud} = \frac{10{,}000}{1} = 10{,}000$$

The use of amplitude-modulated analog carriers to transport digital information is a relatively low-quality, low-cost type of digital modulation and, therefore, is seldom used except for very low-speed telemetry circuits.

2-4   FREQUENCY-SHIFT KEYING

Frequency-shift keying (FSK) is another relatively simple, low-performance type of digital modulation. FSK is a form of constant-amplitude angle modulation similar to standard frequency modulation (FM) except the modulating signal is a binary signal that varies between two discrete voltage levels rather than a continuously changing analog waveform. Consequently, FSK is sometimes called *binary FSK* (BFSK). The general expression for FSK is

$$v_{fsk}(t) = V_c \cos\{2\pi[f_c + v_m(t)\,\Delta f]t\} \qquad (2\text{-}13)$$

where $v_{fsk}(t)$ = binary FSK waveform
V_c = peak analog carrier amplitude (volts)
f_c = analog carrier center frequency (hertz)
Δf = peak change (shift) in the analog carrier frequency (hertz)
$v_m(t)$ = binary input (modulating) signal (volts)

From Equation 2-13, it can be seen that the peak shift in the carrier frequency (Δf) is proportional to the amplitude of the binary input signal ($v_m[t]$), and the direction of the shift

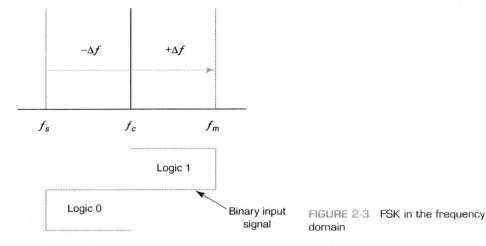

FIGURE 2-3 FSK in the frequency domain

is determined by the polarity. The modulating signal is a normalized binary waveform where a logic 1 = +1 V and a logic 0 = −1 V. Thus, for a logic 1 input, $v_m(t) = +1$, Equation 2-13 can be rewritten as

$$v_{fsk}(t) = V_c \cos[2\pi(f_c + \Delta f)t]$$

For a logic 0 input, $v_m(t) = -1$, Equation 2-13 becomes

$$v_{fsk}(t) = V_c \cos[2\pi(f_c - \Delta f)t]$$

With binary FSK, the carrier center frequency (f_c) is shifted (deviated) up and down in the frequency domain by the binary input signal as shown in Figure 2-3. As the binary input signal changes from a logic 0 to a logic 1 and vice versa, the output frequency shifts between two frequencies: a mark, or logic 1 frequency (f_m), and a space, or logic 0 frequency (f_s). The mark and space frequencies are separated from the carrier frequency by the peak frequency deviation (Δf) and from each other by 2 Δf.

With FSK, frequency deviation is defined as the difference between either the mark or space frequency and the center frequency, or half the difference between the mark and space frequencies. Frequency deviation is illustrated in Figure 2-3 and expressed mathematically as

$$\Delta f = \frac{|f_m - f_s|}{2} \tag{2-14}$$

where Δf = frequency deviation (hertz)
             $|f_m - f_s|$ = absolute difference between the mark and space frequencies (hertz)

Figure 2-4a shows in the time domain the binary input to an FSK modulator and the corresponding FSK output. As the figure shows, when the binary input (f_b) changes from a logic 1 to a logic 0 and vice versa, the FSK output frequency shifts from a mark (f_m) to a space (f_s) frequency and vice versa. In Figure 2-4a, the mark frequency is the higher frequency ($f_c + \Delta f$), and the space frequency is the lower frequency ($f_c - \Delta f$), although this relationship could be just the opposite. Figure 2-4b shows the truth table for a binary FSK modulator. The truth table shows the input and output possibilities for a given digital modulation scheme.

2-4-1 FSK Bit Rate, Baud, and Bandwidth

In Figure 2-4a, it can be seen that the time of one bit (t_b) is the same as the time the FSK output is a mark of space frequency (t_s). Thus, the bit time equals the time of an FSK signaling element, and the bit rate equals the baud.

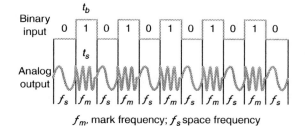

binary input	frequency output
0	space (f_s)
1	mark (f_m)

f_m, mark frequency; f_s space frequency

(a) (b)

FIGURE 2-4 FSK in the time domain: (a) waveform; (b) truth table

The baud for binary FSK can also be determined by substituting $N = 1$ in Equation 2-11:

$$\text{baud} = \frac{f_b}{1} = f_b$$

FSK is the exception to the rule for digital modulation, as the minimum bandwidth is not determined from Equation 2-10. The minimum bandwidth for FSK is given as

$$B = |(f_s - f_b) - (f_m - f_b)|$$
$$= |f_s - f_m| + 2f_b$$

and since $|f_s - f_m|$ equals $2\Delta f$, the minimum bandwidth can be approximated as

$$B = 2(\Delta f + f_b) \qquad (2\text{-}15)$$

where B = minimum Nyquist bandwidth (hertz)
   Δf = frequency deviation ($|f_m - f_s|$) (hertz)
   f_b = input bit rate (bps)

Note how closely Equation 2-15 resembles Carson's rule for determining the approximate bandwidth for an FM wave. The only difference in the two equations is that, for FSK, the bit rate (f_b) is substituted for the modulating-signal frequency (f_m).

Example 2-2

Determine (a) the peak frequency deviation, (b) minimum bandwidth, and (c) baud for a binary FSK signal with a mark frequency of 49 kHz, a space frequency of 51 kHz, and an input bit rate of 2 kbps.

Solution a. The peak frequency deviation is determined from Equation 2-14:

$$\Delta f = \frac{|49\text{kHz} - 51\text{kHz}|}{2}$$
$$= 1 \text{ kHz}$$

b. The minimum bandwidth is determined from Equation 2-15:

$$B = 2(1000 + 2000)$$
$$= 6 \text{ kHz}$$

c. For FSK, $N = 1$, and the baud is determined from Equation 2-11 as

$$\text{baud} = \frac{2000}{1} = 2000$$

Bessel functions can also be used to determine the approximate bandwidth for an FSK wave. As shown in Figure 2-5, the fastest rate of change (highest fundamental frequency) in a nonreturn-to-zero (NRZ) binary signal occurs when alternating 1s and 0s are occurring (i.e., a square wave). Since it takes a high and a low to produce a cycle, the highest fundamental frequency present in a square wave equals the repetition rate of the square wave, which with a binary signal is equal to half the bit rate. Therefore,

$$f_a = \frac{f_b}{2} \qquad (2\text{-}16)$$

where f_a = highest fundamental frequency of the binary input signal (hertz)
        f_b = input bit rate (bps)

The formula used for modulation index in FM is also valid for FSK; thus,

$$h = \frac{\Delta f}{f_a} \qquad \text{(unitless)} \qquad (2\text{-}17)$$

where h = FM modulation index called the h-factor in FSK
        f_a = fundamental frequency of the binary modulating signal (hertz)
        Δf = peak frequency deviation (hertz)

The worst-case modulation index (deviation ratio) is that which yields the widest bandwidth. The worst-case or widest bandwidth occurs when both the frequency deviation and the modulating-signal frequency are at their maximum values. As described earlier, the peak frequency deviation in FSK is constant and always at its maximum value, and the highest fundamental frequency is equal to half the incoming bit rate. Thus,

$$h = \frac{\dfrac{|f_m - f_s|}{2}}{\dfrac{f_b}{2}} \qquad \text{(unitless)}$$

or

$$h = \frac{|f_m - f_s|}{f_b} \qquad (2\text{-}18)$$

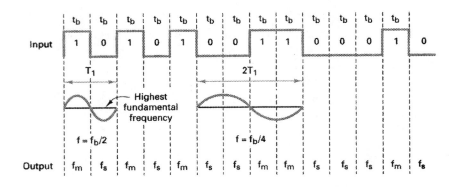

FIGURE 2-5   FSK modulator; t_b, time of one bit = $1/f_b$; f_m, mark frequency; f_s, space frequency; T_1, period of shortest cycle; $1/T_1$, fundamental frequency of binary square wave; f_b, input bit rate (bps)

where h = h-factor (unitless)
         f_m = mark frequency (hertz)
         f_s = space frequency (hertz)
         f_b = bit rate (bits per second)

Example 2-3

Using a Bessel table, determine the minimum bandwidth for the same FSK signal described in Example 2-1 with a mark frequency of 49 kHz, a space frequency of 51 kHz, and an input bit rate of 2 kbps.

Solution   The modulation index is found by substituting into Equation 2-17:

or
$$h = \frac{|49 \text{ kHz} - 51 \text{ kHz}|}{2 \text{ kbps}}$$

$$= \frac{2 \text{ kHz}}{2 \text{ kbps}}$$

$$= 1$$

From a Bessel table, three sets of significant sidebands are produced for a modulation index of one. Therefore, the bandwidth can be determined as follows:
$$B = 2(3 \times 1000)$$
$$= 6000 \text{ Hz}$$

The bandwidth determined in Example 2-3 using the Bessel table is identical to the bandwidth determined in Example 2-2.

2-4-2   FSK Transmitter

Figure 2-6 shows a simplified binary FSK modulator, which is very similar to a conventional FM modulator and is very often a voltage-controlled oscillator (VCO). The center frequency (f_c) is chosen such that it falls halfway between the mark and space frequencies. A logic 1 input shifts the VCO output to the mark frequency, and a logic 0 input shifts the VCO output to the space frequency. Consequently, as the binary input signal changes back and forth between logic 1 and logic 0 conditions, the VCO output shifts or deviates back and forth between the mark and space frequencies.

In a binary FSK modulator, Δf is the peak frequency deviation of the carrier and is equal to the difference between the carrier rest frequency and either the mark or the space frequency (or half the difference between the carrier rest frequency) and either the mark or the space frequency (or half the difference between the mark and space frequencies). A VCO-FSK modulator can be operated in the sweep mode where the peak frequency deviation is

FIGURE 2-6   FSK modulator

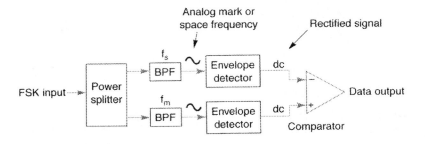

FIGURE 2-7 Noncoherent FSK demodulator

FIGURE 2-8 Coherent FSK demodulator

simply the product of the binary input voltage and the deviation sensitivity of the VCO. With the sweep mode of modulation, the frequency deviation is expressed mathematically as

$$\Delta f = v_m(t)k_l \qquad (2\text{-}19)$$

where
Δf = peak frequency deviation (hertz)
$v_m(t)$ = peak binary modulating-signal voltage (volts)
k_l = deviation sensitivity (hertz per volt).

With binary FSK, the amplitude of the input signal can only be one of two values, one for a logic 1 condition and one for a logic 0 condition. Therefore, the peak frequency deviation is constant and always at its maximum value. Frequency deviation is simply plus or minus the peak voltage of the binary signal times the deviation sensitivity of the VCO. Since the peak voltage is the same for a logic 1 as it is for a logic 0, the magnitude of the frequency deviation is also the same for a logic 1 as it is for a logic 0.

2-4-3 FSK Receiver

FSK demodulation is quite simple with a circuit such as the one shown in Figure 2-7. The FSK input signal is simultaneously applied to the inputs of both bandpass filters (BPFs) through a power splitter. The respective filter passes only the mark or only the space frequency on to its respective envelope detector. The envelope detectors, in turn, indicate the total power in each passband, and the comparator responds to the largest of the two powers. This type of FSK detection is referred to as noncoherent detection; there is no frequency involved in the demodulation process that is synchronized either in phase, frequency, or both with the incoming FSK signal.

Figure 2-8 shows the block diagram for a coherent FSK receiver. The incoming FSK signal is multiplied by a recovered carrier signal that has the exact same frequency and phase as the transmitter reference. However, the two transmitted frequencies (the mark and space frequencies) are not generally continuous; it is not practical to reproduce a local reference that is coherent with both of them. Consequently, coherent FSK detection is seldom used.

FIGURE 2-9 PLL-FSK demodulator

FIGURE 2-10 Noncontinuous FSK waveform

The most common circuit used for demodulating binary FSK signals is the *phase-locked loop* (PLL), which is shown in block diagram form in Figure 2-9. A PLL-FSK demodulator works similarly to a PLL-FM demodulator. As the input to the PLL shifts between the mark and space frequencies, the *dc error voltage* at the output of the phase comparator follows the frequency shift. Because there are only two input frequencies (mark and space), there are also only two output error voltages. One represents a logic 1 and the other a logic 0. Therefore, the output is a two-level (binary) representation of the FSK input. Generally, the natural frequency of the PLL is made equal to the center frequency of the FSK modulator. As a result, the changes in the dc error voltage follow the changes in the analog input frequency and are symmetrical around 0 V.

Binary FSK has a poorer error performance than PSK or QAM and, consequently, is seldom used for high-performance digital radio systems. Its use is restricted to low-performance, low-cost, asynchronous data modems that are used for data communications over analog, voice-band telephone lines.

2-4-4 Continuous-Phase Frequency-Shift Keying

Continuous-phase frequency-shift keying (CP-FSK) is binary FSK except the mark and space frequencies are synchronized with the input binary bit rate. Synchronous simply implies that there is a precise time relationship between the two; it does not mean they are equal. With CP-FSK, the mark and space frequencies are selected such that they are separated from the center frequency by an exact multiple of one-half the bit rate (f_m and $f_s = n[f_b/2]$), where n = any integer). This ensures a smooth phase transition in the analog output signal when it changes from a mark to a space frequency or vice versa. Figure 2-10 shows a noncontinuous FSK waveform. It can be seen that when the input changes from a logic 1 to a logic 0 and vice versa, there is an abrupt phase discontinuity in the analog signal. When this occurs, the demodulator has trouble following the frequency shift; consequently, an error may occur.

Figure 2-11 shows a continuous phase FSK waveform. Notice that when the output frequency changes, it is a smooth, continuous transition. Consequently, there are no phase discontinuities. CP-FSK has a better bit-error performance than conventional binary FSK for a given signal-to-noise ratio. The disadvantage of CP-FSK is that it requires synchronization circuits and is, therefore, more expensive to implement.

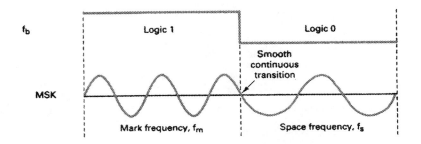

FIGURE 2-11 Continuous-phase MSK waveform

2-5 PHASE-SHIFT KEYING

Phase-shift keying (PSK) is another form of *angle-modulated, constant-amplitude* digital modulation. PSK is an *M*-ary digital modulation scheme similar to conventional phase modulation except with PSK the input is a binary digital signal and there are a limited number of output phases possible. The input binary information is encoded into groups of bits before modulating the carrier. The number of bits in a group ranges from 1 to 12 or more. The number of output phases is defined by *M* as described in Equation 2-6 and determined by the number of bits in the group (*n*).

2-5-1 Binary Phase-Shift Keying

The simplest form of PSK is *binary phase-shift keying* (BPSK), where $N = 1$ and $M = 2$. Therefore, with BPSK, two phases ($2^1 = 2$) are possible for the carrier. One phase represents a logic 1, and the other phase represents a logic 0. As the input digital signal changes state (i.e., from a 1 to a 0 or from a 0 to a 1), the phase of the output carrier shifts between two angles that are separated by 180°. Hence, other names for BPSK are *phase reversal keying* (PRK) and *biphase modulation*. BPSK is a form of square-wave modulation of a *continuous wave* (CW) signal.

2-5-1-1 BPSK transmitter. Figure 2-12 shows a simplified block diagram of a BPSK transmitter. The balanced modulator acts as a phase reversing switch. Depending on

FIGURE 2-12 BPSK transmitter

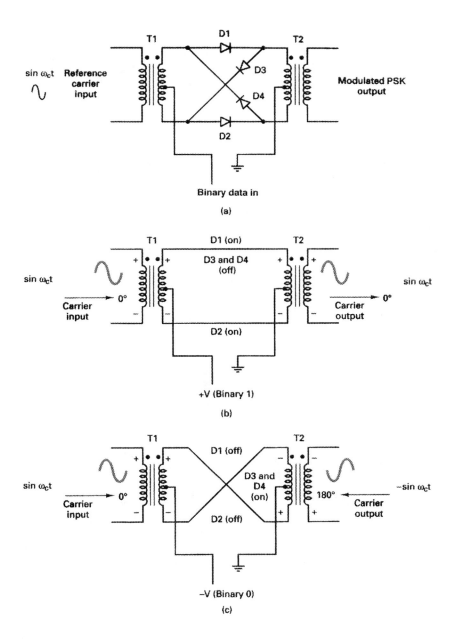

FIGURE 2-13   (a) Balanced ring modulator; (b) logic 1 input; (c) logic 0 input

the logic condition of the digital input, the carrier is transferred to the output either in phase or 180° out of phase with the reference carrier oscillator.

Figure 2-13 shows the schematic diagram of a balanced ring modulator. The balanced modulator has two inputs: a carrier that is in phase with the reference oscillator and the binary digital data. For the balanced modulator to operate properly, the digital input voltage must be much greater than the peak carrier voltage. This ensures that the digital input controls the on/off state of diodes D1 to D4. If the binary input is a logic 1 (positive voltage), diodes D1 and D2 are forward biased and on, while diodes D3 and D4 are reverse biased and off (Figure 2-13b). With the polarities shown, the carrier voltage is developed across

Binary input	Output phase
Logic 0	180°
Logic 1	0°

(a)

(b)

(c)

FIGURE 2-14   BPSK modulator: (a) truth table; (b) phasor
diagram; (c) constellation diagram

transformer T2 in phase with the carrier voltage across T1. Consequently, the output signal is in phase with the reference oscillator.

If the binary input is a logic 0 (negative voltage), diodes D1 and D2 are reverse biased and off, while diodes D3 and D4 are forward biased and on (Figure 2-13c). As a result, the carrier voltage is developed across transformer T2 180° out of phase with the carrier voltage across T1. Consequently, the output signal is 180° out of phase with the reference oscillator. Figure 2-14 shows the truth table, phasor diagram, and constellation diagram for a BPSK modulator. A *constellation diagram,* which is sometimes called a *signal state-space diagram,* is similar to a phasor diagram except that the entire phasor is not drawn. In a constellation diagram, only the relative positions of the peaks of the phasors are shown.

2-5-1-2 Bandwidth considerations of BPSK.   A balanced modulator is a *product modulator;* the output signal is the product of the two input signals. In a BPSK modulator, the carrier input signal is multiplied by the binary data. If $+1$ V is assigned to a logic 1 and -1 V is assigned to a logic 0, the input carrier (sin $\omega_c t$) is multiplied by either a $+$ or -1. Consequently, the output signal is either $+1$ sin $\omega_c t$ or -1 sin $\omega_c t$; the first represents a signal that is *in phase* with the reference oscillator, the latter a signal that is 180° out of phase with the reference oscillator. Each time the input logic condition changes, the output phase changes. Consequently, for BPSK, the output rate of change (baud) is equal to the input rate of change (bps), and the widest output bandwidth occurs when the input binary data are an alternating 1/0 sequence. The fundamental frequency (f_a) of an alternative 1/0 bit sequence is equal to one-half of the bit rate ($f_b/2$). Mathematically, the output of a BPSK modulator is proportional to

$$\text{BPSK output} = [\sin(2\pi f_a t)] \times [\sin(2\pi f_c t)] \tag{2-20}$$

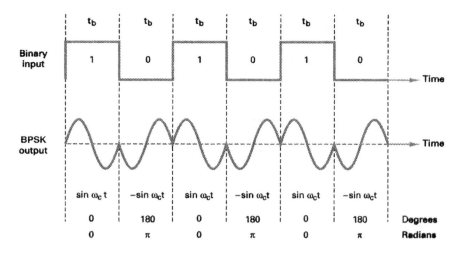

FIGURE 2-15 Output phase-versus-time relationship for a BPSK modulator

where f_a = maximum fundamental frequency of binary input (hertz)
  f_c = reference carrier frequency (hertz)

Solving for the trig identity for the product of two sine functions,

$$\frac{1}{2}\cos[2\pi(f_c - f_a)t] - \frac{1}{2}\cos[2\pi(f_c + f_a)t]$$

Thus, the minimum double-sided Nyquist bandwidth (B) is

$$
\begin{array}{cc}
\begin{array}{r} f_c + f_a \\ -(f_c + f_a) \\ \hline \end{array} & \text{or} \quad
\begin{array}{r} f_c + f_a \\ -f_c + f_a \\ \hline 2f_a \end{array}
\end{array}
$$

and because $f_a = f_b/2$, where f_b = input bit rate,

$$B = \frac{2f_b}{2} = f_b$$

where B is the minimum double-sided Nyquist bandwidth.

Figure 2-15 shows the output phase-versus-time relationship for a BPSK waveform. As the figure shows, a logic 1 input produces an analog output signal with a 0° phase angle, and a logic 0 input produces an analog output signal with a 180° phase angle. As the binary input shifts between a logic 1 and a logic 0 condition and vice versa, the phase of the BPSK waveform shifts between 0° and 180°, respectively. For simplicity, only one cycle of the analog carrier is shown in each signaling element, although there may be anywhere between a fraction of a cycle to several thousand cycles, depending on the relationship between the input bit rate and the analog carrier frequency. It can also be seen that the time of one BPSK signaling element (t_s) is equal to the time of one information bit (t_b), which indicates that the bit rate equals the baud.

Example 2-4

For a BPSK modulator with a carrier frequency of 70 MHz and an input bit rate of 10 Mbps, determine the maximum and minimum upper and lower side frequencies, draw the output spectrum, determine the minimum Nyquist bandwidth, and calculate the baud.

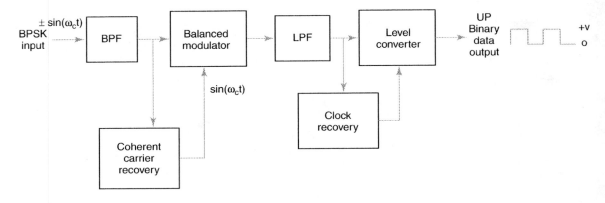

FIGURE 2-16   Block diagram of a BPSK receiver

Solution   Substituting into Equation 2-20 yields

$$\text{output} = (\sin \omega_a t)(\sin \omega_c t)$$

$$= [\sin 2\pi(5 \text{ MHz})t][\sin 2\pi(70 \text{ MHz})t]$$

$$= \underbrace{\frac{1}{2} \cos 2\pi(70 \text{ MHz} - 5 \text{ MHz})t}_{\text{lower side frequency}} - \underbrace{\frac{1}{2} \cos 2\pi(70 \text{ MHz} + 5 \text{ MHz})t}_{\text{upper side frequency}}$$

Minimum lower side frequency (LSF):

$$\text{LSF} = 70 \text{ MHz} - 5 \text{ MHz} = 65 \text{ MHz}$$

Maximum upper side frequency (USF):

$$\text{USF} = 70 \text{ MHz} + 5 \text{ MHz} = 75 \text{ MHz}$$

Therefore, the output spectrum for the worst-case binary input conditions is as follows:
The minimum Nyquist bandwidth (B) is

(Suppressed)

$$B = 75 \text{ MHz} - 65 \text{ MHz} = 10 \text{ MHz}$$

and the baud $= f_b$ or 10 megabaud.

2-5-1-3 BPSK receiver.   Figure 2-16 shows the block diagram of a BPSK receiver.
The input signal may be $+\sin \omega_c t$ or $-\sin \omega_c t$. The coherent carrier recovery circuit detects
and regenerates a carrier signal that is both frequency and phase coherent with the original
transmit carrier. The balanced modulator is a product detector; the output is the product of
the two inputs (the BPSK signal and the recovered carrier). The low-pass filter (LPF) separates the recovered binary data from the complex demodulated signal. Mathematically, the
demodulation process is as follows.

For a BPSK input signal of $+\sin \omega_c t$ (logic 1), the output of the balanced modulator is

$$\text{output} = (\sin \omega_c t)(\sin \omega_c t) = \sin^2 \omega_c t \tag{2-21}$$

or
$$\sin^2 \omega_c t = \frac{1}{2}(1 - \cos 2\omega_c t) = \frac{1}{2} - \frac{1}{2}\cos 2\,\omega_c t \nearrow \text{(filtered out)}$$

leaving
$$\text{output} = +\frac{1}{2}V = \text{logic } 1$$

It can be seen that the output of the balanced modulator contains a positive voltage $(+[1/2]V)$ and a cosine wave at twice the carrier frequency $(2\omega_c)$ The LPF has a cutoff frequency much lower than $2\omega_c$ and, thus, blocks the second harmonic of the carrier and passes only the positive constant component. A positive voltage represents a demodulated logic 1.

For a BPSK input signal of $-\sin \omega_c t$ (logic 0), the output of the balanced modulator is

$$\text{output} = (-\sin \omega_c t)(\sin \omega_c t) = -\sin^2 \omega_c t$$

or
$$-\sin^2 \omega_c t = -\frac{1}{2}(1 - \cos 2\omega_c t) = -\frac{1}{2} + \frac{1}{2}\cos 2\omega_c t \nearrow \text{(filtered out)}$$

leaving
$$\text{output} = -\frac{1}{2}V = \text{logic } 0$$

The output of the balanced modulator contains a negative voltage $(-[1/2]V)$ and a cosine wave at twice the carrier frequency $(2\omega_c)$. Again, the LPF blocks the second harmonic of the carrier and passes only the negative constant component. A negative voltage represents a demodulated logic 0.

2-5-2 Quaternary Phase-Shift Keying

Quaternary phase shift keying (QPSK), or *quadrature* PSK as it is sometimes called, is another form of angle-modulated, constant-amplitude digital modulation. QPSK is an *M*-ary encoding scheme where $N = 2$ and $M = 4$ (hence, the name "quaternary" meaning "4"). With QPSK, four output phases are possible for a single carrier frequency. Because there are four output phases, there must be four different input conditions. Because the digital input to a QPSK modulator is a binary (base 2) signal, to produce four different input combinations, the modulator requires more than a single input bit to determine the output condition. With two bits, there are four possible conditions: 00, 01, 10, and 11. Therefore, with QPSK, the binary input data are combined into groups of two bits, called *dibits*. In the modulator, each dibit code generates one of the four possible output phases $(+45°, +135°, -45°, \text{and} -135°)$. Therefore, for each two-bit dibit clocked into the modulator, a single output change occurs, and the rate of change at the output (baud) is equal to one-half the input bit rate (i.e., two input bits produce one output phase change).

2-5-2-1 QPSK transmitter. A block diagram of a QPSK modulator is shown in Figure 2-17. Two bits (a dibit) are clocked into the bit splitter. After both bits have been serially inputted, they are simultaneously parallel outputted. One bit is directed to the I channel and the other to the Q channel. The I bit modulates a carrier that is in phase with the reference oscillator (hence the name "I" for "in phase" channel), and the Q bit modulates a carrier that is 90° out of phase or in quadrature with the reference carrier (hence the name "Q" for "quadrature" channel).

It can be seen that once a dibit has been split into the I and Q channels, the operation is the same as in a BPSK modulator. Essentially, a QPSK modulator is two BPSK modulators combined in parallel. Again, for a logic 1 = +1 V and a logic 0 = −1 V, two phases are possible at the output of the I balanced modulator $(+\sin \omega_c t \text{ and } -\sin \omega_c t)$, and two

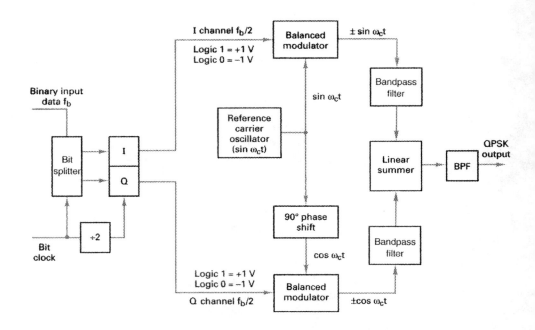

FIGURE 2-17   QPSK modulator

phases are possible at the output of the Q balanced modulator ($+\cos \omega_c t$ and $-\cos \omega_c t$). When the linear summer combines the two quadrature (90° out of phase) signals, there are four possible resultant phasors given by these expressions: $+ \sin \omega_c t + \cos \omega_c t$, $+ \sin \omega_c t - \cos \omega_c t$, $-\sin \omega_c t + \cos \omega_c t$, and $-\sin \omega_c t - \cos \omega_c t$.

Example 2-5

For the QPSK modulator shown in Figure 2-17, construct the truth table, phasor diagram, and constellation diagram.

Solution   For a binary data input of Q = 0 and I = 0, the two inputs to the I balanced modulator are -1 and $\sin \omega_c t$, and the two inputs to the Q balanced modulator are -1 and $\cos \omega_c t$. Consequently, the outputs are

$$\text{I balanced modulator} = (-1)(\sin \omega_c t) = -1 \sin \omega_c t$$
$$\text{Q balanced modulator} = (-1)(\cos \omega_c t) = -1 \cos \omega_c t$$

and the output of the linear summer is

$$-1 \cos \omega_c t - 1 \sin \omega_c t = 1.414 \sin(\omega_c t - 135°)$$

For the remaining dibit codes (01, 10, and 11), the procedure is the same. The results are shown in Figure 2-18a.

In Figures 2-18b and c, it can be seen that with QPSK each of the four possible output phasors has exactly the same amplitude. Therefore, the binary information must be encoded entirely in the phase of the output signal. This constant amplitude characteristic is the most important characteristic of PSK that distinguishes it from QAM, which is explained later in this chapter. Also, from Figure 2-18b, it can be seen that the angular separation between any two adjacent phasors in QPSK is 90°. Therefore, a QPSK signal can undergo almost a +45° or −45° shift in phase during transmission and still retain the correct encoded information when demodulated at the receiver. Figure 2-19 shows the output phase-versus-time relationship for a QPSK modulator.

Binary input		QPSK output phase
Q	I	
0	0	−135°
0	1	−45°
1	0	+135°
1	1	+45°

(a)

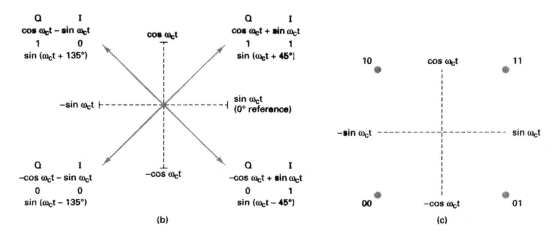

(b)

(c)

FIGURE 2-18 QPSK modulator: (a) truth table; (b) phasor diagram; (c) constellation diagram

FIGURE 2-19 Output phase-versus-time relationship for a QPSK modulator

2-5-2-2 Bandwidth considerations of QPSK. With QPSK, because the input data are divided into two channels, the bit rate in either the I or the Q channel is equal to one-half of the input data rate ($f_b/2$). (Essentially, the bit splitter stretches the I and Q bits to twice their input bit length.) Consequently, the highest fundamental frequency present at the data input to the I or the Q balanced modulator is equal to one-fourth of the input data rate (one-half of $f_b/2 = f_b/4$). As a result, the output of the I and Q balanced modulators requires a minimum double-sided Nyquist bandwidth equal to one-half of the incoming bit rate (f_N = twice $f_b/4$ = $f_b/2$). Thus, with QPSK, a bandwidth compression is realized (the minimum bandwidth is less than the incoming bit rate). Also, because the QPSK output signal does not change phase until two bits (a dibit) have been clocked into the bit splitter, the fastest output rate of change (baud) is also equal to one-half of the input bit rate. As with BPSK, the minimum bandwidth and the baud are equal. This relationship is shown in Figure 2-20.

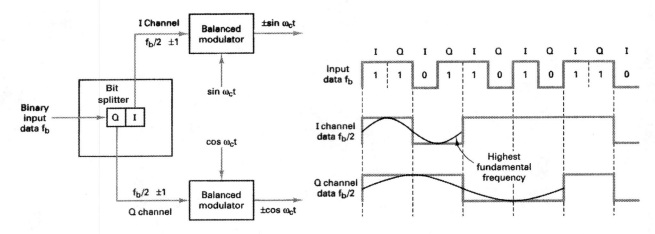

FIGURE 2-20 Bandwidth considerations of a QPSK modulator

In Figure 2-20, it can be seen that the worse-case input condition to the I or Q balanced modulator is an alternative 1/0 pattern, which occurs when the binary input data have a 1100 repetitive pattern. One cycle of the fastest binary transition (a 1/0 sequence) in the I or Q channel takes the same time as four input data bits. Consequently, the highest fundamental frequency at the input and fastest rate of change at the output of the balanced modulators is equal to one-fourth of the binary input bit rate.

The output of the balanced modulators can be expressed mathematically as

$$\text{output} = (\sin \omega_a t)(\sin \omega_c t) \tag{2-22}$$

where

$$\omega_a t = 2\pi \frac{f_b}{4} t \quad \text{and} \quad \omega_c t = 2\pi f_c$$

$$\underbrace{\phantom{\omega_a t = 2\pi \frac{f_b}{4} t}}_{\text{modulating signal}} \qquad \underbrace{}_{\text{carrier}}$$

Thus,

$$\text{output} = \left(\sin 2\pi \frac{f_b}{4} t \right)(\sin 2\pi f_c t)$$

$$\frac{1}{2} \cos 2\pi \left(f_c - \frac{f_b}{4} \right) t - \frac{1}{2} \cos 2\pi \left(f_c + \frac{f_b}{4} \right) t$$

The output frequency spectrum extends from $f_c + f_b/4$ to $f_c - f_b/4$, and the minimum bandwidth (f_N) is

$$\left(f_c + \frac{f_b}{4} \right) - \left(f_c - \frac{f_b}{4} \right) = \frac{2f_b}{4} = \frac{f_b}{2}$$

Example 2-6

For a QPSK modulator with an input data rate (f_b) equal to 10 Mbps and a carrier frequency of 70 MHz, determine the minimum double-sided Nyquist bandwidth (f_N) and the baud. Also, compare the results with those achieved with the BPSK modulator in Example 2-4. Use the QPSK block diagram shown in Figure 2-17 as the modulator model.

Solution The bit rate in both the I and Q channels is equal to one-half of the transmission bit rate, or

$$f_{bQ} = f_{bI} = \frac{f_b}{2} = \frac{10 \text{ Mbps}}{2} = 5 \text{ Mbps}$$

The highest fundamental frequency presented to either balanced modulator is

$$f_a = \frac{f_{bQ}}{2} \text{ or } \frac{f_{bl}}{2} = \frac{5 \text{ Mbps}}{2} = 2.5 \text{ MHz}$$

The output wave from each balanced modulator is

$$(\sin 2\pi f_a t)(\sin 2\pi f_c t)$$

$$\frac{1}{2} \cos 2\pi (f_c - f_a)t - \frac{1}{2} \cos 2\pi (f_c + f_a)t$$

$$\frac{1}{2} \cos 2\pi [(70 - 2.5) \text{ MHz}]t - \frac{1}{2} \cos 2\pi [(70 + 2.5) \text{ MHz}]t$$

$$\frac{1}{2} \cos 2\pi (67.5 \text{ MHz})t - \frac{1}{2} \cos 2\pi (72.5 \text{ MHz})t$$

The minimum Nyquist bandwidth is

$$B = (72.5 - 67.5) \text{ MHz} = 5 \text{ MHz}$$

The symbol rate equals the bandwidth; thus,

$$\text{symbol rate} = 5 \text{ megabaud}$$

The output spectrum is as follows:

(Suppressed)

$$B = 5 \text{ MHz}$$

It can be seen that for the same input bit rate the minimum bandwidth required to pass the output of the QPSK modulator is equal to one-half of that required for the BPSK modulator in Example 2-4. Also, the baud rate for the QPSK modulator is one-half that of the BPSK modulator.

The minimum bandwidth for the QPSK system described in Example 2-6 can also be determined by simply substituting into Equation 2-10:

$$B = \frac{10 \text{ Mbps}}{2}$$

$$= 5 \text{ MHz}$$

2-5-2-3 QPSK receiver. The block diagram of a QPSK receiver is shown in Figure 2-21. The power splitter directs the input QPSK signal to the I and Q product detectors and the carrier recovery circuit. The carrier recovery circuit reproduces the original transmit carrier oscillator signal. The recovered carrier must be frequency and phase coherent with the transmit reference carrier. The QPSK signal is demodulated in the I and Q product detectors, which generate the original I and Q data bits. The outputs of the product detectors are fed to the bit combining circuit, where they are converted from parallel I and Q data channels to a single binary output data stream.

The incoming QPSK signal may be any one of the four possible output phases shown in Figure 2-18. To illustrate the demodulation process, let the incoming QPSK signal be $-\sin \omega_c t + \cos \omega_c t$. Mathematically, the demodulation process is as follows.

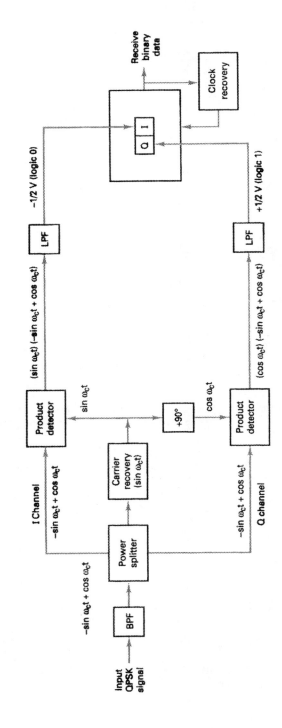

FIGURE 2-21   QPSK receiver

The receive QPSK signal $(-\sin \omega_c t + \cos \omega_c t)$ is one of the inputs to the I product detector. The other input is the recovered carrier $(\sin \omega_c t)$. The output of the I product detector is

$$I = \underbrace{(-\sin \omega_c t + \cos \omega_c t)}_{\text{QPSK input signal}} \underbrace{(\sin \omega_c t)}_{\text{carrier}} \qquad (2\text{-}23)$$

$$= (-\sin \omega_c t)(\sin \omega_c t) + (\cos \omega_c t)(\sin \omega_c t)$$

$$= -\sin^2 \omega_c t + (\cos \omega_c t)(\sin \omega_c t)$$

$$= -\frac{1}{2}(1 - \cos 2\omega_c t) + \frac{1}{2}\sin(\omega_c + \omega_c)t + \frac{1}{2}\sin(\omega_c - \omega_c)t$$

$$I = -\frac{1}{2} + \frac{1}{2}\cos 2\omega_c t \overset{\text{(filtered out)}}{\nearrow} + \frac{1}{2}\sin 2\omega_c t \overset{\text{(equals 0)}}{\nearrow} + \frac{1}{2}\sin 0$$

$$= -\frac{1}{2}V \text{ (logic 0)}$$

Again, the receive QPSK signal $(-\sin \omega_c t + \cos \omega_c t)$ is one of the inputs to the Q product detector. The other input is the recovered carrier shifted 90° in phase $(\cos \omega_c t)$. The output of the Q product detector is

$$Q = \underbrace{(-\sin \omega_c t + \cos \omega_c t)}_{\text{QPSK input signal}} \underbrace{(\cos \omega_c t)}_{\text{carrier}} \qquad (2\text{-}24)$$

$$= \cos^2 \omega_c t - (\sin \omega_c t)(\cos \omega_c t)$$

$$= \frac{1}{2}(1 + \cos 2\omega_c t) - \frac{1}{2}\sin(\omega_c + \omega_c)t - \frac{1}{2}\sin(\omega_c - \omega_c)t$$

$$Q = \frac{1}{2} + \frac{1}{2}\cos 2\omega_c t \overset{\text{(filtered out)}}{\nearrow} - \frac{1}{2}\sin 2\omega_c t \overset{\text{(equals 0)}}{\nearrow} - \frac{1}{2}\sin 0$$

$$= \frac{1}{2}V(\text{logic 1})$$

The demodulated I and Q bits (0 and 1, respectively) correspond to the constellation diagram and truth table for the QPSK modulator shown in Figure 2-18.

2-5-2-4 Offset QPSK. *Offset QPSK* (OQPSK) is a modified form of QPSK where the bit waveforms on the I and Q channels are offset or shifted in phase from each other by one-half of a bit time.

Figure 2-22 shows a simplified block diagram, the bit sequence alignment, and the constellation diagram for a OQPSK modulator. Because changes in the I channel occur at the midpoints of the Q channel bits and vice versa, there is never more than a single bit change in the dibit code and, therefore, there is never more than a 90° shift in the output phase. In conventional QPSK, a change in the input dibit from 00 to 11 or 01 to 10 causes a corresponding 180° shift in the output phase. Therefore, an advantage of OQPSK is the limited phase shift that must be imparted during modulation. A disadvantage of OQPSK is

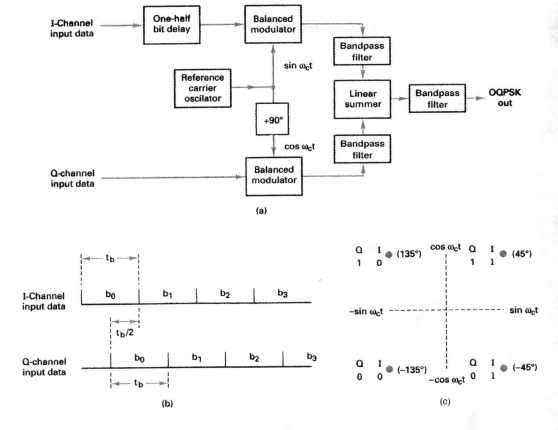

FIGURE 2-22 Offset keyed (OQPSK): (a) block diagram; (b) bit alignment; (c) constellation diagram

that changes in the output phase occur at twice the data rate in either the I or Q channels. Consequently, with OQPSK the baud and minimum bandwidth are twice that of conventional QPSK for a given transmission bit rate. OQPSK is sometimes called OKQPSK (*offset-keyed QPSK*).

2-5-3 8-PSK

With *8-PSK,* three bits are encoded, forming tribits and producing eight different output phases. With 8-PSK, $n = 3$, $M = 8$, and there are eight possible output phases. To encode eight different phases, the incoming bits are encoded in groups of three, called tribits ($2^3 = 8$).

 2-5-3-1 8-PSK transmitter. A block diagram of an 8-PSK modulator is shown in Figure 2-23. The incoming serial bit stream enters the bit splitter, where it is converted to a parallel, three-channel output (the I or in-phase channel, the Q or in-quadrature channel, and the C or control channel). Consequently, the bit rate in each of the three channels is $f_b/3$. The bits in the I and C channels enter the I channel 2-to-4-level converter, and the bits in the Q and $\overline{C}$ channels enter the Q channel 2-to-4-level converter. Essentially, the 2-to-4-level converters are parallel-input *digital-to-analog converters* (DACs). With two input bits, four output voltages are possible. The algorithm for the DACs is quite simple. The I or Q bit determines the polarity of the output analog signal (logic 1 = +V and logic 0 = −V), whereas the C or $\overline{C}$ bit determines the magni-

FIGURE 2-23 8-PSK modulator

I	C	Output
0	0	−0.541 V
0	1	−1.307 V
1	0	+0.541 V
1	1	+1.307 V

(a)

Q	$\bar{C}$	Output
0	1	−1.307 V
0	0	−0.541 V
1	1	+1.307 V
1	0	+0.541 V

(b)

+1.307 V
+0.541 V
0 V
−0.541 V
−1.307 V

(c)

FIGURE 2-24 I- and Q-channel 2-to-4-level converters: (a) I-channel truth table;
(b) Q-channel truth table; (c) PAM levels

tude (logic 1 = 1.307 V and logic 0 = 0.541 V). Consequently, with two magnitudes and two polarities, four different output conditions are possible.

Figure 2-24 shows the truth table and corresponding output conditions for the 2-to-4-level converters. Because the C and $\bar{C}$ bits can never be the same logic state, the outputs from the I and Q 2-to-4-level converters can never have the same magnitude, although they can have the same polarity. The output of a 2-to-4-level converter is an *M*-ary, *pulse-amplitude-modulated* (PAM) signal where *M* = 4.

Example 2-7

For a tribit input of Q = 0, I = 0, and C = 0 (000), determine the output phase for the 8-PSK modulator shown in Figure 2-23.

Solution   The inputs to the I channel 2-to-4-level converter are I = 0 and C = 0. From Figure 2-24 the output is −0.541 V. The inputs to the Q channel 2-to-4-level converter are Q = 0 and $\bar{C}$ = 1. Again from Figure 2-24, the output is −1.307 V.

Thus, the two inputs to the I channel product modulators are −0.541 and sin $\omega_c t$. The output is
$$I = (−0.541)(\sin \omega_c t) = −0.541 \sin \omega_c t$$
The two inputs to the Q channel product modulator are −1.307 V and cos $\omega_c t$. The output is
$$Q = (−1.307)(\cos \omega_c t) = −1.307 \cos \omega_c t$$

The outputs of the I and Q channel product modulators are combined in the linear summer and produce a modulated output of

$$\text{summer output} = -0.541 \sin \omega_c t - 1.307 \cos \omega_c t$$
$$= 1.41 \sin(\omega_c t - 112.5°)$$

For the remaining tribit codes (001, 010, 011, 100, 101, 110, and 111), the procedure is the same. The results are shown in Figure 2-25.

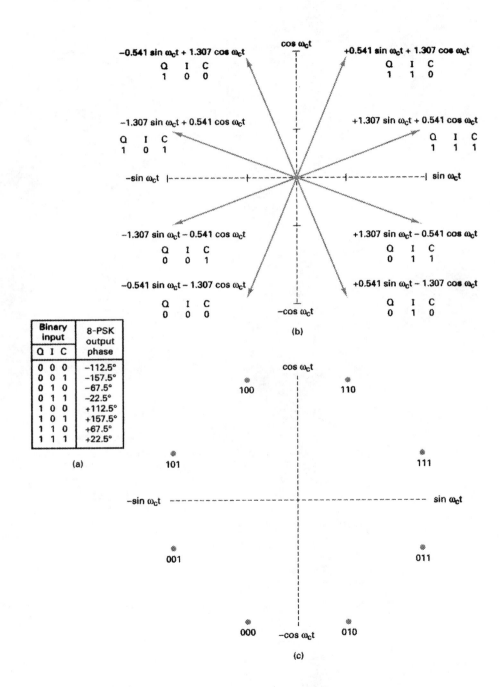

Binary input Q I C	8-PSK output phase
0 0 0	−112.5°
0 0 1	−157.5°
0 1 0	−67.5°
0 1 1	−22.5°
1 0 0	+112.5°
1 0 1	+157.5°
1 1 0	+67.5°
1 1 1	+22.5°

(a)

FIGURE 2-25   8-PSK modulator: (a) truth table; (b) phasor diagram; (c) constellation diagram

Tribit input	QIC 000	QIC 001	QIC 010	QIC 011	QIC 100	QIC 101	QIC 110	QIC 111
8-PSK output phase	−112.5°	−157.5°	−67.5°	−22.5°	+112.5°	+157.5°	+67.5°	+22.5°

FIGURE 2-26 Output phase-versus-time relationship for an 8-PSK modulator

From Figure 2-25, it can be seen that the angular separation between any two adjacent phasors is 45°, half what it is with QPSK. Therefore, an 8-PSK signal can undergo almost a ±22.5° phase shift during transmission and still retain its integrity. Also, each phasor is of equal magnitude; the tribit condition (actual information) is again contained only in the phase of the signal. The PAM levels of 1.307 and 0.541 are relative values. Any levels may be used as long as their ratio is 0.541/1.307 and their arc tangent is equal to 22.5°. For example, if their values were doubled to 2.614 and 1.082, the resulting phase angles would not change, although the magnitude of the phasor would increase proportionally.

It should also be noted that the tribit code between any two adjacent phases changes by only one bit. This type of code is called the *Gray code* or, sometimes, the *maximum distance code*. This code is used to reduce the number of transmission errors. If a signal were to undergo a phase shift during transmission, it would most likely be shifted to an adjacent phasor. Using the Gray code results in only a single bit being received in error.

Figure 2-26 shows the output phase-versus-time relationship of an 8-PSK modulator.

2-5-3-2 Bandwidth considerations of 8-PSK.

With 8-PSK, because the data are divided into three channels, the bit rate in the I, Q, or C channel is equal to one-third of the binary input data rate ($f_b/3$). (The bit splitter stretches the I, Q, and C bits to three times their input bit length.) Because the I, Q, and C bits are outputted simultaneously and in parallel, the 2-to-4-level converters also see a change in their inputs (and consequently their outputs) at a rate equal to $f_b/3$.

Figure 2-27 shows the bit timing relationship between the binary input data; the I, Q, and C channel data; and the I and Q PAM signals. It can be seen that the highest fundamental frequency in the I, Q, or C channel is equal to one-sixth the bit rate of the binary input (one cycle in the I, Q, or C channel takes the same amount of time as six input bits). Also, the highest fundamental frequency in either PAM signal is equal to one-sixth of the binary input bit rate.

With an 8-PSK modulator, there is one change in phase at the output for every three data input bits. Consequently, the baud for 8 PSK equals $f_b/3$, the same as the minimum bandwidth. Again, the balanced modulators are product modulators; their outputs are the product of the carrier and the PAM signal. Mathematically, the output of the balanced modulators is

$$\theta = (X \sin \omega_a t)(\sin \omega_c t) \qquad (2\text{-}25)$$

where

$$\underbrace{\omega_a t = 2\pi \frac{f_b}{6} t}_{\text{modulating signal}} \quad \text{and} \quad \underbrace{\omega_c t = 2\pi f_c t}_{\text{carrier}}$$

and

$$X = \pm 1.307 \text{ or } \pm 0.541$$

Thus,

$$\theta = \left(X \sin 2\pi \frac{f_b}{6} t\right)(\sin 2\pi f_c t)$$

$$= \frac{X}{2} \cos 2\pi \left(f_c - \frac{f_b}{6}\right)t - \frac{X}{2} \cos 2\pi \left(f_c + \frac{f_b}{6}\right)t$$

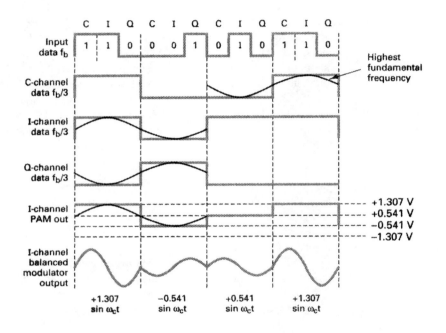

FIGURE 2-27   Bandwidth considerations of an 8-PSK modulator

The output frequency spectrum extends from $f_c + f_b/6$ to $f_c - f_b/6$, and the minimum bandwidth (f_N) is

$$\left(f_c + \frac{f_b}{6}\right) - \left(f_c - \frac{f_b}{6}\right) = \frac{2f_b}{6} = \frac{f_b}{3}$$

Example 2-8

For an 8-PSK modulator with an input data rate (f_b) equal to 10 Mbps and a carrier frequency of 70 MHz, determine the minimum double-sided Nyquist bandwidth (f_N) and the baud. Also, compare the results with those achieved with the BPSK and QPSK modulators in Examples 2-4 and 2-6. Use the 8-PSK block diagram shown in Figure 2-23 as the modulator model.

Solution   The bit rate in the I, Q, and C channels is equal to one-third of the input bit rate, or

$$f_{bC} = f_{bQ} = f_{bI} = \frac{10 \text{ Mbps}}{3} = 3.33 \text{ Mbps}$$

Therefore, the fastest rate of change and highest fundamental frequency presented to either balanced modulator is

$$f_a = \frac{f_{bC}}{2} \text{ or } \frac{f_{bQ}}{2} \text{ or } \frac{f_{bI}}{2} = \frac{3.33 \text{ Mbps}}{2} = 1.667 \text{ Mbps}$$

The output wave from the balance modulators is
$$(\sin 2\pi f_a t)(\sin 2\pi f_c t)$$

$$\frac{1}{2}\cos 2\pi(f_c - f_a)t - \frac{1}{2}\cos 2\pi(f_c + f_a)t$$

$$\frac{1}{2}\cos 2\pi[(70 - 1.667)\text{ MHz}]t - \frac{1}{2}\cos 2\pi[(70 + 1.667)\text{ MHz}]t$$

$$\frac{1}{2}\cos 2\pi(68.333 \text{ MHz})t - \frac{1}{2}\cos 2\pi(71.667 \text{ MHz})t$$

The minimum Nyquist bandwidth is
$$B = (71.667 - 68.333)\text{ MHz} = 3.333 \text{ MHz}$$

The minimum bandwidth for the 8-PSK can also be determined by simply substituting into Equation 2-10:

$$B = \frac{10 \text{ Mbps}}{3}$$
$$= 3.33 \text{ MHz}$$

Again, the baud equals the bandwidth; thus,
$$\text{baud} = 3.333 \text{ megabaud}$$

The output spectrum is as follows:

(Suppressed)

$$B = 3.333 \text{ MHz}$$

It can be seen that for the same input bit rate the minimum bandwidth required to pass the output of an 8-PSK modulator is equal to one-third that of the BPSK modulator in Example 2-4 and 50% less than that required for the QPSK modulator in Example 2-6. Also, in each case the baud has been reduced by the same proportions.

2-5-3-3 8-PSK receiver. Figure 2-28 shows a block diagram of an 8-PSK receiver. The power splitter directs the input 8-PSK signal to the I and Q product detectors and the carrier recovery circuit. The carrier recovery circuit reproduces the original reference oscillator signal. The incoming 8-PSK signal is mixed with the recovered carrier in the I product detector and with a quadrature carrier in the Q product detector. The outputs of the product detectors are 4-level PAM signals that are fed to the 4-to-2-level *analog-to-digital converters* (ADCs). The outputs from the I channel 4-to-2-level converter are the I and C bits, whereas the outputs from the Q channel 4-to-2-level converter are the Q and $\overline{\text{C}}$ bits. The parallel-to-serial logic circuit converts the I/C and Q/$\overline{\text{C}}$ bit pairs to serial I, Q, and C output data streams.

2-5-4 16-PSK
16-PSK is an *M*-ary encoding technique where $M = 16$; there are 16 different output phases possible. With 16-PSK, four bits (called *quadbits*) are combined, producing 16 different output phases. With 16-PSK, $n = 4$ and $M = 16$; therefore, the minimum bandwidth and

FIGURE 2-28 8-PSK receiver

Bit code	Phase	Bit code	Phase
0000	11.25°	1000	191.25°
0001	33.75°	1001	213.75°
0010	56.25°	1010	236.25°
0011	78.75°	1011	258.75°
0100	101.25°	1100	281.25°
0101	123.75°	1101	303.75°
0110	146.25°	1110	326.25°
0111	168.75°	1111	348.75°

(a)

(b)

FIGURE 2-29   16-PSK: (a) truth table; (b) constellation diagram

baud equal one-fourth the bit rate ($f_b/4$). Figure 2-29 shows the truth table and constellation diagram for 16-PSK, respectively. Comparing Figures 2-18, 2-25, and 2-29 shows that as the level of encoding increases (i.e., the values of n and M increase), more output phases are possible and the closer each point on the constellation diagram is to an adjacent point. With 16-PSK, the angular separation between adjacent output phases is only 22.5°. Therefore, 16-PSK can undergo only a 11.25° phase shift during transmission and still retain its integrity. For an M-ary PSK system with 64 output phases ($n = 6$), the angular separation between adjacent phases is only 5.6°. This is an obvious limitation in the level of encoding (and bit rates) possible with PSK, as a point is eventually reached where receivers cannot discern the phase of the received signaling element. In addition, phase impairments inherent on communications lines have a tendency to shift the phase of the PSK signal, destroying its integrity and producing errors.

2-6   QUADRATURE-AMPLITUDE MODULATION

Quadrature-amplitude modulation (QAM) is a form of digital modulation similar to PSK except the digital information is contained in both the amplitude and the phase of the transmitted carrier. With QAM, amplitude and phase-shift keying are combined in such a way that the positions of the signaling elements on the constellation diagrams are optimized to achieve the greatest distance between elements, thus reducing the likelihood of one element being misinterpreted as another element. Obviously, this reduces the likelihood of errors occurring.

2-6-1   8-QAM
8-QAM is an *M*-ary encoding technique where $M = 8$. Unlike 8-PSK, the output signal from an 8-QAM modulator is not a constant-amplitude signal.

2-6-1-1 8-QAM transmitter.   Figure 2-30a shows the block diagram of an 8-QAM transmitter. As you can see, the only difference between the 8-QAM transmitter and the 8-PSK transmitter shown in Figure 2-23 is the omission of the inverter between the C channel and the Q product modulator. As with 8-PSK, the incoming data are divided into groups of three bits (tribits): the I, Q, and C bit streams, each with a bit rate equal to one-third of

FIGURE 2-30 8-QAM transmitter: (a) block diagram; (b) truth table 2-4 level converters

the incoming data rate. Again, the I and Q bits determine the polarity of the PAM signal at the output of the 2-to-4-level converters, and the C channel determines the magnitude. Because the C bit is fed uninverted to both the I and the Q channel 2-to-4-level converters, the magnitudes of the I and Q PAM signals are always equal. Their polarities depend on the logic condition of the I and Q bits and, therefore, may be different. Figure 2-30b shows the truth table for the I and Q channel 2-to-4-level converters; they are identical.

Example 2-9

For a tribit input of Q = 0, I = 0, and C = 0 (000), determine the output amplitude and phase for the 8-QAM transmitter shown in Figure 2-30a.

Solution The inputs to the I channel 2-to-4-level converter are I = 0 and C = 0. From Figure 2-30b, the output is -0.541 V. The inputs to the Q channel 2-to-4-level converter are Q = 0 and C = 0. Again from Figure 2-30b, the output is -0.541 V.

Thus, the two inputs to the I channel product modulator are -0.541 and $\sin \omega_c t$. The output is

$$I = (-0.541)(\sin \omega_c t) = -0.541 \sin \omega_c t$$

The two inputs to the Q channel product modulator are -0.541 and $\cos \omega_c t$. The output is

$$Q = (-0.541)(\cos \omega_c t) = -0.541 \cos \omega_c t$$

The outputs from the I and Q channel product modulators are combined in the linear summer and produce a modulated output of

$$summer\ output = -0.541 \sin \omega_c t - 0.541 \cos \omega_c t$$

$$= 0.765 \sin(\omega_c t - 135°)$$

For the remaining tribit codes (001, 010, 011, 100, 101, 110, and 111), the procedure is the same. The results are shown in Figure 2-31.

Figure 2-32 shows the output phase-versus-time relationship for an 8-QAM modulator. Note that there are two output amplitudes, and only four phases are possible.

2-6-1-2 Bandwidth considerations of 8-QAM.
In 8-QAM, the bit rate in the I and Q channels is one-third of the input binary rate, the same as in 8-PSK. As a result, the highest fundamental modulating frequency and fastest output rate of change in 8-QAM are the same as with 8-PSK. Therefore, the minimum bandwidth required for 8-QAM is $f_b/3$, the same as in 8-PSK.

Binary input			8-QAM output	
Q	I	C	Amplitude	Phase
0	0	0	0.765 V	−135°
0	0	1	1.848 V	−135°
0	1	0	0.765 V	−45°
0	1	1	1.848 V	−45°
1	0	0	0.765 V	+135°
1	0	1	1.848 V	+135°
1	1	0	0.765 V	+45°
1	1	1	1.848 V	+45°

(a)

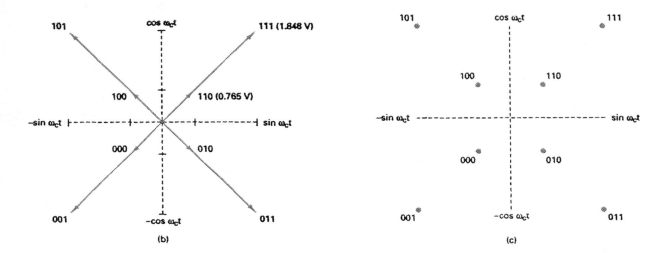

(b)　　　　　　　　　　(c)

FIGURE 2-31　8-QAM modulator: (a) truth table; (b) phasor diagram; (c) constellation diagram

FIGURE 2-32　Output phase and amplitude-versus-time relationship for 8-QAM

2-6-1-3 8-QAM receiver.　An 8-QAM receiver is almost identical to the 8-PSK receiver shown in Figure 2-28. The differences are the PAM levels at the output of the product detectors and the binary signals at the output of the analog-to-digital converters. Because there are two transmit amplitudes possible with 8-QAM that are different from those achievable with 8-PSK, the four demodulated PAM levels in 8-QAM are different from those in 8-PSK. Therefore, the conversion factor for the analog-to-digital converters must also be different. Also, with 8-QAM the binary output signals from the I channel analog-to-digital converter are the I and C bits, and the binary output signals from the Q channel analog-to-digital converter are the Q and C bits.

2-6-2 16-QAM

As with the 16-PSK, *16-QAM* is an *M*-ary system where $M = 16$. The input data are acted on in groups of four ($2^4 = 16$). As with 8-QAM, both the phase and the amplitude of the transmit carrier are varied.

2-6-2-1 QAM transmitter. The block diagram for a 16-QAM transmitter is shown in Figure 2-33. The input binary data are divided into four channels: I, I′, Q, and Q′. The bit rate in each channel is equal to one-fourth of the input bit rate ($f_b/4$). Four bits are serially clocked into the bit splitter; then they are outputted simultaneously and in parallel with the I, I′, Q, and Q′ channels. The I and Q bits determine the polarity at the output of the 2-to-4-level converters (a logic 1 = positive and a logic 0 = negative). The I′ and Q′ bits determine the magnitude (a logic I = 0.821 V and a logic 0 = 0.22 V). Consequently, the 2-to-4-level converters generate a 4-level PAM signal. Two polarities and two magnitudes are possible at the output of each 2-to-4-level converter. They are 0.22 V and ±0.821 V.

The PAM signals modulate the in-phase and quadrature carriers in the product modulators. Four outputs are possible for each product modulator. For the I product modulator, they are +0.821 sin $\omega_c t$, −0.821 sin $\omega_c t$, +0.22 sin $\omega_c t$, and −0.22 sin $\omega_c t$. For the Q product modulator, they are +0.821 cos $\omega_c t$, +0.22 cos $\omega_c t$, −0.821 cos $\omega_c t$, and −0.22 cos $\omega_c t$. The linear summer combines the outputs from the I and Q channel product modulators and produces the 16 output conditions necessary for 16-QAM. Figure 2-34 shows the truth table for the I and Q channel 2-to-4-level converters.

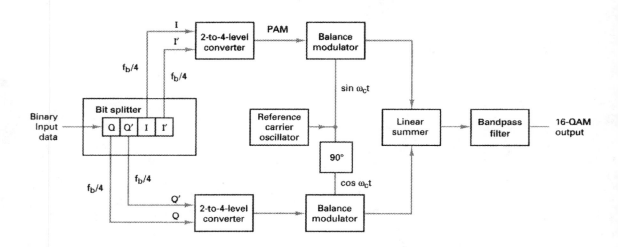

FIGURE 2-33   16-QAM transmitter block diagram

I	I′	Output
0	0	−0.22 V
0	1	−0.821 V
1	0	+0.22 V
1	1	+0.821 V

(a)

Q	Q′	Output
0	0	−0.22 V
0	1	−0.821 V
1	0	+0.22 V
1	1	+0.821 V

(b)

FIGURE 2-34   Truth tables for the I- and Q-channel 2-to-4-level converters: (a) I channel; (b) Q channel

Example 2-10

For a quadbit input of I = 0, I′ = 0, Q = 0, and Q′ = 0 (0000), determine the output amplitude and phase for the 16-QAM modulator shown in Figure 2-33.

Solution   The inputs to the I channel 2-to-4-level converter are I = 0 and I′ = 0. From Figure 2-34, the output is −0.22 V. The inputs to the Q channel 2-to-4-level converter are Q = 0 and Q′ = 0. Again from Figure 2-34, the output is −0.22 V.

Thus, the two inputs to the I channel product modulator are −0.22 V and sin $\omega_c t$. The output is

$$I = (-0.22)(\sin \omega_c t) = -0.22 \sin \omega_c t$$

The two inputs to the Q channel product modulator are −0.22 V and cos $\omega_c t$. The output is

$$Q = (-0.22)(\cos \omega_c t) = -0.22 \cos \omega_c t$$

The outputs from the I and Q channel product modulators are combined in the linear summer and produce a modulated output of

$$\text{summer output} = -0.22 \sin \omega_c t - 0.22 \cos \omega_c t$$
$$= 0.311 \sin(\omega_c t - 135°)$$

For the remaining quadbit codes, the procedure is the same. The results are shown in Figure 2-35.

Binary input				16-QAM output	
Q	Q′	I	I′		
0	0	0	0	0.311 V	−135°
0	0	0	1	0.850 V	−165°
0	0	1	0	0.311 V	−45°
0	0	1	1	0.850 V	−15°
0	1	0	0	0.850 V	−105°
0	1	0	1	1.161 V	−135°
0	1	1	0	0.850 V	−75°
0	1	1	1	1.161 V	−45°
1	0	0	0	0.311 V	135°
1	0	0	1	0.850 V	165°
1	0	1	0	0.311 V	45°
1	0	1	1	0.850 V	15°
1	1	0	0	0.850 V	105°
1	1	0	1	1.161 V	135°
1	1	1	0	0.850 V	75°
1	1	1	1	1.161 V	45°

(a)

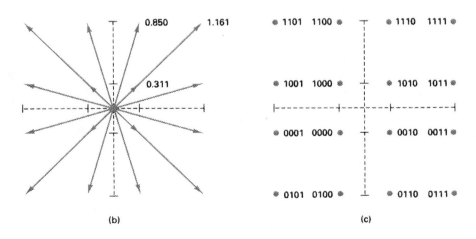

(b)   (c)

FIGURE 2-35   16-QAM modulator: (a) truth table; (b) phasor diagram; (c) constellation diagram

FIGURE 2-36 Bandwidth considerations of a 16-QAM modulator

2-6-2-2 Bandwidth considerations of 16-QAM. With a 16-QAM, because the input data are divided into four channels, the bit rate in the I, I′, Q, or Q′ channel is equal to one-fourth of the binary input data rate ($f_b/4$). (The bit splitter stretches the I, I′, Q, and Q′ bits to four times their input bit length.) Also, because the I, I′, Q, and Q′ bits are outputted simultaneously and in parallel, the 2-to-4-level converters see a change in their inputs and outputs at a rate equal to one-fourth of the input data rate.

Figure 2-36 shows the bit timing relationship between the binary input data; the I, I′, Q, and Q′ channel data; and the I PAM signal. It can be seen that the highest fundamental frequency in the I, I′, Q, or Q′ channel is equal to one-eighth of the bit rate of the binary input data (one cycle in the I, I′, Q, or Q′ channel takes the same amount of time as eight input bits). Also, the highest fundamental frequency of either PAM signal is equal to one-eighth of the binary input bit rate.

With a 16-QAM modulator, there is one change in the output signal (either its phase, amplitude, or both) for every four input data bits. Consequently, the baud equals $f_b/4$, the same as the minimum bandwidth.

Again, the balanced modulators are product modulators and their outputs can be represented mathematically as

$$\text{output} = (X \sin \omega_a t)(\sin \omega_c t) \qquad (2\text{-}26)$$

where

$$\underbrace{\omega_a t = 2\pi \frac{f_b}{8} t}_{\text{modulating signal}} \quad \text{and} \quad \underbrace{\omega_c t = 2\pi f_c t}_{\text{carrier}}$$

and

$$X = \pm 0.22 \text{ or } \pm 0.821$$

Thus,

$$\text{output} = \left(X \sin 2\pi \frac{f_b}{8} t \right)(\sin 2\pi f_c t)$$

$$= \frac{X}{2} \cos 2\pi \left(f_c - \frac{f_b}{8} \right) t = \frac{X}{2} \cos 2\pi \left(f_c + \frac{f_b}{8} \right) t$$

The output frequency spectrum extends from $f_c + f_b/8$ to $f_c - f_b/8$, and the minimum bandwidth (f_N) is

$$\left(f_c + \frac{f_b}{8} \right) - \left(f_c - \frac{f_b}{8} \right) = \frac{2f_b}{8} = \frac{f_b}{4}$$

Example 2-11

For a 16-QAM modulator with an input data rate (f_b) equal to 10 Mbps and a carrier frequency of 70 MHz, determine the minimum double-sided Nyquist frequency (f_N) and the baud. Also, compare the results with those achieved with the BPSK, QPSK, and 8-PSK modulators in Examples 2-4, 2-6, and 2-8. Use the 16-QAM block diagram shown in Figure 2-33 as the modulator model.

Solution The bit rate in the I, I′, Q, and Q′ channels is equal to one-fourth of the input bit rate, or

$$f_{bI} = f_{bI'} = f_{bQ} = f_{bQ'} = \frac{f_b}{4} = \frac{10 \text{ Mbps}}{4} = 2.5 \text{ Mbps}$$

Therefore, the fastest rate of change and highest fundamental frequency presented to either balanced modulator is

$$f_a = \frac{f_{bI}}{2} \text{ or } \frac{f_{bI'}}{2} \text{ or } \frac{f_{bQ}}{2} \text{ or } \frac{f_{bQ'}}{2} = \frac{2.5 \text{ Mbps}}{2} = 1.25 \text{ MHz}$$

The output wave from the balanced modulator is

$$(\sin 2\pi f_a t)(\sin 2\pi f_c t)$$

$$\frac{1}{2} \cos 2\pi (f_c - f_a)t - \frac{1}{2} \cos 2\pi (f_c + f_a)t$$

$$\frac{1}{2} \cos 2\pi [(70 - 1.25) \text{ MHz}]t - \frac{1}{2} \cos 2\pi [(70 + 1.25) \text{ MHz}]t$$

$$\frac{1}{2} \cos 2\pi (68.75 \text{ MHz})t - \frac{1}{2} \cos 2\pi (71.25 \text{ MHz})t$$

The minimum Nyquist bandwidth is

$$B = (71.25 - 68.75) \text{ MHz} = 2.5 \text{ MHz}$$

The minimum bandwidth for the 16-QAM can also be determined by simply substituting into Equation 2-10:

$$B = \frac{10 \text{ Mbps}}{4}$$

$$= 2.5 \text{ MHz}$$

The symbol rate equals the bandwidth; thus,

$$\text{symbol rate} = 2.5 \text{ megabaud}$$

The output spectrum is as follows:

$$B = 2.5 \text{ MHz}$$

For the same input bit rate, the minimum bandwidth required to pass the output of a 16-QAM modulator is equal to one-fourth that of the BPSK modulator, one-half that of QPSK, and 25% less than with 8-PSK. For each modulation technique, the baud is also reduced by the same proportions.

Example 2-12

For the following modulation schemes, construct a table showing the number of bits encoded, number of output conditions, minimum bandwidth, and baud for an information data rate of 12 kbps: QPSK, 8-PSK, 8-QAM, 16-PSK, and 16-QAM.

Solution

Modulation	n	M	B (Hz)	baud
QPSK	2	4	6000	6000
8-PSK	3	8	4000	4000
8-QAM	3	8	4000	4000
16-PSK	4	16	3000	3000
16-QAM	4	16	3000	3000

From Example 2-12, it can be seen that a 12-kbps data stream can be propagated through a narrower bandwidth using either 16-PSK or 16-QAM than with the lower levels of encoding.

Table 2-1 summarizes the relationship between the number of bits encoded, the number of output conditions possible, the minimum bandwidth, and the baud for ASK, FSK, PSK, and QAM. Note that with the three binary modulation schemes (ASK, FSK, and

Table 2-1 ASK, FSK, PSK, and QAM Summary

Modulation	Encoding Scheme	Outputs Possible	Minimum Bandwidth	Baud
ASK	Single bit	2	f_b	f_b
FSK	Single bit	2	f_b	f_b
BPSK	Single bit	2	f_b	f_b
QPSK	Dibits	4	$f_b/2$	$f_b/2$
8-PSK	Tribits	8	$f_b/3$	$f_b/3$
8-QAM	Tribits	8	$f_b/3$	$f_b/3$
16-QAM	Quadbits	16	$f_b/4$	$f_b/4$
16-PSK	Quadbits	16	$f_b/4$	$f_b/4$
32-PSK	Five bits	32	$f_b/5$	$f_b/5$
32-QAM	Five bits	32	$f_b/5$	$f_b/5$
64-PSK	Six bits	64	$f_b/6$	$f_b/6$
64-QAM	Six bits	64	$f_b/6$	$f_b/6$
128-PSK	Seven bits	128	$f_b/7$	$f_b/7$
128-QAM	Seven bits	128	$f_b/7$	$f_b/7$

Note: f_b indicates a magnitude equal to the input bit rate.

BPSK), $n = 1$, $M = 2$, only two output conditions are possible, and the baud is equal to the bit rate. However, for values of $n > 1$, the number of output conditions increases, and the minimum bandwidth and baud decrease. Therefore, digital modulation schemes where $n > 1$ achieve *bandwidth compression* (i.e., less bandwidth is required to propagate a given bit rate). When data compression is performed, higher data transmission rates are possible for a given bandwidth.

2-7 BANDWIDTH EFFICIENCY

Bandwidth efficiency (sometimes called *information density* or *spectral efficiency*) is often used to compare the performance of one digital modulation technique to another. In essence, bandwidth efficiency is the ratio of the transmission bit rate to the minimum bandwidth required for a particular modulation scheme. Bandwidth efficiency is generally normalized to a 1-Hz bandwidth and, thus, indicates the number of bits that can be propagated through a transmission medium for each hertz of bandwidth. Mathematically, bandwidth efficiency is

$$B\eta = \frac{\text{transmission bit rate (bps)}}{\text{minimum bandwidth (Hz)}} \qquad (2\text{-}27)$$

$$= \frac{\text{bits/s}}{\text{hertz}} = \frac{\text{bits/s}}{\text{cycles/s}} = \frac{\text{bits}}{\text{cycle}}$$

where $B\eta$ = bandwidth efficiency

Bandwidth efficiency can also be given as a percentage by simply multiplying $B\eta$ by 100.

Example 2-13

For an 8-PSK system, operating with an information bit rate of 24 kbps, determine (a) baud, (b) minimum bandwidth, and (c) bandwidth efficiency.

Solution   a. Baud is determined by substituting into Equation 2-10:

$$\text{baud} = \frac{24,000}{3} = 8000$$

b. Bandwidth is determined by substituting into Equation 2-11:

$$B = \frac{24,000}{3} = 8000$$

c. Bandwidth efficiency is calculated from Equation 2-27:

$$B\eta = \frac{24,000 \text{ bps}}{8000 \text{ Hz}}$$

$$= 3 \text{ bits per second per cycle of bandwidth}$$

Example 2-14

For 16-PSK and a transmission system with a 10 kHz bandwidth, determine the maximum bit rate.

Solution   The bandwidth efficiency for 16-PSK is 4, which means that four bits can be propagated through the system for each hertz of bandwidth. Therefore, the maximum bit rate is simply the product of the bandwidth and the bandwidth efficiency, or

$$\text{bit rate} = 4 \times 10,000$$
$$= 40,000 \text{ bps}$$

Table 2-2 ASK, FSK, PSK, and QAM Summary

Modulation	Encoding Scheme	Outputs Possible	Minimum Bandwidth	Baud	Bη
ASK	Single bit	2	f_b	f_b	1
FSK	Single bit	2	f_b	f_b	1
BPSK	Single bit	2	f_b	f_b	1
QPSK	Dibits	4	$f_b/2$	$f_b/2$	2
8-PSK	Tribits	8	$f_b/3$	$f_b/3$	3
8-QAM	Tribits	8	$f_b/3$	$f_b/3$	3
16-PSK	Quadbits	16	$f_b/4$	$f_b/4$	4
16-QAM	Quadbits	16	$f_b/4$	$f_b/4$	4
32-PSK	Five bits	32	$f_b/5$	$f_b/5$	5
64-QAM	Six bits	64	$f_b/6$	$f_b/6$	6

Note: f_b indicates a magnitude equal to the input bit rate.

2-7-1 Digital Modulation Summary

The properties of several digital modulation schemes are summarized in Table 2-2.

2-8 CARRIER RECOVERY

Carrier recovery is the process of extracting a phase-coherent reference carrier from a receiver signal. This is sometimes called *phase referencing.*

In the phase modulation techniques described thus far, the binary data were encoded as a precise phase of the transmitted carrier. (This is referred to as *absolute phase encoding.*) Depending on the encoding method, the angular separation between adjacent phasors varied between 30° and 180°. To correctly demodulate the data, a phase-coherent carrier was recovered and compared with the received carrier in a product detector. To determine the absolute phase of the received carrier, it is necessary to produce a carrier at the receiver that is phase coherent with the transmit reference oscillator. This is the function of the carrier recovery circuit.

With PSK and QAM, the carrier is suppressed in the balanced modulators and, therefore, is not transmitted. Consequently, at the receiver the carrier cannot simply be tracked with a standard phase-locked loop (PLL). With suppressed-carrier systems, such as PSK and QAM, sophisticated methods of carrier recovery are required, such as a *squaring loop,* a *Costas loop,* or a *remodulator.*

2-8-1 Squaring Loop

A common method of achieving carrier recovery for BPSK is the *squaring loop.* Figure 2-37 shows the block diagram of a squaring loop. The received BPSK waveform is filtered and then squared. The filtering reduces the spectral width of the received noise. The squaring circuit removes the modulation and generates the second harmonic of the carrier frequency. This harmonic is phase tracked by the PLL. The VCO output frequency from the PLL then is divided by 2 and used as the phase reference for the product detectors.

FIGURE 2-37 Squaring loop carrier recovery circuit for a BPSK receiver

With BPSK, only two output phases are possible: $+\sin \omega_c t$ and $-\sin \omega_c t$. Mathematically, the operation of the squaring circuit can be described as follows. For a receive signal of $+\sin \omega_c t$, the output of the squaring circuit is

$$\text{output} = (+\sin \omega_c t)(+\sin \omega_c t) = +\sin^2 \omega_c t$$

$$= \frac{1}{2}(1 - \cos 2\omega_c t) = \frac{1}{2} - \frac{1}{2}\cos 2\omega_c t$$

(filtered out)

For a received signal of $-\sin \omega_c t$, the output of the squaring circuit is

$$\text{output} = (-\sin \omega_c t)(-\sin \omega_c t) = +\sin^2 \omega_c t$$

$$= \frac{1}{2}(1 - \cos 2\omega_c t) = \frac{1}{2} - \frac{1}{2}\cos 2\omega_c t$$

(filtered out)

It can be seen that in both cases, the output from the squaring circuit contained a constant voltage ($+1/2$ V) and a signal at twice the carrier frequency ($\cos 2\omega_c t$). The constant voltage is removed by filtering, leaving only $\cos 2\omega_c t$.

2-8-2 Costas Loop

A second method of carrier recovery is the Costas, or quadrature, loop shown in Figure 2-38. The Costas loop produces the same results as a squaring circuit followed by an ordinary PLL in place of the BPF. This recovery scheme uses two parallel tracking loops (I and Q) simultaneously to derive the product of the I and Q components of the signal that drives the VCO. The in-phase (I) loop uses the VCO as in a PLL, and the quadrature (Q) loop uses a 90° shifted VCO signal. Once the frequency of the VCO is equal to the suppressed-carrier

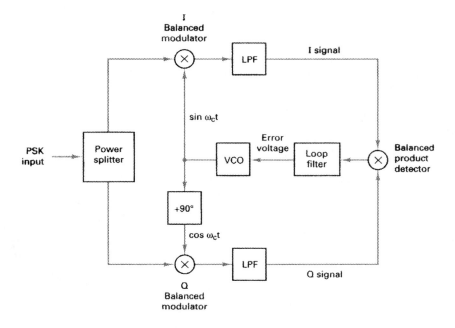

FIGURE 2-38   Costas loop carrier recovery circuit

FIGURE 2-39 Remodulator loop carrier recovery circuit

frequency, the product of the I and Q signals will produce an error voltage proportional to any phase error in the VCO. The error voltage controls the phase and, thus, the frequency of the VCO.

2-8-3   Remodulator

A third method of achieving recovery of a phase and frequency coherent carrier is the remodulator, shown in Figure 2-39. The remodulator produces a loop error voltage that is proportional to twice the phase error between the incoming signal and the VCO signal. The remodulator has a faster acquisition time than either the squaring or the Costas loops.

Carrier recovery circuits for higher-than-binary encoding techniques are similar to BPSK except that circuits that raise the receive signal to the fourth, eighth, and higher powers are used.

2-9   CLOCK RECOVERY

As with any digital system, digital radio requires precise timing or clock synchronization between the transmit and the receive circuitry. Because of this, it is necessary to regenerate clocks at the receiver that are synchronous with those at the transmitter.

Figure 2-40a shows a simple circuit that is commonly used to recover clocking information from the received data. The recovered data are delayed by one-half a bit time and then compared with the original data in an XOR circuit. The frequency of the clock that is recovered with this method is equal to the received data rate (f_b). Figure 2-40b shows the relationship between the data and the recovered clock timing. From Figure 2-40b, it can be seen that as long as the receive data contain a substantial number of transitions (1/0 sequences), the recovered clock is maintained. If the receive data were to undergo an extended period of successive 1s or 0s, the recovered clock would be lost. To prevent this from occurring, the data are scrambled at the transmit end and descrambled at the receive end. Scrambling introduces transitions (pulses) into the binary signal using a prescribed algorithm, and the descrambler uses the same algorithm to remove the transitions.

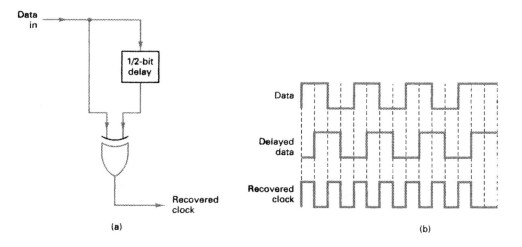

FIGURE 2-40   (a) Clock recovery circuit; (b) timing diagram

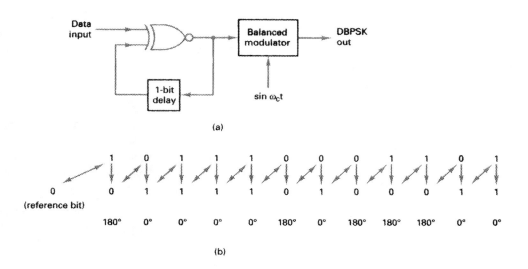

FIGURE 2-41   DBPSK modulator: (a) block diagram; (b) timing diagram

2-10   DIFFERENTIAL PHASE-SHIFT KEYING

Differential phase-shift keying (DPSK) is an alternative form of digital modulation where the binary input information is contained in the difference between two successive signaling elements rather than the absolute phase. With DPSK, it is not necessary to recover a phase-coherent carrier. Instead, a received signaling element is delayed by one signaling element time slot and then compared with the next received signaling element. The difference in the phase of the two signaling elements determines the logic condition of the data.

2-10-1   Differential BPSK

2-10-1-1 DBPSK transmitter.   Figure 2-41a shows a simplified block diagram of a *differential binary phase-shift keying* (DBPSK) transmitter. An incoming information bit is

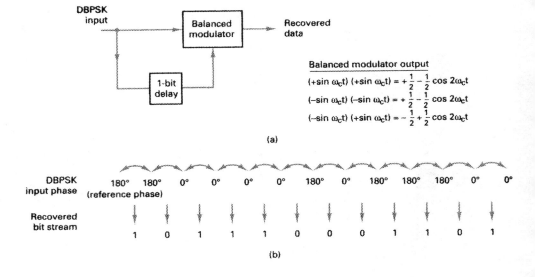

FIGURE 2-42 DBPSK demodulator: (a) block diagram; (b) timing sequence

XNORed with the preceding bit prior to entering the BPSK modulator (balanced modulator). For the first data bit, there is no preceding bit with which to compare it. Therefore, an initial reference bit is assumed. Figure 2-41b shows the relationship between the input data, the XNOR output data, and the phase at the output of the balanced modulator. If the initial reference bit is assumed a logic 1, the output from the XNOR circuit is simply the complement of that shown.

In Figure 2-41b, the first data bit is XNORed with the reference bit. If they are the same, the XNOR output is a logic 1; if they are different, the XNOR output is a logic 0. The balanced modulator operates the same as a conventional BPSK modulator; a logic 1 produces $+\sin \omega_c t$ at the output, and a logic 0 produces $-\sin \omega_c t$ at the output.

2-10-1-2 DBPSK receiver. Figure 2-42 shows the block diagram and timing sequence for a DBPSK receiver. The received signal is delayed by one bit time, then compared with the next signaling element in the balanced modulator. If they are the same, a logic 1 (+ voltage) is generated. If they are different, a logic 0 (− voltage) is generated. If the reference phase is incorrectly assumed, only the first demodulated bit is in error. Differential encoding can be implemented with higher-than-binary digital modulation schemes, although the differential algorithms are much more complicated than for DBPSK.

The primary advantage of DBPSK is the simplicity with which it can be implemented. With DBPSK, no carrier recovery circuit is needed. A disadvantage of DBPSK is that it requires between 1 dB and 3 dB more signal-to-noise ratio to achieve the same bit error rate as that of absolute PSK.

2-11 TRELLIS CODE MODULATION

Achieving data transmission rates in excess of 9600 bps over standard telephone lines with approximately a 3-kHz bandwidth obviously requires an encoding scheme well beyond the quadbits used with 16-PSK or 16-QAM (i.e., *M* must be significantly greater than 16). As might be expected, higher encoding schemes require higher signal-to-noise ratios. Using the Shannon limit for information capacity (Equation 2-4), a data transmission rate of 28.8 kbps through a 3200-Hz bandwidth requires a signal-to-noise ratio of

$$I(\text{bps}) = (3.32 \times B) \log(1 + \text{S/N})$$

therefore,

$$28.8 \text{ kbps} = (3.32)(3200) \log(1 + \text{S/N})$$

$$28,800 = 10,624 \log(1 + \text{S/N})$$

$$\frac{28,800}{10,624} = \log(1 + \text{S/N})$$

$$2.71 = \log(1 + \text{S/N})$$

thus,

$$10^{2.71} = 1 + \text{S/N}$$

$$513 = 1 + \text{S/N}$$

$$512 = \text{S/N}$$

in dB,

$$\text{S/N}_{\text{(dB)}} = 10 \log 512$$

$$= 27 \text{ dB}$$

Transmission rates of 56 kbps require a signal-to-noise ratio of 53 dB, which is virtually impossible to achieve over a standard telephone circuit.

Data transmission rates in excess of 56 kbps can be achieved, however, over standard telephone circuits using an encoding technique called *trellis code modulation* (TCM). Dr. Ungerboeck at IBM Zuerich Research Laboratory developed TCM, which involves using *convolutional* (*tree*) codes, which combines encoding and modulation to reduce the probability of error, thus improving the bit error performance. The fundamental idea behind TCM is introducing controlled redundancy in the bit stream with a convolutional code, which reduces the likelihood of transmission errors. What sets TCM apart from standard encoding schemes is the introduction of redundancy by doubling the number of signal points in a given PSK or QAM constellation.

Trellis code modulation is sometimes thought of as a magical method of increasing transmission bit rates over communications systems using QAM or PSK with fixed bandwidths. Few people fully understand this concept, as modem manufacturers do not seem willing to share information on TCM. Therefore, the following explanation is intended not to fully describe the process of TCM but rather to introduce the topic and give the reader a basic understanding of how TCM works and the advantage it has over conventional digital modulation techniques.

M-ary QAM and PSK utilize a signal set of $2^N = M$, where N equals the number of bits encoded into M different conditions. Therefore, $N = 2$ produces a standard PSK constellation with four signal points (i.e., QPSK) as shown in Figure 2-43a. Using TCM, the number of signal points increases to two times M possible symbols for the same factor-of-M reduction in bandwidth while transmitting each signal during the same time interval. TCM-encoded QPSK is shown in Figure 2-43b.

Trellis coding also defines the manner in which signal-state transitions are allowed to occur, and transitions that do not follow this pattern are interpreted in the receiver as transmission errors. Therefore, TCM can improve error performance by restricting the manner in which signals are allowed to transition. For values of N greater than 2, QAM is the modulation scheme of choice for TCM; however, for simplification purposes, the following explanation uses PSK as it is easier to illustrate.

Figure 2-44 shows a TCM scheme using two-state 8-PSK, which is essentially two QPSK constellations offset by 45°. One four-state constellation is labeled 0-4-2-6, and the other is labeled 1-5-3-7. For this explanation, the signal point labels 0 through 7 are meant not to represent the actual data conditions but rather to simply indicate a convenient method of labeling the various signal points. Each digit represents one of four signal points permitted within each of the two QPSK constellations. When in the 0-4-2-6 constellation and a 0 or 4 is transmitted, the system remains in the same constellation. However, when either a 2 or 6 is transmitted, the system switches to the 1-5-3-7 constellation. Once in the 1-5-3-7

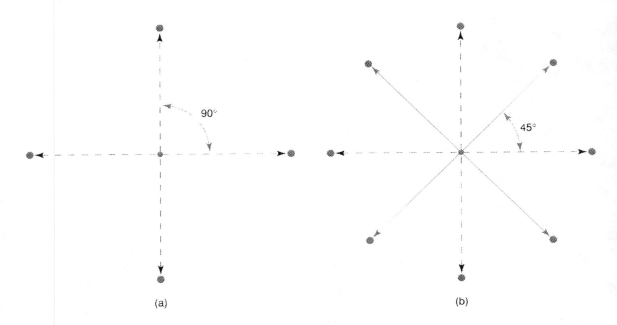

FIGURE 2-43 QPSK constellations: (a) standard encoding format; (b) trellis encoding format

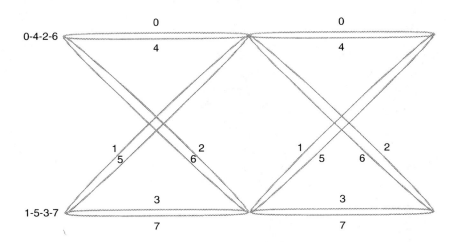

FIGURE 2-44 8-PSK TCM constellations

constellation and a 3 or 7 is transmitted, the system remains in the same constellation, and if a 1 or 5 is transmitted, the system switches to the 0-4-2-6 constellation. Remember that each symbol represents two bits, so the system undergoes a 45° phase shift whenever it switches between the two constellations. A complete error analysis of standard QPSK compared with TCM QPSK would reveal a coding gain for TCM of 2-to-1 1 or 3 dB. Table 2-3 lists the coding gains achieved for TCM coding schemes with several different trellis states.

The maximum data rate achievable using a given bandwidth can be determined by rearranging Equation 2-10:

$$N \times B = f_b$$

Table 2-3   Trellis Coding Gain

Number of Trellis States	Coding Gain (dB)
2	3.0
4	5.5
8	6.0
16	6.5
32	7.1
64	7.3
128	7.3
256	7.4

where N = number of bits encoded (bits)
B = bandwidth (hertz)
f_b = transmission bit rate (bits per second)

Remember that with M-ary QAM or PSK systems, the baud equals the minimum required bandwidth. Therefore, a 3200-Hz bandwidth using a nine-bit trellis code produces a 3200 baud signal with each baud carrying nine bits. Therefore, the transmission rate f_b = 9 × 3200 = 28.8 kbps.

TCM is thought of as a coding scheme that improves on standard QAM by increasing the distance between symbols on the constellation (known as the *Euclidean distance*). The first TCM system used a five-bit code, which included four QAM bits (a quadbit) and a fifth bit used to help decode the quadbit. Transmitting five bits within a single signaling element requires producing 32 discernible signals. Figure 2-45 shows a 128-point QAM constellation.

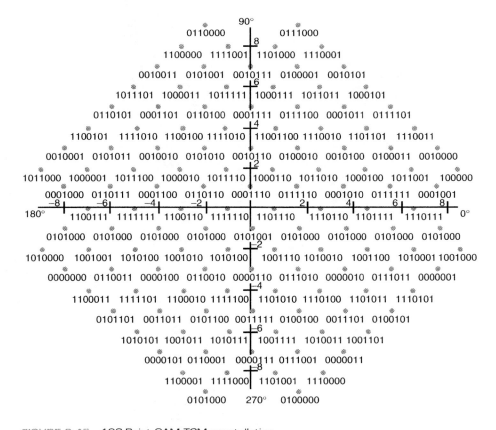

FIGURE 2-45   128-Point QAM TCM constellation

```
                              236 224 216│212 218 228
                          234 205 185 173 164│162 170 181 197 220
                      226 193 165 146 133 123│121 125 137 154 179 207
                  229 189 156 131 110  96  87│ 33  92 100 117 140 172 208
                  201 160 126  98  79  64  58│ 54  62  71  90 112 141 180 221
              222 177 135 102  77  55  41  35│ 31  37  48  65  91 118 155 198
              203 158 119  84  60  39  24  17│ 15  20  30  49  72 101 138 182 230
              194 148 108  75  50  28  13   6│  4   8  21  38  63  93 127 171 219
          238 186 142 103  69  43  22   9   1│  0   5  16  32  56  85 122 163 213
         ────────────────────────────────────┼────────────────────────────────
              190 144 106  73  45  25  11   3│  2   7  18  36  59  88 124 166 217
              199 152 113  80  52  33  19  12│ 10  14  26  42  66  97 134 174 225
              210 167 128  94  67  47  34  27│ 23  29  40  57  81 111 147 187 237
              232 183 149 115  89  68  53  46│ 44  51  61  78  99 132 168 209
                  214 175 139 116  95  82  74│ 70  76  86 104 129 157 195 235
                      205 176 150 130 114 107│105 109 120 136 161 191 227
                          215 184 169 153 145│143 151 159 178 202 231
                              233 211 200 192│188 196 204 223
                                             │239
```

FIGURE 2-46   One-fourth of a 960-Point QAM TCM constellation

A 3200-baud signal using nine-bit TCM encoding produces 512 different codes. The nine data bits plus a redundant bit for TCM requires a 960-point constellation. Figure 2-46 shows one-fourth of the 960-point superconstellation showing 240 signal points. The full superconstellation can be obtained by rotating the 240 points shown by 90°, 180°, and 270°.

2-12 PROBABILITY OF ERROR AND BIT ERROR RATE

Probability of error P(e) and *bit error rate* (BER) are often used interchangeably, although in practice they do have slightly different meanings. $P(e)$ is a theoretical (mathematical) expectation of the bit error rate for a given system. BER is an empirical (historical) record of a system's actual bit error performance. For example, if a system has a $P(e)$ of 10^{-5}, this means that mathematically you can expect one bit error in every 100,000 bits transmitted ($1/10^{-5} = 1/100,000$). If a system has a BER of 10^{-5}, this means that in past performance there was one bit error for every 100,000 bits transmitted. A bit error rate is measured and then compared with the expected probability of error to evaluate a system's performance.

Probability of error is a function of the *carrier-to-noise power ratio* (or, more specifically, the average *energy per bit-to-noise power density ratio*) and the number of possible encoding conditions used (*M*-ary). Carrier-to-noise power ratio is the ratio of the average carrier power (the combined power of the carrier and its associated sidebands) to the *thermal noise power.* Carrier power can be stated in watts or dBm, where

$$C_{\text{(dBm)}} = 10 \log \frac{C_{\text{(watts)}}}{0.001} \tag{2-28}$$

Thermal noise power is expressed mathematically as

$$N = KTB \text{ (watts)} \tag{2-29}$$

where N = thermal noise power (watts)
   K = Boltzmann's proportionality constant (1.38×10^{-23} joules per kelvin)
   T = temperature (kelvin: 0 K = $-273°$ C, room temperature = 290 K)
   B = bandwidth (hertz)

Stated in dBm, $$N_{\text{(dBm)}} = 10 \log \frac{KTB}{0.001} \tag{2-30}$$

Mathematically, the carrier-to-noise power ratio is

$$\frac{C}{N} = \frac{C}{KTB} \text{ (unitless ratio)} \tag{2-31}$$

where C = carrier power (watts)
   N = noise power (watts)

Stated in dB, $$\frac{C}{N}(\text{dB}) = 10 \log \frac{C}{N}$$

$$= C_{\text{(dBm)}} - N_{\text{(dBm)}} \tag{2-32}$$

Energy per bit is simply the energy of a single bit of information. Mathematically, energy per bit is

$$E_b = CT_b \text{ (J/bit)} \tag{2-33}$$

where E_b = energy of a single bit (joules per bit)
   T_b = time of a single bit (seconds)
   C = carrier power (watts)

Stated in dBJ, $$E_{b\text{(dBJ)}} = 10 \log E_b \tag{2-34}$$

and because $T_b = 1/f_b$, where f_b is the bit rate in bits per second, E_b can be rewritten as

$$E_b = \frac{C}{f_b} \text{ (J/bit)} \tag{2-35}$$

Stated in dBJ, $$E_{b\text{ (dBJ)}} = 10 \log \frac{C}{f_b} \tag{2-36}$$

$$= 10 \log C - 10 \log f_b \tag{2-37}$$

Noise power density is the thermal noise power normalized to a 1-Hz bandwidth (i.e., the noise power present in a 1-Hz bandwidth). Mathematically, noise power density is

$$N_0 = \frac{N}{B} \ (\text{W/Hz}) \tag{2-38}$$

where N_0 = noise power density (watts per hertz)
  N = thermal noise power (watts)
  B = bandwidth (hertz)

Stated in dBm, $$N_{0(\text{dBm})} = 10 \log \frac{N}{0.001} - 10 \log B \tag{2-39}$$

$$= N_{(\text{dBm})} - 10 \log B \tag{2-40}$$

Combining Equations 2-29 and 2-38 yields

$$N_0 = \frac{KTB}{B} = KT \ (\text{W/Hz}) \tag{2-41}$$

Stated in dBm, $$N_{0(\text{dBm})} = 10 \log \frac{K}{0.001} + 10 \log T \tag{2-42}$$

Energy per bit-to-noise power density ratio is used to compare two or more digital modulation systems that use different transmission rates (bit rates), modulation schemes (FSK, PSK, QAM), or encoding techniques (M-ary). The energy per bit-to-noise power density ratio is simply the ratio of the energy of a single bit to the noise power present in 1 Hz of bandwidth. Thus, E_b/N_0 normalizes all multiphase modulation schemes to a common noise bandwidth, allowing for a simpler and more accurate comparison of their error performance. Mathematically, E_b/N_0 is

$$\frac{E_b}{N_0} = \frac{C/f_b}{N/B} = \frac{CB}{Nf_b} \tag{2-43}$$

where $E_b N_0$ is the energy per bit-to-noise power density ratio. Rearranging Equation 2-43 yields the following expression:

$$\frac{E_b}{N_0} = \frac{C}{N} \times \frac{B}{f_b} \tag{2-44}$$

where E_b/N_0 = energy per bit-to-noise power density ratio
  C/N = carrier-to-noise power ratio
  B/f_b = noise bandwidth-to-bit rate ratio

Stated in dB, $$\frac{E_b}{N_0} (\text{dB}) = 10 \log \frac{C}{N} + 10 \log \frac{B}{f_b} \tag{2-45}$$

or $$= 10 \log E_b - 10 \log N_0 \tag{2-46}$$

From Equation 2-44, it can be seen that the E_b/N_0 ratio is simply the product of the carrier-to-noise power ratio and the noise bandwidth-to-bit rate ratio. Also, from Equation 2-44, it can be seen that when the bandwidth equals the bit rate, $E_b/N_0 = C/N$.

In general, the minimum carrier-to-noise power ratio required for QAM systems is less than that required for comparable PSK systems, Also, the higher the level of encoding used (the higher the value of M), the higher the minimum carrier-to-noise power ratio. In Chapter 24, several examples are shown for determining the minimum carrier-to-noise power and energy per bit-to-noise density ratios for a given M-ary system and desired $P(e)$.

Example 2-15

For a QPSK system and the given parameters, determine

a. Carrier power in dBm.
b. Noise power in dBm.

c. Noise power density in dBm.
d. Energy per bit in dBJ.
e. Carrier-to-noise power ratio in dB.
f. E_b/N_0 ratio.

$$C = 10^{-12} \text{ W} \qquad f_b = 60 \text{ kbps}$$
$$N = 1.2 \times 10^{-14} \text{ W} \qquad B = 120 \text{ kHz}$$

Solution   a. The carrier power in dBm is determined by substituting into Equation 2-28:

$$C = 10 \log \frac{10^{-12}}{0.001} = -90 \text{ dBm}$$

b. The noise power in dBm is determined by substituting into Equation 2-30:

$$N = 10 \log \frac{1.2 \times 10^{-14}}{0.001} = -109.2 \text{ dBm}$$

c. The noise power density is determined by substituting into Equation 2-40:
$$N_0 = -109.2 \text{ dBm} - 10 \log 120 \text{ kHz} = -160 \text{ dBm}$$

d. The energy per bit is determined by substituting into Equation 2-36:

$$E_b = 10 \log \frac{10^{-12}}{60 \text{ kbps}} = -167.8 \text{ dBJ}$$

e. The carrier-to-noise power ratio is determined by substituting into Equation 2-34:

$$\frac{C}{N} = 10 \log \frac{10^{-12}}{1.2 \times 10^{-14}} = 19.2 \text{ dB}$$

f. The energy per bit-to-noise density ratio is determined by substituting into Equation 2-45:

$$\frac{E_b}{N_0} = 19.2 + 10 \log \frac{120 \text{ kHz}}{60 \text{ kbps}} = 22.2 \text{ dB}$$

2-13   ERROR PERFORMANCE

2-13-1   PSK Error Performance

The bit error performance for the various multiphase digital modulation systems is directly related to the distance between points on a signal state-space diagram. For example, on the signal
state-space diagram for BPSK shown in Figure 2-47a, it can be seen that the two signal points
(logic 1 and logic 0) have maximum separation (d) for a given power level (D). In essence, one
BPSK signal state is the exact negative of the other. As the figure shows, a noise vector (V_N),
when combined with the signal vector (V_S), effectively shifts the phase of the signaling element
(V_{SE}) alpha degrees. If the phase shift exceeds $\pm90°$, the signal element is shifted beyond the
threshold points into the error region. For BPSK, it would require a noise vector of sufficient
amplitude and phase to produce more than a $\pm90°$ phase shift in the signaling element to produce an error. For PSK systems, the general formula for the threshold points is

$$\text{TP} = \pm \frac{\pi}{M} \tag{2-47}$$

where M is the number of signal states.

The phase relationship between signaling elements for BPSK (i.e., 180° out of phase)
is the optimum signaling format, referred to as *antipodal signaling,* and occurs only when
two binary signal levels are allowed and when one signal is the exact negative of the other.
Because no other bit-by-bit signaling scheme is any better, antipodal performance is often
used as a reference for comparison.

The error performance of the other multiphase PSK systems can be compared with
that of BPSK simply by determining the relative decrease in error distance between points

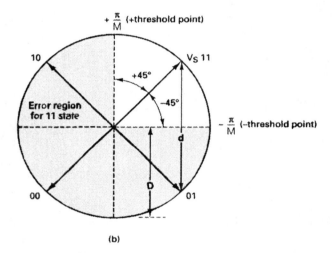

FIGURE 2-47   PSK error region: (a) BPSK; (b) QPSK

on a signal state-space diagram. For PSK, the general formula for the maximum distance between signaling points is given by

$$\sin \theta = \sin \frac{360°}{2M} = \frac{d/2}{D}$$

(2-48)

where d = error distance
 M = number of phases
 D = peak signal amplitude

Rearranging Equation 2-48 and solving for d yields

$$d = \left(2 \sin \frac{180°}{M}\right) \times D$$

(2-49)

Figure 2-47b shows the signal state-space diagram for QPSK. From Figure 2-47 and Equation 2-48, it can be seen that QPSK can tolerate only a $\pm 45°$ phase shift. From Equation 2-47, the maximum phase shift for 8-PSK and 16-PSK is $\pm22.5°$ and $\pm11.25°$, respectively. Consequently, the higher levels of modulation (i.e., the greater the value of M) require a greater energy per bit-to-noise power density ratio to reduce the effect of noise interference. Hence, the higher the level of modulation, the smaller the angular separation between signal points and the smaller the error distance.

The general expression for the bit error probability of an M-phase PSK system is

$$P(e) = \frac{1}{\log_2 M} \, \text{erf}(z) \tag{2-50}$$

where erf = error function
$$z = \sin(\pi/M)(\sqrt{\log_2 M})(\sqrt{E_b/N_0})$$

By substituting into Equation 2-50, it can be shown that QPSK provides the same error performance as BPSK. This is because the 3-dB reduction in error distance for QPSK is offset by the 3-dB decrease in its bandwidth (in addition to the error distance, the relative widths of the noise bandwidths must also be considered). Thus, both systems provide optimum performance. Figure 2-48 shows the error performance for 2-, 4-, 8-, 16-, and 32-PSK systems as a function of E_b/N_0.

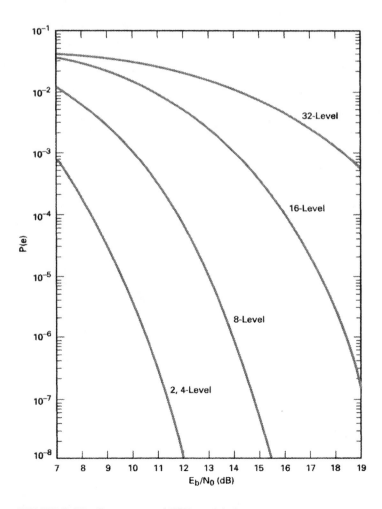

FIGURE 2-48   Error rates of PSK modulation systems

Example 2-16

Determine the minimum bandwidth required to achieve a $P(e)$ of 10^{-7} for an 8-PSK system operating at 10 Mbps with a carrier-to-noise power ratio of 11.7 dB.

Solution   From Figure 2-48, the minimum E_b/N_0 ratio to achieve a $P(e)$ of 10^{-7} for an 8-PSK system is 14.7 dB. The minimum bandwidth is found by rearranging Equation 2-44:

$$\frac{B}{f_b} = \frac{E_b}{N_0} - \frac{C}{N}$$

$$= 14.7 \text{ dB} - 11.7 \text{ dB} = 3 \text{ dB}$$

$$\frac{B}{f_b} = \text{antilog } 3 = 2$$

$$B = 2 \times 10 \text{ Mbps} = 20 \text{ MHz}$$

2-13-2   QAM Error Performance

For a large number of signal points (i.e., M-ary systems greater than 4), QAM outperforms PSK. This is because the distance between signaling points in a PSK system is smaller than the distance between points in a comparable QAM system. The general expression for the distance between adjacent signaling points for a QAM system with L levels on each axis is

$$d = \frac{\sqrt{2}}{L - 1} \times D \tag{2-51}$$

where d = error distance
       L = number of levels on each axis
       D = peak signal amplitude

In comparing Equation 2-49 to Equation 2-51, it can be seen that QAM systems have an advantage over PSK systems with the same peak signal power level.

The general expression for the bit error probability of an L-level QAM system is

$$P(e) = \frac{1}{\log_2 L}\left(\frac{L-1}{L}\right)\text{erfc}(z) \tag{2-52}$$

where erfc(z) is the complementary error function.

$$z = \frac{\sqrt{\log_2 L}}{L - 1}\sqrt{\frac{E_b}{N_0}}$$

Figure 2-49 shows the error performance for 4-, 16-, 32-, and 64-QAM systems as a function of E_b/N_0.

Table 2-4 lists the minimum carrier-to-noise power ratios and energy per bit-to-noise power density ratios required for a probability of error 10^{-6} for several PSK and QAM modulation schemes.

Example 2-16

Which system requires the highest E_b/N_0 ratio for a probability of error of 10^{-6}, a four-level QAM system or an 8-PSK system?

Solution   From Figure 2-49, the minimum E_b/N_0 ratio required for a four-level QAM system is 10.6 dB. From Figure 2-48, the minimum E_b/N_0 ratio required for an 8-PSK system is 14 dB. Therefore, to achieve a $P(e)$ of 10^{-6}, a four-level QAM system would require 3.4 dB less E_b/N_0 ratio.

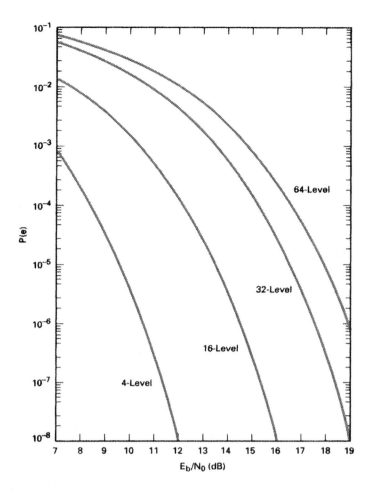

FIGURE 2-49   Error rates of QAM modulation systems

Table 2-4   Performance Comparison of Various Digital Modulation Schemes (BER = 10^{-6})

Modulation Technique	C/N Ratio (dB)	E_b/N_0 Ratio (dB)
BPSK	10.6	10.6
QPSK	13.6	10.6
4-QAM	13.6	10.6
8-QAM	17.6	10.6
8-PSK	18.5	14
16-PSK	24.3	18.3
16-QAM	20.5	14.5
32-QAM	24.4	17.4
64-QAM	26.6	18.8

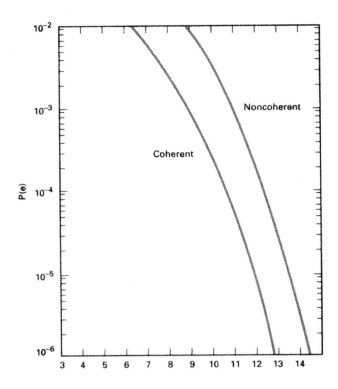

FIGURE 2-50   Error rates for FSK modulation systems

2-13-3   FSK Error Performance

The error probability for FSK systems is evaluated in a somewhat different manner than PSK and QAM. There are essentially only two types of FSK systems: noncoherent (asynchronous) and coherent (synchronous). With noncoherent FSK, the transmitter and receiver are not frequency or phase synchronized. With coherent FSK, local receiver reference signals are in frequency and phase lock with the transmitted signals. The probability of error for noncoherent FSK is

$$P(e) = \frac{1}{2} \exp\left(-\frac{E_b}{2N_0}\right)$$

(2-53)

The probability of error for coherent FSK is

$$P(e) = \text{erfc}\sqrt{\frac{E_b}{N_0}}$$

(2-54)

Figure 2-50 shows probability of error curves for both coherent and noncoherent FSK for several values of E_b/N_0. From Equations 2-53 and 2-54, it can be determined that the probability of error for noncoherent FSK is greater than that of coherent FSK for equal energy per bit-to-noise power density ratios.

QUESTIONS

2-1.   Explain *digital transmission* and *digital radio.*

2-2.   Define *information capacity.*

2-3.   What are the three most predominant modulation schemes used in digital radio systems?

2-4. Explain the relationship between bits per second and baud for an FSK system.

2-5. Define the following terms for FSK modulation: *frequency deviation, modulation index,* and *deviation ratio.*

2-6. Explain the relationship between (a) the minimum bandwidth required for an FSK system and the bit rate and (b) the mark and space frequencies.

2-7. What is the difference between standard FSK and MSK? What is the advantage of MSK?

2-8. Define *PSK.*

2-9. Explain the relationship between bits per second and baud for a BPSK system.

2-10. What is a constellation diagram, and how is it used with PSK?

2-11. Explain the relationship between the minimum bandwidth required for a BPSK system and the bit rate.

2-12. Explain *M*-ary.

2-13. Explain the relationship between bits per second and baud for a QPSK system.

2-14. Explain the significance of the I and Q channels in a QPSK modulator.

2-15. Define *dibit.*

2-16. Explain the relationship between the minimum bandwidth required for a QPSK system and the bit rate.

2-17. What is a coherent demodulator?

2-18. What advantage does OQPSK have over conventional QPSK? What is a disadvantage of OQPSK?

2-19. Explain the relationship between bits per second and baud for an 8-PSK system.

2-20. Define *tribit.*

2-21. Explain the relationship between the minimum bandwidth required for an 8-PSK system and the bit rate.

2-22. Explain the relationship between bits per second and baud for a 16-PSK system.

2-23. Define *quadbit.*

2-24. Define *QAM.*

2-25. Explain the relationship between the minimum bandwidth required for a 16-QAM system and the bit rate.

2-26. What is the difference between PSK and QAM?

2-27. Define *bandwidth efficiency.*

2-28. Define *carrier recovery.*

2-29. Explain the differences between absolute PSK and differential PSK.

2-30. What is the purpose of a clock recovery circuit? When is it used?

2-31. What is the difference between probability of error and bit error rate?

PROBLEMS

2-1. Determine the bandwidth and baud for an FSK signal with a mark frequency of 32 kHz, a space frequency of 24 kHz, and a bit rate of 4 kbps.

2-2. Determine the maximum bit rate for an FSK signal with a mark frequency of 48 kHz, a space frequency of 52 kHz, and an available bandwidth of 10 kHz.

2-3. Determine the bandwidth and baud for an FSK signal with a mark frequency of 99 kHz, a space frequency of 101 kHz, and a bit rate of 10 kbps.

2-4. Determine the maximum bit rate for an FSK signal with a mark frequency of 102 kHz, a space frequency of 104 kHz, and an available bandwidth of 8 kHz.

2-5. Determine the minimum bandwidth and baud for a BPSK modulator with a carrier frequency of 40 MHz and an input bit rate of 500 kbps. Sketch the output spectrum.

2-6. For the QPSK modulator shown in Figure 2-17, change the $+90°$ phase-shift network to $-90°$ and sketch the new constellation diagram.

2-7. For the QPSK demodulator shown in Figure 2-21, determine the I and Q bits for an input signal of $\sin \omega_c t - \cos \omega_c t$.

2-8. For an 8-PSK modulator with an input data rate (f_b) equal to 20 Mbps and a carrier frequency of 100 MHz, determine the minimum double-sided Nyquist bandwidth (f_N) and the baud. Sketch the output spectrum.

2-9. For the 8-PSK modulator shown in Figure 2-23, change the reference oscillator to cos $\omega_c t$ and sketch the new constellation diagram.

2-10. For a 16-QAM modulator with an input bit rate (f_b) equal to 20 Mbps and a carrier frequency of 100 MHz, determine the minimum double-sided Nyquist bandwidth (f_N) and the baud. Sketch the output spectrum.

2-11. For the 16-QAM modulator shown in Figure 2-33, change the reference oscillator to cos $\omega_c t$ and determine the output expressions for the following I, I', Q, and Q' input conditions: 0000, 1111, 1010, and 0101.

2-12. Determine the bandwidth efficiency for the following modulators:
   a. QPSK, f_b = 10 Mbps
   b. 8-PSK, f_b = 21 Mbps
   c. 16-QAM, f_b = 20 Mbps

2-13. For the DBPSK modulator shown in Figure 2-40a, determine the output phase sequence for the following input bit sequence: 00110011010101 (assume that the reference bit = 1).

2-14. For a QPSK system and the given parameters, determine
   a. Carrier power in dBm.
   b. Noise power in dBm.
   c. Noise power density in dBm.
   d. Energy per bit in dBJ.
   e. Carrier-to-noise power ratio.
   f. E_b/N_0 ratio.
   $$C = 10^{-13} \text{ W} \qquad f_b = 30 \text{ kbps}$$
   $$N = 0.06 \times 10^{-15} \text{ W} \qquad B = 60 \text{ kHz}$$

2-15. Determine the minimum bandwidth required to achieve a $P(e)$ of 10^{-6} for an 8-PSK system operating at 20 Mbps with a carrier-to-noise power ratio of 11 dB.

2-16. Determine the minimum bandwidth and baud for a BPSK modulator with a carrier frequency of 80 MHz and an input bit rate f_b = 1 Mbps. Sketch the output spectrum.

2-17. For the QPSK modulator shown in Figure 2-17, change the reference oscillator to cos $\omega_c t$ and sketch the new constellation diagram.

2-18. For the QPSK demodulator shown in Figure 2-21, determine the I and Q bits for an input signal $-\sin \omega_c t + \cos \omega_c t$.

2-19. For an 8-PSK modulator with an input bit rate f_b = 10 Mbps and a carrier frequency f_c = 80 MHz, determine the minimum Nyquist bandwidth and the baud. Sketch the output spectrum.

2-20. For the 8-PSK modulator shown in Figure 2-23, change the $+90°$ phase-shift network to a $-90°$ phase shifter and sketch the new constellation diagram.

2-21. For a 16-QAM modulator with an input bit rate f_b = 10 Mbps and a carrier frequency f_c = 60 MHz, determine the minimum double-sided Nyquist frequency and the baud. Sketch the output spectrum.

2-22. For the 16-QAM modulator shown in Figure 2-33, change the 90° phase shift network to a $-90°$ phase shifter and determine the output expressions for the following I, I', Q, and Q' input conditions: 0000, 1111, 1010, and 0101.

2-23. Determine the bandwidth efficiency for the following modulators:
   a. QPSK, f_b = 20 Mbps
   b. 8-PSK, f_b = 28 Mbps
   c. 16-PSK, f_b = 40 Mbps

2-24. For the DBPSK modulator shown in Figure 2-40a, determine the output phase sequence for the following input bit sequence: 11001100101010 (assume that the reference bit is a logic 1).

CHAPTER 3

Introduction to Data Communications and Networking

OBJECTIVES

- Define the following terms: *data, data communications, data communications circuit,* and *data communications network*
- Give a brief description of the evolution of data communications
- Define *data communications network architecture*
- Describe data communications protocols
- Describe the basic concepts of connection-oriented and connectionless protocols
- Describe syntax and semantics and how they relate to data communications
- Define *data communications standards* and explain why they are necessary
- Describe the following standards organizations: ISO, ITU-T, IEEE, ANSI, EIA, TIA, IAB, ETF, and IRTF
- Define *open systems interconnection*
- Name and explain the functions of each of the layers of the seven-layer OSI model
- Define *station* and *node*
- Describe the fundamental block diagram of a two-station data communications circuit and explain how the following terms relate to it: *source, transmitter, transmission medium, receiver,* and *destination*
- Describe serial and parallel data transmission and explain the advantages and disadvantages of both types of transmissions

- Define *data communications circuit arrangements*
- Describe the following transmission modes: simplex, half duplex, full duplex, and full/full duplex
- Define *data communications network*
- Describe the following network components, functions, and features: servers, clients, transmission media, shared data, shared printers, and network interface card
- Define *local operating system*
- Define *network operating system*
- Describe peer-to-peer client/server and dedicated client/server networks
- Define *network topology* and describe the following: star, bus, ring, mesh, and hybrid
- Describe the following classifications of networks: LAN, MAN, WAN, GAN, building backbone, campus backbone, and enterprise network
- Briefly describe the TCP/IP hierarchical model
- Briefly describe the Cisco three-layer hierarchical model

3-1 INTRODUCTION

Since the early 1970s, technological advances around the world have occurred at a phenomenal rate, transforming the *telecommunications industry* into a highly sophisticated and extremely dynamic field. Where previously telecommunications systems had only voice to accommodate, the advent of very large-scale integration chips and the accompanying low-cost microprocessors, computers, and peripheral equipment has dramatically increased the need for the exchange of digital information. This, of course, necessitated the development and implementation of higher-capacity and much faster means of communicating.

In the data communications world, *data* generally are defined as information that is stored in digital form. The word *data* is plural; a single unit of data is a *datum*. Data communications is the process of transferring digital information (usually in binary form) between two or more points. *Information* is defined as knowledge or intelligence. Information that has been processed, organized, and stored is called data.

The fundamental purpose of a *data communications circuit* is to transfer digital information from one place to another. Thus, *data communications* can be summarized as the transmission, reception, and processing of digital information. The original source information can be in analog form, such as the human voice or music, or in digital form, such as binary-coded numbers or alphanumeric codes. If the source information is in analog form, it must be converted to digital form at the source and then converted back to analog form at the destination.

A *network* is a set of *devices* (sometimes called *nodes* or *stations*) interconnected by media links. *Data communications networks* are systems of interrelated computers and computer equipment and can be as simple as a personal computer connected to a printer or two personal computers connected together through the *public telephone network*. On the other hand, a data communications network can be a complex communications system comprised of one or more mainframe computers and hundreds, thousands, or even millions of remote terminals, personal computers, and workstations. In essence, there is virtually no limit to the capacity or size of a data communications network.

Years ago, a single computer serviced virtually every computing need. Today, the single-computer concept has been replaced by the networking concept, where a large number of separate but interconnected computers share their resources. Data communications networks and systems of networks are used to interconnect virtually all kinds of digital computing equipment, from *automatic teller machines* (ATMs) to bank computers; personal computers to information highways, such as the *Internet;* and workstations to mainframe computers. Data communications networks can also be used for airline and hotel reservation systems, mass media and news networks, and electronic mail delivery systems. The list of applications for data communications networks is virtually endless.

3-2 HISTORY OF DATA COMMUNICATIONS

It is highly likely that data communications began long before recorded time in the form of smoke signals or tom-tom drums, although they surely did not involve electricity or an electronic apparatus, and it is highly unlikely that they were binary coded. One of the earliest means of communicating electrically coded information occurred in 1753, when a proposal submitted to a Scottish magazine suggested running a communications line between villages comprised of 26 parallel wires, each wire for one letter of the alphabet. A Swiss inventor constructed a prototype of the 26-wire system, but current wire-making technology proved the idea impractical.

In 1833, Carl Friedrich Gauss developed an unusual system based on a five-by-five matrix representing 25 letters (I and J were combined). The idea was to send messages over a single wire by deflecting a needle to the right or left between one and five times. The initial set of deflections indicated a row, and the second set indicated a column. Consequently, it could take as many as 10 deflections to convey a single character through the system.

If we limit the scope of data communications to methods that use *binary-coded* electrical signals to transmit information, then the first successful (and practical) data communications system was invented by Samuel F. B. Morse in 1832 and called the *telegraph.* Morse also developed the first practical *data communications code,* which he called the *Morse code.* With telegraph, dots and dashes (analogous to logic 1s and 0s) are transmitted across a wire using electromechanical induction. Various combinations of dots, dashes, and pauses represented binary codes for letters, numbers, and punctuation marks. Because all codes did not contain the same number of dots and dashes, Morse's system combined human intelligence with electronics, as decoding was dependent on the hearing and reasoning ability of the person receiving the message. (Sir Charles Wheatstone and Sir William Cooke allegedly invented the first telegraph in England, but their contraption required six different wires for a single telegraph line.)

In 1840, Morse secured an American patent for the telegraph, and in 1844 the first telegraph line was established between Baltimore and Washington, D.C., with the first message conveyed over this system being "What hath God wrought!" In 1849, the first slow-speed telegraph printer was invented, but it was not until 1860 that high-speed (15-bps) printers were available. In 1850, Western Union Telegraph Company was formed in Rochester, New York, for the purpose of carrying coded messages from one person to another.

In 1874, Emile Baudot invented a telegraph *multiplexer,* which allowed signals from up to six different telegraph machines to be transmitted simultaneously over a single wire. The *telephone* was invented in 1875 by Alexander Graham Bell and, unfortunately, very little new evolved in telegraph until 1899, when Guglielmo Marconi succeeded in sending radio (wireless) telegraph messages. Telegraph was the only means of sending information across large spans of water until 1920, when the first commercial radio stations carrying voice information were installed.

It is unclear exactly when the first electrical computer was developed. Konrad Zuis, a German engineer, demonstrated a computing machine sometime in the late 1930s; however, at the time, Hitler was preoccupied trying to conquer the rest of the world, so the project fizzled out. Bell Telephone Laboratories is given credit for developing the first special-purpose computer in 1940 using electromechanical relays for performing logical operations. However, J. Presper Eckert and John Mauchley at the University of Pennsylvania are given credit by some for beginning modern-day computing when they developed the ENIAC computer on February 14, 1946.

In 1949, the U.S. National Bureau of Standards developed the first all-electronic diode-based computer capable of executing stored programs. The U.S. Census Bureau installed the machine, which is considered the first commercially produced American computer. In the 1950s, computers used punch cards for inputting information, printers for outputting information, and magnetic tape reels for permanently storing information. These early computers could process only one job at a time using a technique called *batch processing.*

The first general-purpose computer was an automatic sequence-controlled calculator developed jointly by Harvard University and International Business Machines (IBM) Corporation. The UNIVAC computer, built in 1951 by Remington Rand Corporation, was the first mass-produced electronic computer.

In the 1960s, batch-processing systems were replaced by on-line processing systems with terminals connected directly to the computer through serial or parallel communications lines. The 1970s introduced microprocessor-controlled microcomputers, and by the 1980s personal computers became an essential item in the home and workplace. Since then, the number of mainframe computers, small business computers, personal computers, and computer terminals has increased exponentially, creating a situation where more and more people have the need (or at least think they have the need) to exchange digital information with each other. Consequently, the need for data communications circuits, networks, and systems has also increased exponentially.

Soon after the invention of the telephone, the American Telephone and Telegraph Company (AT&T) emerged, providing both long-distance and local telephone service and data communications service throughout the United States. The vast AT&T system was referred to by some as the "Bell System" and by others as "Ma Bell." During this time, Western Union Corporation provided telegraph service. Until 1968, the AT&T operating tariff allowed only equipment furnished by AT&T to be connected to AT&T lines. In 1968, a landmark Supreme Court decision, the *Carterfone* decision, allowed non-Bell companies to interconnect to the vast AT&T communications network. This decision started the interconnect industry, which has led to competitive data communications offerings by a large number of independent companies. In 1983, as a direct result of an antitrust suit filed by the federal government, AT&T agreed in a court settlement to divest itself of operating companies that provide basic local telephone service to the various geographic regions of the United States. Since the divestiture, the complexity of the public telephone system in the United States has grown even more involved and complicated.

Recent developments in data communications networking, such as the *Internet, intranets,* and the *World Wide Web* (WWW), have created a virtual explosion in the data communications industry. A seemingly infinite number of people, from homemaker to chief executive officer, now feel a need to communicate over a finite number of facilities. Thus, the demand for higher-capacity and higher-speed data communications systems is increasing daily with no end in sight.

The *Internet* is a public data communications network used by millions of people all over the world to exchange business and personal information. The Internet began to evolve in 1969 at the *Advanced Research Projects Agency* (ARPA). ARPANET was formed in the late 1970s to connect sites around the United States. From the mid-1980s to April 30, 1995, the *National Science Foundation* (NSF) funded a high-speed backbone called NSFNET.

Intranets are private data communications networks used by many companies to exchange information among employees and resources. Intranets normally are used for security reasons or to satisfy specific connectivity requirements. Company intranets are generally connected to the public Internet through a *firewall,* which converts the intranet addressing system to the public Internet addressing system and provides security functionality by filtering incoming and outgoing traffic based on addressing and protocols.

The *World Wide Web* (WWW) is a server-based application that allows subscribers to access the services offered by the Web. Browsers, such as Netscape Communicator and Microsoft Internet Explorer, are commonly used for accessing data over the WWW.

3-3 DATA COMMUNICATIONS NETWORK ARCHITECTURE, PROTOCOLS, AND STANDARDS

3-3-1 Data Communications Network Architecture

A *data communications network* is any system of computers, computer terminals, or computer peripheral equipment used to transmit and/or receive information between two or more locations. *Network architectures* outline the products and services necessary for the individual components within a data communications network to operate together.

In essence, network architecture is a set of equipment, transmission media, and procedures that ensures that a specific sequence of events occurs in a network in the proper order to produce the intended results. Network architecture must include sufficient information to allow a program or a piece of hardware to perform its intended function. The primary goal of network architecture is to give the users of the network the tools necessary for setting up the network and performing data flow control. A network architecture outlines the way in which a data communications network is arranged or structured and generally includes the concept of *levels* or *layers* of functional responsibility within the architecture. The *functional responsibilities* include electrical specifications, hardware arrangements, and software procedures.

Networks and network protocols fall into three general classifications: *current, legacy,* and *legendary.* Current networks include the most modern and sophisticated networks and protocols available. If a network or protocol becomes a legacy, no one really wants to use it, but for some reason it just will not go away. When an antiquated network or protocol finally disappears, it becomes legendary.

In general terms, computer networks can be classified in two different ways: *broadcast* and *point to point.* With broadcast networks, all stations and devices on the network share a single communications channel. Data are propagated through the network in relatively short messages sometimes called *frames, blocks,* or *packets.* Many or all subscribers of the network receive transmitted messages, and each message contains an address that identifies specifically which subscriber (or subscribers) is intended to receive the message. When messages are intended for all subscribers on the network, it is called *broadcasting,* and when messages are intended for a specific group of subscribers, it is called *multicasting.*

Point-to-point networks have only two stations. Therefore, no addresses are needed. All transmissions from one station are intended for and received by the other station. With point-to-point networks, data are often transmitted in long, continuous messages, sometimes requiring several hours to send.

In more specific terms, point-to-point and broadcast networks can be subdivided into many categories in which one type of network is often included as a subnetwork of another.

3-3-2 Data Communications Protocols

Computer networks communicate using *protocols,* which define the procedures that the systems involved in the communications process will use. Numerous protocols are used today to provide networking capabilities, such as how much data can be sent, how it will be sent, how it will be addressed, and what procedure will be used to ensure that there are no undetected errors.

Protocols are arrangements between people or processes. In essence, a protocol is a set of customs, rules, or regulations dealing with formality or precedence, such as diplomatic or military protocol. Each functional layer of a network is responsible for providing a specific service to the data being transported through the network by providing a set of rules, called protocols, that perform a specific function (or functions) within the network. *Data communications protocols* are sets of rules governing the orderly exchange of data within the network or a portion of the network, whereas network architecture is a set of layers and protocols that govern the operation of the network. The list of protocols used by a system is called a *protocol stack,* which generally includes only one protocol per layer. *Layered network architectures* consist of two or more independent levels. Each level has a specific set of responsibilities and functions, including data transfer, flow control, data segmentation and reassembly, sequence control, error detection and correction, and notification.

3-3-2-1 Connection-oriented and connectionless protocols. Protocols can be generally classified as either *connection oriented* or *connectionless.* With a connection-oriented protocol, a logical connection is established between the endpoints (e.g., a *virtual circuit*) prior to the transmission of data. Connection-oriented protocols operate in a manner similar to making a standard telephone call where there is a sequence of actions and acknowledgments, such as setting up the call, establishing the connection, and then disconnecting. The actions and acknowledgments include dial tone, Touch-Tone signaling, ringing and ring-back signals, and busy signals.

Connection-oriented protocols are designed to provide a high degree of reliability for data moving through the network. This is accomplished by using a rigid set of procedures for establishing the connection, transferring the data, acknowledging the data, and then clearing the connection. In a connection-oriented system, each packet of data is assigned a unique sequence number and an associated acknowledgement number to track the data as they travel through a network. If data are lost or damaged, the destination station requests that they be re-sent. A connection-oriented protocol is depicted in Figure 3-1a. Characteristics of connection-oriented protocols include the following:

1. A connection process called a *handshake* occurs between two stations before any data are actually transmitted. Connections are sometimes referred to as *sessions, virtual circuits,* or *logical connections.*
2. Most connection-oriented protocols require some means of acknowledging the data as they are being transmitted. Protocols that use acknowledgment procedures provide a high level of network reliability.
3. Connection-oriented protocols often provide some means of error control (i.e., error detection and error correction). Whenever data are found to be in error, the receiving station requests a retransmission.
4. When a connection is no longer needed, a specific handshake drops the connection.

Connectionless protocols are protocols where data are exchanged in an unplanned fashion without prior coordination between endpoints (e.g., a datagram). Connectionless protocols do not provide the same high degree of reliability as connection-oriented protocols; however, connectionless protocols offer a significant advantage in transmission speed. Connectionless protocols operate in a manner similar to the U.S. Postal Service, where information is formatted, placed in an envelope with source and destination addresses, and then mailed. You can only hope the letter arrives at its destination. A connectionless protocol is depicted in Figure 3-1b. Characteristics of connectionless protocols are as follow:

1. Connectionless protocols send data with a source and destination address without a handshake to ensure that the destination is ready to receive the data.
2. Connectionless protocols usually do not support error control or acknowledgment procedures, making them a relatively unreliable method of data transmission.
3. Connectionless protocols are used because they are often more efficient, as the data being transmitted usually do not justify the extra overhead required by connection-oriented protocols.

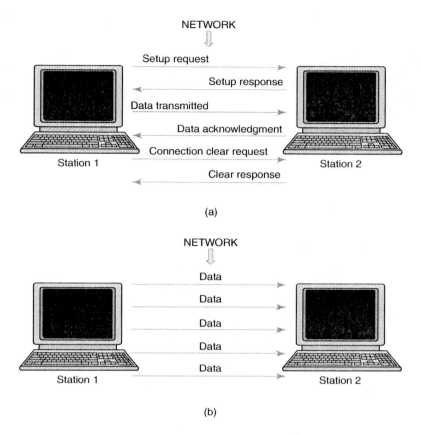

FIGURE 3-1   Network protocols: (a) connection-oriented; (b) connectionless

3-3-2-2 Syntax and semantics.   Protocols include the concepts of *syntax* and *semantics*. Syntax refers to the structure or format of the data within the message, which includes the sequence in which the data are sent. For example, the first byte of a message might be the address of the source and the second byte the address of the destination. Semantics refers to the meaning of each section of data. For example, does a destination address identify only the location of the final destination, or does it also identify the route the data takes between the sending and receiving locations?

3-3-3   Data Communications Standards

During the past several decades, the data communications industry has grown at an astronomical rate. Consequently, the need to provide communications between dissimilar computer equipment and systems has also increased. A major issue facing the data communications industry today is worldwide compatibility. Major areas of interest are software and programming language, electrical and cable interface, transmission media, communications signal, and format compatibility. Thus, to ensure an orderly transfer of information, it has been necessary to establish standard means of governing the physical, electrical, and procedural arrangements of a data communications system.

A standard is an object or procedure considered by an authority or by general consent as a basis of comparison. Standards are authoritative principles or rules that imply a model or pattern for guidance by comparison. *Data communications standards* are guidelines that have been generally accepted by the data communications industry. The guidelines outline procedures and equipment configurations that help ensure an orderly transfer of information between two or more pieces of data communications equipment or two or more data communications networks. Data communications standards are not laws, however—they are simply suggested ways of implementing procedures and accomplishing results. If everyone complies with the standards, everyone's equipment, procedures, and processes will be compatible with everyone else's, and there will be little difficulty communicating information through the system. Today, most companies make their products to comply with standards.

There are two basic types of standards: *proprietary* (closed) system and *open* system. Proprietary standards are generally manufactured and controlled by one company. Other companies are not allowed to manufacture equipment or write software using this standard. An example of a proprietary standard is Apple Macintosh computers. Advantages of proprietary standards are tighter control, easier consensus, and a monopoly. Disadvantages include lack of choice for the customers, higher financial investment, overpricing, and reduced customer protection against the manufacturer going out of business.

With open system standards, any company can produce compatible equipment or software; however, often a royalty must be paid to the original company. An example of an open system standard is IBM's personal computer. Advantages of open system standards are customer choice, compatibility between venders, and competition by smaller companies. Disadvantages include less product control and increased difficulty acquiring agreement between vendors for changes or updates. In addition, standard items are not always as compatible as we would like them to be.

3-4 STANDARDS ORGANIZATIONS FOR DATA COMMUNICATIONS

A consortium of organizations, governments, manufacturers, and users meet on a regular basis to ensure an orderly flow of information within data communications networks and systems by establishing guidelines and standards. The intent is that all data communications equipment manufacturers and users comply with these standards. Standards organizations generate, control, and administer standards. Often, competing companies will form a joint committee to create a compromised standard that is acceptable to everyone. The most prominent organizations relied on in North America to publish standards and make recommendations for the data, telecommunications, and networking industries are shown in Figure 3-2.

3-4-1 International Standards Organization (ISO)

Created in 1946, the *International Standards Organization* (ISO) is the international organization for standardization on a wide range of subjects. The ISO is a voluntary, nontreaty organization whose membership is comprised mainly of members from the standards committees of various governments throughout the world. The ISO creates the sets of rules and standards for graphics and document exchange and provides models for equipment and system compatibility, quality enhancement, improved productivity, and reduced costs. The ISO is responsible for endorsing and coordinating the work of the other standards organizations. The member body of the ISO from the United States is the American National Standards Institute (ANSI).

3-4-2 International Telecommunications Union— Telecommunications Sector

The *International Telecommunications Union—Telecommunications Sector* (ITU-T), formerly the Comité Consultatif Internationale de Télégraphie et Téléphonie (CCITT), is one of four permanent parts of the International Telecommunications Union based in Geneva, Switzerland.

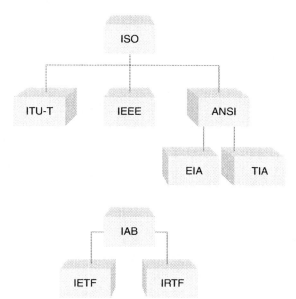

FIGURE 3-2 Standards organizations for data and network communications

Membership in the ITU-T consists of government authorities and representatives from many countries. The ITU-T is now the standards organization for the United Nations and develops the recommended sets of rules and standards for telephone and data communications. The ITU-T has developed three sets of specifications: the V series for modem interfacing and data transmission over telephone lines; the X series for data transmission over public digital networks, e-mail, and directory services; and the I and Q series for Integrated Services Digital Network (ISDN) and its extension Broadband ISDN (sometimes called the Information Superhighway).

The ITU-T is separated into 14 study groups that prepare recommendations on the following topics:

Network and service operation

Tariff and accounting principles

Telecommunications management network and network maintenance

Protection against electromagnetic environment effects

Outside plant

Data networks and open system communications

Characteristics of telematic systems

Television and sound transmission

Language and general software aspects for telecommunications systems

Signaling requirements and protocols

End-to-end transmission performance of networks and terminals

General network aspects

Transport networks, systems, and equipment

Multimedia services and systems

3-4-3 Institute of Electrical and Electronics Engineers

The *Institute of Electrical and Electronics Engineers* (IEEE) is an international professional organization founded in the United States and is comprised of electronics, computer, and communications engineers. The IEEE is currently the world's largest professional society with over 200,000 members. The IEEE works closely with ANSI to develop communications and information processing standards with the underlying goal of advancing theory, creativity, and product quality in any field associated with electrical engineering.

3-4-4 American National Standards Institute

The *American National Standards Institute* (ANSI) is the official standards agency for the United States and is the U.S. voting representative for the ISO. However, ANSI is a completely private, nonprofit organization comprised of equipment manufacturers and users of data processing equipment and services. Although ANSI has no affiliations with the federal government of the United States, it serves as the national coordinating institution for voluntary standardization in the United States. ANSI membership is comprised of people from professional societies, industry associations, governmental and regulatory bodies, and consumer groups.

3-4-5 Electronics Industry Association

The *Electronics Industries Associations* (EIA) is a nonprofit U.S. trade association that establishes and recommends industrial standards. EIA activities include standards development, increasing public awareness, and lobbying. The EIA is responsible for developing the RS (recommended standard) series of standards for data and telecommunications.

3-4-6 Telecommunications Industry Association

The *Telecommunications Industry Association* (TIA) is the leading trade association in the communications and information technology industry. The TIA facilitates business development opportunities and a competitive marketplace through market development, trade promotion, trade shows, domestic and international advocacy, and standards development. The TIA represents manufacturers of communications and information technology products and services providers for the global marketplace through its core competencies. The TIA also facilitates the convergence of new communications networks while working for a competitive and innovative market environment.

3-4-7 Internet Architecture Board

In 1957, the Advanced Research Projects Agency (ARPA), the research arm of the Department of Defense, was created in response to the Soviet Union's launching of *Sputnik*. The original purpose of ARPA was to accelerate the advancement of technologies that could possibly be useful to the U.S. military. When ARPANET was initiated in the late 1970s, ARPA formed a committee to oversee it. In 1983, the name of the committee was changed to the *Internet Activities Board* (IAB). The meaning of the acronym was later changed to the *Internet Architecture Board*.

Today the IAB is a technical advisory group of the Internet Society with the following responsibilities:

1. Oversees the architecture protocols and procedures used by the Internet
2. Manages the processes used to create Internet standards and serves as an appeal board for complaints of improper execution of the standardization processes
3. Is responsible for the administration of the various Internet assigned numbers
4. Acts as representative for Internet Society interests in liaison relationships with other organizations concerned with standards and other technical and organizational issues relevant to the worldwide Internet
5. Acts as a source of advice and guidance to the board of trustees and officers of the Internet Society concerning technical, architectural, procedural, and policy matters pertaining to the Internet and its enabling technologies

3-4-8 Internet Engineering Task Force

The *Internet Engineering Task Force* (IETF) is a large international community of network designers, operators, venders, and researchers concerned with the evolution of the Internet architecture and the smooth operation of the Internet.

3-4-9 Internet Research Task Force

The *Internet Research Task Force* (IRTF) promotes research of importance to the evolution of the future Internet by creating focused, long-term and small research groups working on topics related to Internet protocols, applications, architecture, and technology.

3-5 LAYERED NETWORK ARCHITECTURE

The basic concept of *layering* network responsibilities is that each layer adds value to services provided by sets of lower layers. In this way, the highest level is offered the full set of services needed to run a distributed data application. There are several advantages to using a *layered architecture*. A layered architecture facilitates *peer-to-peer communications protocols* where a given layer in one system can logically communicate with its corresponding layer in another system. This allows different computers to communicate at different levels. Figure 3-3 shows a layered architecture where layer N at the source logically (but not necessarily physically) communicates with layer N at the destination and layer N of any intermediate nodes.

3-5-1 Protocol Data Unit

When technological advances occur in a layered architecture, it is easier to modify one layer's protocol without having to modify all the other layers. Each layer is essentially independent of every other layer. Therefore, many of the functions found in lower layers have been removed entirely from software tasks and replaced with hardware. The primary disadvantage of layered architectures is the tremendous amount of overhead required. With layered architectures, communications between two corresponding layers requires a unit of data called a *protocol data unit* (PDU). As shown in Figure 3-4, a PDU can be a *header* added at the beginning of a message or a *trailer* appended to the end of a message. In a layered architecture, communications occurs between similar layers; however, data must flow through the other layers. Data flows downward through the layers in the source system and upward through the layers in the destination system. In intermediate systems, data flows upward first and then downward. As data passes from one layer into another, headers and trailers are added and removed from the PDU. The process of adding or removing PDU information is called *encapsulation/decapsulation* because it appears as though the PDU from the upper layer is encapsulated in the PDU from the lower layer during the downward

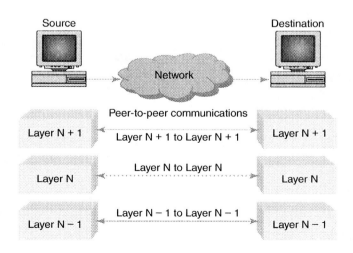

FIGURE 3-3　Peer-to-peer data communications

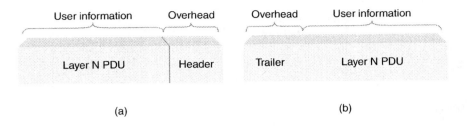

User information	Overhead		Overhead	User information
Layer N PDU	Header		Trailer	Layer N PDU

| (a) | | | (b) | |

FIGURE 3-4   Protocol data unit: (a) header; (b) trailer

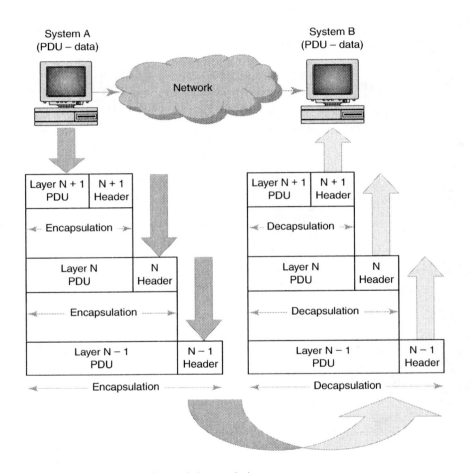

FIGURE 3-5   Encapsulation and decapsulation

movement and decapsulated during the upward movement. *Encapsulate* means to place in a capsule or other protected environment, and *decapsulate* means to remove from a capsule or other protected environment. Figure 3-5 illustrates the concepts of encapsulation and decapsulation.

In a layered protocol such as the one shown in Figure 3-3, layer N receive services from the layer immediately below it (N − 1) and provides services to the layer directly above it (N + 1). Layer N can provide service to more than one entity in layer N + 1 by using a *service access point* (SAP) *address* to define which entity the service is intended.

Information and network information passes from one layer of a multilayered architecture to another layer through a layer-to-layer *interface*. A layer-to-layer interface defines what information and services the lower layer must provide to the upper layer. A well-defined layer and layer-to-layer interface provide modularity to a network.

3-6 OPEN SYSTEMS INTERCONNECTION

Open systems interconnection (OSI) is the name for a set of standards for communicating among computers. The primary purpose of OSI standards is to serve as a structural guideline for exchanging information between computers, workstations, and networks. The OSI is endorsed by both the ISO and ITU-T, which have worked together to establish a set of ISO standards and ITU-T recommendations that are essentially identical. In 1983, the ISO and ITU-T (CCITT) adopted a seven-layer communications architecture reference model. Each layer consists of specific protocols for communicating.

The ISO seven-layer open systems interconnection model is shown in Figure 3-6. This hierarchy was developed to facilitate the intercommunications of data processing equipment by separating network responsibilities into seven distinct layers. As with any layered architecture, overhead information is added to a PDU in the form of headers and trailers. In fact, if all seven levels of the OSI model are addressed, as little as 15% of the transmitted message is actually source information, and the rest is overhead. The result of adding headers to each layer is illustrated in Figure 3-7.

ISO Layer and name   **Function**

Layer 7 Application	User networking applications and interfacing to the network
Layer 6 Presentation	Encoding language used in transmission
Layer 5 Session	Job management tracking
Layer 4 Transport	Data tracking as it moves through a network
Layer 3 Network	Network addressing and packet transmission on the network
Layer 2 Data link	Frame formatting for transmitting data across a physical communications link
Layer 1 Physical	Transmission method used to propagate bits through a network

FIGURE 3-6   OSI seven-layer protocol hierarchy

FIGURE 3-7 OSI seven-layer international protocol hierarchy. H7—applications header, H6—presentation header, H5—session header, H4—transport header, H3—network header, H2—data-link header, H1—physical header

In recent years, the OSI seven-layer model has become more academic than standard, as the hierarchy does not coincide with the Internet's four-layer protocol model. However, the basic functions of the layers are still performed, so the seven-layer model continues to serve as a reference model when describing network functions.

Levels 4 to 7 address the applications aspects of the network that allow for two host computers to communicate directly. The three bottom layers are concerned with the actual mechanics of moving data (at the bit level) from one machine to another. The basic services provided by each layer are discussed in a later chapter of this book. A brief summary of the services provided by each layer is given here.

1. *Physical layer.* The physical layer is the lowest level of the OSI hierarchy and is responsible for the actual propagation of unstructured data bits (1s and 0s) through a transmis-

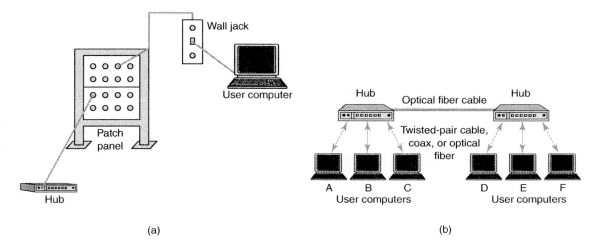

FIGURE 3-8   OSI layer 1—physical: (a) computer-to-hub; (b) connectivity devices

sion medium, which includes how bits are represented, the bit rate, and how bit synchronization is achieved. The physical layer specifies the type of transmission medium and the transmission mode (simplex, half duplex, or full duplex) and the physical, electrical, functional, and procedural standards for accessing data communications networks. Definitions such as connections, pin assignments, interface parameters, timing, maximum and minimum voltage levels, and circuit impedances are made at the physical level. Transmission media defined by the physical layer include metallic cable, optical fiber cable, or wireless radio-wave propagation. The physical layer for a cable connection is depicted in Figure 3-8a.

Connectivity devices connect devices on cabled networks. An example of a connectivity device is a hub. A hub is a transparent device that samples the incoming bit stream and simply repeats it to the other devices connected to the hub. The hub does not examine the data to determine what the destination is; therefore, it is classified as a layer 1 component. Physical layer connectivity for a cabled network is shown in Figure 3-8b.

The physical layer also includes the *carrier system* used to propagate the data signals between points in the network. Carrier systems are simply communications systems that carry data through a system using either metallic or optical fiber cables or wireless arrangements, such as microwave, satellites, and cellular radio systems. The carrier can use analog or digital signals that are somehow converted to a different form (encoded or modulated) by the data and then propagated through the system.

2. *Data-link layer.* The data-link layer is responsible for providing error-free communications across the physical link connecting primary and secondary stations (nodes) within a network (sometimes referred to as *hop-to-hop* delivery). The data-link layer packages data from the physical layer into groups called blocks, frames, or packets and provides a means to activate, maintain, and deactivate the data communications link between nodes. The data-link layer provides the final framing of the information signal, provides synchronization, facilitates the orderly flow of data between nodes, outlines procedures for error detection and correction, and provides the physical addressing information. A block diagram of a network showing data transferred between two computers (A and E) at the data-link level is illustrated in Figure 3-9. Note that the hubs are transparent but that the switch passes the transmission on to only the hub serving the intended destination.

3. *Network layer.* The network layer provides details that enable data to be routed between devices in an environment using multiple networks, subnetworks, or both. Networking components that operate at the network layer include routers and their software. The

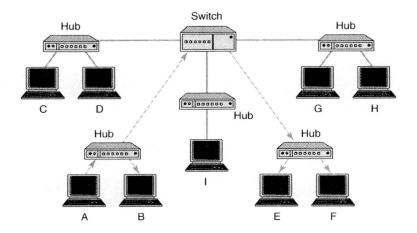

FIGURE 3-9   OSI layer 2—data link

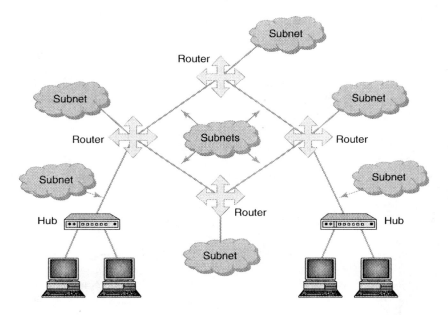

FIGURE 3-10   OSI layer 3—network

network layer determines which network configuration is most appropriate for the function provided by the network and addresses and routes data within networks by establishing, maintaining, and terminating connections between them. The network layer provides the upper layers of the hierarchy independence from the data transmission and switching technologies used to interconnect systems. It accomplishes this by defining the mechanism in which messages are broken into smaller data packets and routed from a sending node to a receiving node within a data communications network. The network layer also typically provides the source and destination network addresses (logical addresses), subnet information, and source and destination node addresses. Figure 3-10 illustrates the network layer of the OSI protocol hierarchy. Note that the network is subdivided into subnetworks that are separated by routers.

    4. *Transport layer.* The transport layer controls and ensures the end-to-end integrity of the data message propagated through the network between two devices, which provides

Computer A   Data   Network   Acknowledgment   Computer B

Data

Acknowledgment

FIGURE 3-11   OSI layer 4—transport

Client

Service request

Hub

Client

Service response

Client

Server

FIGURE 3-12   OSI layer 5—session

for the reliable, transparent transfer of data between two endpoints. Transport layer responsibilities includes message routing, segmenting, error recovery, and two types of basic services to an upper-layer protocol: connectionless oriented and connectionless. The transport layer is the highest layer in the OSI hierarchy in terms of communications and may provide data tracking, connection flow control, sequencing of data, error checking, and application addressing and identification. Figure 3-11 depicts data transmission at the transport layer.

5. *Session layer.* The session layer is responsible for network availability (i.e., data storage and processor capacity). Session layer protocols provide the logical connection entities at the application layer. These applications include file transfer protocols and sending e-mail. Session responsibilities include network log-on and log-off procedures and user authentication. A session is a temporary condition that exists when data are actually in the process of being transferred and does not include procedures such as call establishment, setup, or disconnect. The session layer determines the type of dialogue available (i.e., simplex, half duplex, or full duplex). Session layer characteristics include virtual connections between applications entities, synchronization of data flow for recovery purposes, creation of dialogue units and activity units, connection parameter negotiation, and partitioning services into functional groups. Figure 3-12 illustrates the establishment of a session on a data network.

6. *Presentation layer.* The presentation layer provides independence to the application processes by addressing any code or syntax conversion necessary to present the data to the network in a common communications format. The presentation layer specifies how end-user applications should format the data. This layer provides for translation between local representations of data and the representation of data that will be used for transfer between end users. The results of encryption, data compression, and virtual terminals are examples of the translation service.

FIGURE 3-13 OSI layer 6—presentation

FIGURE 3-14 OSI layer 7—applications

The presentation layer translates between different data formats and protocols. Presentation functions include data file formatting, encoding, encryption and decryption of data messages, dialogue procedures, data compression algorithms, synchronization, interruption, and termination. The presentation layer performs code and character set translation (including ASCII and EBCDIC) and formatting information and determines the display mechanism for messages. Figure 3-13 shows an illustration of the presentation layer.

7. *Application layer.* The application layer is the highest layer in the hierarchy and is analogous to the general manager of the network by providing access to the OSI environment. The applications layer provides distributed information services and controls the sequence of activities within an application and also the sequence of events between the computer application and the user of another application. The application layer (shown in Figure 3-14) communicates directly with the user's application program.

User application processes require application layer service elements to access the networking environment. There are two types of service elements: CASEs (*common application service elements*), which are generally useful to a variety of application processes and SASEs (*specific application service elements*), which generally satisfy particular needs of application processes. CASE examples include association control that establishes, maintains, and terminates connections with a peer application entity and commitment, concurrence, and recovery that ensure the integrity of distributed transactions. SASE examples involve the TCP/IP protocol stack and include FTP (*file transfer protocol*), SNMP (*simple network management protocol*), Telnet (*virtual terminal protocol*), and SMTP (*simple mail transfer protocol*).

The underlying purpose of a data communications circuit is to provide a transmission path between locations and to transfer digital information from one station to another using electronic circuits. A *station* is simply an endpoint where subscribers gain access to the circuit. A station is sometimes called a *node,* which is the location of computers, computer terminals, workstations, and other digital computing equipment. There are almost as many types of data communications circuits as there are types of data communications equipment.

Data communications circuits utilize electronic communications equipment and *facilities* to interconnect digital computer equipment. Communications facilities are physical means of interconnecting stations within a data communications system and can include virtually any type of physical transmission media or wireless radio system in existence. Communications facilities are provided to data communications users through public telephone networks (PTN), public data networks (PDN), and a multitude of private data communications systems.

Figure 3-15 shows a simplified block diagram of a two-station data communications circuit. The fundamental components of the circuit are source of digital information, transmitter, transmission medium, receiver, and destination for the digital information. Although the figure shows transmission in only one direction, bidirectional transmission is possible by providing a duplicate set of circuit components in the opposite direction.

Source. The information source generates data and could be a mainframe computer, personal computer, workstation, or virtually any other piece of digital equipment. The source equipment provides a means for humans to enter data into the system.

Transmitter. Source data is seldom in a form suitable to propagate through the transmission medium. For example, digital signals (pulses) cannot be propagated through a wireless radio system without being converted to analog first. The transmitter encodes the source information and converts it to a different form, allowing it to be more efficiently propagated through the transmission medium. In essence, the transmitter acts as an interface between the source equipment and the transmission medium.

Transmission medium. The transmission medium carries the encoded signals from the transmitter to the receiver. There are many different types of transmission media, such as free-space radio transmission (including all forms of wireless transmission, such as terrestrial microwave, satellite radio, and cellular telephone) and physical facilities, such as metallic and optical fiber cables. Very often, the transmission path is comprised of several different types of transmission facilities.

Receiver. The receiver converts the encoded signals received from the transmission medium back to their original form (i.e., decodes them) or whatever form is used in the destination equipment. The receiver acts as an interface between the transmission medium and the destination equipment.

Destination. Like the source, the destination could be a mainframe computer, personal computer, workstation, or virtually any other piece of digital equipment.

FIGURE 3-15   Simplified block diagram of a two-station data communications circuit

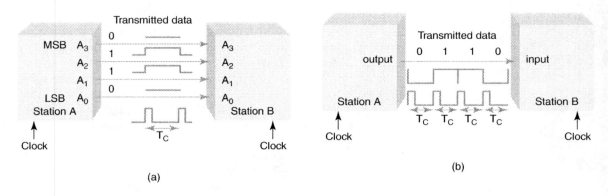

FIGURE 3-16 Data transmission: (a) parallel; (b) serial

3-8 SERIAL AND PARALLEL DATA TRANSMISSION

Binary information can be transmitted either in parallel or serially. Figure 3-16a shows how the binary code 0110 is transmitted from station A to station B in parallel. As the figure shows, each bit position (A_0 to A_3) has its own transmission line. Consequently, all four bits can be transmitted simultaneously during the time of a single clock pulse (T_C). This type of transmission is called *parallel by bit* or *serial by character.*

Figure 3-16b shows the same binary code transmitted serially. As the figure shows, there is a single transmission line and, thus, only one bit can be transmitted at a time. Consequently, it requires four clock pulses ($4T_C$) to transmit the entire four-bit code. This type of transmission is called *serial by bit.*

Obviously, the principal trade-off between parallel and serial data transmission is speed versus simplicity. Data transmission can be accomplished much more rapidly using parallel transmission; however, parallel transmission requires more data lines. As a general rule, parallel transmission is used for short-distance data communications and within a computer, and serial transmission is used for long-distance data communications.

3-9 DATA COMMUNICATIONS CIRCUIT ARRANGEMENTS

Data communications circuits can be configured in a multitude of arrangements depending on the specifics of the circuit, such as how many stations are on the circuit, type of transmission facility, distance between stations, and how many users are at each station. A data communications circuit can be described in terms of circuit configuration and transmission mode.

3-9-1 Circuit Configurations

Data communications networks can be generally categorized as either two point or multipoint. A *two-point* configuration involves only two locations or stations, whereas a *multipoint* configuration involves three or more stations. Regardless of the configuration, each station can have one or more computers, computer terminals, or workstations. A two-point circuit involves the transfer of digital information between a mainframe computer and a personal computer, two mainframe computers, two personal computers, or two data communications networks. A multipoint network is generally used to interconnect a single mainframe computer (host) to many personal computers or to interconnect many personal computers.

3-9-2 Transmission Modes

Essentially, there are four modes of transmission for data communications circuits: *simplex, half duplex, full duplex,* and *full/full duplex.*

3-9-2-1 Simplex. In the simplex (SX) mode, data transmission is unidirectional; information can be sent in only one direction. Simplex lines are also called *receive-only, transmit-only,* or *one-way-only* lines. Commercial radio broadcasting is an example of simplex transmission, as information is propagated in only one direction—from the broadcasting station to the listener.

3-9-2-2 Half duplex. In the half-duplex (HDX) mode, data transmission is possible in both directions but not at the same time. Half-duplex communications lines are also called *two-way-alternate* or *either-way* lines. Citizens band (CB) radio is an example of half-duplex transmission because to send a message, the *push-to-talk* (PTT) switch must be depressed, which turns on the transmitter and shuts off the receiver. To receive a message, the PTT switch must be off, which shuts off the transmitter and turns on the receiver.

3-9-2-3 Full duplex. In the full-duplex (FDX) mode, transmissions are possible in both directions simultaneously, but they must be between the same two stations. Full-duplex lines are also called *two-way simultaneous, duplex,* or *both-way* lines. A local telephone call is an example of full-duplex transmission. Although it is unlikely that both parties would be talking at the same time, they could if they wanted to.

3-9-2-4 Full/full duplex. In the full/full duplex (F/FDX) mode, transmission is possible in both directions at the same time but not between the same two stations (i.e., one station is transmitting to a second station and receiving from a third station at the same time). Full/full duplex is possible only on multipoint circuits. The U.S. postal system is an example of full/full duplex transmission because a person can send a letter to one address and receive a letter from another address at the same time.

3-10 DATA COMMUNICATIONS NETWORKS

Any group of computers connected together can be called a *data communications network,* and the process of sharing resources between computers over a data communications network is called *networking.* In its simplest form, networking is two or more computers connected together through a common transmission medium for the purpose of sharing data. The concept of networking began when someone determined that there was a need to share software and data resources and that there was a better way to do it than storing data on a disk and literally running from one computer to another. By the way, this manual technique of moving data on disks is sometimes referred to as *sneaker net.* The most important considerations of a data communications network are performance, transmission rate, reliability, and security.

Applications running on modern computer networks vary greatly from company to company. A network must be designed with the intended application in mind. A general categorization of networking applications is listed in Table 3-1. The specific application affects how well a network will perform. Each network has a finite capacity. Therefore, network designers and engineers must be aware of the type and frequency of information traffic on the network.

Table 3-1 Networking Applications

Application	Examples
Standard office applications	E-mail, file transfers, and printing
High-end office applications	Video imaging, computer-aided drafting, computer-aided design, and software development
Manufacturing automation	Process and numerical control
Mainframe connectivity	Personal computers, workstations, and terminal support
Multimedia applications	Live interactive video

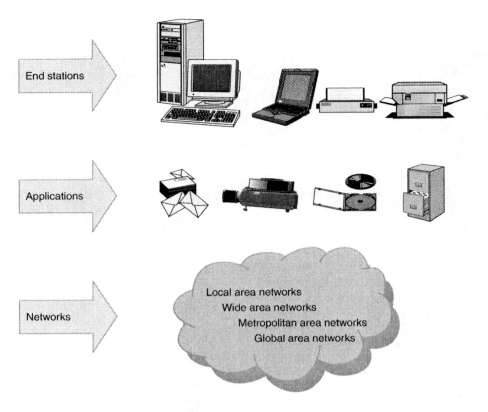

FIGURE 3-17   Basic network components

There are many factors involved when designing a computer network, including the following:

1. Network goals as defined by organizational management
2. Network security
3. Network uptime requirements
4. Network response-time requirements
5. Network and resource costs

The primary balancing act in computer networking is speed versus reliability. Too often, network performance is severely degraded by using error checking procedures, data encryption, and handshaking (acknowledgments). However, these features are often required and are incorporated into protocols.

Some networking protocols are very reliable but require a significant amount of overhead to provide the desired high level of service. These protocols are examples of connection-oriented protocols. Other protocols are designed with speed as the primary parameter and, therefore, forgo some of the reliability features of the connection-oriented protocols. These *quick protocols* are examples of connectionless protocols.

3-10-1   Network Components, Functions, and Features

Computer networks are like snowflakes—no two are the same. The basic components of computer networks are shown in Figure 3-17. All computer networks include some combination of the following: end stations, applications, and a network that will support the data traffic between the end stations. A computer network designed three years ago to support the basic networking applications of the time may have a difficult time supporting recently

File request

Copy of requested file

User computer

File server

FIGURE 3-18 File server operation

developed high-end applications, such as medical imaging and live video teleconferencing. Network designers, administrators, and managers must understand and monitor the most recent types and frequency of networked applications.

Computer networks all share common devices, functions, and features, including servers, clients, transmission media, shared data, shared printers and other peripherals, hardware and software resources, network interface card (NIC), local operating system (LOS), and the network operating system (NOS).

3-10-1-1 Servers. *Servers* are computers that hold shared files, programs, and the network operating system. Servers provide access to network resources to all the users of the network. There are many different kinds of servers, and one server can provide several functions. For example, there are file servers, print servers, mail servers, communications servers, database servers, directory/security servers, fax servers, and Web servers, to name a few.

Figure 3-18 shows the operation of a *file server.* A user (client) requests a file from the file server. The file server sends a copy of the file to the requesting user. File servers allow users to access and manipulate disk resources stored on other computers. An example of a file server application is when two or more users edit a shared spreadsheet file that is stored on a server. File servers have the following characteristics:

1. File servers are loaded with files, accounts, and a record of the access rights of users or groups of users on the network.
2. The server provides a shareable virtual disk to the users (clients).
3. File mapping schemes are implemented to provide the virtualness of the files (i.e., the files are made to look like they are on the user's computer).
4. Security systems are installed and configured to provide the server with the required security and protection for the files.
5. Redirector or shell software programs located on the users' computers transparently activate the client's software on the file server.

3-10-1-2 Clients. *Clients* are computers that access and use the network and shared network resources. Client computers are basically the customers (users) of the network, as they request and receive services from the servers.

3-10-1-3 Transmission media. *Transmission media* are the facilities used to interconnect computers in a network, such as twisted-pair wire, coaxial cable, and optical fiber cable. Transmission media are sometimes called channels, links, or lines.

3-10-1-4 Shared data. *Shared data* are data that file servers provide to clients, such as data files, printer access programs, and e-mail.

3-10-1-5 Shared printers and other peripherals. *Shared printers* and *peripherals* are hardware resources provided to the users of the network by servers. Resources provided include data files, printers, software, or any other items used by clients on the network.

FIGURE 3-19   Network interface card (NIC)

3-10-1-6 Network interface card.   Each computer in a network has a special expansion card called a *network interface card* (NIC). The NIC prepares (formats) and sends data, receives data, and controls data flow between the computer and the network. On the transmit side, the NIC passes frames of data on to the physical layer, which transmits the data to the physical link. On the receive side, the NIC processes bits received from the physical layer and processes the message based on its contents. A network interface card is shown in Figure 3-19. Characteristics of NICs include the following:

1. The NIC constructs, transmits, receives, and processes data to and from a PC and the connected network.
2. Each device connected to a network must have a NIC installed.
3. A NIC is generally installed in a computer as a daughterboard, although some computer manufacturers incorporate the NIC into the motherboard during manufacturing.
4. Each NIC has a unique six-byte media access control (MAC) address, which is typically permanently burned into the NIC when it is manufactured. The MAC address is sometimes called the physical, hardware, node, Ethernet, or LAN address.
5. The NIC must be compatible with the network (i.e., Ethernet—10baseT or token ring) to operate properly.
6. NICs manufactured by different vendors vary in speed, complexity, manageability, and cost.
7. The NIC requires drivers to operate on the network.

3-10-1-7 Local operating system.   A *local operating system* (LOS) allows personal computers to access files, print to a local printer, and have and use one or more disk and CD drives that are located on the computer. Examples of LOSs are MS-DOS, PC-DOS, Unix, Macintosh, OS/2, Windows 3.11, Windows 95, Windows 98, Windows 2000, and Linux. Figure 3-20 illustrates the relationship between a personal computer and its LOS.

3-10-1-8 Network operating system.   The *network operating system* (NOS) is a program that runs on computers and servers that allows the computers to communicate over a network. The NOS provides services to clients such as log-in features, password authenti-

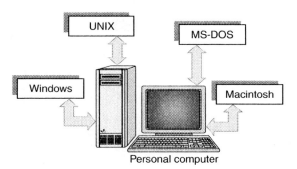

FIGURE 3-20 Local operating system (LOS)

Personal computer

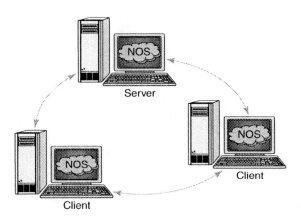

FIGURE 3-21 Network operating system (NOS)

cation, printer access, network administration functions, and data file sharing. Some of the more popular network operating systems are Unix, Novell NetWare, AppleShare, Macintosh System 7, IBM LAN Server, Compaq Open VMS, and Microsoft Windows NT Server. The NOS is software that makes communications over a network more manageable. The relationship between clients, servers, and the NOS is shown in Figure 3-21, and the layout of a local network operating system is depicted in Figure 3-22. Characteristics of NOSs include the following:

1. A NOS allows users of a network to interface with the network transparently.
2. A NOS commonly offers the following services: file service, print service, mail service, communications service, database service, and directory and security services.
3. The NOS determines whether data are intended for the user's computer or whether the data needs to be redirected out onto the network.
4. The NOS implements client software for the user, which allows them to access servers on the network.

3-10-2 Network Models

Computer networks can be represented with two basic network models: *peer-to-peer client/server* and *dedicated client/server*. The client/server method specifies the way in which two computers can communicate with software over a network. Although clients and servers are generally shown as separate units, they are often active in a single computer but not at the same time. With the client/server concept, a computer acting as a client initiates a software request from another computer acting as a server. The server computer responds and attempts

FIGURE 3-22   Network layout using a network operating system (NOS)

FIGURE 3-23   Client/server concept

to satisfy the request from the client. The server computer might then act as a client and request services from another computer. The client/server concept is illustrated in Figure 3-23.

3-10-2-1 Peer-to-peer client/server network.   A *peer-to-peer client/server network* is one in which all computers share their resources, such as hard drives, printers, and so on, with all the other computers on the network. Therefore, the peer-to-peer operating system divides its time between servicing the computer on which it is loaded and servicing

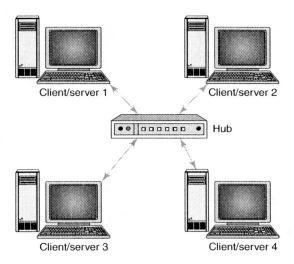

Client/server 1 Client/server 2

Hub

Client/server 3 Client/server 4

FIGURE 3-24   Peer-to-peer
client/server network

requests from other computers. In a peer-to-peer network (sometimes called a *workgroup*), there are no dedicated servers or hierarchy among the computers.

Figure 3-24 shows a peer-to-peer client/server network with four clients/servers (users) connected together through a hub. All computers are equal, hence the name *peer*. Each computer in the network can function as a client and/or a server, and no single computer holds the network operating system or shared files. Also, no one computer is assigned network administrative tasks. The users at each computer determine which data on their computer are shared with the other computers on the network. Individual users are also responsible for installing and upgrading the software on their computer.

Because there is no central controlling computer, a peer-to-peer network is an appropriate choice when there are fewer than 10 users on the network, when all computers are located in the same general area, when security is not an issue, or when there is limited growth projected for the network in the immediate future. Peer-to-peer computer networks should be small for the following reasons:

1. When operating in the server role, the operating system is not optimized to efficiently handle multiple simultaneous requests.
2. The end user's performance as a client would be degraded.
3. Administrative issues such as security, data backups, and data ownership may be compromised in a large peer-to-peer network.

3-10-2-2 Dedicated client/server network.   In a *dedicated client/server network,* one computer is designated the server, and the rest of the computers are clients. As the network grows, additional computers can be designated servers. Generally, the designated servers function only as servers and are not used as a client or workstation. The servers store all the network's shared files and applications programs, such as word processor documents, compilers, database applications, spreadsheets, and the network operating system. Client computers can access the servers and have shared files transferred to them over the transmission medium.

Figure 3-25 shows a dedicated client/server-based network with three servers and three clients (users). Each client can access the resources on any of the servers and also the resources on other client computers. The dedicated client/server-based network is probably

FIGURE 3-25 Dedicated client/server network

the most commonly used computer networking model. There can be a separate dedicated server for each function (i.e., file server, print server, mail server, etc.) or one single general-purpose server responsible for all services.

In some client/server networks, client computers submit jobs to one of the servers. The server runs the software and completes the job and then sends the results back to the client computer. In this type of client/server network, less information propagates through the network than with the file server configuration because only data and not applications programs are transferred between computers.

In general, the dedicated client/server model is preferable to the peer-to-peer client/server model for general-purpose data networks. The peer-to-peer model client/server model is usually preferable for special purposes, such as a small group of users sharing resources.

3-10-3 Network Topologies

Network topology describes the layout or appearance of a network—that is, how the computers, cables, and other components within a data communications network are interconnected, both physically and logically. The *physical topology* describes how the network is actually laid out, and the *logical topology* describes how data actually flow through the network.

In a data communications network, two or more stations connect to a link, and one or more links form a topology. Topology is a major consideration for capacity, cost, and reliability when designing a data communications network. The most basic topologies are *point to point* and *multipoint*. A point-to-point topology is used in data communications networks that transfer high-speed digital information between only two stations. Very often, point-to-point data circuits involve communications between a mainframe computer and another mainframe computer or some other type of high-capacity digital device. A two-point circuit is shown in Figure 3-26a.

A multipoint topology connects three or more stations through a single transmission medium. Examples of multipoint topologies are *star, bus, ring, mesh,* and *hybrid.*

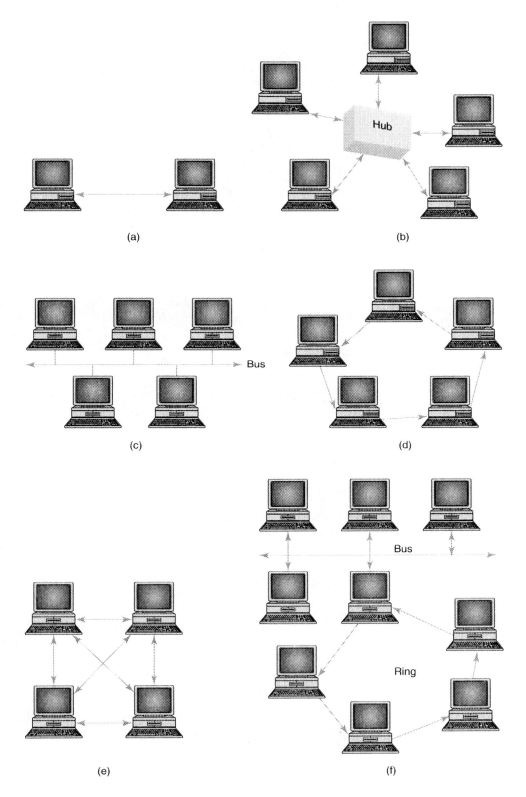

(a)

(b)

Bus

(c)

(d)

Bus

Ring

(e)

(f)

FIGURE 3-26   Network topologies: (a) point-to-point; (b) star; (c) bus; (d) ring; (e) mesh; (f) hybrid

3-10-3-1 Star topology. A *star topology* is a multipoint data communications network where remote stations are connected by cable segments directly to a centrally located computer called a *hub,* which acts like a multipoint connector (see Figure 3-26b). In essence, a star topology is simply a multipoint circuit comprised of many two-point circuits where each remote station communicates directly with a centrally located computer. With a star topology, remote stations cannot communicate directly with one another, so they must relay information through the hub. Hubs also have store-and-forward capabilities, enabling them to handle more than one message at a time.

3-10-3-2 Bus topology. A *bus topology* is a multipoint data communications circuit that makes it relatively simple to control data flow between and among the computers because this configuration allows all stations to receive every transmission over the network. With a bus topology, all the remote stations are physically or logically connected to a single transmission line called a *bus.* The bus topology is the simplest and most common method of interconnecting computers. The two ends of the transmission line never touch to form a complete loop. A bus topology is sometimes called *multidrop* or *linear bus,* and all stations share a common transmission medium. Data networks using the bus topology generally involve one centrally located host computer that controls data flow to and from the other stations. The bus topology is sometimes called a *horizontal bus* and is shown in Figure 3-26c.

3-10-3-3 Ring topology. A *ring topology* is a multipoint data communications network where all stations are interconnected in tandem (series) to form a closed loop or circle. A ring topology is sometimes called a *loop.* Each station in the loop is joined by point-to-point links to two other stations (the transmitter of one and the receiver of the other) (see Figure 3-26d). Transmissions are unidirectional and must propagate through all the stations in the loop. Each computer acts like a repeater in that it receives signals from down-line computers then retransmits them to up-line computers. The ring topology is similar to the bus and star topologies, as it generally involves one centrally located host computer that controls data flow to and from the other stations.

3-10-3-4 Mesh topology. In a *mesh topology,* every station has a direct two-point communications link to every other station on the circuit as shown in Figure 3-26e. The mesh topology is sometimes called *fully connected.* A disadvantage of a mesh topology is a fully connected circuit requires $n(n - 1)/2$ physical transmission paths to interconnect n stations and each station must have $n - 1$ input/output ports. Advantages of a mesh topology are reduced traffic problems, increased reliability, and enhanced security.

3-10-3-5 Hybrid topology. A *hybrid topology* is simply combining two or more of the traditional topologies to form a larger, more complex topology. Hybrid topologies are sometimes called *mixed topologies.* An example of a hybrid topology is the *bus star* topology shown in Figure 3-26f. Other hybrid configurations include the *star ring, bus ring,* and virtually every other combination you can think of.

3-10-4 Network Classifications

Networks are generally classified by size, which includes geographic area, distance between stations, number of computers, transmission speed (bps), transmission media, and the network's physical architecture. The four primary classifications of networks are *local area networks* (LANs), *metropolitan area networks* (MANs), *wide*

Table 3-2 Primary Network Types

Network Type	Characteristics
LAN (local area network)	Interconnects computer users within a department, company, or group
MAN (metropolitan area network)	Interconnects computers in and around a large city
WAN (wide area network)	Interconnects computers in and around an entire country
GAN (global area network)	Interconnects computers from around the entire globe
Building backbone	Interconnects LANs within a building
Campus backbone	Interconnects building LANs
Enterprise network	Interconnects many or all of the above
PAN (personal area network)	Interconnects memory cards carried by people and in computers that are in close proximity to each other
PAN (power line area network, sometimes called PLAN)	Virtually no limit on how many computers it can interconnect and covers an area limited only by the availability of power distribution lines

area networks (WANs), and *global area networks* (GANs). In addition, there are three primary types of interconnecting networks: *building backbone, campus backbone,* and *enterprise network.* Two promising computer networks of the future share the same acronym: the PAN (*personal area network*) and PAN (*power line area network,* sometimes called PLAN). The idea behind a personal area network is to allow people to transfer data through the human body simply by touching each other. Power line area networks use existing ac distribution networks to carry data wherever power lines go, which is virtually everywhere.

When two or more networks are connected together, they constitute an *internetwork* or *internet.* An internet (lowercase *i*) is sometimes confused with the *Internet* (uppercase *I*). The term *internet* is a generic term that simply means to interconnect two or more networks, whereas *Internet* is the name of a specific worldwide data communications network. Table 3-2 summarizes the characteristics of the primary types of networks, and Figure 3-27 illustrates the geographic relationship among computers and the different types of networks.

3-10-4-1 Local area network. *Local area networks* (LANs) are typically privately owned data communications networks in which 10 to 40 computer users share data resources with one or more file servers. LANs use a network operating system to provide two-way communications at bit rates typically in the range of 10 Mbps to 100 Mbps and higher between a large variety of data communications equipment within a relatively small geographical area, such as in the same room, building, or building complex (see Figure 3-28). A LAN can be as simple as two personal computers and a printer or could contain dozens of computers, workstations, and peripheral devices. Most LANs link equipment that are within a few miles of each other or closer. Because the size of most LANs is limited, the longest (or worst-case) transmission time is bounded and known by everyone using the network. Therefore, LANs can utilize configurations that otherwise would not be possible.

LANs were designed for sharing resources between a wide range of digital equipment, including personal computers, workstations, and printers. The resources shared can be software as well as hardware. Most LANs are owned by the company or organization

FIGURE 3-27　Computer network types

that uses it and have a connection to a building backbone for access to other departmental LANs, MANs, WANs, and GANs.

3-10-4-2 Metropolitan area network.　A *metropolitan area network* (MAN) is a high-speed network similar to a LAN except MANs are designed to encompass larger areas, usually that of an entire city (see Figure 3-29). Most MANs support the transmission of both data and voice and in some cases video. MANs typically operate at

FIGURE 3-28   Local area network (LAN) layout

speeds of 1.5 Mbps to 10 Mbps and range from five miles to a few hundred miles in length. A MAN generally uses only one or two transmission cables and requires no switches. A MAN could be a single network, such as a cable television distribution network, or it could be a means of interconnecting two or more LANs into a single, larger network, enabling data resources to be shared LAN to LAN as well as from station to station or computer to computer. Large companies often use MANS to interconnect all their LANs.

A MAN can be owned and operated entirely by a single, private company, or it could lease services and facilities on a monthly basis from the local cable or telephone company. Switched Multimegabit Data Services (SMDS) is an example of a service offered by local telephone companies for handling high-speed data communications for MANs. Other examples of MANs are FDDI (fiber distributed data interface) and ATM (asynchronous transfer mode).

3-10-4-3 Wide area network. *Wide area networks* (WANs) are the oldest type of data communications network that provide relatively slow-speed, long-distance transmission of data, voice, and video information over relatively large and widely dispersed geographical areas, such as a country or an entire continent (see Figure 3-30). WANs typically interconnect cities and states. WANs typically operate at bit rates from 1.5 Mbps to 2.4 Gbps and cover a distance of 100 to 1000 miles.

WANs may utilize both public and private communications systems to provide service over an area that is virtually unlimited; however, WANs are generally obtained through service providers and normally come in the form of leased-line or circuit-switching technology. Often WANs interconnect routers in different locations. Examples of WANs are

FIGURE 3-29   Metropolitan area network (MAN)

ISDN (integrated services digital network), T1 and T3 digital carrier systems, frame relay, X.25, ATM, and using data modems over standard telephone lines.

3-10-4-4 Global area network.   *Global area networks* (GANs) provide connects between countries around the entire globe (see Figure 3-31). The Internet is a good example of a GAN, as it is essentially a network comprised of other networks that interconnects virtually every country in the world. GANs operate from 1.5 Mbps to 100 Gbps and cover thousands of miles

3-10-4-5 Building backbone.   A *building backbone* is a network connection that normally carries traffic between departmental LANs within a single company. A building backbone generally consists of a switch or a router (see Figure 3-32) that can provide connectivity to other networks, such as campus backbones, enterprise backbones, MANs, WANs, or GANs.

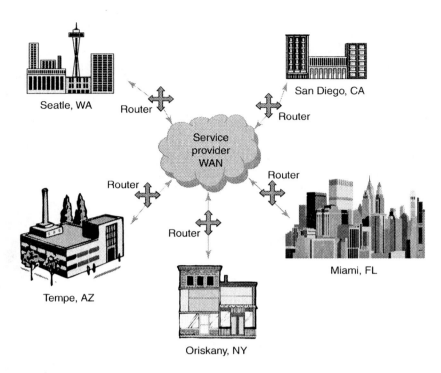

FIGURE 3-30 Wide area network (WAN)

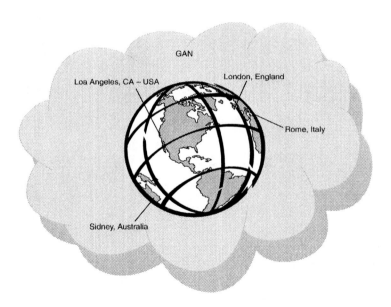

FIGURE 3-31 Global area network (GAN)

3-10-4-6 Campus backbone.   A *campus backbone* is a network connection used to carry traffic to and from LANs located in various buildings on campus (see Figure 3-33). A campus backbone is designed for sites that have a group of buildings at a single location, such as corporate headquarters, universities, airports, and research parks.

A campus backbone normally uses optical fiber cables for the transmission media between buildings. The optical fiber cable is used to connect interconnecting devices, such as

FIGURE 3-32   Building backbone

FIGURE 3-33   Campus backbone

bridges, routers, and switches. Campus backbones must operate at relatively high transmission rates to handle the large volumes of traffic between sites.

3-10-4-7 Enterprise networks.   An *enterprise network* includes some or all of the previously mentioned networks and components connected in a cohesive and manageable fashion.

The functional layers of the OSI seven-layer protocol hierarchy do not line up well with certain data communications applications, such as the Internet. Because of this, there are several other protocols that see widespread use, such as TCP/IP and the Cisco three-layer hierarchical model.

3-11-1 TCP/IP Protocol Suite

The *TCP/IP protocol suite* (*transmission control protocol/Internet protocol*) was actually developed by the Department of Defense before the inception of the seven-layer OSI model. TCP/IP is comprised of several interactive modules that provide specific functionality without necessarily operating independent of one another. The OSI seven-layer model specifies exactly which function each layer performs, whereas TCP/IP is comprised of several relatively independent protocols that can be combined in many ways, depending on system needs. The term *hierarchical* simply means that the upper-level protocols are supported by one or more lower-level protocols. Depending on whose definition you use, TCP/IP is a hierarchical protocol comprised of either three or four layers.

The three-layer version of TCP/IP contains the *network, transport,* and *application* layers that reside above two lower-layer protocols that are not specified by TCP/IP (the physical and data link layers). The network layer of TCP/IP provides internetworking functions similar to those provided by the network layer of the OSI network model. The network layer is sometimes called the *internetwork layer* or *internet layer.*

The transport layer of TCP/IP contains two protocols: TCP (transmission control protocol) and UDP (user datagram protocol). TCP functions go beyond those specified by the transport layer of the OSI model, as they define several tasks defined for the session layer. In essence, TCP allows two application layers to communicate with each other.

The applications layer of TCP/IP contains several other protocols that users and programs utilize to perform the functions of the three uppermost layers of the OSI hierarchy (i.e., the applications, presentation, and session layers).

The four-layer version of TCP/IP specifies the network access, Internet, host-to-host, and process layers:

Network access layer. Provides a means of physically delivering data packets using frames or cells

Internet layer. Contains information that pertains to how data can be routed through the *network*

Host-to-host layer. Services the process and Internet layers to handle the reliability and session aspects of data transmission

Process layer. Provides applications support

TCP/IP is probably the dominant communications protocol in use today. It provides a common denominator, allowing many different types of devices to communicate over a network or system of networks while supporting a wide variety of applications.

3-11-2 Cisco Three-Layer Model

Cisco defines a three-layer logical hierarchy that specifies where things belong, how they fit together, and what functions go where. The three layers are the core, distribution, and access:

Core layer. The core layer is literally the core of the network, as it resides at the top of the hierarchy and is responsible for transporting large amounts of data traffic reliably and quickly. The only purpose of the core layer is to switch traffic as quickly as possible.

Distribution layer. The distribution layer is sometimes called the *workgroup layer.* The distribution layer is the communications point between the access and the core layers that provides routing, filtering, WAN access, and how many data packets are allowed to access the core layer. The distribution layer determines the fastest way to handle service requests, for example, the fastest way to forward a file request to a server. Several functions are performed at the distribution level:

1. Implementation of tools such as access lists, packet filtering, and queuing
2. Implementation of security and network policies, including firewalls and address translation
3. Redistribution between routing protocols
4. Routing between virtual LANS and other workgroup support functions
5. Define broadcast and multicast domains

Access layer. The access layer controls workgroup and individual user access to internetworking resources, most of which are available locally. The access layer is sometimes called the *desktop layer.* Several functions are performed at the access layer level:

1. Access control
2. Creation of separate collision domains (segmentation)
3. Workgroup connectivity into the distribution layer

QUESTIONS

3-1. Define the following terms: *data, information,* and *data communications network.*

3-2. What was the first data communications system that used binary-coded electrical signals?

3-3. Discuss the relationship between network architecture and protocol.

3-4. Briefly describe broadcast and point-to-point computer networks.

3-5. Define the following terms: *protocol, connection-oriented protocols, connectionless protocols,* and *protocol stacks.*

3-6. What is the difference between syntax and semantics?

3-7. What are data communications standards, and why are they needed?

3-8. Name and briefly describe the differences between the two kinds of data communications standards.

3-9. List and describe the eight primary standards organizations for data communications.

3-10. Define the open systems interconnection.

3-11. Briefly describe the seven layers of the OSI protocol hierarchy.

3-12. List and briefly describe the basic functions of the five components of a data communications circuit.

3-13. Briefly describe the differences between serial and parallel data transmission.

3-14. What are the two basic kinds of data communications circuit configurations?

3-15. List and briefly describe the four transmission modes.

3-16. List and describe the functions of the most common components of a computer network.

3-17. What are the differences between servers and clients on a data communications network?

3-18. Describe a peer-to-peer data communications network.

3-19. What are the differences between peer-to-peer client/server networks and dedicated client/server networks?

3-20. What is a data communications network topology?

3-21. List and briefly describe the five basic data communications network topologies.

3-22. List and briefly describe the major network classifications.

3-23. Briefly describe the TCP/IP protocol model.

3-24. Briefly describe the Cisco three-layer protocol model.

C H A P T E R   4

Fundamental Concepts of Data Communications

OBJECTIVES

- Define *data communication code*
- Describe the following data communications codes: Baudot, ASCII, and EBCDIC
- Explain bar code formats
- Define *error control, error detection,* and *error correction*
- Describe the following error-detection mechanisms: redundancy, checksum, LRC, VRC, and CRC
- Describe the following error-correction mechanisms: FEC, ARQ, and Hamming code
- Describe character synchronization and explain the differences between asynchronous and synchronous data formats
- Define the term *data communications hardware*
- Describe data terminal equipment
- Describe data communications equipment
- List and describe the seven components that make up a two-point data communications circuit
- Describe the terms *line control unit* and *front-end processor* and explain the differences between the two
- Describe the basic operation of a UART and outline the differences between UARTs, USRTs, and USARTs
- Describe the functions of a serial interface
- Explain the physical, electrical, and functional characteristics of the RS-232 serial interface
- Compare and contrast the RS-232, RS-449, and RS-530 serial interfaces

- Describe data communications modems
- Explain the block diagram of a modem
- Explain what is meant by Bell System–compatible modems
- Describe modem synchronization and modem equalization
- Describe the ITU-T modem recommendations

4-1 INTRODUCTION

To understand how a data communications network works as an entity, it is necessary first to understand the fundamental concepts and components that make up the network. The fundamental concepts of data communications include data communications code, error control (error detection and correction), and character synchronization, and fundamental hardware includes various pieces of computer and networking equipment, such as line control units, serial interfaces, and data communications modems.

4-2 DATA COMMUNICATIONS CODES

Data communications codes are often used to represent *characters* and *symbols,* such as letters, digits, and punctuation marks. Therefore, data communications codes are called *character codes, character sets, symbol codes,* or *character languages.*

4-2-1 Baudot Code

The *Baudot code* (sometimes called the *Telex code*) was the first *fixed-length character code* developed for machines rather than for people. A French postal engineer named Thomas Murray developed the Baudot code in 1875 and named the code after Emile Baudot, an early pioneer in telegraph printing. The Baudot code (pronounced *baw-dough*) is a *fixed-length source code* (sometimes called a *fixed-length block code*). With fixed-length source codes, all characters are represented in binary and have the same number of symbols (bits). The Baudot code is a five-bit character code that was used primarily for low-speed teletype equipment, such as the TWX/Telex system and radio teletype (RTTY). The latest version of the Baudot code is recommended by the CCITT as the International Alphabet No. 2 and is shown in Table 4-1.

4-2-2 ASCII Code

In 1963, in an effort to standardize data communications codes, the United States adopted the Bell System model 33 teletype code as the *United States of America Standard Code for Information Exchange* (USASCII), better known as ASCII-63. Since its adoption, ASCII (pronounced *as-key*) has progressed through the 1965, 1967, and 1977 versions, with the 1977 version being recommended by the ITU as International Alphabet No. 5, in the United States as ANSI standard X3.4-1986 (R1997), and by the International Standards Organization as ISO-14962 (1997).

ASCII is the standard character set for source coding the alphanumeric character set that humans understand but computers do not (computers only understand 1s and 0s). ASCII is a seven-bit fixed-length character set. With the ASCII code, the least-significant bit (LSB) is designated b_0 and the most-significant bit (MSB) is designated b_7 as shown here:

The terms *least* and *most significant* are somewhat of a misnomer because character codes do not represent weighted binary numbers and, therefore, all bits are equally sig-

Table 4-1 Baudot Code

Letter	Figure	Bit: 4	3	2	1	0
A	—	1	1	0	0	0
B	?	1	0	0	1	1
C	:	0	1	1	1	0
D	$	1	0	0	1	0
E	3	1	0	0	0	0
F	!	1	0	1	1	0
G	&	0	1	0	1	1
H	#	0	0	1	0	1
I	8	0	1	1	0	0
J	'	1	1	0	1	0
K	(	1	1	1	1	0
L	)	0	1	0	0	1
M	.	0	0	1	1	1
N	,	0	0	1	1	0
O	9	0	0	0	1	1
P	0	0	1	1	0	1
Q	1	1	1	1	0	1
R	4	0	1	0	1	0
S	bel	1	0	1	0	0
T	5	0	0	0	0	1
U	7	1	1	1	0	0
V	;	0	1	1	1	1
W	2	1	1	0	0	1
X	/	1	0	1	1	1
Y	6	1	0	1	0	1
Z	"	1	0	0	0	1
Figure shift		1	1	1	1	1
Letter shift		1	1	0	1	1
Space		0	0	1	0	0
Line feed (LF)		0	1	0	0	0
Blank (null)		0	0	0	0	0

nificant. Bit b_7 is not part of the ASCII code but is generally reserved for an error detection bit called the parity bit, which is explained later in this chapter. With character codes, it is more meaningful to refer to bits by their order than by their position; b_0 is the zero-order bit, b_1 the first-order bit, b_7 the seventh-order bit, and so on. However, with serial data transmission, the bit transmitted first is generally called the LSB. With ASCII, the low-order bit (b_0) is transmitted first. ASCII is probably the code most often used in data communications networks today. The 1977 version of the ASCII code with odd parity is shown in Table 4-2 (note that the parity bit is not included in the hex code).

4-2-3 EBCDIC Code

The *extended binary-coded decimal interchange code* (EBCDIC) is an eight-bit fixed-length character set developed in 1962 by the International Business Machines Corporation (IBM). EBCDIC is used almost exclusively with IBM mainframe computers and peripheral equipment. With eight bits, 2^8, or 256, codes are possible, although only 139 of the 256 codes are actually assigned characters. Unspecified codes can be assigned to specialized characters and functions. The name *binary coded decimal* was selected because the second hex character for all letter and digit codes contains only the hex values from 0 to 9, which have the same binary sequence as BCD codes. The EBCDIC code is shown in Table 4-3.

Table 4-2 ASCII-77: Odd Parity

Bit	7	6	5	4	3	2	1	0	Hex	Bit	7	6	5	4	3	2	1	0	Hex
NUL	1	0	0	0	0	0	0	0	00	@	0	1	0	0	0	0	0	0	40
SOH	0	0	0	0	0	0	0	1	01	A	1	1	0	0	0	0	0	1	41
STX	0	0	0	0	0	0	1	0	02	B	1	1	0	0	0	0	1	0	42
ETX	1	0	0	0	0	0	1	1	03	C	0	1	0	0	0	0	1	1	43
EOT	0	0	0	0	0	1	0	0	04	D	1	1	0	0	0	1	0	0	44
ENQ	1	0	0	0	0	1	0	1	05	E	0	1	0	0	0	1	0	1	45
ACK	1	0	0	0	0	1	1	0	06	F	0	1	0	0	0	1	1	0	46
BEL	0	0	0	0	0	1	1	1	07	G	1	1	0	0	0	1	1	1	47
BS	0	0	0	0	1	0	0	0	08	H	1	1	0	0	1	0	0	0	48
HT	1	0	0	0	1	0	0	1	09	I	0	1	0	0	1	0	0	1	49
NL	1	0	0	0	1	0	1	0	0A	J	0	1	0	0	1	0	1	0	4A
VT	0	0	0	0	1	0	1	1	0B	K	1	1	0	0	1	0	1	1	4B
FF	1	0	0	0	1	1	0	0	0C	L	0	1	0	0	1	1	0	0	4C
CR	0	0	0	0	1	1	0	1	0D	M	1	1	0	0	1	1	0	1	4D
SO	0	0	0	0	1	1	1	0	0E	N	1	1	0	0	1	1	1	0	4E
SI	1	0	0	0	1	1	1	1	0F	O	0	1	0	0	1	1	1	1	4F
DLE	0	0	0	1	0	0	0	0	10	P	1	1	0	1	0	0	0	0	50
DC1	0	0	0	1	0	0	0	1	11	Q	0	1	0	1	0	0	0	1	51
DC2	1	0	0	1	0	0	1	0	12	R	0	1	0	1	0	0	1	0	52
DC3	0	0	0	1	0	0	1	1	13	S	1	1	0	1	0	0	1	1	53
DC4	1	0	0	1	0	1	0	0	14	T	0	1	0	1	0	1	0	0	54
NAK	0	0	0	1	0	1	0	1	15	U	1	1	0	1	0	1	0	1	55
SYN	0	0	0	1	0	1	1	0	16	V	1	1	0	1	0	1	1	0	56
ETB	1	0	0	1	0	1	1	1	17	W	0	1	0	1	0	1	1	1	57
CAN	1	0	0	1	1	0	0	0	18	X	0	1	0	1	1	0	0	0	58
EM	0	0	0	1	1	0	0	1	19	Y	1	1	0	1	1	0	0	1	59
SUB	0	0	0	1	1	0	1	0	1A	Z	1	1	0	1	1	0	1	0	5A
ESC	1	0	0	1	1	0	1	1	1B	[	0	1	0	1	1	0	1	1	5B
FS	0	0	0	1	1	1	0	0	1C	\	1	1	0	1	1	1	0	0	5C
GS	1	0	0	1	1	1	0	1	1D	]	0	1	0	1	1	1	0	1	5D
RS	1	0	0	1	1	1	1	0	1E	∧	0	1	0	1	1	1	1	0	5E
US	0	0	0	1	1	1	1	1	1F	-	1	1	0	1	1	1	1	1	5F
SP	0	0	1	0	0	0	0	0	20	`	1	1	1	0	0	0	0	0	60
!	1	0	1	0	0	0	0	1	21	a	0	1	1	0	0	0	0	1	61
"	1	0	1	0	0	0	1	0	22	b	0	1	1	0	0	0	1	0	62
#	0	0	1	0	0	0	1	1	23	c	1	1	1	0	0	0	1	1	63
$	1	0	1	0	0	1	0	0	24	d	0	1	1	0	0	1	0	0	64
%	0	0	1	0	0	1	0	1	25	e	1	1	1	0	0	1	0	1	65
&	0	0	1	0	0	1	1	0	26	f	1	1	1	0	0	1	1	0	66
'	1	0	1	0	0	1	1	1	27	g	0	1	1	0	0	1	1	1	67
(	1	0	1	0	1	0	0	0	28	h	0	1	1	0	1	0	0	0	68
)	0	0	1	0	1	0	0	1	29	i	1	1	1	0	1	0	0	1	69
*	0	0	1	0	1	0	1	0	2A	j	1	1	1	0	1	0	1	0	6A
+	1	0	1	0	1	0	1	1	2B	k	0	1	1	0	1	0	1	1	6B
,	0	0	1	0	1	1	0	0	2C	l	1	1	1	0	1	1	0	0	6C
-	1	0	1	0	1	1	0	1	2D	m	0	1	1	0	1	1	0	1	6D
.	1	0	1	0	1	1	1	0	2E	n	0	1	1	0	1	1	1	0	6E
/	0	0	1	0	1	1	1	1	2F	o	1	1	1	0	1	1	1	1	6F
0	1	0	1	1	0	0	0	0	30	p	0	1	1	1	0	0	0	0	70
1	0	0	1	1	0	0	0	1	31	q	1	1	1	1	0	0	0	1	71
2	0	0	1	1	0	0	1	0	32	r	1	1	1	1	0	0	1	0	72
3	1	0	1	1	0	0	1	1	33	s	0	1	1	1	0	0	1	1	73
4	0	0	1	1	0	1	0	0	34	t	1	1	1	1	0	1	0	0	74
5	1	0	1	1	0	1	0	1	35	u	0	1	1	1	0	1	0	1	75
6	1	0	1	1	0	1	1	0	36	v	0	1	1	1	0	1	1	0	76
7	0	0	1	1	0	1	1	1	37	w	1	1	1	1	0	1	1	1	77
8	0	0	1	1	1	0	0	0	38	x	1	1	1	1	1	0	0	0	78

(Continued)

Table 4-2   (Continued)

Bit	7	6	5	4	3	2	1	0	Hex	Bit	7	6	5	4	3	2	1	0	Hex
9	1	0	1	1	1	0	0	1	39	y	0	1	1	1	1	0	0	1	79
:	1	0	1	1	1	0	1	0	3A	z	0	1	1	1	1	0	1	0	7A
;	0	0	1	1	1	0	1	1	3B	{	1	1	1	1	1	0	1	1	7B
<	1	0	1	1	1	1	0	0	3C	|	0	1	1	1	1	1	0	0	7C
=	0	0	1	1	1	1	0	1	3D	}	1	1	1	1	1	1	0	1	7D
>	0	0	1	1	1	1	1	0	3E	~	1	1	1	1	1	1	1	0	7E
?	1	0	1	1	1	1	1	1	3F	DEL	0	1	1	1	1	1	1	1	7F

NUL = null
SOH = start of heading
STX = start of text
ETX = end of text
EOT = end of transmission
ENQ = enquiry
ACK = acknowledge
BEL = bell
BS = back space
HT = horizontal tab
NL = new line

VT = vertical tab
FF = form feed
CR = carriage return
SO = shift-out
SI = shift-in
DLE = data link escape
DC1 = device control 1
DC2 = device control 2
DC3 = device control 3
DC4 = device control 4
NAK = negative acknowledge

SYN = synchronous
ETB = end of transmission block
CAN = cancel
SUB = substitute
ESC = escape
FS = field separator
GS = group separator
RS = record separator
US = unit separator
SP = space
DEL = delete

Table 4-3   EBCDIC Code

Bit	0	1	2	3	4	5	6	7	Hex	Bit	0	1	2	3	4	5	6	7	Hex
NUL	0	0	0	0	0	0	0	0	00		1	0	0	0	0	0	0	0	80
SOH	0	0	0	0	0	0	0	1	01	a	1	0	0	0	0	0	0	1	81
STX	0	0	0	0	0	0	1	0	02	b	1	0	0	0	0	0	1	0	82
ETX	0	0	0	0	0	0	1	1	03	c	1	0	0	0	0	0	1	1	83
	0	0	0	0	0	1	0	0	04	d	1	0	0	0	0	1	0	0	84
PT	0	0	0	0	0	1	0	1	05	e	1	0	0	0	0	1	0	1	85
	0	0	0	0	0	1	1	0	06	f	1	0	0	0	0	1	1	0	86
	0	0	0	0	0	1	1	1	07	g	1	0	0	0	0	1	1	1	87
	0	0	0	0	1	0	0	0	08	h	1	0	0	0	1	0	0	0	88
	0	0	0	0	1	0	0	1	09	i	1	0	0	0	1	0	0	1	89
	0	0	0	0	1	0	1	0	0A		1	0	0	0	1	0	1	0	8A
	0	0	0	0	1	0	1	1	0B		1	0	0	0	1	0	1	1	8B
FF	0	0	0	0	1	1	0	0	0C		1	0	0	0	1	1	0	0	8C
	0	0	0	0	1	1	0	1	0D		1	0	0	0	1	1	0	1	8D
	0	0	0	0	1	1	1	0	0E		1	0	0	0	1	1	1	0	8E
	0	0	0	0	1	1	1	1	0F		1	0	0	0	1	1	1	1	8F
DLE	0	0	0	1	0	0	0	0	10		1	0	0	1	0	0	0	0	90
SBA	0	0	0	1	0	0	0	1	11	j	1	0	0	1	0	0	0	1	91
EUA	0	0	0	1	0	0	1	0	12	k	1	0	0	1	0	0	1	0	92
IC	0	0	0	1	0	0	1	1	13	l	1	0	0	1	0	0	1	1	93
	0	0	0	1	0	1	0	0	14	m	1	0	0	1	0	1	0	0	94
NL	0	0	0	1	0	1	0	1	15	n	1	0	0	1	0	1	0	1	95
	0	0	0	1	0	1	1	0	16	o	1	0	0	1	0	1	1	0	96
	0	0	0	1	0	1	1	1	17	p	1	0	0	1	0	1	1	1	97
	0	0	0	1	1	0	0	0	18	q	1	0	0	1	1	0	0	0	98
EM	0	0	0	1	1	0	0	1	19	r	1	0	0	1	1	0	0	1	99
	0	0	0	1	1	0	1	0	1A		1	0	0	1	1	0	1	0	9A
	0	0	0	1	1	0	1	1	1B		1	0	0	1	1	0	1	1	9B
DUP	0	0	0	1	1	1	0	0	1C		1	0	0	1	1	1	0	0	9C
SF	0	0	0	1	1	1	0	1	1D		1	0	0	1	1	1	0	1	9D
FM	0	0	0	1	1	1	1	0	1E		1	0	0	1	1	1	1	0	9E

(Continued)

Table 4–3 (Continued)

Bit	|	Binary Code								Hex	Bit	|	Binary Code								Hex
	0	1	2	3	4	5	6	7				0	1	2	3	4	5	6	7	
ITB	0	0	0	1	1	1	1	1	1F		1	0	0	1	1	1	1	1	9F
	0	0	1	0	0	0	0	0	20		1	0	1	0	0	0	0	0	A0
	0	0	1	0	0	0	0	1	21	~	1	0	1	0	0	0	0	1	A1
	0	0	1	0	0	0	1	0	22	s	1	0	1	0	0	0	1	0	A2
	0	0	1	0	0	0	1	1	23	t	1	0	1	0	0	0	1	1	A3
	0	0	1	0	0	1	0	0	24	u	1	0	1	0	0	1	0	0	A4
	0	0	1	0	0	1	0	1	25	v	1	0	1	0	0	1	0	1	A5
ETB	0	0	1	0	0	1	1	0	26	w	1	0	1	0	0	1	1	0	A6
ESC	0	0	1	0	0	1	1	1	27	x	1	0	1	0	0	1	1	1	A7
	0	0	1	0	1	0	0	0	28	y	1	0	1	0	1	0	0	0	A8
	0	0	1	0	1	0	0	1	29	z	1	0	1	0	1	0	0	1	A9
	0	0	1	0	1	0	1	0	2A		1	0	1	0	1	0	1	0	AA
	0	0	1	0	1	0	1	1	2B		1	0	1	0	1	0	1	1	AB
	0	0	1	0	1	1	0	0	2C		1	0	1	0	1	1	0	0	AC
ENQ	0	0	1	0	1	1	0	1	2D		1	0	1	0	1	1	0	1	AD
	0	0	1	0	1	1	1	0	2E		1	0	1	0	1	1	1	0	AE
	0	0	1	0	1	1	1	1	2F		1	0	1	0	1	1	1	1	AF
	0	0	1	1	0	0	0	0	30		1	0	1	1	0	0	0	0	B0
	0	0	1	1	0	0	0	1	31		1	0	1	1	0	0	0	1	B1
SYN	0	0	1	1	0	0	1	0	32		1	0	1	1	0	0	1	0	B2
	0	0	1	1	0	0	1	1	33		1	0	1	1	0	0	1	1	B3
	0	0	1	1	0	1	0	0	34		1	0	1	1	0	1	0	0	B4
	0	0	1	1	0	1	0	1	35		1	0	1	1	0	1	0	1	B5
	0	0	1	1	0	1	1	0	36		1	0	1	1	0	1	1	0	B6
BOT	0	0	1	1	0	1	1	1	37		1	0	1	1	0	1	1	1	B7
	0	0	1	1	1	0	0	0	38		1	0	1	1	1	0	0	0	B8
	0	0	1	1	1	0	0	1	39		1	0	1	1	1	0	0	1	B9
	0	0	1	1	1	0	1	0	3A		1	0	1	1	1	0	1	0	BA
	0	0	1	1	1	0	1	1	3B		1	0	1	1	1	0	1	1	BB
RA	0	0	1	1	1	1	0	0	3C		1	0	1	1	1	1	0	0	BC
NAK	0	0	1	1	1	1	0	1	3D		1	0	1	1	1	1	0	1	BD
	0	0	1	1	1	1	1	0	3E		1	0	1	1	1	1	1	0	BE
SUB	0	0	1	1	1	1	1	1	3F		1	0	1	1	1	1	1	1	BF
SP	0	1	0	0	0	0	0	0	40	{	1	1	0	0	0	0	0	0	C0
	0	1	0	0	0	0	0	1	41	A	1	1	0	0	0	0	0	1	C1
	0	1	0	0	0	0	1	0	42	B	1	1	0	0	0	0	1	0	C2
	0	1	0	0	0	0	1	1	43	C	1	1	0	0	0	0	1	1	C3
	0	1	0	0	0	1	0	0	44	D	1	1	0	0	0	1	0	0	C4
	0	1	0	0	0	1	0	1	45	E	1	1	0	0	0	1	0	1	C5
	0	1	0	0	0	1	1	0	46	F	1	1	0	0	0	1	1	0	C6
	0	1	0	0	0	1	1	1	47	G	1	1	0	0	0	1	1	1	C7
	0	1	0	0	1	0	0	0	48	H	1	1	0	0	1	0	0	0	C8
	0	1	0	0	1	0	0	1	49	I	1	1	0	0	1	0	0	1	C9
¢	0	1	0	0	1	0	1	0	4A		1	1	0	0	1	0	1	0	CA
-	0	1	0	0	1	0	1	1	4B		1	1	0	0	1	0	1	1	CB
<	0	1	0	0	1	1	0	0	4C		1	1	0	0	1	1	0	0	CC
(	0	1	0	0	1	1	0	1	4D		1	1	0	0	1	1	0	1	CD
+	0	1	0	0	1	1	1	0	4E		1	1	0	0	1	1	1	0	CE
|	0	1	0	0	1	1	1	1	4F		1	1	0	0	1	1	1	1	CF
&	0	1	0	1	0	0	0	0	50	}	1	1	0	1	0	0	0	0	D0
	0	1	0	1	0	0	0	1	51	J	1	1	0	1	0	0	0	1	D1
	0	1	0	1	0	0	1	0	52	K	1	1	0	1	0	0	1	0	D2
	0	1	0	1	0	0	1	1	53	L	1	1	0	1	0	0	1	1	D3
	0	1	0	1	0	1	0	0	54	M	1	1	0	1	0	1	0	0	D4
	0	1	0	1	0	1	0	1	55	N	1	1	0	1	0	1	0	1	D5
	0	1	0	1	0	1	1	0	56	O	1	1	0	1	0	1	1	0	D6

(Continued)

Table 4-3 (*Continued*)

Bit	0	1	2	3	4	5	6	7	Hex	Bit	0	1	2	3	4	5	6	7	Hex
	0	1	0	1	0	1	1	1	57	P	1	1	0	1	0	1	1	1	D7
	0	1	0	1	1	0	0	0	58	Q	1	1	0	1	1	0	0	0	D8
	0	1	0	1	1	0	0	1	59	R	1	1	0	1	1	0	0	1	D9
!	0	1	0	1	1	0	1	0	5A		1	1	0	1	1	0	1	0	DA
$	0	1	0	1	1	0	1	1	5B		1	1	0	1	1	0	1	1	DB
*	0	1	0	1	1	1	0	0	5C		1	1	0	1	1	1	0	0	DC
)	0	1	0	1	1	1	0	1	5D		1	1	0	1	1	1	0	1	DD
:	0	1	0	1	1	1	1	0	5E		1	1	0	1	1	1	1	0	DE
¬	0	1	0	1	1	1	1	1	5F		1	1	0	1	1	1	1	1	DF
−	0	1	1	0	0	0	0	0	60	\	1	1	1	0	0	0	0	0	E0
/	0	1	1	0	0	0	0	1	61		1	1	1	0	0	0	0	1	E1
−	0	1	1	0	0	0	1	0	62	S	1	1	1	0	0	0	1	0	E2
	0	1	1	0	0	0	1	1	63	T	1	1	1	0	0	0	1	1	E3
	0	1	1	0	0	1	0	0	64	U	1	1	1	0	0	1	0	0	E4
	0	1	1	0	0	1	0	1	65	V	1	1	1	0	0	1	0	1	E5
	0	1	1	0	0	1	1	0	66	W	1	1	1	0	0	1	1	0	E6
	0	1	1	0	0	1	1	1	67	X	1	1	1	0	0	1	1	1	E7
	0	1	1	0	1	0	0	0	68	Y	1	1	1	0	1	0	0	0	E8
	0	1	1	0	1	0	0	1	69	Z	1	1	1	0	1	0	0	1	E9
	0	1	1	0	1	0	1	0	6A		1	1	1	0	1	0	1	0	EA
	0	1	1	0	1	0	1	1	6B		1	1	1	0	1	0	1	1	EB
%	0	1	1	0	1	1	0	0	6C		1	1	1	0	1	1	0	0	EC
	0	1	1	0	1	1	0	1	6D		1	1	1	0	1	1	0	1	ED
>	0	1	1	0	1	1	1	0	6E		1	1	1	0	1	1	1	0	EE
?	0	1	1	0	1	1	1	1	6F		1	1	1	0	1	1	1	1	EF
	0	1	1	1	0	0	0	0	70	0	1	1	1	1	0	0	0	0	F0
	0	1	1	1	0	0	0	1	71	1	1	1	1	1	0	0	0	1	F1
	0	1	1	1	0	0	1	0	72	2	1	1	1	1	0	0	1	0	F2
	0	1	1	1	0	0	1	1	73	3	1	1	1	1	0	0	1	1	F3
	0	1	1	1	0	1	0	0	74	4	1	1	1	1	0	1	0	0	F4
	0	1	1	1	0	1	0	1	75	5	1	1	1	1	0	1	0	1	F5
	0	1	1	1	0	1	1	0	76	6	1	1	1	1	0	1	1	0	F6
	0	1	1	1	0	1	1	1	77	7	1	1	1	1	0	1	1	1	F7
	0	1	1	1	1	0	0	0	78	8	1	1	1	1	1	0	0	0	F8
▲	0	1	1	1	1	0	0	1	79	9	1	1	1	1	1	0	0	1	F9
:	0	1	1	1	1	0	1	0	7A		1	1	1	1	1	0	1	0	FA
#	0	1	1	1	1	0	1	1	7B		1	1	1	1	1	0	1	1	FB
@	0	1	1	1	1	1	0	0	7C		1	1	1	1	1	1	0	0	FC
▲	0	1	1	1	1	1	0	1	7D		1	1	1	1	1	1	0	1	FD
−	0	1	1	1	1	1	1	0	7E		1	1	1	1	1	1	1	0	FE
"	0	1	1	1	1	1	1	1	7F		1	1	1	1	1	1	1	1	FF

DLE = data-link escape	ITB = end of intermediate transmission block
DUP = duplicate	NUL = null
EM = end of medium	PT = program tab
ENQ = enquiry	RA = repeat to address
EOT = end of transmission	SBA = set buffer address
ESC = escape	SF = start field
ETB = end of transmission block	SOH = start of heading
ETX = end of text	SP = space
EUA = erase unprotected to address	STX = start of text
FF = form feed	SUB = substitute
FM = field mark	SYN = synchronous
IC = insert cursor	NAK = negative acknowledge

FIGURE 4-1 Typical bar code

4-3 BAR CODES

Bar codes are those omnipresent black-and-white striped stickers that seem to appear on virtually every consumer item in the United States and most of the rest of the world. Although bar codes were developed in the early 1970s, they were not used extensively until the mid-1980s. A bar code is a series of vertical black bars separated by vertical white bars (called spaces). The widths of the bars and spaces along with their reflective abilities represent binary 1s and 0s, and combinations of bits identify specific items. In addition, bar codes may contain information regarding cost, inventory management and control, security access, shipping and receiving, production counting, document and order processing, automatic billing, and many other applications. A typical bar code is shown in Figure 4-1.

There are several standard bar code formats. The format selected depends on what types of data are being stored, how the data are being stored, system performance, and which format is most popular with business and industry. Bar codes are generally classified as being discrete, continuous, or two-dimensional (2D).

Discrete code. A discrete bar code has spaces or gaps between characters. Therefore, each character within the bar code is independent of every other character. Code 39 is an example of a discrete bar code.

Continuous code. A continuous bar code does not include spaces between characters. An example of a continuous bar code is the Universal Product Code (UPC).

2D code. A 2D bar code stores data in two dimensions in contrast with a conventional linear bar code, which stores data along only one axis. 2D bar codes have a larger storage capacity than one-dimensional bar codes (typically 1 kilobyte or more per data symbol).

4-3-1 Code 39

One of the most popular bar codes was developed in 1974 and called *Code 39* (also called *Code 3 of 9* and *3 of 9 Code*). Code 39 uses an alphanumeric code similar to the ASCII code. Code 39 is shown in Table 4-4. Code 39 consists of 36 unique codes representing the 10 digits and 26 uppercase letters. There are seven additional codes used for special characters, and an exclusive start/stop character coded as an asterisk (*). Code 39 bar codes are ideally suited for making labels, such as name badges.

Each Code 39 character contains nine vertical elements (five bars and four spaces). The logic condition (1 or 0) of each element is encoded in the width of the bar or space (i.e., *width modulation*). A wide element, whether it be a bar or a space, represents a logic 1, and a narrow element represents a logic 0. Three of the nine elements in each Code 39 character must be logic 1s, and the rest must be logic 0s. In addition, of the three logic 1s, two must be bars and one a space. Each character begins and ends with a black bar with alternating white bars in between. Since Code 39 is a discrete code, all characters are separated with an intercharacter gap, which is usually one character wide. The asterisks at the beginning and end of the bar code are start and stop characters, respectively.

Table 4-4 Code 39 Character Set

Character	Binary Code									Bars $b_8b_6b_4b_2b_0$	Spaces $b_7b_5b_3b_1$	Check Sum Value
	b_8	b_7	b_6	b_5	b_4	b_3	b_2	b_1	b_0			
0	0	0	0	1	1	0	1	0	0	00110	0100	0
1	1	0	0	1	0	0	0	0	1	10001	0100	1
2	0	0	1	1	0	0	0	0	1	01001	0100	2
3	1	0	1	1	0	0	0	0	0	11000	0100	3
4	0	0	0	1	1	0	0	0	1	00101	0100	4
5	1	0	0	1	1	0	0	0	0	10100	0100	5
6	0	0	1	1	1	0	0	0	0	01100	0100	6
7	0	0	0	1	0	0	1	0	1	00011	0100	7
8	1	0	0	1	0	0	1	0	0	10010	0100	8
9	0	0	1	1	0	0	1	0	0	01010	0100	9
A	1	0	0	0	0	1	0	0	1	10001	0010	10
B	0	0	1	0	0	1	0	0	1	01001	0010	11
C	1	0	1	0	0	1	0	0	0	11000	0010	12
D	0	0	0	0	1	1	0	0	1	00101	0010	13
E	1	0	0	0	1	1	0	0	0	10100	0010	14
F	0	0	1	0	1	1	0	0	0	01100	0010	15
G	0	0	0	0	0	1	1	0	1	00011	0010	16
H	1	0	0	0	0	1	1	0	0	10010	0010	17
I	0	0	1	0	0	1	1	0	0	01010	0010	18
J	0	0	0	0	1	1	1	0	0	00110	0010	19
K	1	0	0	0	0	0	0	1	1	10001	0001	20
L	0	0	1	0	0	0	0	1	1	01001	0001	21
M	1	0	1	0	0	0	0	1	0	11000	0001	22
N	0	0	0	0	1	0	0	1	1	00101	0001	23
O	1	0	0	0	1	0	0	1	0	10100	0001	24
P	0	0	1	0	1	0	0	1	0	01100	0001	25
Q	0	0	0	0	0	0	1	1	1	00011	0001	26
R	1	0	0	0	0	0	1	1	0	10010	0001	27
S	0	0	1	0	0	0	1	1	0	01010	0001	28
T	0	0	0	0	1	0	1	1	0	00110	0001	29
U	1	1	0	0	0	0	0	0	1	10001	1000	30
V	0	1	1	0	0	0	0	0	1	01001	1000	31
W	1	1	1	0	0	0	0	0	0	11000	1000	32
X	0	1	0	0	1	0	0	0	1	00101	1000	33
Y	1	1	0	0	1	0	0	0	0	10100	1000	34
Z	0	1	1	0	1	0	0	0	0	01100	1000	35
–	0	1	0	0	0	0	1	0	1	00011	1000	36
.	1	1	0	0	0	0	1	0	0	10010	1000	37
space	0	1	1	0	0	0	1	0	0	01010	1000	38
*	0	1	0	0	1	0	1	0	0	00110	1000	—
$	0	1	0	1	0	1	0	0	0	00000	1110	39
/	0	1	0	1	0	0	0	1	0	00000	1101	40
+	0	1	0	0	0	1	0	1	0	00000	1011	41
%	0	0	0	1	0	1	0	1	0	00000	0111	42

Figure 4-2 shows the Code 39 representation of the start/stop code (*) followed by an intercharacter gap and then the Code 39 representation of the letter A.

4-3-2 Universal Product Code

The grocery industry developed the *Universal Product Code* (UPC) sometime in the early 1970s to identify their products. The *National Association of Food Chains* officially adopted the UPC code in 1974. Today UPC codes are found on virtually every grocery item from a candy bar to a can of beans.

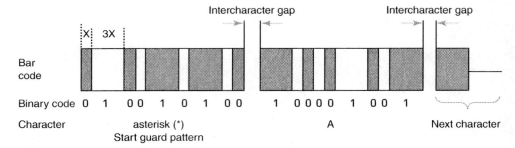

X = width of narrow bar or space
3X = width of wide bar or space

FIGURE 4-2   Code 39 bar code

Figures 4-3a, b, and c show the character set, label format, and sample bit patterns for the standard UPC code. Unlike Code 39, the UPC code is a continuous code since there are no intercharacter spaces. Each UPC label contains a 12-digit number. The two long bars shown in Figure 4-3b on the outermost left- and right-hand sides of the label are called the *start guard pattern* and the *stop guard pattern,* respectively. The start and stop guard patterns consist of a 101 (bar-space-bar) sequence, which is used to frame the 12-digit UPC number. The left and right halves of the label are separated by a *center guard pattern,* which consists of two *long bars* in the center of the label (they are called long bars because they are physically longer than the other bars on the label). The two long bars are separated with a space between them and have spaces on both sides of the bars. Therefore, the UPC center guard pattern is 01010 as shown in Figure 4-3b. The first six digits of the UPC code are encoded on the left half of the label (called the *left-hand characters*), and the last six digits of the UPC code are encoded on the right half (called the *right-hand characters*). Note in Figure 4-3a that there are two binary codes for each character. When a character appears in one of the first six digits of the code, it uses a left-hand code, and when a character appears in one of the last six digits, it uses a right-hand code. Note that the right-hand code is simply the complement of the left-hand code. For example, if the second and ninth digits of a 12-digit code UPC are both 4s, the digit is encoded as a 0100011 in position 2 and as a 1011100 in position 9. The UPC code for the 12-digit code 012345 543210 is

The first left-hand digit in the UPC code is called the *UPC number system character,* as it identifies how the UPC symbol is used. Table 4-5 lists the 10 UPC number system characters. For example, the UPC number system character 5 indicates that the item is intended to be used with a coupon. The other five left-hand characters are data characters. The first five right-hand characters are data characters, and the sixth right-hand character is a check character, which is used for error detection. The decimal value of the number system character is always printed to the left of the UPC label, and on most UPC labels the decimal value of the check character is printed on the right side of the UPC label.

With UPC codes, the width of the bars and spaces does not correspond to logic 1s and 0s. Instead, the digits 0 through 9 are encoded into a combination of two variable-

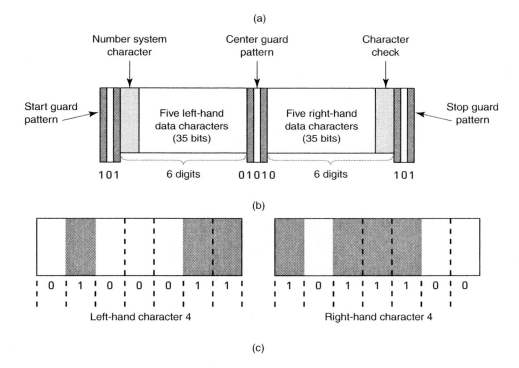

UPC Character Set

Left-hand character	Decimal digit	Right-hand character
0001101	0	1110010
0011001	1	1100110
0010011	2	1101100
0111101	3	1000010
0100011	4	1011100
0110001	5	1001110
0101111	6	1010000
0111011	7	1000100
0110111	8	1001000
0001011	9	1110100

(a)

Number system character

Center guard pattern

Character check

Start guard pattern

Five left-hand data characters (35 bits)

Five right-hand data characters (35 bits)

Stop guard pattern

101   6 digits   01010   6 digits   101

(b)

0 1 0 0 0 1 1 1
Left-hand character 4

1 0 1 1 1 1 0 0
Right-hand character 4

(c)

FIGURE 4-3   (a) UPC version A character set; (b) UPC label format; (c) left- and right-hand bit sequence for the digit 4

width bars and two variable-width spaces that occupy the equivalent of seven bit positions. Figure 4-3c shows the variable-width code for the UPC character 4 when used in one of the first six digit positions of the code (i.e., left-hand bit sequence) and when used in one of the last six digit positions of the code (i.e., right-hand bit sequence). A single bar (one bit position) represents a logic 1, and a single space represents a logic 0. However, close examination of the UPC character set in Table 4-5 will reveal that all UPC digits are comprised of bit patterns that yield two variable-width bars and two variable-width spaces, with the bar and space widths ranging from one to four bits. For the UPC character 4 shown in Figure 4-3c, the left-hand character is comprised of a one-bit space followed in order by a one-bit bar, a three-bit space, and a two-bit bar. The right-hand character is comprised of a one-bit bar followed in order by a one-bit space, a three-bit bar, and a two-bit space.

Table 4-5 UPC Number System Characters

Character	Intended Use
0	Regular UPC codes
1	Reserved for future use
2	Random-weight items that are symbol marked at the store
3	National Drug Code and National Health Related Items Code
4	Intended to be used without code format restrictions and with check digit protection for in-store marking of nonfood items
5	For use with coupons
6	Regular UPC codes
7	Regular UPC codes
8	Reserved for future use
9	Reserved for future use

Left-hand version of the character 0   Right-hand version of the character 0

FIGURE 4-4 UPC character 0

Example 4-1

Determine the UPC label structure for the digit 0.

Solution From Figure 4-3a, the binary sequence for the digit 0 in the left-hand character field is 0001101, and the binary sequence for the digit 0 in the right-hand character field is 1110010.

The left-hand sequence is comprised of three successive 0s, followed by two 1s, one 0, and one 1. The three successive 0s are equivalent to a space three bits long. The two 1s are equivalent to a bar two bits long. The single 0 and single 1 are equivalent to a space and a bar, each one bit long.

The right-hand sequence is comprised of three 1s followed by two 0s, a 1, and a 0. The three 1s are equivalent to a bar three bits long. The two 0s are equivalent to a space two bits long. The single 1 and single 0 are equivalent to a bar and a space, each one bit long each. The UPC pattern for the digit 0 is shown in Figure 4-4.

4-4 ERROR CONTROL

A data communications circuit can be as short as a few feet or as long as several thousand miles, and the transmission medium can be as simple as a pair of wires or as complex as a microwave, satellite, or optical fiber communications system. Therefore, it is inevitable that errors will occur, and it is necessary to develop and implement error-control procedures. Transmission errors are caused by electrical interference from natural sources, such as lightning, as well as from man-made sources, such as motors, generators, power lines, and fluorescent lights.

Data communications errors can be generally classified as *single bit, multiple bit,* or *burst.* Single-bit errors are when only one bit within a given data string is in error. Single-bit errors affect only one character within a message. A multiple-bit error is when two or more nonconsecutive bits within a given data string are in error. Multiple-bit errors can affect one or more characters within a message. A burst error is when two or more consecutive bits within a given data string are in error. Burst errors can affect one or more characters within a message.

Error performance is the rate in which errors occur, which can be described as either an expected or an empirical value. The theoretical (mathematical) expectation of the rate at which errors will occur is called *probability of error* ($P[e]$), whereas the actual historical record of a system's error performance is called *bit error rate* (BER). For example, if a system has a $P(e)$ of 10^{-5}, this means that mathematically the system can expect to experience one bit error for every 100,000 bits transported through the system ($10^{-5} = 1/10^5 = 1/100,000$). If a system has a BER of 10^{-5}, this means that in the past there was one bit error for every 100,000 bits transported. Typically, a BER is measured and then compared with the probability of error to evaluate system performance. Error control can be divided into two general categories: *error detection* and *error correction.*

4-5 ERROR DETECTION

Error detection is the process of monitoring data transmission and determining when errors have occurred. Error-detection techniques neither correct errors nor identify which bits are in error—they indicate only when an error has occurred. The purpose of error detection is not to prevent errors from occurring but to prevent undetected errors from occurring.

The most common error-detection techniques are redundancy checking, which includes vertical redundancy checking, checksum, longitudinal redundancy checking, and cyclic redundancy checking.

4-5-1 Redundancy Checking

Duplicating each data unit for the purpose of detecting errors is a form of error detection called *redundancy.* Redundancy is an effective but rather costly means of detecting errors, especially with long messages. It is much more efficient to add bits to data units that check for transmission errors. Adding bits for the sole purpose of detecting errors is called *redundancy checking.* There are four basic types of redundancy checks: vertical redundancy checking, checksums, longitudinal redundancy checking, and cyclic redundancy checking.

4-5-1-1 Vertical redundancy checking. *Vertical redundancy checking* (VRC) is probably the simplest error-detection scheme and is generally referred to as *character parity* or simply *parity.* With character parity, each character has its own error-detection bit called the *parity bit.* Since the parity bit is not actually part of the character, it is considered a redundant bit. An n-character message would have n redundant parity bits. Therefore, the number of error-detection bits is directly proportional to the length of the message.

With character parity, a single parity bit is added to each character to force the total number of logic 1s in the character, including the parity bit, to be either an odd number (*odd parity*) or an even number (*even parity*). For example, the ASCII code for the letter C is 43 hex, or P1000011 binary, where the P bit is the parity bit. There are three logic 1s in the code, not counting the parity bit. If odd parity is used, the P bit is made a logic 0, keeping the total number of logic 1s at three, which is an odd number. If even parity is used, the P bit is made a logic 1, making the total number of logic 1s four, which is an even number.

The primary advantage of parity is its simplicity. The disadvantage is that when an even number of bits are received in error, the parity checker will not detect them because when the logic condition of an even number of bits is changed, the parity of the character remains the same. Consequently, over a long time, parity will theoretically detect only 50% of the transmission errors (this assumes an equal probability that an even or an odd number of bits could be in error).

Example 4-2

Determine the odd and even parity bits for the ASCII character R.

Solution The hex code for the ASCII character R is 52, which is P1010010 in binary, where P designates the parity bit.

For odd parity, the parity bit is a 0 because 52 hex contains three logic 1s, which is an odd number. Therefore, the odd-parity bit sequence for the ASCII character R is 01010010.

For even parity, the parity bit is 1, making the total number of logic 1s in the eight-bit sequence four, which is an even number. Therefore, the even-parity bit sequence for the ASCII character R is 11010010.

Other forms of parity include *marking parity* (the parity bit is always a 1), *no parity* (the parity bit is not sent or checked), and *ignored parity* (the parity bit is always a 0 bit if it is ignored). Marking parity is useful only when errors occur in a large number of bits. Ignored parity allows receivers that are incapable of checking parity to communicate with devices that use parity.

4-5-1-2 Checksum. *Checksum* is another relatively simple form of redundancy error checking where each character has a numerical value assigned to it. The characters within a message are combined together to produce an error-checking character (checksum), which can be as simple as the arithmetic sum of the numerical values of all the characters in the message. The checksum is appended to the end of the message. The receiver replicates the combining operation and determines its own checksum. The receiver's checksum is compared to the checksum appended to the message, and if they are the same, it is assumed that no transmission errors have occurred. If the two checksums are different, a transmission error has definitely occurred.

4-5-1-3 Longitudinal redundancy checking. *Longitudinal redundancy checking* (LRC) is a redundancy error detection scheme that uses parity to determine if a transmission error has occurred within a message and is therefore sometimes called *message parity*. With LRC, each bit position has a parity bit. In other words, b_0 from each character in the message is XORed with b_0 from all the other characters in the message. Similarly, b_1, b_2, and so on are XORed with their respective bits from all the characters in the message. Essentially, LRC is the result of XORing the "character codes" that make up the message, whereas VRC is the XORing of the bits within a single character. With LRC, even parity is generally used, whereas with VRC, odd parity is generally used.

The LRC bits are computed in the transmitter while the data are being sent and then appended to the end of the message as a redundant character. In the receiver, the LRC is recomputed from the data, and the recomputed LRC is compared to the LRC appended to the message. If the two LRC characters are the same, most likely no transmission errors have occurred. If they are different, one or more transmission errors have occurred.

Example 4-3 shows how are VRC and LRC are calculated and how they can be used together.

Example 4-3

Determine the VRCs and LRC for the following ASCII-encoded message: THE CAT. Use odd parity for the VRCs and even parity for the LRC.

Solution

Character		T	H	E	sp	C	A	T	LRC
Hex		54	48	45	20	43	41	54	2F
ASCII code	b_0	0	0	1	0	1	1	0	1
	b_1	0	0	0	0	1	0	0	1
	b_2	1	0	1	0	0	0	1	1
	b_3	0	1	0	0	0	0	0	1
	b_4	1	0	0	0	0	0	1	0
	b_5	0	0	0	1	0	0	0	1
	b_6	1	1	1	0	1	1	1	0
Parity bit (VRC)	b_7	0	1	0	0	0	1	0	0

The LRC is 00101111 binary (2F hex), which is the character "/" in ASCII. Therefore, after the LRC character is appended to the message, it would read "THE CAT/."

The group of characters that comprise a message (i.e., THE CAT) is often called a *block* or *frame* of data. Therefore, the bit sequence for the LRC is often called a *block check sequence* (BCS) or *frame check sequence* (FCS).

With longitudinal redundancy checking, all messages (regardless of their length) have the same number of error-detection characters. This characteristic alone makes LRC a better choice for systems that typically send long messages.

Historically, LRC detects between 95% and 98% of all transmission errors. LRC will not detect transmission errors when an even number of characters has an error in the same bit position. For example, if b_4 in an even number of characters is in error, the LRC is still valid even though multiple transmission errors have occurred.

4-5-1-4 Cyclic redundancy checking. Probably the most reliable redundancy checking technique for error detection is a convolutional coding scheme called *cyclic redundancy checking* (CRC). With CRC, approximately 99.999% of all transmission errors are detected. In the United States, the most common CRC code is CRC-16. With CRC-16, 16 bits are used for the block check sequence. With CRC, the entire data stream is treated as a long continuous binary number. Because the BCS is separate from the message but transported within the same transmission, CRC is considered a *systematic code*. Cyclic block codes are often written as (*n, k*) cyclic codes where n = bit length of transmission and k = bit length of message. Therefore, the length of the BCC in bits is

$$BCC = n - k$$

A CRC-16 block check character is the remainder of a binary division process. A data message polynominal $G(x)$ is divided by a unique generator polynominal function $P(x)$, the quotient is discarded, and the remainder is truncated to 16 bits and appended to the message as a BCS. The generator polynominal must be a prime number (i.e., a number divisible by only itself and 1). CRC-16 detects all single-bit errors, all double-bit errors (provided the divisor contains at least three logic 1s), all odd number of bit errors (provided the division contains a factor 11), all error bursts of 16 bits or less, and 99.9% of error bursts greater than 16 bits long. For randomly distributed errors, it is estimated that the likelihood of CRC-16 not detecting an error is 10^{-14}, which equates to one undetected error every two years of continuous data transmission at a rate of 1.544 Mbps.

With CRC generation, the division is not accomplished with standard arithmetic division. Instead, modulo-2 division is used, where the remainder is derived from an exclusive OR (XOR) operation. In the receiver, the data stream, including the CRC code, is divided by the same generating function $P(x)$. If no transmission errors have occurred, the remainder will be zero. In the receiver, the message and CRC character pass through a block check register. After the entire message has passed through the register, its contents should be zero if the receive message contains no errors.

Mathematically, CRC can be expressed as

$$\frac{G(x)}{P(x)} = Q(x) + R(x) \tag{4-1}$$

where $G(x)$ = message polynominal
            $P(x)$ = generator polynominal
            $Q(x)$ = quotient
            $R(x)$ = remainder

The generator polynomial for CRC-16 is

$$P(x) = x^{16} + x^{15} + x^2 + x^0$$

CRC-16 polynominal, $G(x) = X^{16} + X^{15} + X^2 + X^0$

FIGURE 4-5 CRC-16 generating circuit

The number of bits in the CRC code is equal to the highest exponent of the generating polynomial. The exponents identify the bit positions in the generating polynomial that contain a logic 1. Therefore, for CRC-16, b_{16}, b_{15}, b_2, and b_0 are logic 1s, and all other bits are logic 0s. The number of bits in a CRC character is always twice the number of bits in a data character (i.e., eight-bit characters use CRC-16, six-bit characters use CRC-12, and so on).

Figure 4-5 shows the block diagram for a circuit that will generate a CRC-16 BCC. A CRC generating circuit requires one shift register for each bit in the BCC. Note that there are 16 shift registers in Figure 4-5. Also note that an XOR gate is placed at the output of the shift registers for each bit position of the generating polynomial that contains a logic 1, except for x^0. The BCC is the content of the 16 registers after the entire message has passed through the CRC generating circuit.

Example 4-4

Determine the BCS for the following data and CRC generating polynomials:

$$\text{Data } G(x) = x^7 + x^5 + x^4 + x^2 + x^1 + x^0$$
$$= 10110111$$

$$\text{CRC } P(x) = x^5 + x^4 + x^1 + x^0$$
$$= 110011$$

Solution First, $G(x)$ is multiplied by the number of bits in the CRC code, which is 5:

$$x^5(x^7 + x^5 + x^4 + x^2 + x^1 + x^0) = x^{12} + x^{10} + x^9 + x^7 + x^6 + x^5 = 1011011100000$$

Then the result is divided by $P(x)$:

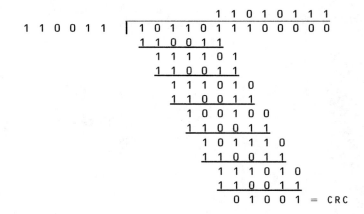

The CRC is appended to the data to give the following data stream:

$$G(x) \qquad\qquad \text{CRC}$$

1 0 1 1 0 1 1 1 0 1 0 0 1

At the receiver, the data are again divided by $P(x) =:$

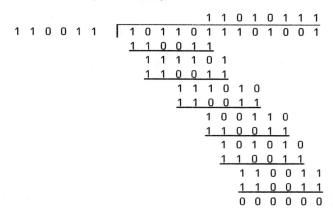

```
                                        1 1 0 1 0 1 1 1
     1 1 0 0 1 1  │ 1 0 1 1 0 1 1 1 0 1 0 0 1
                    1 1 0 0 1 1
                    1 1 1 1 0 1
                    1 1 0 0 1 1
                        1 1 1 0 1 0
                        1 1 0 0 1 1
                            1 0 0 1 1 0
                            1 1 0 0 1 1
                                1 0 1 0 1 0
                                1 1 0 0 1 1
                                    1 1 0 0 1 1
                                    1 1 0 0 1 1
                                    0 0 0 0 0 0   Remainder = 0,
                                                  which means there
                                                  were no transmis-
                                                  sion errors
```

4-6 ERROR CORRECTION

Although detecting errors is an important aspect of data communications, determining what to do with data that contain errors is another consideration. There are two basic types of error messages: *lost message* and *damaged message.* A lost message is one that never arrives at the destination or one that arrives but is damaged to the extent that it is unrecognizable. A damaged message is one that is recognized at the destination but contains one or more transmission errors.

Data communications network designers have developed two basic strategies for handling transmission errors: *error-detecting codes* and *error-correcting codes.* Error-detecting codes include enough redundant information with each transmitted message to enable the receiver to determine when an error has occurred. Parity bits, block and frame check characters, and cyclic redundancy characters are examples of error-detecting codes. Error-correcting codes include sufficient extraneous information along with each message to enable the receiver to determine when an error has occurred and which bit is in error.

Transmission errors can occur as single-bit errors or as bursts of errors, depending on the physical processes that caused them. Having errors occur in bursts is an advantage when data are transmitted in blocks or frames containing many bits. For example, if a typical frame size is 10,000 bits and the system has a probability of error of 10^{-4} (one bit error in every 10,000 bits transmitted), independent bit errors would most likely produce an error in every block. However, if errors occur in bursts of 1000, only one or two blocks out of every 1000 transmitted would contain errors. The disadvantage of bursts of errors is they are more difficult to detect and even more difficult to correct than isolated single-bit errors. In the modern world of data communications, there are two primary methods used for error correction: *retransmission* and *forward error correction.*

4-6-1 Retransmission

Retransmission, as the name implies, is when a receive station requests the transmit station to resend a message (or a portion of a message) when the message is received in error. Because the receive terminal automatically calls for a retransmission of the entire message, retransmission is often called ARQ, which is an old two-way radio term that means *automatic repeat request* or *automatic retransmission request.* ARQ is probably the most reliable method of error correction, although it is not necessarily the most efficient. Impairments on transmission media often occur in bursts. If short messages are used, the likelihood that impairments will occur during a transmission is small. However, short messages require more *acknowledgments* and *line turnarounds* than do long messages. Acknowledgments are when the recipient of data sends a short message back to the sender acknowledging receipt of the last transmission. The acknowledgment can indicate a successful transmission (positive acknowledgment) or an unsuccessful transmission (negative acknowledgment). Line turnarounds are when a receive station becomes the transmit station, such as when acknowledgments are sent or when retransmissions are sent in response to a negative acknowledgment. Acknowledgments and line turnarounds for error control are forms of overhead (data other than user information that must be transmitted). With long messages, less turnaround time is needed, although the likelihood that a transmission error will occur is higher than for short messages. It can be shown statistically that messages between 256 and 512 characters long are the optimum size for ARQ error correction.

There are two basic types of ARQ: discrete and continuous. *Discrete ARQ* uses *acknowledgments* to indicate the successful or unsuccessful reception of data. There are two basic types of acknowledgments: positive and negative. The destination station responds with a *positive acknowledgment* when it receives an error-free message. The destination station responds with a negative *acknowledgment* when it receives a message containing errors to call for a retransmission. If the sending station does not receive an acknowledgment after a predetermined length of time (called a *time-out*), it retransmits the message. This is called *retransmission after time-out.*

Another type of ARQ, called *continuous ARQ,* can be used when messages are divided into smaller blocks or frames that are sequentially numbered and transmitted in succession, without waiting for acknowledgments between blocks. Continuous ARQ allows the destination station to asynchronously request the retransmission of a specific frame (or frames) of data and still be able to reconstruct the entire message once all frames have been successfully transported through the system. This technique is sometimes called *selective repeat,* as it can be used to call for a retransmission of an entire message or only a portion of a message.

4-6-2   Forward Error Correction

Forward error correction (FEC) is the only error-correction scheme that actually detects and corrects transmission errors when they are received without requiring a retransmission. With FEC, redundant bits are added to the message before transmission. When an error is detected, the redundant bits are used to determine which bit is in error. Correcting the bit is a simple matter of complementing it. The number of redundant bits necessary to correct errors is much greater than the number of bits needed to simply detect errors. Therefore, FEC is generally limited to one-, two-, or three-bit errors.

FEC is ideally suited for data communications systems when acknowledgments are impractical or impossible, such as when simplex transmissions are used to transmit messages to many receivers or when the transmission, acknowledgment, and retransmission time is excessive, for example when communicating to far away places, such as deep-space vehicles. The purpose of FEC codes is to eliminate the time wasted for retransmissions. However, the addition of the FEC bits to each message wastes time itself. Obviously, a trade-off is made between ARQ and FEC, and system requirements determine which method is best suited to a particular application. Probably the most popular error-correction code is the Hamming code.

   4-6-2-1 Hamming code.   A mathematician named Richard W. Hamming, who was an early pioneer in the development of error-detection and -correction procedures, devel-

One data unit contains $m + n$ bits

m data bits · n Hamming bits

FIGURE 4-6 Data unit comprised of m character bits and n Hamming bits

oped the *Hamming code* while working at Bell Telephone Laboratories. The Hamming code is an *error-correcting code* used for correcting transmission errors in synchronous data streams. However, the Hamming code will correct only single-bit errors. It cannot correct multiple-bit errors or burst errors, and it cannot identify errors that occur in the Hamming bits themselves. The Hamming code, as with all FEC codes, requires the addition of overhead to the message, consequently increasing the length of a transmission.

Hamming bits (sometimes called *error bits*) are inserted into a character at random locations. The combination of the data bits and the Hamming bits is called the Hamming code. The only stipulation on the placement of the Hamming bits is that both the sender and the receiver must agree on where they are placed. To calculate the number of redundant Hamming bits necessary for a given character length, a relationship between the character bits and the Hamming bits must be established. As shown in Figure 4-6, a data unit contains m character bits and n Hamming bits. Therefore, the total number of bits in one data unit is $m + n$. Since the Hamming bits must be able to identify which bit is in error, n Hamming bits must be able to indicate at least $m + n + 1$ different codes. Of the $m + n$ codes, one code indicates that no errors have occurred, and the remaining $m + n$ codes indicate the bit position where an error has occurred. Therefore, $m + n$ bit positions must be identified with n bits. Since n bits can produce 2^n different codes, 2^n must be equal to or greater than $m + n + 1$. Therefore, the number of Hamming bits is determined by the following expression:

$$2^n \geq m + n + 1 \tag{4-2}$$

where n = number of Hamming bits
          m = number of bits in each data character

A seven-bit ASCII character requires four Hamming bits ($2^4 > 7 + 4 + 1$), which could be placed at the end of the character bits, at the beginning of the character bits, or interspersed throughout the character bits. Therefore, including the Hamming bits with ASCII-coded data requires transmitting 11 bits per ASCII character, which equates to a 57% increase in the message length.

Example 4-5

For a 12-bit data string of 101100010010, determine the number of Hamming bits required, arbitrarily place the Hamming bits into the data string, determine the logic condition of each Hamming bit, assume an arbitrary single-bit transmission error, and prove that the Hamming code will successfully detect the error.

Solution   Substituting $m = 12$ into Equation 4-2, the number of Hamming bits is

for $n = 4$ $2^4 = 16 \geq 12 + 4 + 1 = 17$

Because $16 < 17$, four Hamming bits are insufficient:

for $n = 5$ $2^5 = 32 \geq 12 + 5 + 1 = 18$

Because $32 > 18$, five Hamming bits are sufficient, and a total of 17 bits make up the data stream (12 data plus five Hamming).

Arbitrarily placing five Hamming bits into bit positions 4, 8, 9, 13, and 17 yields

bit position	17	16	15	14	13	12	11	10	9	8	7	6	5	4	3	2	1
	H	1	0	1	H	1	0	0	H	H	0	1	0	H	0	1	0

To determine the logic condition of the Hamming bits, express all bit positions that contain a logic 1 as a five-bit binary number and XOR them together:

Bit position	Binary number
2	00010
6	00110
XOR	00100
12	01100
XOR	01000
14	01110
XOR	00110
16	10000
XOR	10110 = Hamming bits

$$b_{17} = 1, \quad b_{13} = 0, \quad b_9 = 1, \quad b_8 = 1, \quad b_4 = 0$$

The 17-bit Hamming code is

	H			H				H	H				H			
1	1	0	1	0	1	0	0	1	1	0	1	0	0	0	1	0

Assume that during transmission, an error occurs in bit position 14. The received data stream is

$$1\ 1\ 0\ \underline{0}\ 0\ 1\ 0\ 0\ 1\ 1\ 0\ 1\ 0\ 0\ 0\ 1\ 0$$

error

At the receiver, to determine the bit position in error, extract the Hamming bits and XOR them with the binary code for each data bit position that contains a logic 1:

Bit position	Binary number
Hamming bits	10110
2	00010
XOR	10100
6	00110
XOR	10010
12	01100
XOR	11110
16	10000
XOR	01110 = 14

Therefore, bit position 14 contains an error.

4-7 CHARACTER SYNCHRONIZATION

In essence, *synchronize* means to harmonize, coincide, or agree in time. *Character synchronization* involves identifying the beginning and end of a character within a message. When a continuous string of data is received, it is necessary to identify which bits belong to which characters and which bits are the MSBS and LSBS of the character. In essence, this is *character synchronization:* identifying the beginning and end of a character code. In data communications circuits, there are two formats commonly used to achieve character synchronization: asynchronous and synchronous.

4-7-1 Asynchronous Serial Data

The term asynchronous literally means "without synchronism," which in data communications terminology means "without a specific time reference." Asynchronous data transmis-

| (1) | (1) | 1 or 0 or b₇ (MSB) | b₆ MSB | b₅ | b₄ | b₃ | b₂ | b₁ | b₀ LSB | 0 |

Stop bits (1, 1.5, or 2)   Data or Parity bit (odd/even)   Data bits (5 to 8)   Start bit

Time

FIGURE 4-7   Asynchronous data format

sion is sometimes called *start-stop transmission* because each data character is framed between *start* and *stop bits.* The start and stop bits identify the beginning and end of the character, so the time gaps between characters do not present a problem. For asynchronously transmitted serial data, framing characters individually with start and stop bits is sometimes said to occur on a *character-by-character* basis.

Figure 4-7 shows the format used to frame a character for asynchronous serial data transmission. The first bit transmitted is the start bit, which is always a logic 0. The character bits are transmitted next, beginning with the LSB and ending with the MSB. The data character can contain between five and eight bits. The parity bit (if used) is transmitted directly after the MSB of the character. The last bit transmitted is the stop bit, which is always a logic 1, and there can be either one, one and a half, or two stop bits. Therefore, a data character may be comprised of between seven and 11 bits.

A logic 0 is used for the start bit because an idle line condition (no data transmission) on a data communications circuit is identified by the transmission of continuous logic 1s (called *idle line 1s*). Therefore, the start bit of a character is identified by a high-to-low transition in the received data, and the bit that immediately follows the start bit is the LSB of the character code. All stop bits are logic 1s, which guarantees a high-to-low transition at the beginning of each character. After the start bit is detected, the data and parity bits are clocked into the receiver. If data are transmitted in real time (i.e., as the operator types data into the computer terminal), the number of idle line 1s between each character will vary. During this *dead time,* the receive will simply wait for the occurrence of another start bit (i.e., high-to-low transition) before clocking in the next character. Obviously, both slipping over and slipping under produce errors. However, the errors are somewhat self-inflicted, as they occur in the receiver and are not a result of an impairment that occurred during transmission.

With asynchronous data, it is not necessary that the transmit and receive clocks be continuously synchronized; however, their frequencies should be close, and they should be synchronized at the beginning of each character. When the transmit and receive clocks are substantially different, a condition called *clock slippage* may occur. If the transmit clock is substantially lower than the receive clock, *underslipping* occurs. If the transmit clock is substantially higher than the receive clock, a condition called *overslipping* occurs. With overslipping, the receive clock samples the receive data slower than the bit rate. Consequently, each successive sample occurs later in the bit time until finally a bit is completely skipped.

Example 4-6

For the following sequence of bits, identify the ASCII-encoded character, the start and stop bits, and the parity bits (assume even parity and two stop bits):

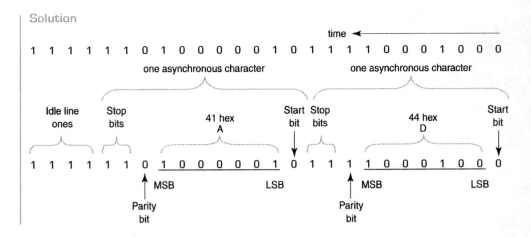

4-7-2 Synchronous Serial Data

Synchronous data generally involves transporting serial data at relatively high speeds in groups of characters called blocks or frames. Therefore, synchronous data are not sent in real time. Instead, a message is composed or formulated and then the entire message is transmitted as a single entity with no time lapses between characters. With synchronous data, rather than frame each character independently with start and stop bits, a unique sequence of bits, sometimes called a synchronizing (SYN) character, is transmitted at the beginning of each message. For synchronously transmitted serial data, framing characters in blocks is sometimes said to occur on a *block-by-block* basis. For example, with ASCII code, the SYN character is 16 hex. The receiver disregards incoming data until it receives one or more SYN characters. Once the synchronizing sequence is detected, the receiver clocks in the next eight bits and interprets them as the first character of the message. The receiver continues clocking in bits, interpreting them in groups of eight until it receives another unique character that signifies the end of the message. The end-of-message character varies with the type of protocol being used and what type of message it is associated with. With synchronous data, the transmit and receive clocks must be synchronized because character synchronization occurs only once at the beginning of a message.

With synchronous data, each character has two or three bits added to each character (one start and either one, one and a half, or two stop bits). These bits are additional overhead and, thus, reduce the efficiency of the transmission (i.e., the ratio of information bits to total transmitted bits). Synchronous data generally has two SYN characters (16 bits of overhead) added to each message. Therefore, asynchronous data are more efficient for short messages, and synchronous data are more efficient for long messages.

Example 4-7

For the following string of ASCII-encoded characters, identify each character (assume odd parity):

Solution

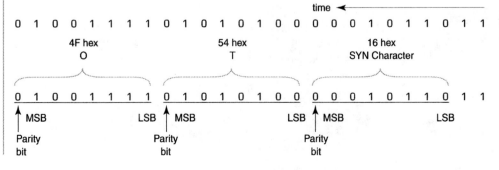

Digital information sources, such as personal computers, communicate with each other using the POTS (plain old telephone system) telephone network in a manner very similar to the way analog information sources, such as human conversations, communicate with each other using the POTS telephone network. With both digital and analog information sources, special devices are necessary to interface the sources to the telephone network.

Figure 4-8 shows a comparison between human speech (analog) communications and computer data (digital) communications using the POTS telephone network. Figure 4-8a shows how two humans communicate over the telephone network using standard analog telephone sets. The telephone sets interface human speech signals to the telephone network and vice versa. At the transmit end, the telephone set converts acoustical energy (information) to electrical energy and, at the receive end, the telephone set converts electrical energy back to acoustical energy. Figure 4-8b shows how digital data are transported over the telephone network. At the transmitting end, a telco interface converts digital data from the transceiver to analog electrical energy, which is transported through the telephone network. At the receiving end, a telco interface converts the analog electrical energy received from the telephone network back to digital data.

In simplified terms, a data communications system is comprised of three basic elements: a *transmitter* (source), a *transmission path* (data channel), and a *receiver* (destination). For two-way communications, the transmission path would be bidirectional and the source and destination interchangeable. Therefore, it is usually more appropriate to describe a data communications system as connecting two *endpoints* (sometimes called *nodes*) through a common communications channel. The two endpoints may not possess the same computing capabilities; however, they must be configured with the same basic components. Both endpoints must be equipped with special devices that perform unique functions, make the physical connection to the data channel, and process the data before they are transmitted and after they have been received. Although the special devices are

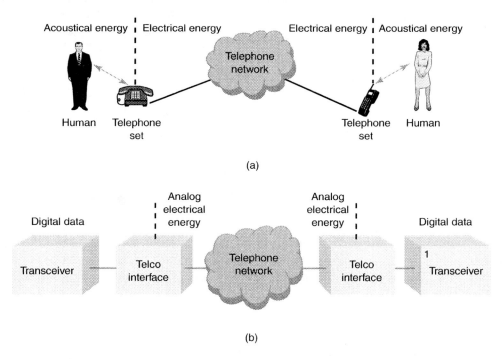

(a)

(b)

FIGURE 4-8   Telephone communications network: (a) human communications; (b) digital data communications sometimes implemented as a single unit, it is generally easier to describe them as separate entities. In essence, all endpoints must have three fundamental components: *data terminal equipment, data communications equipment,* and a *serial interface.*

4-8-1 Data Terminal Equipment

Data terminal equipment (DTE) can be virtually any binary digital device that generates, transmits, receives, or interprets data messages. In essence, a DTE is where information originates or terminates. DTEs are the data communications equivalent to the person in a telephone conversation. DTEs contain the hardware and software necessary to establish and control communications between endpoints in a data communications system; however, DTEs seldom communicate directly with other DTEs. Examples of DTEs include video display terminals, printers, and personal computers.

Over the past 50 years, data terminal equipment has evolved from simple on-line printers to sophisticated high-level computers. Data terminal equipment includes the concept of *terminals, clients, hosts,* and *servers.* Terminals are devices used to input, output, and display information, such as keyboards, printers, and monitors. A client is basically a modern-day terminal with enhanced computing capabilities. Hosts are high-powered, high-capacity mainframe computers that support terminals. Servers function as modern-day hosts except with lower storage capacity and less computing capability. Servers and hosts maintain local databases and programs and distribute information to clients and terminals.

4-8-2 Data Communications Equipment

Data communications equipment (DCE) is a general term used to describe equipment that interfaces data terminal equipment to a transmission channel, such as a digital T1 carrier or an analog telephone circuit. The output of a DTE can be digital or analog, depending on the application. In essence, a DCE is a *signal conversion device,* as it converts signals from a DTE to a form more suitable to be transported over a transmission channel. A DCE also converts those signals back to their original form at the receive end of a circuit. DCEs are transparent devices responsible for transporting bits (1s and 0s) between DTEs through a data communications channel. The DCEs neither know nor do they care about the content of the data.

There are several types of DCEs, depending on the type of transmission channel used. Common DCEs are *channel service units* (CSUs), *digital service units* (DSUs), and *data modems.* CSUs and DSUs are used to interface DTEs to digital transmission channels. Data modems are used to interface DTEs to analog telephone networks. Because data communications channels are terminated at each end in a DCE, DCEs are sometimes called *data circuit-terminating equipment* (DCTE). CSUs and DSUs are described in a later chapter of this book, whereas data modems are described in subsequent sections of this chapter.

4-9 DATA COMMUNICATIONS CIRCUITS

A data modem is a DCE used to interface a DTE to an analog telephone circuit commonly called a POTS. Figure 4-9a shows a simplified diagram for a two-point data communications circuit using a POTS link to interconnect the two endpoints (endpoint A and endpoint B). As shown in the figure, a two-point data communications circuit is comprised of the seven basic components:

1. DTE at endpoint A
2. DCE at endpoint A
3. DTE/DCE interface at endpoint A
4. Transmission path between endpoint A and endpoint B
5. DCE at endpoint B
6. DTE at endpoint B
7. DTE/DCE interface at endpoint B

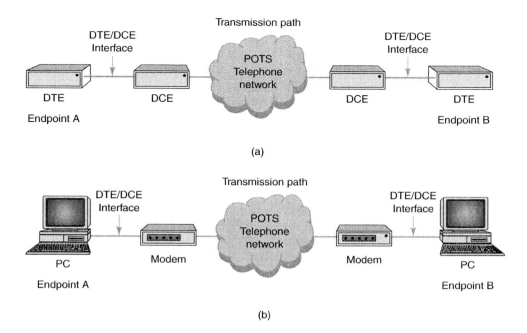

(a)

(b)

FIGURE 4-9 Two point data communications circuit: (a) DTE/DCE representation; (b) device representation

The DTEs can be terminal devices, personal computers, mainframe computers, front-end processors, printers, or virtually any other piece of digital equipment. If a digital communications channel were used, the DCE would be a CSU or a DSU. However, because the communications channel is a POTS link, the DCE is a data modem.

Figure 4-9b shows the same equivalent circuit as is shown in Figure 4-9a, except the DTE and DCE have been replaced with the actual devices they represent—the DTE is a personal computer, and the DCE is a modem. In most modern-day personal computers for home use, the modem is simply a card installed inside the computer.

Figure 4-10 shows the block diagram for a centralized multipoint data communications circuit using several POTS data communications links to interconnect three endpoints. The circuit is arranged in a bus topology with central control provided by a mainframe computer (host) at endpoint A. The host station is sometimes called the *primary station.* Endpoints B and C are called *secondary stations.* The primary station is responsible for establishing and maintaining the data link and for ensuring an orderly flow of data between itself and each of the secondary stations. Data flow is controlled by an applications program stored in the mainframe computer at the primary station.

At the primary station, there is a mainframe computer, a front-end processor (DTE), and a data modem (DCE). At each secondary station, there is a modem (DCE), a line control unit (DTE), and a *cluster* of terminal devices (personal computers, printers, and so on). The line control unit at the secondary stations is referred to as a *cluster controller,* as it controls data flow between several terminal devices and the data communications channel. Line control units at secondary stations are sometimes called station controllers (STACOs), as they control data flow to and from all the data communications equipment located at that station.

For simplicity, Figure 4-10 only shows one data circuit served by the mainframe computer at the primary station. However, there can be dozens of different circuits served by one mainframe computer. Therefore, the primary station line control unit (i.e., the front-end processor) must have enhanced capabilities for storing, processing, and retransmitting data it receives from all secondary stations on all the circuits it serves. The primary station stores software for database management of all the circuits it serves. Obviously, the duties

FIGURE 4-10　Multipoint data communications circuit using POTS links

performed by the front-end processor at the primary station are much more involved than the duties performed by the line control units at the secondary stations. The FEP directs data traffic to and from many different circuits, which could all have different parameters (i.e., different bit rates, character codes, data formats, protocols, and so on). The LCU at the secondary stations directs data traffic between one data communications link and a relative few terminal devices, which all transmit and receive data at the same speed and use the same data-link protocol, character code, data format, and so on.

4-10　LINE CONTROL UNIT

As previously stated, a line control unit (LCU) is a DTE, and DTEs have several important functions. At the primary station, the LCU is often called a FEP because it processes information and serves as an interface between the host computer and all the data communications circuits it serves. Each circuit served is connected to a different port on the FEP. The FEP directs the flow of input and output data between data communications circuits and their respective application programs. The data interface between the mainframe computer and the FEP transfers data in parallel at relatively high bit rates. However, data transfers between the modem and the FEP are accomplished in serial and at a much lower bit rate. The FEP at the primary station and the LCU at the secondary stations perform parallel-to-serial and serial-to-parallel conversions. They also house the circuitry that performs error detection and correction. In addition, data-link control characters are inserted and deleted in the FEP and LCUs (data-link control characters are described in Chapter 23).

Within the FEP and LCUs, a single special-purpose integrated circuit performs many of the fundamental data communications functions. This integrated circuit is called a *universal asynchronous receiver/transmitter* (UART) if it is designed for asynchronous data transmission, a *universal synchronous receiver/transmitter* (USRT) if it is designed for synchronous data transmission, and a *universal synchronous/asynchronous receiver/transmitter* (USART) if it is designed for either asynchronous or synchronous data transmission. All three types of circuits specify general-purpose integrated-circuit chips located in an LCU or FEP that allow DTEs to interface with DCEs. In modern-day integrated circuits, UARTs and USRTs are often combined into a single USART chip that is probably more popular today simply because it can be adapted to either asynchronous or synchronous data transmission. USARTs are available in 24- to 64-pin dual in-line packages (DIPs).

UARTS, USRTS, and USARTS are devices that operate external to the central processor unit (CPU) in a DTE that allow the DTE to communicate serially with other data communications equipment, such as DCEs. They are also essential data communications components in terminals, workstations, PCs, and many other types of serial data communications devices. In most modern computers, USARTs are normally included on the motherboard and connected directly to the serial port. UARTs, USRTs, and USARTs designed to interface to specific microprocessors often have unique manufacturer-specific names. For example, Motorola manufactures a special purpose UART chip it calls an *asynchronous communications interface adapter* (ACIA).

4-10-1 UART

A UART is used for asynchronous transmission of serial data between a DTE and a DCE. Asynchronous data transmission means that an asynchronous data format is used, and there is no clocking information transferred between the DTE and the DCE. The primary functions performed by a UART are the following:

1. Parallel-to-serial data conversion in the transmitter and serial-to-parallel data conversion in the receiver
2. Error detection by inserting parity bits in the transmitter and checking parity bits in the receiver
3. Insert start and stop bits in the transmitter and detect and remove start and stop bits in the receiver
4. Formatting data in the transmitter and receiver (i.e., combining items 1 through 3 in a meaningful sequence)
5. Provide transmit and receive status information to the CPU
6. Voltage level conversion between the DTE and the serial interface and vice versa
7. Provide a means of achieving bit and character synchronization

Transmit and receive functions can be performed by a UART simultaneously because the transmitter and receiver have separate control signals and clock signals and share a bidirectional data bus, which allows them to operate virtually independently of one another. In addition, input and output data are double buffered, which allows for continuous data transmission and reception.

Figure 4-11 shows a simplified block diagram of a line control unit showing the relationship between the UART and the CPU that controls the operation of the UART. The CPU coordinates data transfer between the line-control unit (or FEP) and the modem. The CPU is responsible for programming the UART's control register, reading the UART's status register, transferring parallel data to and from the UART transmit and receive buffer registers, providing clocking information to the UART, and facilitating the transfer of serial data between the UART and the modem.

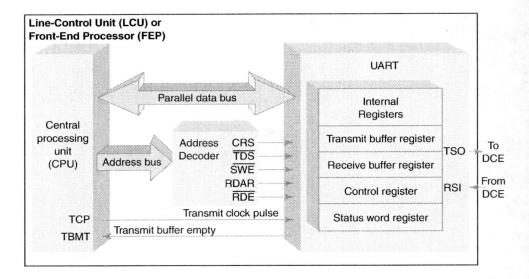

FIGURE 4-11   Line control unit UART interface

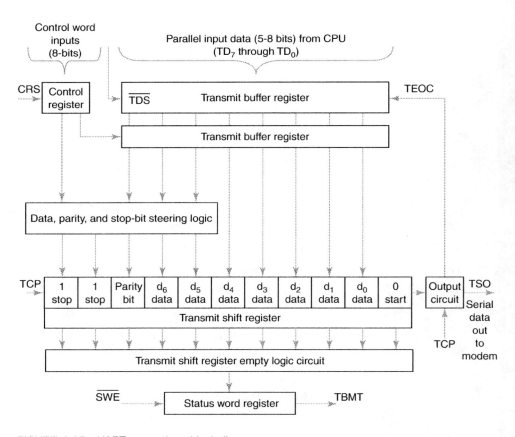

FIGURE 4-12   UART transmitter block diagram

Table 4-6   UART Control Register Inputs

D_7 and D_6
  Number of stop bits

NSB1	NSB2	No. of Bits
0	0	Invalid
0	1	1
1	0	1.5
1	1	2

D_5 and D_4
  NPB (parity or no parity)

1	No parity bit (RPE disabled in receiver)
0	Insert parity bits in transmitter and check parity bits in receiver

POE (parity odd or even)

1	Even parity
0	Odd parity

D_3 and D_2
  Character length

NDB1	NDB2	Bits per Word
0	0	5
0	1	6
1	0	7
1	1	8

D_1 and D_0
  Receive clock (baud rate factor)

RC1	RC2	Clock Rate
0	0	Synchronous mode
0	1	1X
1	0	16X
1	1	32X

A UART can be divided into two functional sections: the transmitter and the receiver. Figure 4-12 shows a simplified block diagram of a UART transmitter. Before transferring data in either direction, an eight-bit control word must be programmed into the UART control register to specify the nature of the data. The control word specifies the number of data bits per character; whether a parity bit is included with each character and, if so, whether it is odd or even parity; the number of stop bits inserted at the end of each character; and the receive clock frequency relative to the transmit clock frequency. Essentially, the start bit is the only bit in the UART that is not optional or programmable, as there is always one start bit, and it is always a logic 0. Table 4-6 shows the control-register coding format for a typical UART.

As specified in Table 4-6, the parity bit is optional and, if used, can be either odd or even. To select parity, NPB is cleared (logic 0), and to exclude the parity bit, NBP is set (logic 1). Odd parity is selected by clearing POE (logic 0), and even parity is selected by setting POE (logic 1). The number of stop bits is established with the NSB1 and NSB2 bits and can be one, one and a half, or two. The character length is determined by NDB1 and NDB2 and can be five, six, seven, or eight bits long. The maximum character length is 11 bits (i.e., one start bit, eight data bits, and two stop bits or one start bit, seven data bits, one parity bit, and two stop bits). Using a 22-bit character format with ASCII encoding is sometimes called *full ASCII*.

Figure 4-13 shows three of the character formats possible with a UART. Figure 4-13a shows an 11-bit data character comprised of one start bit, seven ASCII data bits, one odd-parity bit, and two stop bits (i.e., full ASCII). Figure 4-13b shows a nine-bit data character comprised of one start bit, seven ARQ data bits, and one stop bit, and Figure 4-13c shows another nine-bit data character comprised of one start bit, five Baudot data bits, one odd parity bit, and two stop bits.

A UART also contains a *status word register,* which is an *n*-bit data register that keeps track of the status of the UART's transmit and receive buffer registers. Typical status

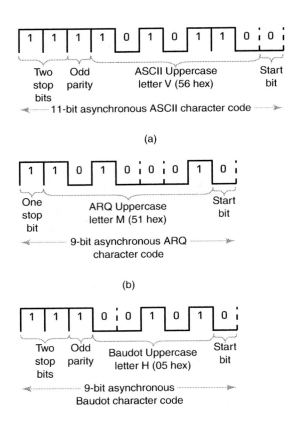

FIGURE 4-13 Asynchronous characters: (a) ASCII character; (b) ARQ character; (c) Baudot character

conditions compiled by the status word register for the UART transmitter include the following conditions:

> *TBMT: transmit buffer empty.* Transmit shift register has completed transmission of a data character
>
> *RPE: receive parity error.* Set when a received character has a parity error in it
>
> *RFE: receive framing error.* Set when a character is received without any or with an improper number of stop bits
>
> *ROR: receiver overrun.* Set when a character in the receive buffer register is written over by another receive character because the CPU failed to service an active condition on REA before the next character was received from the receive shift register
>
> *RDA: receive data available.* A data character has been received and loaded into the receive data register

4-10-1-1 UART transmitter. The operation of the typical UART transmitter shown in Figure 4-12a is quite logical. However, before the UART can send or receive data, the UART control register must be loaded with the desired mode instruction word. This is accomplished by the CPU in the DTE, which applies the mode instruction word to the control word bus and then activates the control-register strobe (CRS).

Figure 4-14 shows the signaling sequence that occurs between the CPU and the UART transmitter. On receipt of an active *status word enable* (SWE) signal, the UART sends a *transmit buffer empty* (TBMT) signal from the status word register to the CPU to indicate that the transmit buffer register is empty and the UART is ready to receive more

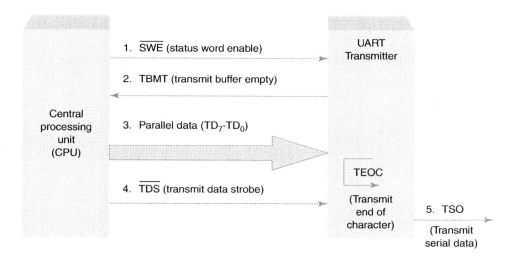

FIGURE 4-14   UART transmitter signal sequence

data. When the CPU senses an active condition of TBMT, it applies a parallel data character to the transmit data lines (TD_7 through TD_0) and strobes them into the transmit buffer register with an active signal on the *transmit data strobe* ($\overline{TDS}$) signal. The contents of the transmit buffer register are transferred to the transmit shift register when the *transmit end-of-character* (TEOC) signal goes active (the TEOC signal is internal to the UART and simply tells the transmit buffer register when the transmit shift register is empty and available to receive data). The data pass through the steering logic circuit, where it picks up the appropriate start, stop, and parity bits. After data have been loaded into the transmit shift register, they are serially outputted on the *transmit serial output* (TSO) pin at a bit rate equal to the transmit clock (TCP) frequency. While the data in the transmit shift register are serially clocked out of the UART, the CPU applies the next character to the input of the transmit buffer register. The process repeats until the CPU has transferred all its data.

4-10-1-2 UART receiver.   A simplified block diagram for a UART receiver is shown in Figure 4-15. The number of stop bits and data bits and the parity bit parameters specified for the UART receiver must be the same as those of the UART transmitter. The UART receiver ignores the reception of idle line 1s. When a valid start bit is detected by the start bit verification circuit, the data character is clocked into the receive shift register. If parity is used, the parity bit is checked in the parity checker circuit. After one complete data character is loaded into the shift register, the character is transferred in parallel into the receive buffer register, and the *receive data available* (RDA) flag is set in the status word register. The CPU reads the status register by activating the *status word enable* ($\overline{SWE}$) signal and, if RDA is active, the CPU reads the character from the receive buffer register by placing an active signal on the receive data enable (RDE) pin. After reading the data, the CPU places an active signal on *the receive data available reset* ($\overline{RDAR}$) pin, which resets the RDA pin. Meanwhile, the next character is received and clocked into the receive shift register, and the process repeats until all the data have been received. Figure 4-16 shows the receive signaling sequence that occurs between the CPU and the UART.

4-10-1-3 Start-bit verification circuit.   With asynchronous data transmission, precise timing is less important than following an agreed-on format or pattern for the data. Each transmitted data character must be preceded by a start bit and end with one or more

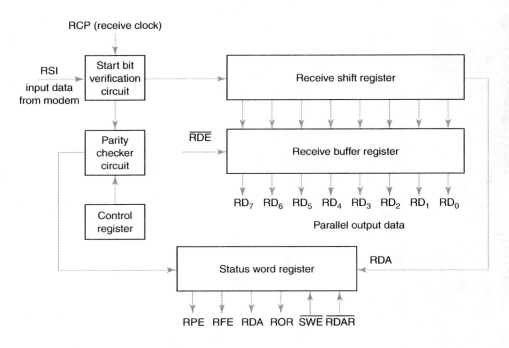

FIGURE 4-15 UART receiver block diagram

FIGURE 4-16 UART receive signal sequence

stop bits. Because data received by a UART have been transmitted from a distant UART whose clock is asynchronous to the receive UART, bit synchronization is achieved by establishing a timing reference at the center of each start bit. Therefore, it is imperative that a UART detect the occurrence of a valid start bit early in the bit cell and establish a timing reference before it begins to accept data.

The primary function of the start bit verification circuit is to detect valid start bits, which indicate the beginning of a data character. Figure 4-17a shows an example of how a noise hit can be misinterpreted as a start bit. The input data consist of a continuous string

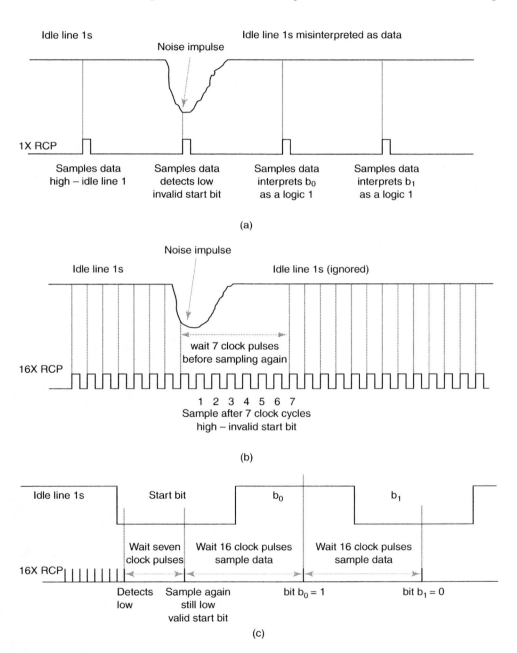

FIGURE 4-17   Start bit verification: (a) 1X RCP; (b) 16X RCP; (c) valid start bit

of idle line 1s, which are typically transmitted when there is no information. Idle line 1s are interpreted by a receiver as continuous stop bits (i.e., no data). If a noise impulse occurs that causes the receive data to go low at the same time the receiver clock is active, the receiver will interpret the noise impulse as a start bit. If this happens, the receiver will misinterpret the logic condition present during the next clock as the first data bit (b_0) and the following clock cycles as the remaining data bits (b_1, b_2, and so on). The likelihood of misinterpreting noise hits as start bits can be reduced substantially by clocking the UART receiver at a rate higher than the incoming data. Figure 4-17b shows the same situation as shown in Figure 4-17a, except the receive clock pulse (RCP) is 16 times (16×) higher than the receive serial data input (RSI). Once a low is detected, the UART waits seven clock cycles before resampling the input data. Waiting seven clock cycles places the next sample very near the center of the start bit. If the next sample detects a low, it assumes that a valid start bit has been detected. If the data have reverted to the high condition, it is assumed that the high-to-low transition was simply a noise pulse and, therefore, is ignored. Once a valid start bit has been detected and verified (Figure 4-17c), the start bit verification circuit samples the incoming data once every 16 clock cycles, which essentially makes the sample rate equal to the receive data rate (i.e., 16 RCP/16 = RCP). The UART continues sampling the data once every 16 clock cycles until the stop bits are detected, at which time the start bit verification circuit begins searching for another valid start bit. UARTs are generally programmed for receive clock rates of 16, 32, or 64 times the receive data rate (i.e., 16×, 32×, and 64×).

Another advantage of clocking a UART receiver at a rate higher than the actual receive data is to ensure that a high-to-low transition (valid start bit) is detected as soon as possible. This ensures that once the start bit is detected, subsequent samples will occur very near the center of each data bit. The difference in time between when a sample is taken (i.e., when a data bit is clocked into the receive shift register) and the actual center of a data bit is called the sampling error. Figure 4-18 shows a receive data stream sampled at a rate 16 times higher (16 RCP) than the actual data rate (RCP). As the figure shows, the start bit is not immediately detected. The difference in time between the beginning of a start bit and when it is detected is called the *detection error*. The maximum detection error is equal to the time of one receive clock cycle ($t_{cl} = 1/R_{cl}$). If the receive clock rate equaled the receive data rate, the maximum detection error would approach the time of one bit, which would mean that a start bit would not be detected until the very end of the bit time. Obviously, the higher the receive clock rate, the earlier a start bit would be detected.

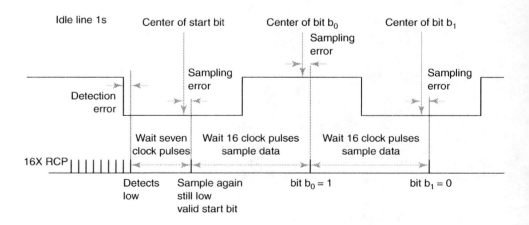

FIGURE 4-18　16X receive clock rate

Because of the detection error, successive samples occur slightly off from the center of the data bit. This would not present a problem with synchronous clocks, as the sampling error would remain constant from one sample to the next. However, with asynchronous clocks, the magnitude of the sampling error for each successive sample would increase (the clock would slip over or slip under the data), eventually causing a data bit to be either sampled twice or not sampled at all, depending on whether the receive clock is higher or lower than the transmit clock.

Figure 4-19 illustrates how sampling at a higher rate reduces the sampling error. Figures 4-19a and b show data sampled at a rate eight times the data rate (8×) and 16 times the data rate (16×), respectively. It can be seen that increasing the sample rate moves the sample time closer to the center of the data bit, thus decreasing the sampling error.

Placing stop bits at the end of each data character also helps reduce the *clock slip-page* (sometimes called *clock skew*) problem inherent when using asynchronous transmit and receive clocks. Start and stop bits force a high-to-low transition at the beginning of each character, which essentially allows the receiver to resynchronize to the start bit at the beginning of each data character. It should probably be mentioned that with UARTs the data rates do not have to be the same in each direction of propagation (e.g., you could transmit data at 1200 bps and receive at 600 bps). However, the rate at which data leave a transmitter must be the same as the rate at which data enter the receiver at the other end of the circuit. If you transmit at 1200 bps, it must be received at the other end at 1200 bps.

4-10-2 Universal Synchronous Receiver/Transmitter

A *universal synchronous receiver/transmitter* (USRT) is used for synchronous transmission of data between a DTE and a DCE. Synchronous data transmission means that a synchronous data format is used, and clocking information is generally transferred between the DTE and the DCE. A USRT performs the same basic functions as a UART, except for

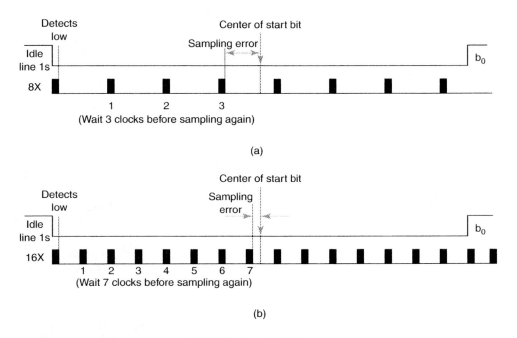

(a)

(b)

FIGURE 4-19 Sampling error: (a) 8X RCP; (b) 16X RCP

synchronous data (i.e., the start and stop bits are omitted and replaced by unique synchronizing characters). The primary functions performed by a USRT are the following:

1. Serial-to-parallel and parallel-to-serial data conversions
2. Error detection by inserting parity bits in the transmitter and checking parity bits in the receiver.
3. Insert and detect unique data synchronization (SYN) characters
4. Formatting data in the transmitter and receiver (i.e., combining items 1 through 3 in a meaningful sequence)
5. Provide transmit and receive status information to the CPU
6. Voltage-level conversion between the DTE and the serial interface and vice versa
7. Provide a means of achieving bit and character synchronization

4-11 SERIAL INTERFACES

To ensure an orderly flow of data between a DTE and a DCE, a standard serial interface is used to interconnect them. The serial interface coordinates the flow of data, control signals, and timing information between the DTE and the DCE.

Before serial interfaces were standardized, every company that manufactured data communications equipment used a different interface configuration. More specifically, the cable arrangement between the DTE and the DCE, the type and size of the connectors, and the voltage levels varied considerably from vender to vender. To interconnect equipment manufactured by different companies, special level converters, cables, and connectors had to be designed, constructed, and implemented for each application. A serial interface standard should provide the following:

1. A specific range of voltages for transmit and receive signal levels
2. Limitations for the electrical parameters of the transmission line, including source and load impedance, cable capacitance, and other electrical characteristics outlined later in this chapter
3. Standard cable and cable connectors
4. Functional description of each signal on the interface

In 1962, the Electronics Industries Association (EIA), in an effort to standardize interface equipment between data terminal equipment and data communications equipment, agreed on a set of standards called the *RS-232 specifications* (RS meaning "recommended standard"). The official name of the RS-232 interface is *Interface Between Data Terminal Equipment and Data Communications Equipment Employing Serial Binary Data Interchange.* In 1969, the third revision, RS-232C, was published and remained the industrial standard until 1987, when the RS-232D was introduced, which was followed by the RS-232E in the early 1990s. The RS-232D standard is sometimes referred to as the EIA-232 standard. Versions D and E of the RS-232 standard changed some of the pin designations. For example, data set ready was changed to DCE ready, and data terminal ready was changed to DTE ready.

The RS-232 specifications identify the mechanical, electrical, functional, and procedural descriptions for the interface between DTEs and DCEs. The RS-232 interface is similar to the combined ITU-T standards V.28 (electrical specifications) and V.24 (functional description) and is designed for serial transmission up to 20 kbps over a maximum distance of 50 feet (approximately 15 meters).

4-11-1 RS-232 Serial Interface Standard

The mechanical specification for the RS-232 interface specifies a cable with two connectors. The standard RS-232 cable is a sheath containing 25 wires with a DB25P-compatible

(a)   (b)

(c)   (d)

FIGURE 4-20 RS-232 serial interface connector: [a] DB25P; [b] DB25S; [c] DB9P; [d] DB9S

FIGURE 4-21 EIA-561 modular connector

male connector (plug) on one end and a DB25S-compatible female connector (receptacle) on the other end. The DB25P-compatible and DB25S-compatible connectors are shown in Figures 4-20a and b, respectively. The cable must have a plug on one end that connects to the DTE and a receptacle on the other end that connects to the DCE. There is also a special PC nine-pin version of the RS-232 interface cable with a DB9P-compatible male connector on one end and a DB9S-compatible connector at the other end. The DB9P-compatible and DB9S-compatible connectors are shown in Figures 4-20c and d, respectively (note that there is no correlation between the pin assignments for the two connectors). The nine-pin version of the RS-232 interface is designed for transporting asynchronous data between a DTE and a DCE or between two DTEs, whereas the 25-pin version is designed for transporting either synchronous or asynchronous data between a DTE and a DCE. Figure 4-21 shows the eight-pin EIA-561 modular connector, which is used for transporting asynchronous data between a DTE and a DCE when the DCE is connected directly to a standard two-wire telephone line attached to the public switched telephone network. The EIA-561 modular connector is designed exclusively for dial-up telephone connections.

Although the RS-232 interface is simply a cable and two connectors, the standard also specifies limitations on the voltage levels that the DTE and DCE can output onto or receive from the cable. The DTE and DCE must provide circuits that convert their internal logic levels to RS-232-compatible values. For example, a DTE using TTL logic interfaced to a DCE using CMOS logic is not compatible. *Voltage-leveling circuits* convert the internal voltage levels from the DTE and DCE to RS-232 values. If both the DCE and the DTE output and accept RS-232 levels, they are electrically compatible regardless of which logic family they use internally. A voltage leveler is called a *driver* if it outputs signals onto the cable and a

Table 4-7 RS-232 Voltage Specifications

	Data Signals		Control Signals	
	Logic 1	Logic 0	Enable (On)	Disable (Off)
Driver (output)	−5 V to −15 V	+5 V to +15 V	+5 V to +15 V	−5 V to −15 V
Terminator (input)	−3 V to −25 V	+3 V to +25 V	+3 V to +25 V	−3 V to −25 V

terminator if it accepts signals from the cable. In essence, a driver is a transmitter, and a terminator is a receiver. Table 4-7 lists the voltage limits for RS-232-compatible drivers and terminators. Note that the data and control lines use *non–return to zero, level* (NRZ-L) bipolar encoding. However, the data lines use negative logic, while the control lines use positive logic.

From examining Table 4-7, it can be seen that the voltage limits for a driver are more inclusive than the voltage limits for a terminator. The output voltage range for a driver is between +5 V and +15 V or between −5 V and −15 V, depending on the logic level. However, the voltage range in which a terminator will accept is between +3 V and +25 V or between −3 V and −25 V. Voltages between ±3 V are undefined and may be interpreted by a terminator as a high or a low. The difference in the voltage levels between the driver output and the terminator input is called *noise margin* (NM). The noise margin reduces the susceptibility to interface caused by noise transients induced into the cable. Figure 4-22a shows the relationship between the driver and terminator voltage ranges. As shown in Figure 4-22a, the noise margin for the minimum driver output voltage is 2 V (5 − 3), and the noise margin for the maximum driver output voltage is 10 V (25 – 15). (The minimum noise margin of 2 V is called the *implied noise margin*.) Noise margins will vary, of course, depending on what specific voltages are used for highs and lows. When the noise margin of a circuit is a high value, it is said to have *high noise immunity,* and when the noise margin is a low value, it has *low noise immunity.* Typical RS-232 voltage levels are +10 V for a high and −10 V for a low, which produces a noise margin of 7 V in one direction and 15 V in the other direction. The noise margin is generally stated as the minimum value. This relationship is shown in Figure 4-22b. Figure 4-22c illustrates the immunity of the RS-232 interface to noise signals for logic levels of +10 V and −10 V.

The RS-232 interface specifies single-end (unbalanced) operation with a common ground between the DTE and DCE. A common ground is reasonable when a short cable is used. However, with longer cables and when the DTE and DCE are powered from different electrical buses, this may not be true.

Example 4-8

Determine the noise margins for an RS-232 interface with driver signal voltages of ±6 V.

Solution The noise margin is the difference between the driver signal voltage and the terminator receive voltage, or

$$NM = 6 - 3 = 3 \text{ V or } NM = 25 - 6 = 19 \text{ V}$$

The minimum noise margin is 3 V.

4-11-1-1 RS-232 electrical equivalent circuit. Figure 4-23 shows the equivalent electrical circuit for the RS-232 interface, including the driver and terminator. With these electrical specifications and for a bit rate of 20 kbps, the nominal maximum length of the RS-232 interface cable is approximately 50 feet.

4-11-1-2 RS-232 functional description. The pins on the RS-232 interface cable are functionally categorized as either ground (signal and chassis), data (transmit and re-

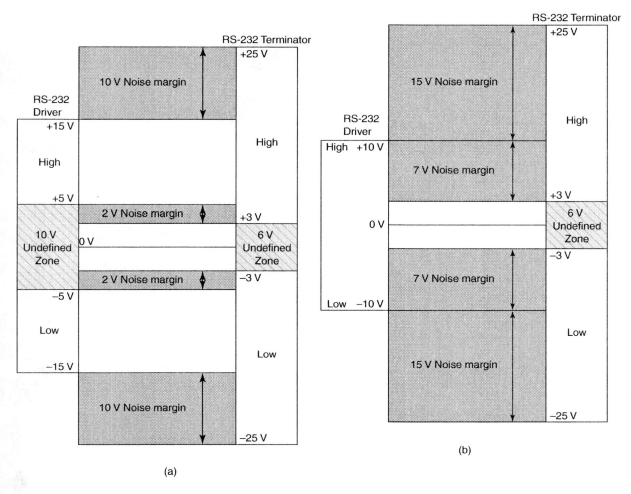

(a)

(b)

FIGURE 4-22   RS-232 logic levels and noise margin: (a) driver and terminator voltage ranges; (b) noise margin with a +10 V high and −10 V low (*Continued*)

ceive), control (handshaking and diagnostic), or timing (clocking signals). Although the RS-232 interface as a unit is bidirectional (signals propagate in both directions), each individual wire or pin is unidirectional. That is, signals on any given wire are propagated either from the DTE to the DCE or from the DCE to the DTE but never in both directions. Table 4-8 lists the 25 pins (wires) of the RS-232 interface and gives the direction of signal propagation (i.e., either from the DTE toward the DCE or from the DCE toward the DTE). The RS-232 specification designates the first letter of each pin with the letters A, B, C, D, or S. The letter categorizes the signal into one of five groups, each representing a different type of circuit. The five groups are as follows:

A—ground
B—data
C—control
D—timing (clocking)
S—secondary channel

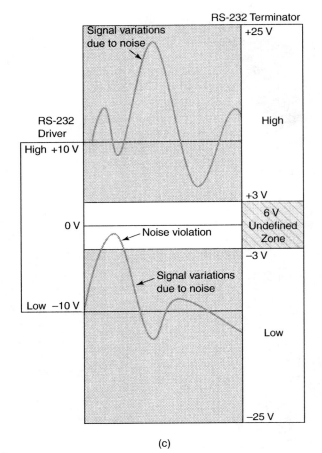

FIGURE 4-22 (*Continued*)
(c) noise violation

(c)

V_{out} — open-circuit voltage at the output of a driver (±5 V to ±15 V)
V_i — terminated voltage at the input to a terminator (±3 V to ±25 V)
C_L — load capacitance associated with the terminator, including the cable (2500 pF maximum)
C_O — capacitance seen by the driver including the cable (2500 pF maximum)
R_L — terminator input resistance (3000 Ω to 7000 Ω)
R_{out} — driver output resistance (300 Ω maximum)

FIGURE 4-23   RS-232 Electrical specifications

Table 4-8   EIA RS-232 Pin Designations and Direction of Propagation

Pin Number	Pin Name	Direction of Propagation
1	Protective ground (frame ground or chassis ground)	None
2	Transmit data (send data)	DTE to DCE
3	Receive data	DCE to DTE
4	Request to send	DTE to DCE
5	Clear to send	DCE to DTE
6	Data set ready (modem ready)	DCE to DTE
7	Signal ground (reference ground)	None
8	Receive line signal detect (carrier detect or data carrier detect)	DCE to DTE
9	Unassigned	None
10	Unassigned	None
11	Unassigned	None
12	Secondary receive line signal detect (secondary carrier detect or secondary data carrier detect)	DCE to DTE
13	Secondary clear to send	DCE to DTE
14	Secondary transmit data (secondary send data)	DTE to DCE
15	Transmit signal element timing—DCE (serial clock transmit—DCE)	DCE to DTE
16	Secondary receive data	DCE to DTE
17	Receive signal element timing (serial clock receive)	DCE to DTE
18	Unassigned	None
19	Secondary request to send	DTE to DCE
20	Data terminal ready	DTE to DCE
21	Signal quality detect	DCE to DTE
22	Ring indicator	DCE to DTE
23	Data signal rate selector	DTE to DCE
24	Transmit signal element timing—DTE (serial clock transmit—DTE)	DTE to DCE
25	Unassigned	None

Because the letters are nondescriptive designations, it is more practical and useful to use acronyms to designate the pins that reflect the functions of the pins. Table 4-9 lists the EIA signal designations plus the nomenclature more commonly used by industry in the United States to designate the pins.

Twenty of the 25 pins on the RS-232 interface are designated for specific purposes or functions. Pins 9, 10, 11, 18, and 25 are unassigned (unassigned does not necessarily imply unused). Pins 1 and 7 are grounds; pins 2, 3, 14, and 16 are data pins; pins 15, 17, and 24 are timing pins; and all the other pins are used for control or handshaking signals. Pins 1 through 8 are used with both asynchronous and synchronous modems. Pins 15, 17, and 24 are used only with synchronous modems. Pins 12, 13, 14, 16, and 19 are used only when the DCE is equipped with a secondary data channel. Pins 20 and 22 are used exclusively when interfacing a DTE to a modem that is connected to standard dial-up telephone circuits on the public switched telephone network.

There are two full-duplex data channels available with the RS-232 interface; one channel is for *primary data* (actual information), and the second channel is for *secondary data* (diagnostic information and handshaking signals). The secondary channel is sometimes used as a reverse or backward channel, allowing the receive DCE to communicate with the transmit DCE while data are being transmitted on the primary data channel.

Table 4-9 EIA RS-232 Pin Designations and Designations

Pin Number	Pin Name	EIA Nomenclature	Common U.S. Acronyms
1	Protective ground (frame ground or chassis ground)	AA	GWG, FG, or CG
2	Transmit data (send data)	BA	TD, SD, TxD
3	Receive data	BB	RD, RxD
4	Request to send	CA	RS, RTS
5	Clear to send	CB	CS, CTS
6	Data set ready (modem ready)	CC	DSR, MR
7	Signal ground (reference ground)	AB	SG, GND
8	Receive line signal detect (carrier detect or data carrier detect)	CF	RLSD, CD, DCD
9	Unassigned	—	—
10	Unassigned	—	—
11	Unassigned	—	—
12	Secondary receive line signal detect (secondary carrier detect or secondary data carrier detect)	SCF	SRLSD, SCD, SDCD
13	Secondary clear to send	SCB	SCS, SCTS
14	Secondary transmit data (secondary send data)	SBA	STD, SSD, STxD
15	Transmit signal element timing—DCE (serial clock transmit—DCE)	DB	TSET, SCT-DCE
16	Secondary receive data	SBB	SRD, SRxD
17	Receive signal element timing (serial clock receive)	DD	RSET, SCR
18	Unassigned	—	—
19	Secondary request to send	SCA	SRS, SRTS
20	Data terminal ready	CD	DTR
21	Signal quality detect	CG	SQD
22	Ring indicator	CE	RI
23	Data signal rate selector	CH	DSRS
24	Transmit signal element timing—DTE (serial clock transmit—DTE)	DA	TSET, SCT-DTE
25	Unassigned	—	—

The functions of the 25 RS-232 pins are summarized here for a DTE interfacing with a DCE where the DCE is a data communications modem:

Pin 1—protective ground, frame ground, or *chassis ground* (GWG, FG, or CG). Pin 1 is connected to the chassis and used for protection against accidental electrical shock. Pin 1 is generally connected to signal ground (pin 7).

Pin 2—transmit data or *send data* (TD, SD, or TxD). Serial data on the primary data channel are transported from the DTE to the DCE on pin 2. Primary data are the actual source information transported over the interface. The transmit data line is a transmit line for the DTE but a receive line for the DCE. The DTE may hold the TD line at a logic 1 voltage level when no data are being transmitted and between characters when asynchronous data are being transmitted. Otherwise, the TD driver is enabled by an active condition on pin 5 (clear to send).

Pin 3—receive data (RD or RxD). Pin 3 is the second primary data pin. Serial data are transported from the DCE to the DTE on pin 3. Pin 3 is the receive data pin for the DTE and the transmit data pin for the DCE. The DCE may hold the TD line at a logic 1 voltage level when no data are being transmitted or when pin 8 (RLSD) is inactive. Otherwise, the RD driver is enabled by an active condition on pin 8.

Pin 4—request to send (RS or RTS). For half-duplex data transmission, the DTE uses pin 4 to request permission from the DCE to transmit data on the primary data channel. When the DCE is a modem, an active condition on RTS turns on the modem's analog carrier. The RTS and CTS signals are used together to coordinate half-duplex data transmission between the DTE and DCE. For full-duplex data transmission, RTS can be held active permanently. The RTS driver is enabled by an active condition on pin 6 (data set ready).

Pin 5—clear to send (CS or CTS). The CTS signal is a handshake from the DCE to the DTE (i.e., modem to LCU) in response to an active condition on RTS. An active condition on CTS enables the TD driver in the DTE. There is a predetermined time delay between when the DCE receives an active condition on the RTS signal and when the DCE responds with an active condition on the CTS signal.

Pin 6—data set ready or *modem ready* (DSR or MR). DSR is a signal sent from the DCE to the DTE to indicate the availability of the communications channel. DSR is active only when the DCE and the communications channel are available. Under normal operation, the modem and the communications channel are always available. However, there are five situations when the modem or the communications channel are not available:

1. The modem is shut off (i.e., has no power).
2. The modem is disconnected from the communications line so that the line can be used for normal telephone voice traffic (i.e., in the voice rather than the data mode).
3. The modem is in one of the self-test modes (i.e., analog or digital loopback).
4. The telephone company is testing the communications channel.
5. On dial-up circuits, DSR is held inactive while the telephone switching system is establishing a call and when the modem is transmitting a specific response (answer) signal to the calling station's modem.

An active condition on the DSR lead enables the request to send driver in the DTE, thus giving the DSR lead the highest priority of the RS-232 control leads.

Pin 7—signal ground or *reference ground* (SG or GND). Pin 7 is the signal reference (return line) for all data, control, and timing signals (i.e., all pins except pin 1, chassis ground).

Pin 8—receive line signal detect, carrier detect, or *data carrier detect* (RLSD, CD, or DCD). The DCE uses this pin to signal the DTE when it determines that it is receiving a valid analog carrier (data carrier). An active RLSD signal enables the RD terminator in the DTE, allowing it to accept data from the DCE. An inactive RLSD signal disables the terminator for the DTE's receive data pin, preventing it from accepting invalid data. On half-duplex data circuits, RLSD is held inactive whenever RTS is active.

Pin 9—unassigned. Pin 9 is non–EIA specified; however, it is often held at $+12$ Vdc for test purposes ($+$P).

Pin 10—unassigned. Pin 10 is non–EIA specified; however, it is often held at -12 Vdc for test purposes ($-$P).

Pin 11—unassigned. Pin 11 is non–EIA specified; however, it is often designated as *equalizer mode* (EM) and used by the modem to signal the DTE when the modem is self-adjusting its internal equalizers because error performance is suspected to be poor. When the carrier detect signal is active and the circuit is inactive, the modem is retraining (resynchronizing), and the probability of error is high. When the receive line signal detect (pin 8) is active and EM is inactive, the modem is trained, and the probability of error is low.

Pin 12—secondary receive line signal detect, secondary carrier detect, or *secondary data carrier detect* (SRLSD, SCD, or SDCD). Pin 12 is the same as RLSD (pin 8), except for the secondary data channel.

Pin 13—secondary clear to send. The SCTS signal is sent from DCE to the DTE as a response (handshake) to the secondary request to send signal (pin 19).

Pin 14—secondary transmit data or *secondary send data* (STD, STD, or STxD). Diagnostic data are transmitted from the DTE to the DCE on this pin. STD is enabled by an active condition on SCTS.

Pin 15—transmission signal element timing or (*serial clock transmit*) *DCE* (TSET, SCT-DCE). With synchronous modems, the transmit clocking signal is sent from the DCE to the DTE on this pin.

Pin 16—secondary received data (SRD or SRxD). Diagnostic data are transmitted from the DCE to the DTE on this pin. The SRD driver is enabled by an active condition on secondary receive line signal detect (SRLSD).

Pin 17—receiver signal element timing or *serial clock receive* (RSET or SCR). When synchronous modems are used, clocking information recovered by the DCE is sent to the DTE on this pin. The receive clock is used to clock data out of the DCE and into the DTE on the receive data line. The clock frequency is equal to the bit rate on the primary data channel.

Pin 18—unassigned. Pin 11 is non–EIA specified; however, it is often used for the *local loopback* (LL) signal. Local loopback is a control signal sent from the DTE to the DCE placing the DCE (modem) into an analog loopback condition. Analog and digital loopbacks are described in a later section of this chapter.

Pin 19—secondary request to send (SRS or SRTS). SRTS is used by the DTE to bid for the secondary data channel from the DCE. SRTS and SCTS coordinate the flow of data on the secondary data channel.

Pin 20—data terminal ready (DTR). The DTE sends signals to the DCE on the DTR line concerning the availability of the data terminal equipment. DTR is used primarily with dial-up circuits to handshake with ring indicator (pin 22). The DTE disables DTR when it is unavailable, thus instructing the DCE not to answer an incoming call.

Pin 21—signal quality detector (SQD). The DCE sends signals to the DTE on this line indicating the quality of the received analog carrier. An inactive (low) signal on SQD tells the DTE that the incoming signal is marginal and that there is a high likelihood that errors are occurring.

Pin 22—ring indicator (RI). The RI line is used primarily on dial-up data circuits for the DCE to inform the DTE that there is an incoming call. If the DTE is ready to receive data, it responds to an active condition on RI with an active condition on DTR. DTR is a handshaking signal in response to an active condition on RI.

Pin 23—data signal rate selector (DSRS). The DTE used this line to select one of two transmission bit rates when the DCE is equipped to offer two rates. (The data rate selector line can be used to change the transmit clock frequency.)

Pin 24—transmit signal element timing or *serial clock transmit–DTE* (TSET, SCT-DTE). When synchronous modems are used, the transmit clocking signal is sent from the DTE to the DCE on this pin. Pin 24 is used only when the master clock is located in the DTE.

Pin 25—unassigned. Pin 5 is non–EIA specified; however, it is sometimes used as a control signal from the DCE to the DTE to indicate that the DCE is in either the remote or local loopback mode.

For asynchronous transmission using either the DB9P/S-modular connector, only the following nine pins are provided:

1. Receive line signal detect
2. Receive data

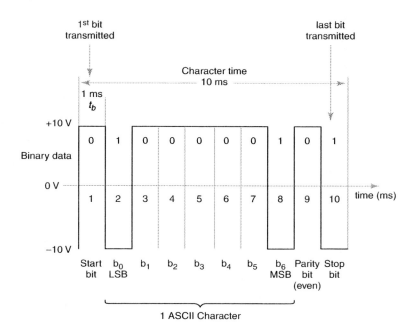

FIGURE 4-24   RS-232 data timing diagram—ASCII upper case letter A, 1 start bit, even parity, and one stop bit

3. Transmit data
4. Data terminal ready
5. Signal ground
6. Data set ready
7. Request to send
8. Clear to send
9. Ring indicator

4-11-1-3 RS-232 signals.   Figure 4-24 shows the timing diagram for the transmission of one asynchronous data character over the RS-232 interface. The character is comprised of one start bit, one stop bit, seven ASCII character bits, and one even-parity bit. The transmission rate is 1000 bps, and the voltage level for a logic 1 is −10 V and for a logic 0 is +10 V. The time of one bit is 1 ms; therefore, the total time to transmit one ASCII character is 10 ms.

4-11-1-4 RS-232.   Asynchronous Data Transmission. Figures 4-25a and b show the functional block diagram for the drivers and terminators necessary for transmission of asynchronous data over the RS-232 interface between a DTE and a DCE that is a modem. As shown in the figure, only the first eight pins of the interface are required, which includes the following signals: signal ground and chassis ground, transmit data and receive data, request to send, clear to send, data set ready, and receive line signal detect.

Figure 4-26a shows the transmitter timing diagram for control and data signals for a typical asynchronous data transmission over an RS-232 interface with the following parameters:

Modem RTS-CTS delay = 50 ms

DTE primary data message length = 100 ms

(a)

(b)

FIGURE 4-25 Functional block diagram for the drivers and terminators necessary for transmission of asynchronous data over the RS-232 interface between a DTE and a DCE (modem): (a) transmit circuits; (b) receive circuits

Modem training sequence = 50 ms

Propagation time = 10 ms

Modem RLSD turn-off delay time = 5 ms

When the DTE wishes to transmit data on the primary channel, it enables request to send ($t = 0$). After a predetermined RTS/CTS time delay time, which is determined by the modem (50 ms for this example), CTS goes active. During the 50-ms RTS/CTS delay, the modem outputs an analog carrier that is modulated by a unique bit pattern called a *training sequence*. The training sequence for asynchronous modems is generally nothing more than a series of logic 1s that produce 50 ms of continuous mark frequency. The analog carrier is used to initialize the communications channel and the distant receive modem (with synchronous modems, the training sequence is more involved, as it would also synchronize the carrier and clock recovery circuits in the distant modem). After the RTS/CTS delay, the transmit data (TD) line is enabled, and the DTE begins transmitting user data. When the transmission is

(a)

(b)

FIGURE 4-26 Typical timing diagram for control and data signals for asynchronous data transmission over the RS-232 interface between a DTE and a DCE (modem): (a) transmit timing diagram; (b) receive timing diagram complete ($t = 150$ ms), RTS goes low, which turns off the modem's analog carrier. The modem acknowledges the inactive condition of RTS with an inactive condition on CTS.

At the distant end (see Figure 4-26b), the receive modem receives a valid analog carrier after a 10-ms propagation delay (P_d) and enables RLSD. The DCE sends an active RLSD signal across the RS-232 interface cable to the DT, which enables the receive data line (RD). However, the first 50 ms of the receive data is the training sequence, which is ignored by the DTE, as it is simply a continuous stream of logic 1s. The DTE identifies the beginning of the user data by recognizing the high-to-low transition caused by the first start bit ($t = 60$ ms). At the end of the message, the DCE holds RLSD active for a predetermined RLSD turn-off delay time (10 ms) to ensure that all the data received have been demodulated and outputted onto the RS-232 interface.

4-11-2 RS-449 Serial Interface Standards

In the mid-1970s, it appeared that data rates had exceeded the capabilities of the RS-232 interface. Consequently, in 1977, the EIA introduced the RS-449 serial interface with the intention of replacing the RS-232 interface. The RS-449 interface specifies a 37-pin primary connector (DB37) and a nine-pin secondary connector (DB9) for a total of 46 pins, which provide more functions, faster data transmission rates, and spans greater distances than the RS-232 interface. The RS-449 is essentially an updated version of the RS-232 interface except the RS-449 standard outlines only the mechanical and functional specifications of the interface.

The RS-449 primary cable is for serial data transmission, while the secondary cable is for diagnostic information. Table 4-10a lists the 37 pins of the RS-449 primary cable and their designations, and Table 4-10b lists the nine pins of the diagnostic cable and their designations. Note that the acronyms used with the RS-449 interface are more descriptive than those recommended by the EIA for the RS-232 interface. The functions specified by the RS-449 are very similar to the functions specified by the RS-232. The major difference

Table 4-10a RS-449 Pin Designations (37-Pin Connector)

Pin Number	Pin Name	EIA Nomenclature
1	Shield	None
19	Signal	SG
37	Send common	SC
20	Receive common	RC
28	Terminal in service	IS
15	Incoming call	IC
12, 30	Terminal ready	TR
11, 29	Data mode	DM
4, 22	Send data	SD
6, 24	Receive data	RD
17, 35	Terminal timing	TT
5, 23	Send timing	ST
8, 26	Receive timing	RT
7, 25	Request to send	RS
9, 27	Clear to send	CS
13, 31	Receiver ready	RR
33	Signal quality	SQ
34	New signal	NS
16	Select frequency	SF
2	Signal rate indicator	SI
10	Local loopback	LL
14	Remote loopback	RL
18	Test mode	TM
32	Select standby	SS
36	Standby indicator	SB

Table 4-10b RS-449 Pin Designations (Nine-Pin Connector)

Pin Number	Pin Name	EIA Nomenclature
1	Shield	None
5	Signal ground	SG
9	Send common	SC
2	Receive common	RC
3	Secondary send data	SSD
4	Secondary receive data	SRD
7	Secondary request to send	SRS
8	Secondary clear to send	SCS
6	Secondary receiver ready	SRF

between the two standards is the separation of the primary data and secondary diagnostic channels onto two separate cables.

The electrical specifications for the RS-449 were specified by the EIA in 1978 as either the RS-422 or the RS-423 standard. The RS-449 standard, when combined with RS-422A or RS-423A, were intended to replace the RS-232 interface. The primary goals of the new specifications are listed here:

1. Compatibility with the RS-232 interface standard
2. Replace the set of circuit names and mnemonics used with the RS-232 interface with more meaningful and descriptive names
3. Provide separate cables and connectors for the primary and secondary data channels
4. Provide single-ended or balanced transmission
5. Reduce crosstalk between signal wires
6. Offer higher data transmission rates
7. Offer longer distances over twisted-pair cable
8. Provide loopback capabilities
9. Improve performance and reliability
10. Specify a standard connector

The RS-422A standard specifies a balanced interface cable capable of operating up to 10 Mbps and span distances up to 1200 meters. However, this does not mean that 10 Mbps can be transmitted 1200 meters. At 10 Mbps, the maximum distance is approximately 15 meters, and 90 kbps is the maximum bit rate that can be transmitted 1200 meters.

The RS-423A standard specifies an unbalanced interface cable capable of operating at a maximum transmission rate of 100 kbps and span a maximum distance of 90 meters. The RS-442A and RS-443A standards are similar to ITU-T V.11 and V.10, respectively. With a bidirectional unbalanced line, one wire is at ground potential, and the currents in the two wires may be different. With an unbalanced line, interference is induced into only one signal path and, therefore, does not cancel in the terminator.

The primary objective of establishing the RS-449 interface standard was to maintain compatibility with the RS-232 interface standard. To achieve this goal, the EIA divided the RS-449 into two categories: *category I* and *category II* circuits. Category I circuits include only circuits that are compatible with the RS-232 standard. The remaining circuits are classified as category II. Category I and category II circuits are listed in Table 4-11.

Category I circuits can function with either the RS-422A (balanced) or the RS-423A (unbalanced) specifications. Category I circuits are allotted two adjacent wires for each RS-232-compatible signal, which facilitates either balanced or unbalanced operation. Category II circuits are assigned only one wire and, therefore, can facilitate only unbalanced (RS-423A) specifications.

Table 4-11 RS-449 Category I and Category II Circuits

Category I	
SD	Send data (4, 22)
RD	Receive data (6, 24)
TT	Terminal timing (17, 35)
ST	Send timing (5, 23)
RT	Receive timing (8, 26)
RS	Request to send (7, 25)
CS	Clear to send (9, 27)
RR	Receiver ready (13, 31)
TR	Terminal ready (12, 30)
DM	Data mode (11, 29)
Category II	
SC	Send common (37)
RC	Receive common (20)
IS	Terminal in service (28)
NS	New signal (34)
SF	Select frequency (16)
LL	Local loopback (10)
RL	Remote loopback (14)
TM	Test mode (18)
SS	Select standby (32)
SB	Standby indicator (36)

The RS-449 interface provides 10 circuits not specified in the RS-232 standard:

1. *Local loopback* (LL, pin 10). Used by the DTE to request a local (analog) loopback from the DCE
2. *Remote loopback* (RL, pin 14). Used by the DTE to request a remote (digital) loopback from the distant DCE
3. *Select frequency* (SF, pin 16). Allows the DTE to select the DCE's transmit and receive frequencies
4. *Test mode* (TM, pin 18). Used by the DTE to signal the DCE that a test is in progress
5. *Receive common* (RC, pin 20). Common return wire for unbalanced signals propagating from the DCE to the DTE
6. *Terminal in service* (IS, pin 28). Used by the DTE to signal the DCE whether it is operational
7. *Select standby* (SS, pin 32). Used by the DTE to request that the DCE switch to standby equipment in the event of a failure on the primary equipment
8. *New signal* (NS, pin 34). Used with a modem at the primary location of a multipoint data circuit so that the primary can resynchronize to whichever secondary is transmitting at the time
9. *Standby indicator* (SB, pin 36). Intended to be by the DCE as a response to the SS signal to notify the DTE that standby equipment has replaced the primary equipment
10. *Send common* (SC, pin 37). Common return wire for unbalanced signals propagating from the DTE to the DCE

4-11-3 RS-530 Serial Interface Standards

Since the data communications industry did not readily adopt the RS-449 interface, it came and went virtually unnoticed by most of industry. Consequently, in 1987 the EIA introduced another new standard, the RS-530 serial interface, which was intended to operate at data rates

Table 4-12   RS-530 Pin Designations

Signal Name	Pin Number(s)
Shield	1
Transmit data[a]	2, 14
Receive data[a]	3, 16
Request to send[a]	4, 19
Clear to send[a]	5, 13
DCE ready[a]	6, 22
DTE ready[a]	20, 23
Signal ground	7
Receive line signal detect[a]	8, 10
Transmit signal element timing (DCE source)[a]	15, 12
Receive signal element timing (DCE source)[a]	17, 9
Local loopback[b]	18
Remote loopback[b]	21
Transmit signal element timing (DTE source)[a]	24, 11
Test mode[b]	25

[a]Category I circuits (RS-422A).
[b]Category II circuits (RS-423A).

between 20 kbps and 2 Mbps using the same 25-pin DB-25 connector used by the RS-232 interface. The pin functions of the RS-530 interface are essentially the same as the RS-449 category I pins with the addition of three category II pins: local loopback, remote loopback, and test mode. Table 4-12 lists the 25 pins for the RS-530 interface and their designations.

Like the RS-449 standard, the RS-530 interface standard does not specify electrical parameters. The electrical specifications for the RS-530 are outlined by either the RS-422A or the RS-423A standard. The RS-232, RS-449, and RS-530 interface standards provide specifications for answering calls, but do not provide specifications for initiating calls (i.e., dialing). The EIA has a different standard, RS-366, for automatic calling units. The principal use of the RS-366 is for dial backup of private-line data circuits and for automatic dialing of remote terminals.

4-12   DATA COMMUNICATIONS MODEMS

The most common type of data communications equipment (DEC) is the *data communications modem.* Alternate names include *datasets, dataphones,* or simply *modems.* The word *modem* is a contraction derived from the words *modulator* and *demodulator.*

In the 1960s, the business world recognized a rapidly increasing need to exchange digital information between computers, computer terminals, and other computer-controlled equipment separated by substantial distances. The only transmission facilities available at the time were analog voice-band telephone circuits. Telephone circuits were designed for transporting analog voice signals within a bandwidth of approximately 300 Hz to 3000 Hz. In addition, telephone circuits often included amplifiers and other analog devices that could not propagate digital signals. Therefore, voice-band data modems were designed to communicate with each other using analog signals that occupied the same bandwidth used for standard voice telephone communications. Data communications modems designed to operate over the limited bandwidth of the public telephone network are called *voice-band modems.*

Because digital information cannot be transported directly over analog transmission media (at least not in digital form), the primary purpose of a *data communications modem* is to interface computers, computer networks, and other digital terminal equipment to analog communications facilities. Modems are also used when computers are too far apart to be directly interconnected using standard computer cables. In the transmitter (modulator) section of a modem, digital signals are encoded onto an analog carrier. The digital signals modulate the carrier, producing digitally modulated analog signals that are capable of being transported through the analog communications media. Therefore, the output of a modem is an analog signal that is carrying digital information. In the receiver section of a modem, digitally modulated analog signals are demodulated. Demodulation is the reverse process of modulation. Therefore, modem receivers (demodulators) simply extract digital information from digitally modulated analog carriers.

The most common (and simplest) modems available are ones intended to be used to interface DTEs through a serial interface to standard voice-band telephone lines and provide reliable data transmission rates from 300 bps to 56 kbps. These types of modems are sometimes called *telephone-loop modems* or *POTS modems,* as they are connected to the telephone company through the same local loops that are used for voice telephone circuits. More sophisticated modems (sometimes called *broadband modems*) are also available that are capable of transporting data at much higher bit rates over wideband communications channels, such as those available with optical fiber, coaxial cable, microwave radio, and satellite communications systems. Broadband modems can operate using a different set of standards and protocols than telephone loop modems.

A modem is, in essence, a transparent repeater that converts electrical signals received in digital form to electrical signals in analog form and vice versa. A modem is transparent, as it does not interpret or change the information contained in the data. It is a repeater, as it is not a destination for data—it simply repeats or retransmits data. A modem is physically located between digital terminal equipment (DTE) and the analog communications channel. Modems work in pairs with one located at each end of a data communications circuit. The two modems do not need to be manufactured by the same company; however, they must use compatible modulation schemes, data encoding formats, and transmission rates.

Figure 4-27 shows how a typical modem is used to facilitate the transmission of digital data between DTEs over a POTS telephone circuit. At the transmit end, a modem receives discrete digital pulses (which are usually in binary form) from a DTE through a serial digital interface (such as the RS-232). The DCE converts the digital pulses to analog signals. In essence, a modem transmitter is a *digital-to-analog converter* (DAC). The analog signals are then outputted onto an analog communications channel where they are transported through the system to a distant receiver. The equalizers and bandpass filters shape and band-limit the signal. At the destination end of a data communications system, a modem receives analog signals from the communications channel and converts them to digital pulses. In essence, a modem receiver is an *analog-to-digital converter* (ADC). The demodulated digital pulses are then outputted onto a serial digital interface and transported to the DTE.

FIGURE 4-27 Data communications modems - POTS analog channel

4-12-1　Bits per Second versus Baud

The parameters *bits per second* (bps) and *baud* are often misunderstood and, consequently, misused. Baud, like bit rate, is a rate of change; however, baud refers to the rate of change of the signal on the transmission medium after encoding and modulation have occurred. Bit rate refers to the rate of change of a digital information signal, which is usually binary. Baud is the reciprocal of the time of one output *signaling element,* and a signaling element may represent several information bits. A signaling element is sometimes called a *symbol* and could be encoded as a change in the amplitude, frequency, or phase. For example, binary signals are generally encoded and transmitted one bit at a time in the form of discrete voltage levels representing logic 1s (highs) and logic 0s (lows). A baud is also transmitted one at a time; however, a baud may represent more than one information bit. Thus, the baud of a data communications system may be considerably less than the bit rate.

4-12-2　Bell System–Compatible Modems

At one time, Bell System modems were virtually the only modems in existence. This is because AT&T operating companies once owned 90% of the telephone companies in the United States, and the AT&T operating tariff allowed only equipment manufactured by Western Electric Company (WECO) and furnished by Bell System operating companies to be connected to AT&T telephone lines. However, in 1968, AT&T lost a landmark Supreme Court decision, the *Carterfone decision,* which allowed equipment manufactured by non-Bell companies to interconnect to the vast AT&T communications network, provided that the equipment met Bell System specifications. The Carterfone decision began the *interconnect industry,* which has led to competitive data communications offerings by a large number of independent companies.

　　The operating parameters for Bell System modems are the models from which the international standards specified by the ITU-T evolved. Bell System modem specifications apply only to modems that existed in 1968; therefore, their specifications pertain only to modems operating at data transmission rate of 9600 bps or less. Table 4-11 summarizes the parameters for Bell System–equivalent modems.

4-12-3　Modem Block Diagram

Figure 4-28 shows a simplified block diagram for a data communications modem. For simplicity, only the primary functional blocks of the transmitter and receiver are shown.

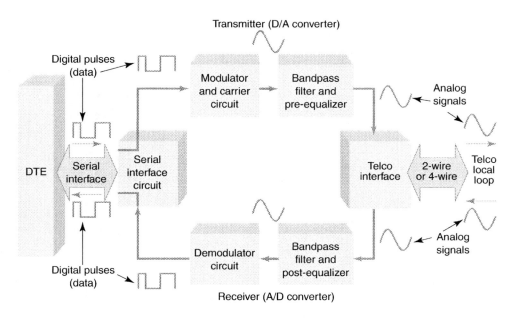

FIGURE 4-28　Simplified block diagram for an asynchronous FSK modem

The basic principle behind a modem transmitter is to convert information received from the DTE in the form of binary digits (bits) to digitally modulated analog signals. The reverse process is accomplished in the modem receiver.

The primary blocks of a modem are described here:

1. *Serial interface circuit.* Interfaces the modem transmitter and receiver to the serial interface. The transmit section accepts digital information from the serial interface, converts it to the appropriate voltage levels, and then directs the information to the modulator. The receive section receives digital information from the demodulator circuit, converts it to the appropriate voltage levels, and then directs the information to the serial interface. In addition, the serial interface circuit manages the flow of control, timing, and data information transferred between the DTE and the modem, which includes handshaking signals and clocking information.

2. *Modulator circuit.* Receives digital information from the serial interface circuit. The digital information modulates an analog carrier, producing a digitally modulated analog signal. In essence, the modulator converts digital changes in the information to analog changes in the carrier. The output from the modulator is directed to the transmit bandpass filter and equalizer circuit.

3. *Bandpass filter and equalizer circuit.* There are bandpass filter and equalizer circuits in both the transmitter and receiver sections of the modem. The transmit bandpass filter limits the bandwidth of the digitally modulated analog signals to a bandwidth appropriate for transmission over a standard telephone circuit. The receive bandpass filter limits the bandwidth of the signals allowed to reach the demodulator circuit, thus reducing noise and improving system performance. Equalizer circuits compensate for bandwidth and gain imperfections typically experienced on voiceband telephone lines.

4. *Telco interface circuit.* The primary functions of the telco interface circuit are to match the impedance of the modem to the impedance of the telephone line and regulate the amplitude of the transmit signal. The interface also provides electrical isolation and protection and serves as the demarcation (separation) point between subscriber equipment and telephone company–provided equipment. The telco line can be two-wire or four-wire, and the modem can operate half or full duplex. When the telephone line is two wire, the telco interface circuit would have to perform four-wire-to-two-wire and two-wire-to-four-wire conversions.

5. *Demodulator circuit.* Receives modulated signals from the bandpass filter and equalizer circuit and converts the digitally modulated analog signals to digital signals. The output from the demodulator is directed to the serial interface circuit, where it is passed on to the serial interface.

6. *Carrier and clock generation circuit.* The carrier generation circuit produces the analog carriers necessary for the modulation and demodulation processes. The clock generation circuit generates the appropriate clock and timing signals required for performing transmit and receive functions in an orderly and timely fashion.

4-12-4 Modem Classifications

Data communications modems can be generally classified as either *asynchronous* or *synchronous* and use one of the following digital modulation schemes: amplitude-shift keying (ASK), frequency-shift keying (FSK), phase-shift keying (PSK), or quadrature amplitude modulation (QAM). However, there are several additional ways modems can be classified, depending on which features or capabilities you are trying to distinguish. For example, modems can be categorized as internal or external; low speed, medium speed, high speed, or very high speed; wide band or voice band; and personal or commercial. Regardless of how modems are classified, they all share a common goal, namely, to convert digital pulses to analog signals in the transmitter and analog signals to digital pulses in the receiver.

Some of the common features provided data communications modems are listed here:

1. Automatic dialing, answering, and redialing
2. Error control (detection and correction)
3. Caller ID recognition
4. Self-test capabilities, including analog and digital loopback tests
5. Fax capabilities (transmit and receive)
6. Data compression and expansion
7. Telephone directory (telephone number storage)
8. Adaptive transmit and receive data transmission rates (300 bps to 56 kbps)
9. Automatic equalization
10. Synchronous or asynchronous operation

4-12-5 Asynchronous Voice-Band Modems

Asynchronous modems can be generally classified as low-speed voice-band modems, as they are typically used to transport asynchronous data (i.e., data framed with start and stop bits). Synchronous data are sometimes used with an asynchronous modem; however, it is not particularly practical or economical. Synchronous data transported by asynchronous modems is called *isochronous transmission.* Asynchronous modems use relatively simple modulation schemes, such as ASK or FSK, and are restricted to relatively low-speed applications (generally less than 2400 bps), such as telemetry and caller ID.

There are several standard asynchronous modems designed for low-speed data applications using the switched public telephone network. To operate full duplex with a two-wire dial-up circuit, it is necessary to divide the usable bandwidth of a voice-band circuit in half, creating two equal-capacity data channels. A popular modem that does this is the Bell System 103–compatible modem.

4-12-5-1 Bell system 103–compatible modem.
The 103 modem is capable of full-duplex operation over a two-wire telephone line at bit rates up to 300 bps. With the 103 modem, there are two data channels, each with their own mark and space frequencies. One data channel is called the *low-band channel* and occupies a bandwidth from 300 Hz to 1650 Hz (i.e., the lower half of the usable voice band). A second data channel, called the *high-band channel,* occupies a bandwidth from 1650 Hz to 3000 Hz (i.e., the upper half of the usable voice band). The mark and space frequencies for the low-band channel are 1270 Hz and 1070 Hz, respectively. The mark and space frequencies for the high-band channel are 2225 Hz and 2025 Hz, respectively. Separating the usable bandwidth into two narrower bands is called *frequency-division multiplexing* (FDM). FDM allows full-duplex (FDX) transmission over a two-wire circuit, as signals can propagate in both directions at the same time without interfering with each other because the frequencies for the two directions of propagation are different. FDM allows full-duplex operation over a two-wire telephone circuit. Because FDM reduces the effective bandwidth in each direction, it also reduces the maximum data transmission rates. A 103 modem operates at 300 baud and is capable of simultaneous transmission and reception of 300 bps.

4-12-5-2 Bell system 202T/S modem.
The 202T and 202S modem are identical except the 202T modem specifies four-wire, full-duplex operation, and the 202S modem specifies two-wire, half-duplex operation. Therefore, the 202T is utilized on four-wire private-line data circuits, and the 202S modem is designed for the two-wire switched public telephone network. Probably the most common application of the 202 modem today is caller ID, which is a simplex system with the transmitter in the telephone office and the receiver at the subscriber's location. The 202 modem is an asynchronous 1200-baud transceiver utilizing FSK with a transmission bit rate of 1200 bps over a standard voice-grade telephone line.

Synchronous modems use PSK or quadrature amplitude modulation (QAM) to transport synchronous data (i.e., data preceded by unique SYN characters) at transmission rates between 2400 bps and 56,000 bps over standard voice-grade telephone lines. The modulated carrier is transmitted to the distant modem, where a coherent carrier is recovered and used to demodulate the data. The transmit clock is recovered from the data and used to clock the received data into the DTE. Because of the addition of clock and carrier recovery circuits, synchronous modems are more complicated and, thus, more expensive than asynchronous modems.

PSK is commonly used in medium speed synchronous voice-band modems, typically operating between 2400 bps and 4800 bps. More specifically, QPSK is generally used with 2400-bps modems and 8-PSK with 4800-bps modems. QPSK has a bandwidth efficiency of 2 bps/Hz; therefore, the baud rate and minimum bandwidth for a 2400-bps synchronous modem are 1200 baud and 1200 Hz, respectively. The standard 2400-bps synchronous modem is the Bell System 201C or equivalent. The 201C modem uses a 1600-Hz carrier frequency and has an output spectrum that extends from approximately 1000 Hz to 2200 Hz. Because 8-PSK has a bandwidth efficiency of 3 bps/Hz, the baud rate and minimum bandwidth for 4800-bps synchronous modems are 1600 baud and 1600 Hz, respectively. The standard 4800-bps synchronous modem is the Bell System 208A. The 208A modem also uses a 1600-Hz carrier frequency but has an output spectrum that extends from approximately 800 Hz to 2400 Hz. Both the 201C and the 208A are full-duplex modems designed to be used with four-wire private-line circuits. The 201C and 208A modems can operate over two-wire dial-up circuits but only in the simplex mode. There are also half-duplex two-wire versions of both modems: the 201B and 208B.

High-speed synchronous voice-band modems operate at 9600 bps and use 16-QAM modulation. 16-QAM has a bandwidth efficiency of 4 bps/Hz; therefore, the baud and minimum bandwidth for 9600-bps synchronous modems is 2400 baud and 2400 Hz, respectively. The standard 9600-bps modem is the Bell System 209A or equivalent. The 209A uses a 1650-Hz carrier frequency and has an output spectrum that extends from approximately 450 Hz to 2850 Hz. The Bell System 209A is a four-wire synchronous voice-band modem designed to be used on full-duplex private-line circuits. The 209B is the two-wire version designed for half-duplex operation on dial-up circuits.

Table 4-13 summarizes the Bell System voice-band modem specifications. The modems listed in the table are all relatively low speed by modern standards. Today, the Bell System–compatible modems are used primarily on relatively simple telemetry circuits, such as remote alarm systems and on metropolitan and wide-area private-line data networks, such as those used by department stores to keep track of sales and inventory. The more advanced, higher-speed data modems are described in a later section of this chapter.

4-12-7 Modem Synchronization

During the request-to-send/clear-to-send (RTS/CTS) delay, a transmit modem outputs a special, internally generated bit pattern called a *training sequence*. This bit pattern is used to synchronize (train) the receive modem at the distant end of the communications channel. Depending on the type of modulation, transmission bit rate, and modem complexity, the training sequence accomplishes one or more of the following functions:

1. Initializes the communications channel, which includes disabling echo and establishing the gain of automatic gain control (AGC) devices
2. Verifies continuity (activates RLSD in the receive modem)
3. Initialize descrambler circuits in receive modem
4. Initialize automatic equalizers in receive modem
5. Synchronize the receive modem's carrier to the transmit modem's carrier
6. Synchronize the receive modem's clock to the transmit modem's clock

Table 4-13   Bell System Modem Specifications

Bell System Designation	Transmission Facility	Operating Mode	Circuit Arrangement	Synchronization Mode	Modulation	Transmission Rate
103	Dial-up	FDM/FDX	Two wire	Asynchronous	FSK	300 bps
113A/B	Dial-up	FDM/FDX	Two wire	Asynchronous	FSK	300 bps
201B	Dial-up	HDX	Two wire	Synchronous	QPSK	2400 bps
201C	Private line	FDX	Four wire	Synchronous	QPSK	2400 bps
202S	Dial-up	HDX	Two wire	Asynchronous	FSK	1200 bps
202T	Private line	FDX	Four wire	Asynchronous	FSK	1800 bps
208A	Private line	FDX	Four wire	Synchronous	8-PSK	4800 bps
208B	Dial-up	HDX	Two wire	Synchronous	8-PSK	4800 bps
209A	Private line	FDX	Four wire	Synchronous	16-QAM	9600 bps
209B	Dial-up	HDX	Two wire	Synchronous	16-QAM	9600 bps
212A	Dial up	HDX	Two wire	Asynchronous	FSK	600 bps
212B	Private line	FDX	Four wire	Synchronous	QPSK	1200 bps

Dial-up = switched telephone network
Private line = dedicated circuit
FDM = frequency-division multiplexing
HDX = half duplex
FDX = full duplex
FSK = frequency-shift keying
QPSK = four-phase PSK
8-PSK = eight-phase PSK
16-QAM = 16-state QAM

4-12-8   Modem Equalizers

Equalization is the compensation for phase delay distortion and amplitude distortion inherently present on telephone communications channels. One form of equalization provided by the telephone company is C-type conditioning, which is available only on private-line circuits. Additional equalization may be performed by the modems themselves. *Compromise equalizers* are located in the transmit section of a modem and provide *preequalization*—they shape the transmitted signal by altering its delay and gain characteristics before the signal reaches the telephone line. It is an attempt by the modem to compensate for impairments anticipated in the bandwidth parameters of the communications line. When a modem is installed, the compromise equalizers are manually adjusted to provide the best error performance. Typically, compromise equalizers affect the following:

1. Amplitude only
2. Delay only
3. Amplitude and delay
4. Neither amplitude nor delay

Compromise equalizer settings may be applied to either the high- or low-voice-band frequencies or symmetrically to both at the same time. Once a compromise equalizer setting has been selected, it can be changed only manually. The setting that achieves the best error performance is dependent on the electrical length of the circuit and the type of facilities that comprise it (i.e., one or more of the following: twisted-pair cable, coaxial cable, optical fiber cable, microwave, digital T-carriers, and satellite).

Adaptive equalizers are located in the receiver section of a modem, where they provide postequalization to the received signals. Adaptive equalizers automatically adjust their gain and delay characteristics to compensate for phase and amplitude impairments encountered on the communications channel. Adaptive equalizers may determine the quality of the received signal within its own circuitry, or they may acquire this information from the demodulator or descrambler circuits. Whatever the case, the adaptive equalizer may continuously vary its settings to achieve the best overall bandwidth characteristics for the circuit.

4-13 ITU-T MODEM RECOMMENDATIONS

Since the late 1980s, the International Telecommunications Union (ITU-T, formerly CCITT), which is headquartered in Geneva, Switzerland, has developed transmission standards for data modems outside the United States. The ITU-T specifications are known as the V-series, which include a number indicating the standard (V.21, V.23, and so on). Sometimes the V-series is followed by the French word *bis,* meaning "second," which indicates that the standard is a revision of an earlier standard. If the standard includes the French word *terbo,* meaning "third," the bis standard also has been modified. Table 4-14 lists some of the ITU-T modem recommendations.

4-13-1 ITU-T Modem Recommendation V.29

The ITU-T V.29 specification is the first internationally accepted standard for a 9600-bps data transmission rate. The V.29 standard is intended to provide synchronous data transmission over four-wire leased lines. V.29 uses 16-QAM modulation of a 1700-Hz carrier frequency. Data are clocked into the modem in groups of four bits called quadbits, resulting in a 2400-baud transmission rate. Occasionally, V.29-compatible modems are used in the half-duplex mode over two-wire switched telephone lines. Pseudo full-duplex operation can be achieved over the two-wire lines using a method called *ping-pong.* With ping-pong, data sent to the modem at each end of the circuit by their respective DTE are buffered and automatically exchanged over the data link by rapidly turning the carriers on and off in succession.

Pseudo full-duplex operation over a two-wire line can also be accomplished using *statistical duplexing.* Statistical duplexing utilizes a 300-bps reverse data channel. The reverse channel allows a data operator to enter keyboard data while simultaneously receiving a file from the distant modem. By monitoring the data buffers inside the modem, the direction of data transmission can be determined, and the high- and low-speed channels can be reversed.

4-13-2 ITU-T Modem Recommendation V.32

The ITU-T V.32 specification provides for a 9600-bps data transmission rate with true full-duplex operation over four-wire leased private lines or two-wire switched telephone lines. V.32 also provides for data rates of 2400 bps and 4800 bps. V.32 specifies QAM with a carrier frequency of 1800 Hz. V.32 is similar to V.29, except with V.32 the advanced coding technique *trellis encoding* is specified (see Chapter 12). Trellis encoding produces a superior signal-to-noise ratio by dividing the incoming data stream into groups of five bits called *quintbits* (*M*-ary, where $M = 2^5 = 32$). The constellation diagram for 32-state trellis encoding was developed by Dr. Ungerboeck at the IBM Zuerich Research Laboratory and combines coding and modulation to improve bit error performance. The basic idea behind trellis encoding is to introduce controlled redundancy, which reduces channel error rates by doubling the number of signal points on the QAM constellation. The trellis encoding constellation used with V.32 is shown in Figure 4-29.

Full-duplex operation over two-wire switched telephone lines is achieved with V.32 using a technique called *echo cancellation.* Echo cancellation involves adding an inverted replica of the transmitted signal to the received signal. This allows the data transmitted from each modem to simultaneously use the same carrier frequency, modulation scheme, and bandwidth.

4-13-3 ITU-T Modem Recommendation V.32bis and V.32terbo

ITU-T recommendation V.32bis was introduced in 1991 and created a new benchmark for the data modem industry by allowing transmission bit rates of 14.4 kbps over standard

Table 4-14   ITU-T V-Series Modem Standards

ITU-T Designation	Specification
V.1	Defines binary 0/1 data bits as space/mark line conditions
V.2	Limits output power levels of modems used on telephone lines
V.4	Sequence of bits within a transmitted character
V.5	Standard synchronous signaling rates for dial-up telephone lines
V.6	Standard synchronous signaling rates for private leased communications lines
V.7	List of modem terminology in English, Spanish, and French
V.10	Unbalanced high-speed electrical interface specifications (similar to RS-423)
V.11	Balanced high-speed electrical interface specifications (similar to RS-422)
V.13	Simulated carrier control for full-duplex modem operating in the half-duplex mode
V.14	Asynchronous-to-synchronous conversion
V.15	Acoustical couplers
V.16	Electrocardiogram transmission over telephone lines
V.17	Application-specific modulation scheme for Group III fax (provides two-wire, half-duplex trellis-coded transmission at 7.2 kbps, 9.6 kbps, 12 kbps, and 14.4 kbps)
V.19	Low-speed parallel data transmission using DTMF modems
V.20	Parallel data transmission modems
V.21	0-to-300 bps full-duplex two-wire modems similar to Bell System 103
V.22	1200/600 bps full-duplex modems for switched or dedicated lines
V.22bis	1200/2400 bps two-wire modems for switched or dedicated lines
V.23	1200/75 bps modems (host transmits 1200 bps and terminal transmits 75 bps). V.23 also supports 600 bps in the high channel speed. V.23 is similar to Bell System 202. V.23 is used in Europe to support some videotext applications.
V.24	Known in the United States as RS-232. V.24 defines only the functions of the interface circuits, whereas RS-232 also defines the electrical characteristics of the connectors.
V.25	Automatic answering equipment and parallel automatic dialing similar to Bell System 801 (defines the 2100-Hz answer tone that modems send)
V.25bis	Serial automatic calling and answering—CCITT equivalent to the Hayes AT command set used in the United States
V.26	2400-bps four-wire modems identical to Bell System 201 for four-wire leased lines
V.26bis	2400/1200 bps half-duplex modems similar to Bell System 201 for two-wire switched lines
V.26terbo	2400/1200 bps full-duplex modems for switched lines using echo canceling
V.27	4800 bps four-wire modems for four-wire leased lines similar to Bell System 208 with manual equalization
V.27bis	4800/2400 bps four-wire modems same as V.27 except with automatic equalization
V.28	Electrical characteristics for V.24
V.29	9600-bps four-wire full-duplex modems similar to Bell System 209 for leased lines
V.31	Older electrical characteristics rarely used today
V.31bis	V.31 using optocouplers
V.32	9600/4800 bps full-duplex modems for switched or leased facilities
V.32bis	4.8-kbps, 7.2-kbps, 9.6-kbps, 12-kbps, and 14.4-kbps modems and rapid rate regeneration for full-duplex leased lines
V.32terbo	Same as V.32bis except with the addition of adaptive speed leveling, which boosts transmission rates to as high as 21.6 kbps
V.33	12.2 kbps and 14.4 kbps for four-wire leased communications lines
V.34	(V. fast) 28.8-kbps data rates without compression
V.34+	Enhanced specifications of V.34
V.35	48-kbps four-wire modems (no longer used)
V.36	48-kbps four-wire full-duplex modems
V.37	72-kbps four-wire full-duplex modems
V.40	Method teletypes use to indicate parity errors
V.41	An older obsolete error-control scheme
V.42	Error-correcting procedures for modems using asynchronous-to-synchronous conversion (V.22, B.22bis, V.26terbo, V.32, and V.32bis, and LAP M protocol)
V.42bis	Lempel-Ziv-based data compression scheme used with V.42 LAP M
V.50	Standard limits for transmission quality for modems
V.51	Maintenance of international data circuits

(Continued)

Table 4-14 (*Continued*)

ITU-T Designation	Specification
V.52	Apparatus for measuring distortion and error rates for data transmission
V.53	Impairment limits for data circuits
V.54	Loop test devices of modems
V.55	Impulse noise-measuring equipment
V.56	Comparative testing of modems
V.57	Comprehensive tests set for high-speed data transmission
V.90	Asymmetrical data transmission—receive data rates up to 56 kbps but restricts transmission bit rates to 33.6 kbps
V.92	Asymmetrical data transmission—receive data rates up to 56 kbps but restricts transmission bit rates to 48 kbps
V.100	Interconnection between public data networks and public switched telephone networks
V.110	ISDN terminal adaptation
V.120	ISDN terminal adaptation with statistical multiplexing
V.230	General data communications interface, ISO layer 1

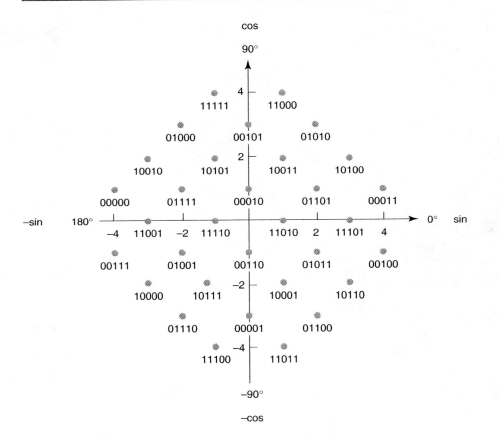

FIGURE 4-29   V.32 constellation diagram using Trellis encoding

voice-band telephone channels. V.32bis uses a 64-point signal constellation with each signaling condition representing six bits of data. The constellation diagram for V.32 is shown in Figure 4-30. The transmission bit rate for V.32 is six bits/code × 2400 codes/second = 14,400 bps. The signaling rate (baud) is 2400.

V.32bis also includes automatic *fall-forward* and *fall-back* features that allow the modem to change its transmission rate to accommodate changes in the quality of the commu-

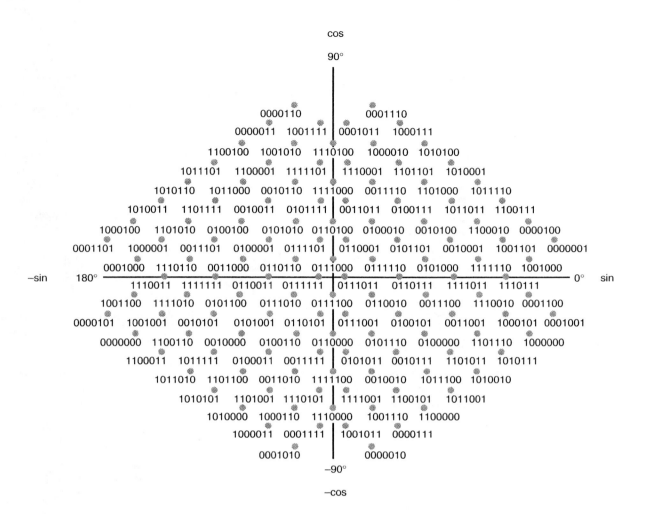

FIGURE 4-30   V.33 signal constellation diagram using Trellis encoding

nications line. The fall-back feature slowly reduces the transmission bit rate to 12.2 kbps, 9.6 kbps, or 4.8 kbps if the quality of the communications line degrades. The fall-forward feature gives the modem the ability to return to the higher transmission rate when the quality of the communications channel improves. V.32bis support Group III fax, which is the transmission standard that outlines the connection procedures used between two fax machines or fax modems. V.32bis also specifies the data compression procedure used during transmissions.

In August 1993, U.S. Robotics introduced V.32terbo. V.32terbo includes all the features of V.32bis plus a proprietary technology called *adaptive speed leveling*. V.32terbo includes two categories of new features: increased data rates and enhanced fax abilities. V.32terbo also outlines the new 19.2-kbps data transmission rate developed by AT&T.

4-13-4   ITU-T Modem Recommendation V.33

ITU-T specification V.33 is intended for modems that operate over dedicated two-point, private-line four-wire circuits. V.33 uses trellis coding and is similar to V.32 except a V.33 signaling element includes six information bits and one redundant bit, resulting in a data transmission rate of 14.4 kbps, 2400 baud, and an 1800-Hz carrier. The 128-point constellation used with V.33 is shown in Figure 4-30.

4-13-5 ITU-T Modem Recommendation V.42 and V.42bis

In 1988, the ITU adopted the V.42 standard *error-correcting procedures for DCEs* (modems). V.42 specifications address asynchronous-to-synchronous transmission conversions and error control that includes both detection and correction. V.42's primary purpose specifies a relatively new modem protocol called Link Access Procedures for Modems (LAP M). LAP M is almost identical to the packet-switching protocol used with the X.25 standard.

V.42bis is a specification designed to enhance the error-correcting capabilities of modems that implement the V.42 standard. Modems employing data compression schemes have proven to significantly surpass the data throughput performance of the predecessors. The V.42bis standard is capable of achieving somewhere between 3-to-1 and 4-to-1 compression ratios for ASCII-coded text. The compression algorithm specified is British Telecom's BTLZ. Throughput rates of up to 56 kbps can be achieved using V.42bis data compression.

4-13-6 ITU-T Modem Recommendation V.32 (V.fast)

Officially adopted in 1994, V.fast is considered the next generation in data transmission. Data rates of 28.8 kbps without compression are possible using V.34. Using current data compression techniques, V.fast modems will be able to transmit data at two to three times current data rates. V.32 automatically adapts to changes in transmission-line characteristics and dynamically adjusts data rates either up or down, depending on the quality of the communication channel.

V.34 innovations include the following:

1. Nonlinear coding, which offsets the adverse effects of system nonlinearities that produce harmonic and intermodulation distortion and amplitude proportional noise
2. Multidimensional coding and constellation shaping, which enhance data immunity to channel noise
3. Reduced complexity in decoders found in receivers
4. Precoding of data for more of the available bandwidth of the communications channel to be used by improving transmission of data in the outer limits of the channel where amplitude, frequency, and phase distortion are at their worst
5. Line probing, which is a technique that receive modems to rapidly determine the best correction to compensate for transmission-line impairments

4-13-7 ITU-T Modem Recommendation V.34+

V.34+ is an enhanced standard adopted by the ITU in 1996. V.34+ adds 31.2 kbps and 33.6 kbps to the V.34 specification. Theoretically, V.34+ adds 17% to the transmission rate; however, it is not significant enough to warrant serious consideration at this time.

4-13-8 ITU-T Modem Recommendation V.90

The ITU-T developed the V.90 specification in February 1998 during a meeting in Geneva, Switzerland. The V.90 recommendation is similar to 3COM's x2 and Lucent's K56flex in that it defines an asymmetrical data transmission technology where the upstream and downstream data rates are not the same. V.90 allows modem downstream (receive) data rates up to 56 kbps and upstream (transmit) data rates up to 33.6 kbps. These data rates are inappropriate in the United States and Canada, as the FCC and CRTC limit transmission rates offered by telephone companies to no more than 53 kbps.

4-13-9 ITU-T Modem Recommendation V.92

In 2000, the ITU approved a new modem standard called V.92. V.92 offers three improvements over V.90 that can be achieved only if both the transmit and receive modems and the Internet Service Provider (ISP) have V.92 compliant modems. V.92 offers (1) upstream transmission rate of 48 kbps, (2) faster call setup capabilities, and (3) incorporation of a hold option.

4-1. Define *data communications code.*

4-2. Give some of the alternate names for data communications codes.

4-3. Briefly describe the following data communications codes: Baudot, ASCII, and EBCDIC.

4-4. Describe the basic concepts of *bar codes.*

4-5. Describe a *discrete bar code; continuous bar code; 2D bar code.*

4-6. Explain the encoding formats used with *Code 39* and *UPC* bar codes.

4-7. Describe what is meant by *error control.*

4-8. Explain the difference between *error detection* and *error correction.*

4-9. Describe the difference between *redundancy* and *redundancy checking.*

4-10. Explain *vertical redundancy checking.*

4-11. Define *odd parity; even parity; marking parity.*

4-12. Explain the difference between *no parity* and *ignored parity.*

4-13. Describe how checksums are used for error detection.

4-14. Explain *longitudinal redundancy checking.*

4-15. Describe the difference between *character* and *message parity.*

4-16. Describe *cyclic redundancy checking.*

4-17. Define *forward error correction.*

4-18. Explain the difference between using *ARQ* and a *Hamming code.*

4-19. What is meant by *character synchronization*?

4-20. Compare and contrast *asynchronous* and *synchronous serial data formats.*

4-21. Describe the basic format used with asynchronous data.

4-22. Define the *start* and *stop bits.*

4-23. Describe *synchronous data.*

4-24. What is a *SYN character*?

4-25. Define and give some examples of *data terminal equipment.*

4-26. Define and give examples of *data communications equipment.*

4-27. List and describe the basic components that make up a *data communications circuit.*

4-28. Define *line control unit* and describe its basic functions in a data communications circuit.

4-29. Describe the basic functions performed by a *UART.*

4-30. Describe the operation of a UART transmitter and receiver.

4-31. Explain the operation of a *start bit verification circuit.*

4-32. Explain *clock slippage* and describe the effects of *slipping over* and *slipping under.*

4-33. Describe the differences between UARTs, USRTs, and USARTs.

4-34. List the features provided by *serial interfaces.*

4-35. Describe the purpose of a serial interface.

4-36. Describe the physical, electrical, and functional characteristics of the *RS-232 interface.*

4-37. Describe the *RS-449 interface* and give the primary differences between it and the RS-232 interface.

4-38. Describe *data communications modems* and explain where they are used in data communications circuits.

4-39. What is meant by a *Bell System–compatible* modem?

4-40. What is the difference between *asynchronous* and *synchronous* modems?

4-41. Define *modem synchronization* and list its functions.

4-42. Describe modem *equalization.*

4-43. Briefly describe the following ITU-T modem recommendations: V.29, V.32, V.32bis, V.32terbo, V.33, V.42, V.42bis, V.32fast, and V.34+.

4-1. Determine the hex codes for the following Baudot codes: C, J, 4, and /.

4-2. Determine the hex codes for the following ASCII codes: C, J, 4, and /.

4-3. Determine the hex codes for the following EBCDIC codes: C, J, 4, and /.

4-4. Determine the left- and right-hand UPC label format for the digit 4.

4-5. Determine the LRC and VRC for the following message (use even parity for LRC and odd parity for VCR):

D A T A sp C O M M U N I C A T I O N S

4-6. Determine the LRC and VRC for the following message (use even parity for LRC and odd parity for VCR):

A S C I I sp C O D E

4-7. Determine the BCS for the following data- and CRC-generating polynomials:

$$G(x) = x^7 + x^4 + x^2 + x^0 = 1\,0\,0\,1\,0\,1\,0\,1$$
$$P(x) = x^5 + x^4 + x^1 + x^0 = 1\,1\,0\,0\,1\,1$$

4-8. Determine the BCC for the following data- and CRC-generating polynomials:

$$G(x) = x^8 + x^5 + x^2 + x^0$$
$$P(x) = x^5 + x^4 + x^1 + x^0$$

4-9. How many Hamming bits are required for a single EBCDIC character?

4-10. Determine the Hamming bits for the ASCII character "B." Insert the hamming bits into every other bit location starting from the left.

4-11. Determine the Hamming bits for the ASCII character "C" (use odd parity and two stop bits). Insert the Hamming bits into every other location starting at the right.

4-12. Determine the noise margins for an RS-232 interface with driver output signal voltages of ±12 V.

4-13. Determine the noise margins for an RS-232 interface with driver output signal voltages of ±11 V.

CHAPTER 5

Data-Link Protocols and Data Communications Networks

OBJECTIVES

- Define *data-link protocol*
- Define and describe the following data-link protocol functions: line discipline, flow control, and error control
- Define *character-* and *bit-oriented protocols*
- Describe asynchronous data-link protocols
- Describe synchronous data-link protocols
- Explain binary synchronous communications
- Define and describe *synchronous data-link control*
- Define and describe *high-level data-link control*
- Describe the concept of a public data network
- Describe the X.25 protocol
- Define and describe the basic concepts of asynchronous transfer mode
- Explain the basic concepts of integrated services digital network
- Define and describe the fundamental concepts of local area networks
- Describe the fundamental concepts of Ethernet
- Describe the differences between the various types of Ethernet
- Describe the Ethernet II and IEEE 802.3 frame formats

The primary goal of *network architecture* is to give users of a network the tools necessary for setting up the network and performing data flow control. A network architecture outlines the way in which a data communications network is arranged or structured and generally includes the concepts of levels or layers within the architecture. Each layer within the network consists of specific *protocols* or rules for communicating that perform a given set of functions.

Protocols are arrangements between people or processes. A *data-link protocol* is a set of rules implementing and governing an orderly exchange of data between layer two devices, such as line control units and front-end processors.

5-2 DATA-LINK PROTOCOL FUNCTIONS

For communications to occur over a data network, there must be at least two devices working together (one transmitting and one receiving). In addition, there must be some means of controlling the exchange of data. For example, most communication between computers on networks is conducted half duplex even though the circuits that interconnect them may be capable of operating full duplex. Most data communications networks, especially local area networks, transfer data half duplex where only one device can transmit at a time. Half-duplex operation requires coordination between stations. Data-link protocols perform certain network functions that ensure a coordinated transfer of data. Some data networks designate one station as the *control station* (sometimes called the *primary station*). This is sometimes referred to as *primary-secondary* communications. In centrally controlled networks, the primary station enacts procedures that determine which station is transmitting and which is receiving. The transmitting station is sometimes called the *master station,* whereas the receiving station is called the *slave station.* In primary-secondary networks, there can never be more than one master at a time; however, there may be any number of slave stations. In another type of network, all stations are equal, and any station can transmit at any time. This type of network is sometimes called a *peer-to-peer network.* In a peer-to-peer network, all stations have equal access to the network, but when they have a message to transmit, they must contend with the other stations on the network for access to the transmission medium.

Data-link protocol *functions* include line discipline, flow control, and error control. *Line discipline* coordinates hop-to-hop data delivery where a hop may be a computer, a network controller, or some type of network-connecting device, such as a router. *Line discipline* determines which device is transmitting and which is receiving at any point in time. *Flow control* coordinates the rate at which data are transported over a link and generally provides an acknowledgment mechanism that ensures that data are received at the destination. *Error control* specifies means of detecting and correcting transmission errors.

5-2-1 Line Discipline

In essence, line discipline is coordinating half-duplex transmission on a data communications network. There are two fundamental ways that line discipline is accomplished in a data communications network: *enquiry/acknowledgment* (ENQ/ACK) and *poll/select.*

5-2-1-1 ENQ/ACK.

Enquiry/acknowledgment (ENQ/ACK) is a relatively simple data-link-layer line discipline that works best in simple network environments where there is no doubt as to which station is the intended receiver. An example is a network comprised of only two stations (i.e., a two-point network) where the stations may be interconnected permanently (hardwired) or on a temporary basis through a switched network, such as the public telephone network.

Before data can be transferred between stations, procedures must be invoked that establish logical continuity between the source and destination stations and ensure that the destination station is ready and capable of receiving data. These are the primary purposes of line discipline procedures. ENQ/ACK line discipline procedures determine which device on a network can initiate a transmission and whether the intended receiver is available and ready to receive a message. Assuming all stations on the network have equal access to the transmission medium, a data session can be initiated by any station using ENQ/ACK. An exception would be a receive-only device, such as most printers, which cannot initiate a session with a computer.

The initiating station begins a session by transmitting a *frame, block,* or *packet* of data called an *enquiry* (ENQ), which identifies the receiving station. There does not seem to be any universally accepted standard definition of frames, blocks, and packets other than by size. Typically, packets are smaller than frames or blocks, although sometimes the term *packet* means only the information and not any overhead that may be included with the message. The terms *block* and *frame,* however, can usually be used interchangeably.

In essence, the ENQ sequence solicits the receiving station to determine if it is ready to receive a message. With half-duplex operation, after the initiating station sends an ENQ, it waits for a response from the destination station indicating its readiness to receive a message. If the destination station is ready to receive, it responds with a *positive acknowledgment* (ACK), and if it is not ready to receive, it responds with a *negative acknowledgment* (NAK). If the destination station does not respond with an ACK or a NAK within a specified period of time, the initiating station retransmits the ENQ. How many enquiries are made varies from network to network, but generally after three unsuccessful attempts to establish communications, the initiating station gives up (this is sometimes called a *time-out*). The initiating station may attempt to establish a session later, however, after several unsuccessful attempts; the problem is generally referred to a higher level of authority (such as a human).

A NAK transmitted by the destination station in response to an ENQ generally indicates a temporary unavailability, and the initiating station will simply attempt to establish a session later. An ACK from the destination station indicates that it is ready to receive data and tells the initiating station it is free to transmit its message. All transmitted message frames end with a unique terminating sequence, such as *end of transmission* (EOT), which indicates the end of the message frame. The destination station acknowledges all message frames received with either an ACK or a NAK. An ACK transmitted in response to a received message indicates the message was received without errors, and a NAK indicates that the message was received containing errors. A NAK transmitted in response to a message is usually interpreted as an automatic request for retransmission of the rejected message.

Figure 5-1 shows how a session is established and how data are transferred using ENQ/ACK procedures. Station A initiates the session by sending an ENQ to station B. Station B responds with an ACK indicating that it is ready to receive a message. Station A transmits message frame 1, which is acknowledged by station B with an ACK. Station A then transmits message frame 2, which is rejected by station B with a NAK, indicating that the message was received with errors. Station A then retransmits message frame 2, which is received without errors and acknowledged by station B with an ACK.

5-2-1-2 Poll/select.   The poll/select line discipline is best suited to *centrally controlled* data communications networks using a multipoint topology, such as a bus, where one station or device is designated as the primary or host station and all other stations are designated as secondaries. Multipoint data communications networks using a single transmission medium must coordinate access to the transmission medium to prevent more than one station from attempting to transmit data at the same time. In addition, all exchanges of data must occur through the primary station. Therefore, if a secondary station wishes to transmit data to another secondary station, it must do so through the primary station. This is analogous to transferring data between memory devices in a computer using a central

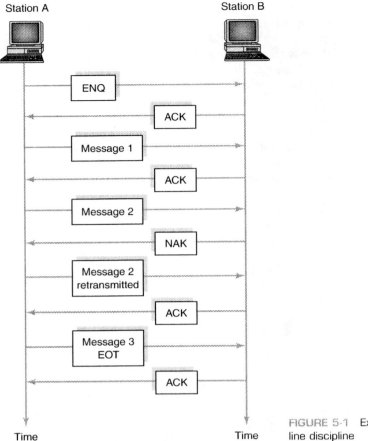

Station A   Station B

ENQ

ACK

Message 1

ACK

Message 2

NAK

Message 2
retransmitted

ACK

Message 3
EOT

ACK

Time   Time

FIGURE 5-1 Example of ENQ/ACK
line discipline

processing unit (CPU) where all data are read into the CPU from the source memory and
then written to the destination memory.

In a poll/select environment, the primary station controls the data link, while secondary stations simply respond to instructions from the primary. The primary determines
which device or station has access to the transmission channel (medium) at any given time.
Hence, the primary initiates all data transmissions on the network with polls and selections.

A *poll* is a solicitation sent from the primary to a secondary to determine if the secondary has data to transmit. In essence, the primary designates a secondary as a transmitter (i.e., the master) with a poll. A *selection* is how the primary designates a secondary as a
destination or recipient of data. A selection is also a query from the primary to determine if
the secondary is ready to receive data. With two-point networks using ENQ/ACK procedures, there was no need for addresses because transmissions from one station were obviously intended for the other station. On multipoint networks, however, addresses are necessary because all transmissions from the primary go to all secondaries, and addresses are
necessary to identify which secondary is being polled or selected. All secondary stations receive all polls and selections transmitted from the primary. With poll/select procedures,
each secondary station is assigned one or more address for identification. It is the secondaries' responsibility to examine the address and determine if the poll or selection is intended
for them. The primary has no address because transmissions from all secondary stations go
only to the primary. A primary can poll only one station at a time; however, it can select
more than one secondary at a time using *group* (more than one station) or *broadcast* (all stations) addresses.

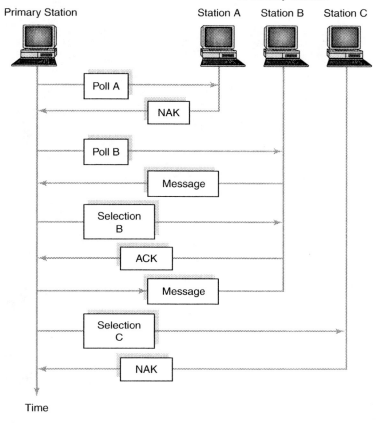

FIGURE 5-2 Example of poll/select line discipline

When a primary polls a secondary, it is soliciting the secondary for a message. If the secondary has a message to send, it responds to the poll with the message. This is called a positive acknowledgment to a poll. If the secondary has no message to send, it responds with a negative acknowledgment to the poll, which confirms that it received the poll but indicates that it has no messages to send at that time. This is called a negative acknowledgment to a poll.

When a primary selects a secondary, it is identifying the secondary as a receiver. If the secondary is available and ready to receive data, it responds with an ACK. If it is not available or ready to receive data, it responds with a NAK. These are called, respectively, positive and negative acknowledgments to a selection.

Figure 5-2 shows how polling and selections are accomplished using poll/select procedures. The primary polls station A, which responds with a negative acknowledgment to a poll (NAK) indicating it received the poll but has no message to send. Then the primary polls station B, which responds with a positive acknowledgment to a poll (i.e., a message). The primary then selects station B to see if it ready to receive a message. Station B responds with a positive acknowledgment to the selection (ACK), indicating that it is ready to receive a message. The primary transmits the message to station B. The primary then selects station C, which responds with a negative acknowledgment to the selection (NAK), indicating it is not ready to receive a message.

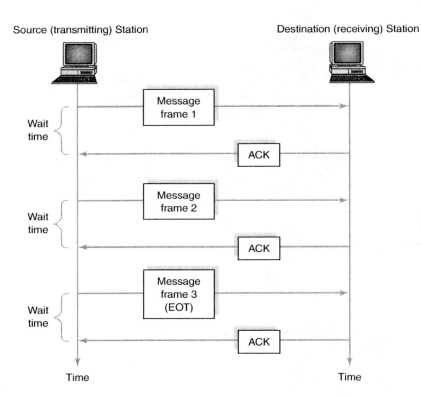

Source (transmitting) Station   Destination (receiving) Station

Wait
time

Message
frame 1

ACK

Wait
time

Message
frame 2

ACK

Wait
time

Message
frame 3
(EOT)

ACK

Time   Time

FIGURE 5-3   Example of stop-and-wait flow control

5-2-2   Flow Control

Flow control defines a set of procedures that tells the transmitting station how much data it can send before it must stop transmitting and wait for an acknowledgment from the destination station. The amount of data transmitted must not exceed the storage capacity of the destination station's buffer. Therefore, the destination station must have some means of informing the transmitting station when its buffers are nearly at capacity and telling it to temporarily stop sending data or to send data at a slower rate. There are two common methods of flow control: stop-and-wait and sliding window.

5-2-2-1 Stop-and-wait flow control.   With *stop-and-wait* flow control, the transmitting station sends one message frame and then waits for an acknowledgment before sending the next message frame. After it receives an acknowledgment, it transmits the next frame. The transmit/acknowledgment sequence continues until the source station sends an end-of-transmission sequence. The primary advantage of stop-and-wait flow control is simplicity. The primary disadvantage is speed, as the time lapse between each frame is wasted time. Each frame takes essentially twice as long to transmit as necessary because both the message and the acknowledgment must traverse the entire length of the data link before the next frame can be sent.

Figure 5-3 shows an example of stop-and-wait flow control. The source station sends message frame 1, which is acknowledged by the destination station. After stopping transmission and waiting for the acknowledgment, the source station transmits the next frame (message frame 2). After sending the second frame, there is another lapse in time while the destination station acknowledges reception of frame 2. The time it takes the source station to transport three frames equates to at least three times as long as it would have taken to send the message in one long frame.

With *sliding window* flow control, a source station can transmit several frames in succession before receiving an acknowledgment. There is only one acknowledgment for several transmitted frames, thus reducing the number of acknowledgments and considerably reducing the total elapsed transmission time as compared to stop-and-wait flow control.

The term *sliding window* refers to imaginary receptacles at the source and destination stations with the capacity of holding several frames of data. Message frames can be acknowledged any time before the window is filled with data. To keep track of which frames have been acknowledged and which have not, sliding window procedures require a modulo-n numbering system where each transmitted frame is identified with a unique sequence number between 0 and $n - 1$. n is any integer value equal to 2^x, where x equals the number of bits in the numbering system. With a three-bit binary numbering system, there are 2^3, or eight, possible numbers (0, 1, 2, 3, 4, 5, 6, and 7), and therefore the windows must have the capacity of holding $n - 1$ (seven) frames of data. The reason for limiting the number of frames to $n - 1$ is explained in Section 5-6-1-3.

The primary advantage of sliding window flow control is network utilization. With fewer acknowledgments (i.e., fewer line turnarounds), considerably less network time is wasted acknowledging messages, and more time can be spent actually sending messages. The primary disadvantages of sliding window flow control are complexity and hardware capacity. Each secondary station on a network must have sufficient buffer space to hold $2(n - 1)$ frames of data ($n - 1$ transmit frames and $n - 1$ receive frames), and the primary station must have sufficient buffer space to hold $m(2[n - 1])$, where m equals the number of secondary stations on the network. In addition, each secondary must store each unacknowledged frame it has transmitted and keep track of the number of each unacknowledged frame it transmits and receives. The primary station must store and keep track of all unacknowledged frames it has transmitted and received for each secondary station on the network.

5-2-3 Error Control

Error control includes both error detection and error correction. However, with the data-link layer, error control is concerned primarily with error detection and message retransmission, which is the most common method of error correction.

With poll/select line disciplines, all polls, selections, and message transmissions end with some type of end-of-transmission sequence. In addition, all messages transported from the primary to a secondary or from a secondary to the primary are acknowledged with ACK or NAK sequences to verify the validity of the message. An ACK means the message was received with no transmission errors, and a NAK means there were errors in the received message. A NAK is an automatic call for retransmission of the last message.

Error detection at the data-link layer can be accomplished with any of the methods described in Chapter 22, such as VRC, LRC, or CRC. Error correction is generally accomplished with a type of retransmission called *automatic repeat request* (ARQ) (sometimes called *automatic request for retransmission*). With ARQ, when a transmission error is detected, the destination station sends a NAK back to the source station requesting retransmission of the last message frame or frames. ARQ also calls for retransmission of missing or lost frames, which are frames that either never reach the secondary or are damaged so severely that the destination station does not recognize them. ARQ also calls for retransmission of frames where the acknowledgments (either ACKs or NAKs) are lost or damaged.

There are two types of ARQ: stop-and-wait and sliding window. Stop-and-wait flow control generally incorporates *stop-and-wait ARQ,* and sliding window flow control can implement ARQ in one of two variants: *go-back-n* frames or *selective reject* (SREJ). With go-back-n frames, the destination station tells the source station to go back n frames and retransmit all of them, even if all the frames did not contain errors. Go-back-n requests retransmission of the damaged frame plus any other frames that were transmitted after it. If the second frame in a six-frame message were received in error, five frames would be retransmitted. With selective reject, the destination station tells the source station to retransmit only the frame (or frames) received in error. Go-back-*n* is easier to implement, but it also wastes more time, as most of the frames retransmitted were not received in error. Selective reject is more complicated to implement but saves transmission time, as only those frames actually damaged are retransmitted.

5-3 CHARACTER- AND BIT-ORIENTED DATA-LINK PROTOCOLS

All data-link protocols transmit control information either in separate control frames or in the form of overhead that is added to the data and included in the same frame. Data-link protocols can be generally classified as either character or bit oriented.

5-3-1 Character-Oriented Protocols

Character-oriented protocols interpret a frame of data as a group of successive bits combined into predefined patterns of fixed length, usually eight bits each. Each group of bits represents a unique character. Control information is included in the frame in the form of standard characters from an existing character set, such as ASCII. Control characters convey important information pertaining to line discipline, flow control, and error control.

With character-oriented protocols, unique data-link control characters, such as start of text (STX) and end of text (ETX), no matter where they occur in a transmission, warrant the same action or perform the same function. For example, the ASCII code 02 hex represents the STX character. Start of text, no matter where 02 hex occurs within a data transmission, indicates that the next character is the first character of the text or information portion of the message. Care must be taken to ensure that the bit sequences for data-link control characters do not occur within a message unless they are intended to perform their designated data-link functions.

Character-oriented protocols are sometimes called *byte-oriented* protocols. Examples of character-oriented protocols are XMODEM, YMODEM, ZMODEM, KERMIT, BLAST, IBM 83B Asynchronous Data Link Protocol, and IBM Binary Synchronous Communications (BSC—bisync). Bit-oriented protocols are more efficient than character-oriented protocols.

5-3-2 Bit-Oriented Protocols

A *bit-oriented protocol* is a discipline for serial-by-bit information transfer over a data communications channel. With bit-oriented protocols, data-link control information is transferred as a series of successive bits that may be interpreted individually on a bit-by-bit basis or in groups of several bits rather than in a fixed-length group of *n* bits where *n* is usually the number of bits in a data character. In a bit-oriented protocol, there are no dedicated data-link control characters. With bit-oriented protocols, the control field within a frame may convey more than one control function.

Bit-oriented typically convey more information into shorter frames than character-oriented protocols. The most popular bit-oriented protocol are Synchronous Data Link Communications (SDLC) and High-Level Data Link Communications (HDLC).

5-4 ASYNCHRONOUS DATA-LINK PROTOCOLS

Asynchronous data-link protocols are relatively simple, character-oriented protocols generally used on two-point networks using asynchronous data and asynchronous modems. Asynchronous protocols, such as XMODEM and YMODEM, are commonly used to facilitate communications between two personal computers over the public switched telephone network.

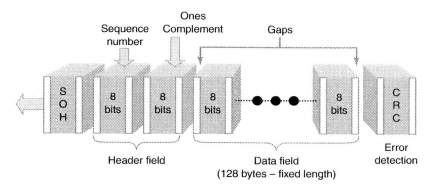

*Each 8-bit character contains start and stop bits (white bars)
and characters are separated from each other with gaps.

FIGURE 5-4 XMODEM frame format

5-4-1 XMODEM

In 1979, a man named Ward Christiansen developed the first *file transfer protocol* designed to facilitate transferring data between two personal computers (PCs) over the public switched telephone network. Christiansen's protocol is now called *XMODEM*. XMODEM is a relatively simple data-link protocol intended for low-speed applications. Although XMODEM was designed to provide communications between two PCs, it can also be used between a PC and a mainframe or host computer.

XMODEM specifies a half-duplex stop-and-wait protocol using a data frame comprised of four fields. The frame format for XMODEM contains four fields as shown in Figure 5-4. The four fields for XMODEM are the SOH field, header field, data field, and error-detection field. The first field of an XMODEM frame is simply a one-byte start of heading (SOH) field. SOH is a data-link control character that is used to indicate the beginning of a header. Headers are used for conveying system information, such as the message number. SOH simply indicates that the next byte is the first byte of the header. The second field is a two-byte sequence that is the actual header for the frame. The first header byte is called the sequence number, as it contains the number of the current frame being transmitted. The second header byte is simply the 2-s complement of the first byte, which is used to verify the validity of the first header byte (this is sometimes called *complementary redundancy*). The next field is the information field, which contains the actual user data. The information field has a maximum capacity of 128 bytes (e.g., 128 ASCII characters). The last field of the frame is an eight-bit CRC frame check sequence, which is used for error detection.

Data transmission and control are quite simple with the XMODEM protocol—too simple for most modern-day data communications networks. The process of transferring data begins when the destination station sends a NAK character to the source station. Although NAK is the acronym for a negative acknowledgment, when transmitted by the destination station at the beginning of an XMODEM data transfer, it simply indicates that the destination station is ready to receive data. After the source station receives the initial NAK character, it sends the first data frame and then waits for an acknowledgment from the destination station. If the data are received without errors, the destination station responds with an ACK character (positive acknowledgment). If the data is received with errors, the destination station responds with a NAK character, which calls for a retransmission of the data. After the originate station receives the NAK character, it retransmits the same frame. Each time the destination station receives a frame, it responds with either a NAK or an ACK, depending on whether a transmission error has occurred. If the source station does not receive an ACK or NAK after a predetermined length of time, it retransmits the last frame. A timeout is treated the same as a NAK. When the destination station wishes to prematurely terminate a transmission, it inserts a cancel (CAN) character.

5-4-2 YMODEM
YMODEM is a protocol similar to XMODEM except with the following exceptions:

1. The information field has a maximum capacity of 1024 bytes.
2. Two CAN characters are required to abort a transmission.
3. ITU-T-CRC 16 is used to calculate the frame check sequence.
4. Multiple frames can be sent in succession and then acknowledged with a single ACK or NAK character.

5-5 SYNCHRONOUS DATA-LINK PROTOCOLS

With *synchronous data-link protocols,* remote stations can have more than one PC or printer. A group of computers, printers, and other digital devices is sometimes called a *cluster.* A single line control unit (LCU) can serve a cluster with as many as 50 devices. Synchronous data-link protocols are generally used with synchronous data and synchronous modems and can be either character or bit oriented. One of the most common synchronous data-link protocols is IBM's binary synchronous communications (BSC).

5-5-1 Binary Synchronous Communications
Binary synchronous communications (BSC) is a synchronous character-oriented data-link protocol developed by IBM. BSC is sometimes called *bisync* or *bisynchronous communications.* With BSC, each data transmission is preceded by a unique synchronization (SYN) character as shown here:

$$
\begin{matrix}
S & S & \\
Y & Y & \text{message} \\
N & N &
\end{matrix}
$$

The message can be a poll, a selection, an acknowledgment, or a message containing user information.

The SYN character with ASCII is 16 hex and with EBCDIC 32 hex. The SYN character places the receiver in the character (byte) mode and prepares it to receive data in eight-bit groupings. With BSC, SYN characters are always transmitted in pairs (hence the name *bisync* or *bisynchronous communications*). Received data are shifted serially one bit at a time through the detection circuit, where they are monitored in groups of 16 bits looking for two SYN characters. Two SYN characters are used to avoid misinterpreting a random eight-bit sequence in the middle of a message with the same bit sequence as a SYN character. For example, if the ASCII characters A and b were received in succession, the following bit sequence would occur:

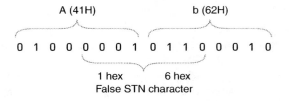

As you can see, it appears that a SYN character has been received when in fact it has not. To avoid this situation, SYN characters are always transmitted in pairs and, consequently, if only one is detected, it is ignored. The likelihood of two false SYN characters occurring one immediately after the other is remote.

5-5-1-1 BSC polling sequences. BSC uses a poll/select format to control data transmission. There are two polling formats used with bisync: general and specific. The format for a *general poll* is

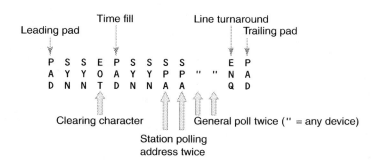

where

	P			S	
	A	= pad		Y	= synchronization character
	D			N	
	E			S	
	O	= end of transmission		P	= station polling address
	T			A	
	"	= identifies a general poll			
	E				
	N	= inquiry			
	Q				

The PAD character at the beginning of the sequence is called a *leading pad* and is either 55 hex or AA hex (01010101 or 10101010). A leading pad is simply a string of alternating 1s and 0s for clock synchronization. Immediately following the leading pad are two SYN characters that establish character synchronization. The EOT character is a *clearing character* that places all secondary stations into the line monitor mode. The PAD character immediately following the second SYN character is simply a string of successive logic 1s that serves as a time fill, giving each of the secondary stations time to clear. The number of logic 1s transmitted during this time fill is not necessarily a multiple of eight bits. Consequently, two more SYN characters are transmitted to reestablish character synchronization. Two *station polling address* (SPA) characters are transmitted for error detection (character redundancy). A secondary will not recognize or respond to a poll unless its SPA appears twice in succession. The two quotation marks signify that the poll is a general poll for any device at that station that has a formatted message to send. The enquiry (ENQ) character is sometimes called a *format* or *line turnaround* character because it simply completes the polling sequence and initiates a line turnaround.

The PAD character at the end of the polling sequence is a trailing pad (FF). The purpose of the trailing pad is to ensure that the RLSD signal in the receive modem is held active long enough for the entire message to be demodulated.

Table 5-1 Station and Device Addresses

Station or Device Number	SPA	SSA	DA	Station or Device Number	SPA	SSA	DA
0	sp	—	sp	16	&	0	&
1	A	/	A	17	J	1	J
2	B	S	B	18	K	2	K
3	C	T	C	19	L	3	L
4	D	U	D	20	M	4	M
5	E	V	E	21	N	5	N
6	F	W	F	22	O	6	O
7	G	X	G	23	P	7	P
8	H	Y	H	24	Q	8	Q
9	I	Z	I	25	R	9	R
10	[	-	[	26	]	:	]
11	.	,	.	27	$	#	$
12	<	%	<	28	*	@	*
13	(	—	(	29	)	`	)
14	+	>	+	30	;	=	;
15	!	?	!	31	^	"	^

With BSC, there is a second polling sequence called a *specific poll*. The format for a specific poll is

The character sequence for a specific poll is identical to a general poll except two device address (DA) characters are substituted for the two quotation marks. With a specific poll, both the station and the device address are included. Therefore, a specific poll is an invitation for only one specific device at a given secondary station to transmit its message. Again, two DA characters are transmitted for redundancy error detection.

Table 5-1 lists the station polling addresses, station selection addresses, and device addresses for a BSC system with a maximum of 32 stations and 32 devices.

With bisync, there are only two ways in which a secondary station can respond to a poll: with a formatted message or with an ACK. The character sequence for a ACK is

```
P   S   S   E   P
A   Y   Y   O   A
D   N   N   T   D
```

5-5-1-2 BSC selection sequence. The format for a selection with BSC is

The sequence for a selection is very identical to a specific poll except two SSA characters are substituted for the two SPA characters. SSA stands for *station selection address*. All selections are specific, as they are for a specific device at the selected station.

A secondary station can respond to a selection with either a positive or a negative acknowledgment. A positive acknowledgment to a selection indicates that the device selected is ready to receive. The character sequence for a positive acknowledgment is

```
P   S   S   D       P
A   Y   Y   L   0   A
D   N   N   E       D
```

A negative acknowledgment to a selection indicates that the selected device is not ready to receive. A negative acknowledgment is called a reverse interrupt (RVI). The character sequence for a negative acknowledgment to a selection is

```
P   S   S   D       P
A   Y   Y   L   6   A
D   N   N   E       D
```

5-5-1-3 BSC message sequence.   Bisync uses stop-and-wait flow control and stop-and-wait ARQ. Formatted messages are sent from secondary stations to the primary station in response to a poll and sent from primary stations to secondary stations after the secondary has been selected. Formatted messages use the following format:

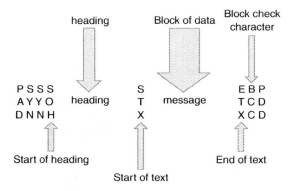

The *block check character* (BCC) uses longitudinal redundancy checking (LRC) with ASCII-coded messages and cyclic redundancy checking (CRC-16) for EBCDIC-coded messages (when CRC-16 is used, there are two BCCs). The BCC is sometimes called a block check sequence (BCS) because it does not represent a character; it is simply a sequence of bits used for error detection.

The BCC is computed beginning with the first character after SOH and continues through and includes the *end of text* (ETX) character. (If there is no heading, the BCC is computed beginning with the first character after start of text.) Data are transmitted in blocks or frames that are generally between 256 and 1500 bytes long. ETX is used to terminate the last block of a message. *End of block* (ETB) is used for multiple block messages to terminate all message blocks except the last one. The last block of a message is always terminated with ETX. The receiving station must acknowledge all BCCs.

A positive acknowledgment to a BCC indicates that the BCC was good, and a negative acknowledgment to a BCC indicates that the BCC was bad. A negative acknowledgment is an automatic request for retransmission (ARQ). The character sequences for positive and negative acknowledgments are the following:

Positive responses to BCCs (messages):

```
P   S   S   D       P
A   Y   Y   L   0   A       even-numbered blocks 2
D   N   N   E       D
        or
P   S   S   D       P
A   Y   Y   L   1   A       odd-numbered blocks 2
D   N   N   E       D
```

Negative response to BCCs (messages):

```
P   S   S   N   P
A   Y   Y   A   A
D   N   N   K   D
```

where

```
N
A  = negative acknowledgment
K
```

5-5-1-4 BSC transparency.   It is possible that a device attached to one or more of the ports of a station controller is not a computer terminal or printer. For example, a microprocessor-controlled system used to monitor environmental conditions (temperature, humidity, and so on) or a security alarm system. If so, the data transferred between it and the primary are not ASCII- or EBCDIC-encoded characters. Instead, they could be microprocessor op-codes or binary-encoded data. Consequently, it would be possible that an eight-bit sequence could occur within the message that is equivalent to a data-link control character. For example, if the binary code 00000011 (03 hex) occurred in a message, the controller would misinterpret it as the ASCII code for the ETX. If this happened, the controller would terminate the message and interpret the next sequence of bits as the BCC. To prevent this from occurring, the controller is made *transparent* to the data. With bisync, a *data-link escape* (DLE) character is used to achieve transparency. To place a controller into the transparent mode, STX is preceded by a DLE. This causes the controller to transfer the data to the selected device without searching through the message looking for data-link control characters. To come out of the transparent mode, DLE ETX is transmitted. To transmit a bit sequence equivalent to DLE as part of the text, it must be preceded by a DLE character (i.e., DLE DLE). There are only three additional circumstances with transparent data when it is necessary to precede a character with DLE:

1. *DLE ETB.* Used to terminate all blocks of data except the final block.
2. *DLE ITB.* Used to terminate blocks of transparent text other than the final block when ITB (end of intermittent block) is used for a block-terminating character.
3. *DLE SYN.* With bisync, two SYN characters are inserted in the text in messages lasting longer than 1 second to ensure that the receive controller maintains character synchronization.

5-6 SYNCHRONOUS DATA-LINK CONTROL

Synchronous data-link control (SDLC) is a synchronous bit-oriented protocol developed in the 1970s by IBM for use in *system network architecture* (SNA) environments. SDLC was the first link-layer protocol based on synchronous, bit-oriented operation. The Inter-

F	A	C	I	FCS	F
Flag field 8 bits	Address field 8 bits	Control field 8 bits	Information field (Variable length in 8 bit groupings)	Frame check sequence (CRC-16)	Flag field 8 bits

01111110
7E hex
◄──────── Span of CRC accumulation ────────►
01111110
7E hex
◄──────── Span of zero insertion ────────►

FIGURE 5-5   SDLC frame format

national Organization for Standardization modified SDLC and created high-level data-link control (HDLC) and the International Telecommunications Union—Telecommunications Standardization Sector (ITU-T) subsequently modified HDLC to create Link Access Procedures (LAP). The Institute of Electrical and Electronic Engineers (IEEE) modified HDLC and created IEEE 802.2. Although each of these protocol variations is important in its own domain, SDLC remains the primary SNA link-layer protocol for wide-area data networks.

SDLC can transfer data simplex, half duplex, or full duplex and can support a variety of link types and topologies. SDLC can be used on point-to-point or multipoint networks over both circuit- and packet-switched networks. SDLC is a bit-oriented protocol (BOP) where there is a single control field within a message *frame* that performs essentially all the data-link control functions. SDLC frames are generally limited to 256 characters in length. EBCDIC was the original character language used with SDLC.

There are two types of network nodes defined by SDLC: *primary stations* and *secondary stations*. There is only one primary station in an SDLC circuit, which controls data exchange on the communications channel and issues *commands*. All other stations on an SDLC network are secondary stations, which receive commands from the primary and return (transmit) *responses* to the primary station.

There are three transmission states with SDLC: transient, idle, and active. The *transient state* exists before and after an initial transmission and after each line turnaround. A secondary station assumes the circuit is in an idle state after receiving 15 or more consecutive logic 1s. The *active state* exists whenever either the primary or one of the secondary stations is transmitting information or control signals.

5-6-1   SDLC Frame Format

Figure 5-5 shows an SDLC frame format. Frames transmitted from the primary and secondary stations use exactly the same format. There are five *fields* included in an SDLC frame:

1. Flag field (beginning and ending)
2. Address field
3. Control field
4. Information (or text) field
5. Frame check sequence field

5-6-1-1 SDLC flag field.   There are two *flag fields* per frame, each with a minimum length of one byte. The two flag fields are the beginning flag and ending flag. Flags are used for the *delimiting sequence* for the frame and to achieve *frame and character synchronization*. The delimiting sequence sets the limits of the frame (i.e., when the frame begins and when it ends). The flag is used with SDLC in a manner similar to the way SYN characters are used with bisync—to achieve character synchronization. The bit sequence for a flag is 01111110 (7E hex), which is the character "=" in the EBCDIC code. There are several variations to how flags are transmitted with SDLC:

1. One beginning and one ending flag for each frame:

2. The ending flag from one frame is used for the beginning flag for the next frame:

3. The last zero of an ending flag can be the first zero of the beginning flag of the next frame:

4. Flags are transmitted continuously during the time between frames in lieu of idle line 1s:

01111110011111100111111001111110   Address   Control   Text   FCC   0111111001111110

   Flag   Flag   Flag   Flag   Flag   Flag

5-6-1-2 SDLC address field. An SDLC address field contains eight bits; therefore, 256 addresses are possible. The address 00 hex (00000000) is called the *null* address and is never assigned to a secondary station. The null address is used for network testing. The address FF hex (11111111) is called the *broadcast* address. The primary station is the only station that can transmit the broadcast address. When a frame is transmitted with the broadcast address, it is intended for all secondary stations. The remaining 254 addresses can be used as unique station addresses intended for one secondary station only or as group addresses that are intended for more than one secondary station but not all of them.

In frames sent by the primary station, the address field contains the address of the secondary station (i.e., the address of the destination). In frames sent from a secondary station, the address field contains the address of the secondary (i.e., the address of the station sending the message). The primary station has no address because all transmissions from secondary stations go to the primary.

5-6-1-3 SDLC control field. The control field is an eight-bit field that identifies the type of frame being transmitted. The control field is used for polling, confirming previously received frames, and several other data-link management functions. There are three frame formats with SDLC: information, supervisory, and unnumbered.

Information frame. With an *information frame*, there must be an information field, which must contain user data. Information frames are used for transmitting sequenced information that must be acknowledged by the destination station. The bit pattern for the control field of an information frame is

Bit:	b_0	b_1	b_2	b_3	b_4	b_5	b_6	b_7
Function:		nr		P or F $\overline{P}$ or $\overline{F}$		ns		0 Indicates information frame

A logic 0 in the high-order bit position identifies an information frame (I-frame). With information frames, the primary can select a secondary station, send formatted information, confirm previously received information frames, and poll a secondary station—with a single transmission.

Bit b_3 of an information frame is called a *poll* (P) or *not-a-poll* ($\overline{P}$) bit when sent by the primary and a *final* (F) or *not-a-final* ($\overline{F}$) bit when sent by a secondary. In frames sent from the primary, if the primary desires to poll the secondary (i.e., solicit it for information), the P bit in the control field is set (logic 1). If the primary does not wish to poll the secondary, the P bit is reset (logic 0). With SDLC, a secondary cannot transmit frames unless it receives a frame addressed to it with the P bit set. This is called the *synchronous response mode*. When the primary is transmitting multiple frames to the same secondary, b_3 is a logic 0 in all but the last frame. In the last frame, b_3 is set, which demands a response from the secondary. When a secondary is transmitting multiple frames to the primary, b_3 in the control field is a logic 0 in all frames except the last frame. In the last frame, b_3 is set, which simply indicates that the frame is the last frame in the message sequence.

In information frames, bits b_4, b_5, and b_6 of the control field are *ns* bits, which are used in the transmit sequence number (*ns* stands for "number sent"). All information frames must be numbered. With three bits, the binary numbers 000 through 111 (0 through 7) can be represented. The first frame transmitted by each station is designated frame 000, the second frame 001, and so on up to frame 111 (the eighth frame), at which time the count cycles back to 000 and repeats.

SDLC uses a sliding window ARQ for error correction. In information frames, bits b_0, b_1, and b_2 in the control field are the *nr* bits, which are the receive numbering sequence used to indicate the status of previously received information frames (*nr* stands for "number received"). The *nr* bits are used to confirm frames received without errors and to automatically request retransmission of information frames received with errors. The *nr* is the number of the next information frame the transmitting station expects to receive or the number of the next information frame the receiving station will transmit. The *nr* confirms received frames through *nr* − 1. Frame *nr* − 1 is the last information frame received without a transmission error. For example, when a station transmits *nr* = 5, it is confirming successful reception of previously unconfirmed frames up through frame 4. Together, the *ns* and *nr* bits are used for error correction (ARQ). The primary station must keep track of the *ns* and *nr* for each secondary station. Each secondary station must keep track of only its *ns* and *nr*. After all frames have been confirmed, the primary station's *ns* must agree with the secondary station's *nr* and vice versa.

For the following example, both the primary and secondary stations begin with their *nr* and *ns* counters reset to 000. The primary begins the information exchange by sending three information frames numbered 0, 1, and 2 (i.e., the *ns* bits in the control character for the three frames are 000, 001, and 010). In the control character for the three frames, the primary transmits an $nr = 0$ (i.e., 000). An $nr = 0$ is transmitted because the next frame the primary expects to receive from the secondary is frame 0, which is the secondary's present ns. The secondary responds with two information frames ($ns = 0$ and 1). The secondary received all three frames from the primary without any errors; therefore, the nr transmitted in the secondary's control field is 3, which is the number of the next frame the primary will send. The primary now sends information frames 3 and 4 with an $nr = 2$, which confirms the correct reception of frames 0 and 1 from the secondary. The secondary responds with frames $ns = 2$, 3, and 4 with an $nr = 4$. The $nr = 4$ confirms reception of only frame 3 from the primary ($nr - 1$). Consequently, the primary retransmits frame 4. Frame 4 is transmitted together with four additional frames ($ns = 5, 6, 7$, and 0). The primary's $nr = 5$, which confirms frames 2, 3, and 4 from the secondary. Finally, the secondary sends information frame 5 with an $nr = 1$, which confirms frames 4, 5, 6, 7, and 0 from the primary. At this point, all frames transmitted have been confirmed except frame 5 from the secondary. The preceding exchange of information frames is shown in Figure 5-6.

With SDLC, neither the primary nor the secondary station can send more than seven numbered information frames in succession without receiving a confirmation. For example, if the primary sent eight frames ($ns = 0, 1, 2, 3, 4, 5, 6$, and 7) and the secondary responded with an $nr = 0$, it is ambiguous which frames are being confirmed. Does $nr = 0$

Primary Station

Status												
ns	0	1	2		3	4		4	5	6	7	0
nr:	0	0	0		2	2		5	5	5	5	5
P/$\bar{P}$	0	0	1		0	1		0	0	0	0	1

Control Field												
b_0	0	0	0		0	0		1	1	1	1	1
b_1	0	0	0		1	1		0	0	0	0	0
b_2	0	0	0		0	0		1	1	1	1	1
b_3	0	0	1		0	1		0	0	0	0	1
b_4	0	0	0		0	1		1	1	1	1	0
b_5	0	0	1		1	0		0	0	1	1	0
b_6	0	1	0		1	0		0	1	0	1	0
b_7	0	0	0		0	0		0	0	0	0	0
hex code	00	02	14		46	58		A8	AA	AC	AE	B0

Secondary Station

Status						
ns:	0	1	2	3	4	5
nr:	3	3	4	4	4	1
F/$\bar{F}$	0	1	0	0	1	1

Control Field						
b_0	0	0	1	1	1	0
b_1	1	1	0	0	0	0
b_2	1	1	0	0	0	1
b_3	0	1	0	0	1	1
b_4	0	0	0	0	1	1
b_5	0	0	1	1	0	0
b_6	0	1	0	1	0	1
b_7	0	0	0	0	0	0
hex code	60	72	84	86	98	3A

FIGURE 5-6   SDLC exchange of information frames

mean that all eight frames were received correctly, or does it mean that frame 0 had an error in it and all eight frames must be retransmitted? (All frames beginning with $nr - 1$ must be retransmitted.)

Example 5-1

Determine the bit pattern for the control field of an information frame sent from the primary to a secondary station for the following conditions:

a. Primary is sending information frame 3 ($ns = 3$)
b. Primary is polling the secondary (P = 1)
c. Primary is confirming correct reception of frames 2, 3, and 4 from the secondary ($nr = 5$)

Solution

Example 5-2

Determine the bit pattern for the control field of an information frame sent from a secondary station to the primary for the following conditions:

a. Secondary is sending information frame 7 ($ns = 7$)
b. Secondary is not sending its final frame (F = 0)
c. Secondary is confirming correct reception of frames 2 and 3 from the primary ($nr = 4$)

Solution

Supervisory frame. With *supervisory frames,* an information field is not allowed. Consequently, supervisory frames cannot be used to transfer numbered information; however, they can be used to assist in the transfer of information. Supervisory frames can be used to confirm previously received information frames, convey ready or busy conditions, and for a primary to poll a secondary when the primary does not have any numbered information to send to the secondary. The bit pattern for the control field of a supervisory frame is

Bit:	b_0	b_1	b_2	b_3	b_4	b_5	b_6	b_7
Function:		nr		P or F $\overline{P}$ or $\overline{F}$	X	X	0	1
					Function code		Indicates supervisory frame	

A supervisory frame is identified with a 01 in bit positions b_6 and b_7, respectively, of the control field. With the supervisory format, bit b_3 is again the poll/not-a-poll or final/not-a-final bit, and b_0, b_1, and b_2 are the nr bits. Therefore, supervisory frames can be used by a primary to poll a secondary, and both the primary and the secondary stations can use supervisory frames to confirm previously received information frames. Bits b_4 and b_5 in a supervisory are the function code that either indicate the receive status of the station transmitting the frame or request transmission or retransmission of sequenced information frames. With two bits, there are four combinations possible. The four combinations and their functions are the following:

b_4	b_5	Receive Status
0	0	Ready to receive (RR)
0	1	Ready not to receive (RNR)
1	0	Reject (REJ)
1	1	Not used with SDLC

When a primary station sends a supervisory frame with the P bit set and a status of ready to receive, it is equivalent to a general poll. Primary stations can use supervisory frames for polling and also to confirm previously received information frames without sending any information. A secondary uses the supervisory format for confirming previously received information frames and for reporting its receive status to the primary. If a secondary sends a supervisory frame with RNR status, the primary cannot send it numbered information frames until that status is cleared. RNR is cleared when a secondary sends an information frame with the F bit = 1 or a supervisory frame indicating RR or REJ with the F bit = 0. The REJ command/response is used to confirm information frames through $nr - 1$ and to request transmission of numbered information frames beginning with the frame number identified in the REJ frame. An information field is prohibited with a supervisory frame, and the REJ command/response is used only with full-duplex operation.

Example 5-3

Determine the bit pattern for the control field of a supervisory frame sent from a secondary station to the primary for the following conditions:
a. Secondary is ready to receive (RR)
b. It is a final frame
c. Secondary station is confirming correct reception of frames 3, 4, and 5 ($nr = 6$)

Solution

Bit:	b_0	b_1	b_2	b_3	b_4	b_5	b_6	b_7
	1	1	0	1	0	0	0	1

$\underbrace{\quad nr \quad}$ $\underbrace{F}$ $\underbrace{RR}$ $\underbrace{Supervisory}$
6   final   frame

Unnumbered frame. An *unnumbered frame* is identified by making bits b_6 and b_7 in the control field both logic 1s. The bit pattern for the control field of an unnumbered frame is

With an unnumbered frame, bit b_3 is again either the poll/not-a-poll or final/not-a-final bit. There are five X bits (b_0, b_1, b_2, b_4, and b_5) included in the control field of an unnumbered frame that contain the function code, which is used for various unnumbered commands and responses. With five bits available, there are 32 unnumbered commands/

Table 5-2 Unnumbered Commands and Responses

Binary Configuration			Acronym	Command	Response	I Field Prohibited	Resets *ns* and *nr*
b_0		b_7					
000	P/F	0011	UI	Yes	Yes	No	No
000	F	0111	RIM	No	Yes	Yes	No
000	P	0111	SIM	Yes	No	Yes	Yes
100	P	0011	SNRM	Yes	No	Yes	Yes
000	F	1111	DM	No	Yes	Yes	No
010	P	0011	DISC	Yes	No	Yes	No
011	F	0011	UA	No	Yes	Yes	No
100	F	0111	FRMR	No	Yes	No	No
111	F	1111	BCN	No	Yes	Yes	No
110	P/F	0111	CFGR	Yes	Yes	No	No
010	F	0011	RD	No	Yes	Yes	No
101	P/F	1111	XID	Yes	Yes	No	No
111	P/F	0011	TEST	Yes	Yes	No	No

responses possible. The control field in an unnumbered frame sent from a primary station is called a command, and the control field in an unnumbered frame sent from a secondary station is called a response. With unnumbered frames, there are neither *ns* nor *nr* bits included in the control field. Therefore, numbered information frames cannot be sent or confirmed with the unnumbered format. Unnumbered frames are used to send network control and status information. Two examples of control functions are placing a secondary station on- or off-line and initializing a secondary station's line control unit (LCU).

Table 5-2 lists several of the more common unnumbered commands and responses. Numbered information frames are prohibited with all unnumbered frames. Therefore, user information cannot be transported with unnumbered frames and, thus, the control field in unnumbered frames does not include *nr* and *ns* bits. However, information fields containing control information are allowed with the following unnumbered commands and responses: UI, FRMR, CFGR, TEST, and XID.

A secondary station must be in one of three modes: *initialization mode, normal response mode,* or *normal disconnect mode.* The procedures for placing a secondary station into the initialization mode are system specified and vary considerably. A secondary in the normal response mode cannot initiate unsolicited transmissions; it can transmit only in response to a frame received with the P bit set. When in the normal disconnect mode, a secondary is off-line. In this mode, a secondary station will accept only the TEST, XID, CFGR, SNRM, or SIM commands from the primary station and can respond only if the P bit is set.

The unnumbered commands and responses are summarized here:

1. *Unnumbered information (UI).* UI can be a command or a response that is used to send unnumbered information. Unnumbered information transmitted in the I-field is not acknowledged.

2. *Set initialization mode (SIM).* SIM is a command that places a secondary station into the initialization mode. The initialization procedure is system specified and varies from a simple self-test of the station controller to executing a complete IPL (initial program logic) program. SIM resets the *ns* and *nr* counters at the primary and secondary stations. A secondary is expected to respond to a SIM command with an unnumbered acknowledgment (UA) response.

3. *Request initialization mode (RIM).* RIM is a response sent by a secondary station to request the primary to send a SIM command.

4. *Set normal response mode (SNRM).* SNRM is a command that places a secondary into the normal response mode (NRM). A secondary station cannot send or receive numbered information frames unless it is in the normal response mode. Essentially, SNRM places a secondary station on-line. SNRM resets the *ns* and *nr* counters at both the primary and secondary stations. UA is the normal response to a SNRM command. Unsolicited responses are not allowed when a secondary is in the NRM. A secondary station remains in the NRM until it receives a disconnect (DISC) or SIM command.

5. *Disconnect mode (DM).* DM is a response transmitted from a secondary station if the primary attempts to send numbered information frames to it when the secondary is in the normal disconnect mode.

6. *Request disconnect (RD).* RD is a response sent by a secondary when it wants the primary to place it in the disconnect mode.

7. *Disconnect (DISC).* DISC is a command that places a secondary station in the normal disconnect mode (NDM). A secondary cannot send or receive numbered information frames when it is in the normal disconnect mode. When in the NDM, a secondary can receive only SIM or SNRM commands and can transmit only a DM response. The expected response to a DISC is UA.

8. *Unnumbered acknowledgment (UA).* UA is an affirmative response that indicates compliance to SIM, SNRM, or DISC commands. UA is also used to acknowledge unnumbered information frames.

9. *Frame reject (FRMR).* FRMR is for reporting procedural errors. The FRMR response is an answer transmitted by a secondary after it has received an invalid frame from the primary. A received frame may be invalid for any one of the following reasons:
   a. The control field contains an invalid or unassigned command.
   b. The amount of data in the information field exceeds the buffer space in the secondary station's controller.
   c. An information field is received in a frame that does not allow information fields.
   d. The *nr* received is incongruous with the secondary's *ns,* for example, if the secondary transmitted *ns* frames 2, 3, and 4 and then the primary responded with an *nr* = 7.

   A secondary station cannot release itself from the FRMR condition, nor does it act on the frame that caused the condition. The secondary repeats the FRMR response until it receives one of the following mode-setting commands: SNRM, DISC, or SIM. The information field for a FRMR response must contain three bytes (24 bits) and has the following format:

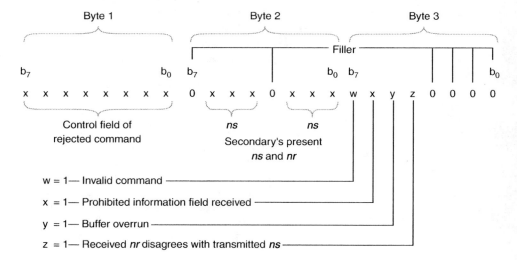

10. *TEST.* The TEST command/response is an exchange of frames between the primary station and a secondary station. An information field may be included with the TEST command; however, it cannot be sequenced (numbered). The primary sends a TEST command to a secondary in any mode to solicit a TEST response. If an information field is included with the command, the secondary returns it with its response. The TEST command/response is exchanged for link testing purposes.

11. *Exchange station identification (XID).* XID can be a command or a response. As a command, XID solicits the identification of a secondary station. An information field can be included in the frame to convey the identification data of either the primary or the secondary. For dial-up circuits, it is often necessary that the secondary station identify itself before the primary will exchange information frames with it, although XID is not restricted only to dial-up circuits.

5-6-1-4 SDLC information field. All information transmitted in an SDLC frame must be in the information field (I-field), and the number of bits in the information field must be a multiple of eight. An information field is not allowed with all SDLC frames; however, the data within an information field can be user information or control information.

5-6-1-5 Frame Check Character (FCC) field. The FCC field contains the error detection mechanism for SDLC. The FCC is equivalent to the BCC used with binary synchronous communications (BSC). SDLC uses CRC-16 and the following generating polynomial: $x^{16} + x^{12} + x^5 + x^1$. Frame check characters are computed on the data in the address, control and information fields.

5-6-2 SDLC Loop Operation

An SDLC loop operates half-duplex. The primary difference between the loop and bus configurations is that in a loop, all transmissions travel in the same direction on the communications channel. In a loop configuration, only one station transmits at a time. The primary station transmits first, then each secondary station responds sequentially. In an SDLC loop, the transmit port of the primary station controller is connected to the receive port of the controller in the first down-line secondary station. Each successive secondary station is connected in series with the transmission path with the transmit port of the last secondary station's controller on the loop connected to the receive port of the primary station's controller. Figure 5-7 shows the physical layout for an SDLC loop.

In an SDLC loop, the primary transmits sequential frames where each frame may be addressed to any or all of the secondary stations. Each frame transmitted by the primary station contains an address of the secondary station to which that frame is directed. Each secondary station, in turn, decodes the address field of every frame and then serves as a repeater for all stations that are down-loop from it. When a secondary station detects a frame with its address, it copies the frame, then passes it on to the next down-loop station. All frames transmitted by the primary are returned to the primary. When the primary has completed transmitting, it follows the last flag with eight consecutive logic 0s. A flag followed by eight consecutive logic 0s is called a *turnaround sequence*, which signals the end of the primary's transmissions. Immediately following the turnaround sequence, the primary transmits continuous logic 1s, which is called the go-ahead sequence. A secondary station cannot transmit until it receives a frame address to it with the P bit set, a turnaround sequence, and then a go-ahead sequence. Once the primary has begun transmitting continuous logic 1s, it goes into the receive mode.

The first down-loop secondary station that receives a frame addressed to it with the P bit set changes the go-ahead sequence to a flag, which becomes the beginning flag of that secondary station's response frame or frames. After the secondary station has transmitted its last frame, it again becomes a repeater for the idle line 1s from the primary, which become the go-ahead sequence for the next down-loop secondary station. The next secondary station that receives a frame addressed to it with the P bit set detects the turnaround sequence, any frames transmitted from up-loop

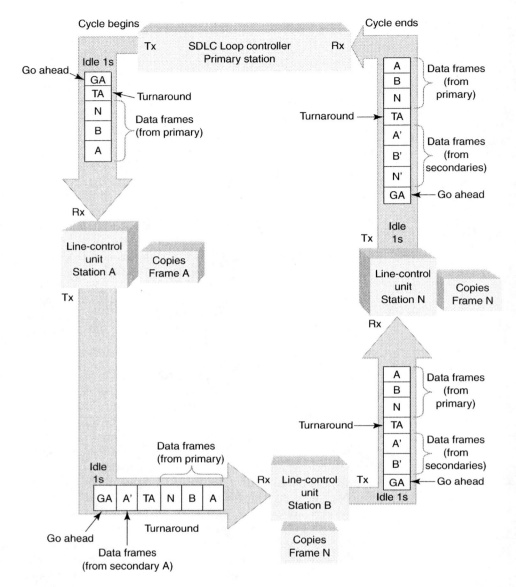

FIGURE 5-7 SDLC loop configuration

secondary stations, and then the go-ahead sequence. Each secondary station inserts its response frames immediately after the last frame transmitted by an up-loop secondary. Frames transmitted from the primary are separated from frames transmitted by the secondaries by the turnaround sequence. Without the separation, it would be impossible to tell which frames were from the primary and which were from a secondary, as their frame formats (including the address field) are identical. The cycle is completed when the primary station receives its own turnaround sequence, a series of response frames, and then the go-ahead sequence.

The previously described sequence is summarized here:

1. Primary transmits sequential frames to one or more secondary stations.
2. Each transmitted frame contains a secondary station's address.
3. After a primary has completed transmitting, it follows the last flag of the last frame with eight consecutive logic 0s (turnaround sequence) followed by continuous logic 1s (go-ahead sequence -0111111111111 - - - -).

4. The turnaround sequence alerts secondary stations of the end of the primary's transmissions.
5. Each secondary, in turn, decodes the address field of each frame and removes frames addressed to them.
6. Secondary stations serve as repeaters for any down-line secondary stations.
7. Secondary stations cannot transmit frames of their own unless they receive a frame with the P bit set.
8. The first secondary station that receives a frame addressed to it with the P bit set changes the seventh logic 1 in the go-ahead sequence to a logic 0, thus creating a flag. The flag becomes the beginning flag for the secondary station's response frames.
9. The next down-loop secondary station that receives a frame addressed to it with the P bit set detects the turnaround sequence, any frames transmitted by other up-loop secondary stations, and then the go-ahead sequence.
10. Each secondary station's response frames are inserted immediately after the last repeated frame.
11. The cycle is completed when the primary receives its own turnaround sequence, a series of response frames, and the go-ahead sequence.

5-6-2-1 SDLC loop configure command/response. The configure command/response (CFGR) is an unnumbered command/response that is used only in SDLC loop configurations. CFGR contains a one-byte *function descriptor* (essentially a subcommand) in the information field. A CFGR command is acknowledged with a CFGR response. If the low-order bit of the function descriptor is set, a specified function is initiated. If it is reset, the specified function is cleared. There are six subcommands that can appear in the configure command/response function field:

1. *Clear* (00000000). A *clear* subcommand causes all previously set functions to be cleared by the secondary. The secondary's response to a clear subcommand is another clear subcommand, 00000000.
2. *Beacon test* (*BCN*) (0000000X). The *beacon test* subcommand causes the secondary receiving it to turn on (00000001) or turn off (00000000) its carrier. The beacon response is called a carrier, although it is not a carrier in the true sense of the word. The beacon test command causes a secondary station to begin transmitting a beacon response, which is not a carrier. However, if modems were used in the circuit, the beacon response would cause the modem's carrier to turn on. The beacon test is used to isolate open-loop continuity problems. In addition, whenever a secondary station detects a loss of signal (either data or idle line ones), it automatically begins to transmit its beacon response. The secondary will continue transmitting the beacon until the loop resumes normal status.
3. *Monitor mode* (0000010X). The *monitor* command (00000101) causes the addressed secondary station to place itself into the monitor (receive-only) mode. Once in the monitor mode, a secondary cannot transmit until it receives either a monitor mode clear (00000100) or a clear (00000000) subcommand.
4. *Wrap* (0000100X). The *wrap* command (00001001) causes a secondary station to loop its transmissions directly to its receiver input. The wrap command places the secondary effectively off-line for the duration of the test. A secondary station takes itself out of the wrap mode when it receives a wrap clear (00001000) or clear (00000000) subcommand.
5. *Self-test* (0000101X). The self-test subcommand (00001011) causes the addressed secondary to initiate a series of internal diagnostic tests. When the tests are completed, the secondary will respond. If the P bit in the configure command is set, the secondary will respond following completion of the self-test or at its earliest opportunity. If the P bit is reset, the secondary will respond following completion of the test to the next poll-type frame it receives from the primary.

All other transmissions are ignored by the secondary while it is performing a self-test; however, the secondary will repeat all frames received to the next down-loop station. The secondary reports the results of the self-test by setting or clearing the low-order bit (X) of its self-test response. A logic 1 means that the tests were unsuccessful, and a logic 0 means that they were successful.

6. *Modified link test* (0000110X). If the *modified link test* function is set (X bit set), the secondary station will respond to a TEST command with a TEST response that has an information field containing the first byte of the TEST command information field repeated *n* times. The number *n* is system specified. If the X bit is reset, the secondary station will respond with a zero-length information field. The modified link test is an optional subcommand and is used only to provide an alternative form of link test to that previously described for the TEST command.

5-6-2-2 SDLC transparency. With SDLC, the flag bit sequence (01111110) can occur within a frame where it is not intended to be a flag. For instance, within the address, control, or information fields, a combination of one or more bits from one character combined with one or more bits from an adjacent character could produce a 01111110 pattern. If this were to happen, the receive controller would misinterpret the sequence for a flag, thus destroying the frame. Therefore, the pattern 01111110 must be prohibited from occurring except when it is intended to be a flag.

One solution to the problem would be to prohibit certain sequences of characters from occurring, which would be difficult to do. A more practical solution would be to make a receiver transparent to all data located between beginning and ending flags. This is called *transparency*. The *transparency mechanism* used with SDLC is called *zero-bit insertion* or *zero stuffing*. With zero-bit insertion, a logic 0 is automatically inserted after any occurrence of five consecutive logic 1s except in a designated flag sequence (i.e., flags are not zero inserted). When five consecutive logic 1s are received and the next bit is a 0, the 0 is automatically deleted or removed. If the next bit is a logic 1, it must be a valid flag. An example of zero insertion/deletion is shown here:

Original frame bits at the transmit station:

01111110 01101111 11010011 1110001100110101 01111110

| Beginning flag | Address | Control | Frame check character | Ending flag |

After zero insertion but prior to transmission:

01111110 01101111 101010011 1110000110011 0101 01111110

| Beginning flag | Address | Control | Frame check character | Ending flag |

Inserted zeros

After zero deletion at the receive end:

01111110 01101111 11010011 1110001100110101 01111110

| Beginning flag | Address | Control | Frame check character | Ending flag |

5-6-3 Message Abort

Message abort is used to prematurely terminate an SDLC frame. Generally, this is done only to accommodate high-priority messages, such as emergency link recovery procedures. A message abort is any occurrence of seven to 14 consecutive logic 1s. Zeros are not inserted in an abort sequence. A message abort terminates an existing frame and immediately begins the higher-

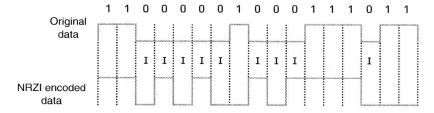

1 1 0 0 0 0 0 1 0 0 0 1 1 1 1 0 1 1

Original data

NRZI encoded data

*I indicates to invert

FIGURE 5-8   NRZI encoding

priority frame. If more than 14 consecutive logic 1s occur in succession, it is considered an idle line condition. Therefore, 15 or more contiguous logic 1s places the circuit into the idle state.

5-6-4   Invert-on-Zero Encoding

With binary synchronous transmission such as SDLC, transmission and reception of data must be time synchronized to enable identification of sequential binary digits. Synchronous data communications assumes that bit or time synchronization is provided by either the DCE or the DTE. The master transmit clock can come from the DTE or, more likely, the DCE. However, the receive clock must be recovered from the data by the DCE and then transferred to the DTE. With synchronous data transmission, the DTE receiver must sample the incoming data at the same rate that it was outputted from the transmit DTE. Although minor variations in timing can exist, the receiver in a synchronous modem provides data clock recovery and dynamically adjusted sample timing to keep sample times midway between bits. For a DCE to recover the data clock, it is necessary that transitions occur in the data. Traditional unipolar (UP) logic levels, such as TTL (0 V and +5 V), do not provide transitions for long strings of logic 0s or logic 1s. Therefore, they are inadequate for clock recovery without placing restrictions on the data. *Invert-on-zero coding* is the encoding scheme used with SDLC because it guarantees at least one transition in the data for every seven bits transmitted. Invert-on-zero coding is also called NRZI (*nonreturn-to-zero inverted*).

With NRZI encoding, the data are encoded in the controller at the transmit end and then decoded in the controller at the receive end. Figure 5-8 shows examples of NRZI encoding and decoding. The encoded waveform is unchanged by 1s in the NRZI encoder. However, logic 0s cause the encoded transmission level to invert from its previous state (i.e., either from a high to a low or from a low to a high). Consequently, consecutive logic 0s are converted to an alternating high/low sequence. With SDLC, there can never be more than six logic 1s in succession (a flag). Therefore, a high-to-low transition is guaranteed to occur at least once every seven bits transmitted except during a message abort or an idle line condition. In a NRZI decoder, whenever a high/low or low/high transition occurs in the received data, a logic 0 is generated. The absence of a transition simply generates a logic 1. In Figure 5-8, a high level is assumed prior to encoding the incoming data.

NRZI encoding was originally intended for asynchronous modems that do not have clock recovery capabilities. Consequently, the receive DTE must provide time synchronization, which is aided by using NRZI-encoded data. Synchronous modems have built-in scrambler and descrambler circuits that ensure transitions in the data and, thus, NRZI encoding is unnecessary. The NRZI encoder/decoder is placed in between the DTE and the DCE.

5-7   HIGH-LEVEL DATA-LINK CONTROL

In 1975, the International Organization for Standardization (ISO) defined several sets of substandards that, when combined, are called *high-level data-link control* (HDLC). HDLC is a superset of SDLC; therefore, only the added capabilities are explained.

HDLC comprises three standards (subdivisions) that outline the frame structure, control standards, and class of operation for a bit-oriented data-link control (DLC):

1. ISO 3309
2. ISO 4335
3. ISO 7809

5-7-1 ISO 3309

The ISO 3309 standard defines the frame structure, delimiting sequence, transparency mechanism, and error-detection method used with HDLC. With HDLC, the frame structure and delimiting sequence are essentially the same as with SDLC. An HDLC frame includes a beginning flag field, an address field, a control field, an information field, a frame check character field, and an ending flag field. The delimiting sequence with HDLC is a binary 01111110, which is the same flag sequence used with SDLC. However, HDLC computes the frame check characters in a slightly different manner. HDLC can use either CRC-16 with a generating polynomial specified by CCITT V.41 for error detection. At the transmit station, the CRC characters are computed such that when included in the FCC computations at the receive end, the remainder for an errorless transmission is always FOB8. HDLC also offers an optional 32-bit CRC checksum.

HDLC has extended addressing capabilities. HDLC can use an eight-bit address field or an *extended addressing* format, which is virtually limitless. With extended addressing, the address field may be extended recursively. If b_0 in the address field is a logic 1, the seven remaining bits are the secondary's address (the ISO defines the low-order bit as b_0, whereas SDLC designates the high-order bit as b_0). If b_0 is a logic 0, the next byte is also part of the address. If b_0 of the second byte is a logic 0, a third address byte follows and so on until an address byte with a logic 1 for the low-order bit is encountered. Essentially, there are seven bits available in each address byte for address encoding. An example of a three-byte extended addressing scheme is shown in the following. Bit b_0 in the first two bytes of the address field are logic 0s, indicating that one or more additional address bytes follow. However, b_0 in the third address byte is a logic 1, which terminates the address field. There are a total of 21 address bits (seven in each byte):

5-7-2 Information Field

HDLC permits any number of bits in the information field of an information command or response. With HDLC, any number of bits may be used for a character in the I field as long as all characters have the same number of bits.

5-7-3 Elements of Procedure

The ISO 3309 standard defines the elements of procedure for HDLC. The control and information fields have increased capabilities over SDLC, and there are two additional operational modes allowed with HDLC.

5-7-3-1 Control field. With HDLC, the control field can be extended to 16 bits. Seven bits are for the *ns,* and seven bits are for the *nr.* Therefore, with the extended control format, there can be a maximum of 127 outstanding (unconfirmed) frames at any given time. In essence, a primary station can send 126 successive information frames to a secondary station with the P bit = 0 before it would have to send a frame with the P bit = 1.

With HDLC, the supervisory format includes a fourth status condition: selective reject (SREJ). SREJ is identified by two logic 1s in bit positions b_4 and b_5 of a supervisory control field. With SREJ, a single frame can be rejected. A SREJ calls for the retransmission of only one frame identified by the three-bit *nr* code. A REJ calls for the retransmission of all frames beginning with frame identified by the three-bit *nr* code. For example, the primary sends I frames *ns* = 2, 3, 4, and 5. If frame 3 were received in error, a REJ with an *nr* of 3 would call for a retransmission of frames 3, 4, and 5. However, a SREJ with an *nr* of 3 would call for the retransmission of only frame 3. SREJ can be used to call for the retransmission of any number of frames except only one at a time.

5-7-3-2 HDLC operational modes.
SDLC specifies only one operational mode, called the *normal response mode* (NRM), which allows secondaries to communicate with the primary only after the primary has given the secondary permission to transmit. With SDLC, when a station is logically disconnected from the network, it is said to be in the *normal disconnect mode.*

HDLC has two additional operational modes: *asynchronous response mode* (ARM) and *asynchronous balanced mode* (ABM). With ARM, secondary stations are allowed to send unsolicited responses (i.e., communicate with the primary without permission). To transmit, a secondary does not need to have received a frame from the primary with the P bit set. However, if a secondary receives a frame with the P bit set, it must respond with a frame with the F bit set. HDLC also specifies an *asynchronous disconnect mode,* which is identical to the normal disconnect mode except that the secondary can initiate an asynchronous DM or RIM response at any time.

The ISO 7809 standard combines previous standards 6159 (unbalanced) and 6256 (balanced) and outlines the class of operation necessary to establish the link-level protocol. Unbalanced operation is a class of operation logically equivalent to a multipoint private-line circuit with a polling environment. There is a single primary station responsible for central control of the network. Data transmission may be either half or full duplex.

Asynchronous balanced mode is a mode of operation logically equivalent to a two-point private-line circuit where each station has equal data-link responsibilities (a station can operate as a primary or as a secondary), which enables a station to initiate data transmission without receiving permission from any other station. Channel access is accomplished through contention on a two-wire circuit using the asynchronous response mode. Data transmission is half duplex on a two-wire circuit or full duplex over a four-wire circuit.

5-8 PUBLIC SWITCHED DATA NETWORKS

A *public switched data network* (PDN or PSDN) is a switched data communications network similar to the public telephone network except a PDN is designed for transferring data only. A public switched data network is comprised of one or more wide-area data networks designed to provide access to a large number of subscribers with a wide variety of computer equipment.

The basic principle behind a PDN is to transport data from a source to a destination through a network of intermediate *switching nodes* and transmission media. The switching nodes are not concerned with the content of the data, as their purpose is to provide *end stations* access to transmission media and other switching nodes that will transport data from node to node until it reaches its final destination. Figure 5-9 shows a public switched data network comprised of several switching nodes interconnected with *transmission links* (channels). The end-station devices can be personal computers, servers, mainframe computers, or any other piece of computer hardware capable of sending or receiving data. End stations are connected to the network through switching nodes. Data enter the network where they are routed through one or more intermediate switching nodes until reaching their destination.

Some switching nodes connect only to other switching nodes (sometimes called *tandem switching nodes* or *switchers switches*), while some switching nodes are connected to end stations as well. Node-to-node communications links generally carry multiplexed data

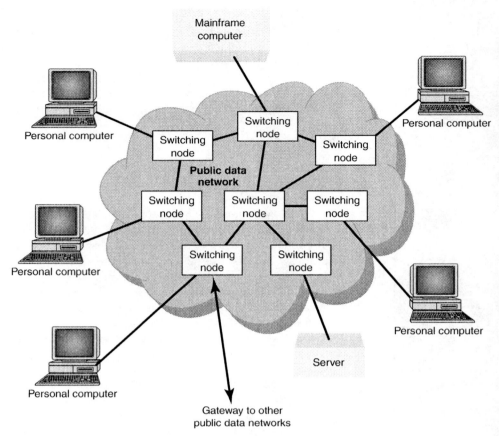

FIGURE 5-9 Public switched data network

(usually time-division multiplexing). Public data networks are not *direct connected;* that is, they do not provide direct communications links between every possible pair of nodes.

Public switched data networks combine the concepts of *value-added networks* (VANs) and *packet switching networks.*

5-8-1 Value-Added Network

A value-added network "adds value" to the services or facilities provided by a common carrier to provide new types of communication services. Examples of added values are error control, enhanced connection reliability, dynamic routing, failure protection, logical multiplexing, and data format conversions. A VAN comprises an organization that leases communications lines from common carriers such as AT&T and MCI and adds new types of communications services to those lines. Examples of value-added networks are GTE Telnet, DATAPAC, TRANSPAC, and Tymnet Inc.

5-8-2 Packet Switching Network

Packet switching involves dividing data messages into small bundles of information and transmitting them through communications networks to their intended destinations using computer-controlled switches. Three common switching techniques are used with public data networks: *circuit switching, message switching,* and *packet switching.*

5-8-2-1 Circuit switching. Circuit switching is used for making a standard telephone call on the public telephone network. The call is established, information is transferred, and then the call is disconnected. The time required to establish the call is called the *setup* time. Once the call has been established, the circuits interconnected by the network switches are allocated to a single user for the duration of the call. After a call has been established, information is transferred in *real time*. When a call is terminated, the circuits and switches are once again available for another user. Because there are a limited number of circuits and switching paths available, *blocking* can occur. Blocking is the inability to complete a call because there are no facilities or switching paths available between the source and destination locations. When circuit switching is used for data transfer, the terminal equipment at the source and destination must be compatible; they must use compatible modems and the same bit rate, character set, and protocol.

A circuit switch is a *transparent* switch. The switch is transparent to the data; it does nothing more than interconnect the source and destination terminal equipment. A circuit switch adds no value to the circuit.

5-8-2-2 Message switching. Message switching is a form of *store-and-forward* network. Data, including source and destination identification codes, are transmitted into the network and stored in a switch. Each switch within the network has message storage capabilities. The network transfers the data from switch to switch when it is convenient to do so. Consequently, data are not transferred in real time; there can be a delay at each switch. With message switching, blocking cannot occur. However, the delay time from message transmission to reception varies from call to call and can be quite long (possibly as long as 24 hours). With message switching, once the information has entered the network, it is converted to a more suitable format for transmission through the network. At the receive end, the data are converted to a format compatible with the receiving data terminal equipment. Therefore, with message switching, the source and destination data terminal equipment do not need to be compatible. Message switching is more efficient than circuit switching because data that enter the network during busy times can be held and transmitted later when the load has decreased.

A message switch is a *transactional* switch because it does more than simply transfer the data from the source to the destination. A message switch can store data or change its format and bit rate, then convert the data back to their original form or an entirely different form at the receive end. Message switching multiplexes data from different sources onto a common facility.

5-8-2-3 Packet switching. With packet switching, data are divided into smaller segments, called *packets,* prior to transmission through the network. Because a packet can be held in memory at a switch for a short period of time, packet switching is sometimes called a *hold-and-forward* network. With packet switching, a message is divided into packets, and each packet can take a different path through the network. Consequently, all packets do not necessarily arrive at the receive end at the same time or in the same order in which they were transmitted. Because packets are small, the hold time is generally quite short, message transfer is near real time, and blocking cannot occur. However, packet switching networks require complex and expensive switching arrangements and complicated protocols. A packet switch is also a transactional switch. Circuit, message, and packet switching techniques are summarized in Table 5-3.

5-9 CCITT X.25 USER-TO-NETWORK INTERFACE PROTOCOL

In 1976, the CCITT designated the X.25 user interface as the international standard for packet network access. Keep in mind that X.25 addresses only the physical, data-link, and network layers in the ISO seven-layer model. X.25 uses existing standards when possible. For example, X.25 specifies X.21, X.26, and X.27 standards as the physical interface, which correspond to EIA RS-232, RS-423A, and RS-422A standards, respectively. X.25 defines HDLC as the international standard for the data-link layer and the American National Standards Institute (ANSI) 3.66 *Advanced Data Communications Control Procedures*

Table 5-3   Switching Summary

Circuit Switching	Message Switching	Packet Switching
Dedicated transmission path	No dedicated transmission path	No dedicated transmission path
Continuous transmission of data	Transmission of messages	Transmission of packets
Operates in real time	Not real time	Near real time
Messages not stored	Messages stored	Messages held for short time
Path established for entire message	Route established for each message	Route established for each packet
Call setup delay	Message transmission delay	Packet transmission delay
Busy signal if called party busy	No busy signal	No busy signal
Blocking may occur	Blocking cannot occur	Blocking cannot occur
User responsible for message-loss protection	Network responsible for lost messages	Network may be responsible for each packet but not for entire message
No speed or code conversion	Speed and code conversion	Speed and code conversion
Fixed bandwidth transmission (i.e., fixed information capacity)	Dynamic use of bandwidth	Dynamic use of bandwidth
No overhead bits after initial setup delay	Overhead bits in each message	Overhead bits in each packet

Table 5-4   LAPB Commands

Command	Bit Number			
	8 7 6	5	4 3 2	1
1 (information)	nr	P	ns	0
RR (receiver ready)	nr	P	0 0 0	1
RNR (receiver not ready)	nr	P	0 1 0	1
REJ (reject)	nr	P	1 0 0	1
SABM (set asynchronous balanced mode)	0 0 1	P	1 1 1	1
DISC (disconnect)	0 1 0	P	0 0 1	1

(ADCCP) as the U.S. standard. ANSI 3.66 and ISO HDLC were designed for private-line data circuits with a polling environment. Consequently, the addressing and control procedures outlined by them are not appropriate for packet data networks. ANSI 3.66 and HDLC were selected for the data-link layer because of their frame format, delimiting sequence, transparency mechanism, and error-detection method.

At the link level, the protocol specified by X.25 is a subset of HDLC, referred to as *Link Access Procedure Balanced* (LAPB). LAPB provides for two-way, full-duplex communications between DTE and DCE at the packet network gateway. Only the address of the DTE or DCE may appear in the address field of a LAPB frame. The address field refers to a link address, not a network address. The network address of the destination terminal is embedded in the packet header, which is part of the information field.

Tables 5-4 and 5-5 show the commands and responses, respectively, for an LAPB frame. During LAPB operation, most frames are commands. A response frame is compelled only when a command frame is received containing a poll (P bit) = 1. SABM/UA is a command/response pair used to initialize all counters and timers at the beginning of a session. Similarly, DISC/DM is a command/response pair used at the end of a session. FRMR is a response to any illegal command for which there is no indication of transmission errors according to the frame check sequence field.

Information (I) commands are used to transmit packets. Packets are never sent as responses. Packets are acknowledged using *ns* and *nr* just as they were in SDLC. RR is sent by a station when it needs to respond (acknowledge) something but has no information packets to send. A response to an information command could be RR with F = 1. This procedure is called *checkpointing*.

Table 5-5 LAPB Responses

Response	Bit Number			
	8 7 6	5	4 3 2	1
RR (receiver ready)	*nr*	F	0 0 0	1
RNR (receiver not ready)	*nr*	F	0 1 0	1
REJ (reject)	*nr*	F	1 0 0	1
UA (unnumbered acknowledgment)	0 1 1	F	0 0 1	1
DM (disconnect mode)	0 0 0	F	1 1 1	1
FRMR (frame rejected)	1 0 0	F	0 1 1	1

REJ is another way of requesting transmission of frames. RNR is used for the flow control to indicate a busy condition and prevents further transmissions until cleared with an RR.

The network layer of X.25 specifies three switching services offered in a switched data network: permanent virtual circuit, virtual call, and datagram.

5-9-1 Permanent Virtual Circuit

A *permanent virtual circuit* (PVC) is logically equivalent to a two-point dedicated private-line circuit except slower. A PVC is slower because a hardwired, end-to-end connection is not provided. The first time a connection is requested, the appropriate switches and circuits must be established through the network to provide the interconnection. A PVC identifies the routing between two predetermined subscribers of the network that is used for all subsequent messages. With a PVC, a source and destination address are unnecessary because the two users are fixed.

5-9-2 Virtual Call

A *virtual call* (VC) is logically equivalent to making a telephone call through the DDD network except no direct end-to-end connection is made. A VC is a one-to-many arrangement. Any VC subscriber can access any other VC subscriber through a network of switches and communication channels. Virtual calls are temporary virtual connections that use common usage equipment and circuits. The source must provide its address and the address of the destination before a VC can be completed.

5-9-3 Datagram

A *datagram* (DG) is, at best, vaguely defined by X.25 and, until it is completely outlined, has very limited usefulness. With a DG, users send small packets of data into the network. Each packet is self-contained and travels through the network independent of other packets of the same message by whatever means available. The network does not acknowledge packets, nor does it guarantee successful transmission. However, if a message will fit into a single packet, a DG is somewhat reliable. This is called a *single-packet-per-segment* protocol.

5-9-4 X.25 Packet Format

A virtual call is the most efficient service offered for a packet network. There are two packet formats used with virtual calls: a call request packet and a data transfer packet.

5-9-4-1 Call request packet. Figure 5-10 shows the field format for a call request packet. The delimiting sequence is 01111110 (an HDLC flag), and the error-detection/correction mechanism is CRC-16 with ARQ. The link address field and the control field have little use and, therefore, are seldom used with packet networks. The rest of the fields are defined in sequence.

Format identifier. The format identifier identifies whether the packet is a new call request or a previously established call. The format identifier also identifies the packet numbering sequence (either 0–7 or 0–127).

Logical channel identifier (*LCI*). The LCI is a 12-bit binary number that identifies the source and destination users for a given virtual call. After a source user has

Flag	Link address field	Link control field	Format identifier	Logical channel identifier	Packet type	Calling address length	Called address length	Called address up to	Calling address up to
8 bits	8 bits	8 bits	4 bits	12 bits	8 bits	4 bits	4 bits	60 bits	60 bits

Null field	Facilities length field	Facilities field up to	Protocol ID	User data up to	Frame check sequence	Flag
2 zeros	6 bits	512 bits	32 bits	96 bits	16 bits	8 bits

FIGURE 5-10   X.25 call request packet format

gained access to the network and has identified the destination user, they are assigned an LCI. In subsequent packets, the source and destination addresses are unnecessary; only the LCI is needed. When two users disconnect, the LCI is relinquished and can be reassigned to new users. There are 4096 LCIs available. Therefore, there may be as many as 4096 virtual calls established at any given time.

Packet type. This field is used to identify the function and the content of the packet (new request, call clear, call reset, and so on).

Calling address length. This four-bit field gives the number of digits (in binary) that appear in the calling address field. With four bits, up to 15 digits can be specified.

Called address length. This field is the same as the calling address field except that it identifies the number of digits that appear in the called address field.

Called address. This field contains the destination address. Up to 15 BCD digits (60 bits) can be assigned to a destination user.

Calling address. This field is the same as the called address field except that it contains up to 15 BCD digits that can be assigned to a source user.

Facilities length field. This field identifies (in binary) the number of eight-bit octets present in the facilities field.

Facilities field. This field contains up to 512 bits of optional network facility information, such as reverse billing information, closed user groups, and whether it is a simplex transmit or simplex receive connection.

Protocol identifier. This 32-bit field is reserved for the subscriber to insert user-level protocol functions such as log-on procedures and user identification practices.

User data field. Up to 96 bits of user data can be transmitted with a call request packet. These are unnumbered data that are not confirmed. This field is generally used for user passwords.

5-9-4-2 Data transfer packet.   Figure 5-11 shows the field format for a data transfer packet. A data transfer packet is similar to a call request packet except that a data transfer packet has considerably less overhead and can accommodate a much larger user data field. The data transfer packet contains a send-and-receive packet sequence field that was not included with the call request format.

The flag, link address, link control, format identifier, LCI, and FCS fields are identical to those used with the call request packet. The send and receive packet sequence fields are described as follows:

Send packet sequence field. The P(s) field is used in the same manner that the *ns* and *nr* sequences are used with SDLC and HDLC. P(s) is analogous to *ns,* and P(r) is analogous

Flag	Link address field	Link control field	Format identifier	Logical channel identifier	Send packet sequence number P(s)	Null field
8 bits	8 bits	8 bits	4 bits	12 bits	3 or 7 bits	5 or 1 zeros

Receive packet sequence number P(r)	Null field	User data	Frame check sequence	Flag
3 or 7 bits	5 or 1 zeros	up to 1024 bits	16 bits	8 bits

FIGURE 5-11   X.25 data transfer packet format

to *nr.* Each successive data transfer packet is assigned the next P(s) number in sequence. The P(s) can be a 14- or seven-bit binary number and, thus, number packets from either 0–7 or 0–127. The numbering sequence is identified in the format identifier. The send packet field always contains eight bits, and the unused bits are reset.

Receive packet sequence field. P(r) is used to confirm received packets and call for retransmission of packets received in error (ARQ). The I field in a data transfer packet can have considerably more source information than an I field in a call request packet.

5-9-5   The X Series of Recommended Standards
X.25 is part of the X series of ITU-T-recommended standards for public data networks. The X series is classified into two categories: X.1 through X.39, which deal with services and facilities, terminals, and interfaces, and X.40 through X.199, which deal with network architecture, transmission, signaling, switching, maintenance, and administrative arrangements. Table 5-6 lists the most important X standards with their titles and descriptions.

5-10   INTEGRATED SERVICES DIGITAL NETWORK

The data and telephone communications industry is continually changing to meet the demands of contemporary telephone, video, and computer communications systems. Today, more and more people have a need to communicate with each other than ever before. In order to meet these needs, old standards are being updated and new standards developed and implemented almost on a daily basis.

The *Integrated Services Digital Network* (ISDN) is a proposed network designed by the major telephone companies in conjunction with the ITU-T with the intent of providing worldwide telecommunications support of voice, data, video, and facsimile information within the same network (in essence, ISDN is the integrating of a wide range of services into a single multipurpose network). ISDN is a network that proposes to interconnect an unlimited number of independent users through a common communications network.

To date, only a small number of ISDN facilities have been developed; however, the telephone industry is presently implementing an ISDN system so that in the near future, subscribers will access the ISDN system using existing public telephone and data networks. The basic principles and evolution of ISDN have been outlined by the International Telecommunication Union-Telephony (ITU-T) in its recommendation ITU-T I.120 (1984). ITU-T I.120 lists the following principles and evolution of ISDN.

Table 5-6   ITU-T X Series Standards

X.1	International user classes of service in public data networks. Assigns numerical class designations to different terminal speeds and types.
X.2	International user services and facilities in public data networks. Specifies essential and additional services and facilities.
X.3	Packet assembly/disassembly facility (PAD) in a public data network. Describes the packet assembler/disassembler, which normally is used at a network gateway to allow connection of a start/stop terminal to a packet network.
X.20bis	Use on public data networks of DTE designed for interfacing to asynchronous full-duplex V-series modems. Allows use of V.24/V.28 (essentially the same as EIA RS-232).
X.21bis	Use on public data networks of DTE designed for interfacing to synchronous full-duplex V-series modems. Allows use of V.24/V.28 (essentially the same as EIA RS-232) or V.35.
X.25	Interface between DTE and DCE for terminals operating in the packet mode on public data networks. Defines the architecture of three levels of protocols existing in the serial interface cable between a packet mode terminal and a gateway to a packet network.
X.28	DTE/DCE interface for a start/stop mode DTE accessing the PAD in a public data network situated in the same country. Defines the architecture of protocols existing in a serial interface cable between a start/stop terminal and an X.3 PAD.
X.29	Procedures for the exchange of control information and user data between a PAD and a packet mode DTE or another PAD. Defines the architecture of protocols behind the X.3 PAD, either between two PADs or between a PAD and a packet mode terminal on the other side of the network.
X.75	Terminal and transit call control procedures and data transfer system on international circuits between packet-switched data networks. Defines the architecture of protocols between two public packet networks.
X.121	International numbering plan for public data networks. Defines a numbering plan including code assignments for each nation.

5-10-1   Principles of ISDN

The main feature of the ISDN concept is to support a wide range of voice (telephone) and nonvoice (digital data) applications in the same network using a limited number of standardized facilities. ISDNs support a wide variety of applications, including both switched and nonswitched (dedicated) connections. Switched connections include both circuit- and packet-switched connections and their concatenations. Whenever practical, new services introduced into an ISDN should be compatible with 64-kbps switched digital connections. The 64-kbps digital connection is the basic building block of ISDN.

An ISDN will contain intelligence for the purpose of providing service features, maintenance, and network management functions. In other words, ISDN is expected to provide services beyond the simple setting up of switched circuit calls.

A layered protocol structure should be used to specify the access procedures to an ISDN and can be mapped into the open system interconnection (OSI) model. Standards already developed for OSI-related applications can be used for ISDN, such as X.25 level 3 for access to packet switching services.

It is recognized that ISDNs may be implemented in a variety of configurations according to specific national situations. This accommodates both single-source or competitive national policy.

5-10-2   Evolution of ISDN

ISDNs will be based on the concepts developed for telephone ISDNs and may evolve by progressively incorporating additional functions and network features including those of any other dedicated networks such as circuit and packet switching for data so as to provide for existing and new services.

The transition from an existing network to a comprehensive ISDN may require a period of time extending over one or more decades. During this period, arrangements must be developed for the internetworking of services on ISDNs and services on other networks.

FIGURE 5-12   Subscriber's conceptual view of ISDN

In the evolution toward an ISDN, digital end-to-end connectivity will be obtained via plant and equipment used in existing networks, such as digital transmission, time-division multiplex, and/or space-division multiplex switching. Existing relevant recommendations for these constituent elements of an ISDN are contained in the appropriate series of recommendations of ITU-T and CCIR.

In the early stages of the evolution of ISDNs, some interim user-network arrangements may need to be adopted in certain countries to facilitate early penetration of digital service capabilities. An evolving ISDN may also include at later stages switched connections at bit rates higher and lower than 64 kbps.

5-10-3   Conceptual View of ISDN

Figure 5-12 shows a view of how ISDN can be conceptually viewed by a subscriber (customer) of the system. Customers gain access to the ISDN system through a local interface connected to a digital transmission medium called a *digital pipe*. There are several sizes of pipe available with varying capacities (i.e., bit rates), depending on customer need. For example, a residential customer may require only enough capacity to accommodate a telephone and a personal computer. However, an office complex may require a pipe with sufficient capacity to handle a large number of digital telephones interconnected through an on-premise private branch exchange (PBX) or a large number of computers on a local area network (LAN).

Figure 5-13 shows the ISDN user network, which illustrates the variety of network users and the need for more than one capacity pipe. A single residential telephone is at the low end of the ISDN demand curve, followed by a multiple-drop arrangement serving a telephone, a personal computer, and a home alarm system. Industrial complexes would be at the high end of the demand curve, as they require sufficient capacity to handle hundreds of telephones and several LANs. Although a pipe has a fixed capacity, the traffic on the pipe can be comprised of data from a dynamic variety of sources with varying signal types and bit rates that have been multiplexed into a single high-capacity pipe. Therefore, a customer can gain access to both circuit- and packet-switched services through the same

☐ ISDN user-to-network interface

FIGURE 5-13   ISDN user network

pipe. Because of the obvious complexity of ISDN, it requires a rather complex control system to facilitate multiplexing and demultiplexing data to provide the required services.

5-10-4   ISDN Objectives

The key objectives of developing a worldwide ISDN system are the following:

1. *System standardization.* Ensure universal access to the network.
2. *Achieving transparency.* Allow customers to use a variety of protocols and applications.
3. *Separating functions.* ISDN should not provide services that preclude competitiveness.
4. *Variety of configurations.* Provide private-line (leased) and switched services.
5. *Addressing cost-related tariffs.* ISDN service should be directly related to cost and independent of the nature of the data.
6. *Migration.* Provide a smooth transition while evolving.
7. *Multiplexed support.* Provide service to low-capacity personal subscribers as well as to large companies.

5-10-5   ISDN Architecture

Figure 5-14 shows a block diagram of the architecture for ISDN functions. The ISDN network is designed to support an entirely new physical connector for the customer, a digital subscriber loop, and a variety of transmission services.

A common physical is defined to provide a standard interface connection. A single interface will be used for telephones, computer terminals, and video equipment. Therefore, various protocols are provided that allow the exchange of control information between the customer's device and the ISDN network. There are three basic types of ISDN channels:

1. B channel: 64 kbps
2. D channel: 16 kbps or 64 kbps
3. H channel: 384 kbps (H_0), 1536 kbps (H_{11}), or 1920 kbps (H_{12})

ISDN standards specify that residential users of the network (i.e., the subscribers) be provided a *basic access* consisting of three full-duplex, time-division multiplexed digital channels, two operating at 64 kbps (designated the B channels, for *bearer*) and one at 16 kbps (designated the D channel, for *data*). The B and D bit rates were selected to be compatible with existing DS1–DS4 digital carrier systems. The D channel is used for carrying signaling

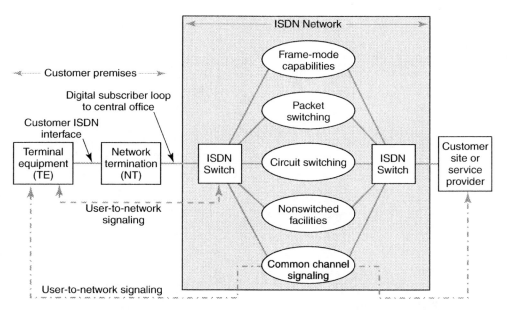

FIGURE 5-14 ISDN architecture

information and for exchanging network control information. One B channel is used for digitally encoded voice and the other for applications such as data transmission, PCM-encoded digitized voice, and videotex. The 2B + D service is sometimes called the *basic rate interface* (BRI). BRI systems require bandwidths that can accommodate two 64-kbps B channels and one 16-kbps D channel plus framing, synchronization, and other overhead bits for a total bit rate of 192 kbps. The H channels are used to provide higher bit rates for special services such as fast facsimile, video, high-speed data, and high-quality audio.

There is another service called the *primary service, primary access,* or *primary rate interface* (PRI) that will provide multiple 64-kbps channels intended to be used by the higher-volume subscribers to the network. In the United States, Canada, Japan, and Korea, the primary rate interface consists of 23 64-kbps B channels and one 64-kbps D channel (23B + D) for a combined bit rate of 1.544 Mbps. In Europe, the primary rate interface uses 30 64-kbps B channels and one 64-kbps D channel for a combined bit rate of 2.048 Mbps.

It is intended that ISDN provide a circuit-switched B channel with the existing telephone system; however, packet-switched B channels for data transmission at nonstandard rates would have to be created.

The subscriber's loop, as with the twisted-pair cable used with a common telephone, provides the physical signal path from the subscriber's equipment to the ISDN central office. The subscriber loop must be capable of supporting full-duplex digital transmission for both basic and primary data rates. Ideally, as the network grows, optical fiber cables will replace the metallic cables.

Table 5-7 lists the services provided to ISDN subscribers. BC designates a circuit-switched B channel, BP designates a packet-switched B channel, and D designates a D channel.

5-10-6 ISDN System Connections and Interface Units

ISDN subscriber units and interfaces are defined by their function and reference within the network. Figure 5-15 shows how users may be connected to an ISDN. As the figure shows, subscribers must access the network through one of two different types of entry devices: *terminal equipment type 1* (TE1) or *terminal equipment type 2* (TE2). TE1 equipment supports standard ISDN interfaces and, therefore, requires no protocol translation. Data enter

Table 5-7   ISDN Services

Service	Transmission Rate	Channel
Telephone	64 kbps	BC
System alarms	100 bps	D
Utility company metering	100 bps	D
Energy management	100 bps	D
Video	2.4–64 kbps	BP
Electronic mail	4.8–64 kbps	BP
Facsimile	4.8–64 kbps	BC
Slow-scan television	64 kbps	BC

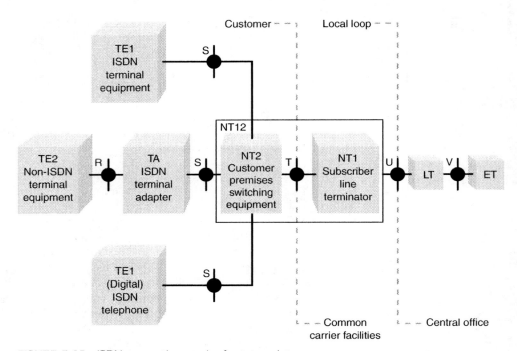

FIGURE 5-15   ISDN connections and reference points

the network and are immediately configured into ISDN protocol format. TE2 equipment is classified as non-ISDN; thus, computer terminals are connected to the system through physical interfaces such as the RS-232 and host computers with X.25. Translation between non-ISDN data protocol and ISDN protocol is performed in a device called a *terminal adapter* (TA), which converts the user's data into the 64-kbps ISDN channel B or the 16-kbps channel D format and X.25 packets into ISDN packet formats. If any additional signaling is required, it is added by the terminal adapter. The terminal adapters can also support traditional analog telephones and facsimile signals by using a 3.1-kHz audio service channel. The analog signals are digitized and put into ISDN format before entering the network.

User data at points designated as *reference point S* (*system*) are presently in ISDN format and provide the 2B + D data at 192 kbps. These reference points separate user terminal equipment from network-related system functions. *Reference point T* (*terminal*) locations correspond to a minimal ISDN network termination at the user's location. These reference points separate the network provider's equipment from the user's equipment. *Reference point R* (*rate*) provides an interface between non-ISDN-compatible user equipment and the terminal adapters.

Network termination 1 (NT1) provides the functions associated with the physical interface between the user and the common carrier and are designated by the letter *T* (these functions correspond to OSI layer 1). The NT1 is a boundary to the network and may be controlled by the ISDN provider. The NT1 performs line maintenance functions and supports multiple channels at the physical level (e.g., 2B + D). Data from these channels are time-division multiplexed together. Network terminal 2 devices are intelligent and can perform *concentration* and switching functions (functionally up through OSI level 3). NT2 terminations can also be used to terminate several S-point connections and provide local switching functions and two-wire-to-four-wire and four-wire-to-two-wire conversions. *U-reference points* refer to interfaces between the common carrier subscriber loop and the *central office switch*. A *U loop* is the media interface point between an NT1 and the central office.

Network termination 1,2 (NT12) constitutes one piece of equipment that combines the functions of NT1 and NT2. U loops are terminated at the central office by a *line termination* (LT) unit, which provides physical layer interface functions between the central office and the loop lines. The LT unit is connected to an *exchange termination* (ET) at *reference point* V. An ET routes data to an outgoing channel or central office user.

There are several types of transmission channels in addition to the B and D types described in the previous section. They include the following:

HO channel. This interface supports multiple 384-kbps HO channels. These structures are 3HO + D and 4HO + D for the 1.544-Mbps interface and 5HO + D for the 2.048-Mbps interface.

H11 channel. This interface consists of one 1.536-Mbps H11 channel (24 64-kbps channels).

H12 channel. European version of H11 that uses 30 channels for a combined data rate of 1.92 Mbps.

E channel. Packet switched using 64 kbps (similar to the standard D channel).

5-10-7 Broadband ISDN

Broadband ISDN (BISDN) is defined by the ITU-T as a service that provides transmission channels capable of supporting transmission rates greater than the primary data rate. With BISDN, services requiring data rates of a magnitude beyond those provided by ISDN, such as video transmission, will become available. With the advent of BISDN, the original concept of ISDN is being referred to as *narrowband* ISDN.

In 1988, the ITU-T first recommended as part of its I-series recommendations relating to BISDN: I.113, *Vocabulary of terms for broadband aspects of ISDN,* and I.121, *Broadband aspects of ISDN.* These two documents are a consensus concerning the aspects of the future of BISDN. They outline preliminary descriptions of future standards and development work.

The new BISDN standards are based on the concept of an *asynchronous transfer mode* (ATM), which will incorporate optical fiber cable as the transmission medium for data transmission. The BISDN specifications set a maximum length of 1 km per cable length but are making provisions for repeated interface extensions. The expected data rates on the optical fiber cables will be either 11 Mbps, 155 Mbps, or 600 Mbps, depending on the specific application and the location of the fiber cable within the network.

ITU-T classifies the services that could be provided by BISDN as interactive and distribution services. *Interactive services* include those in which there is a two-way exchange

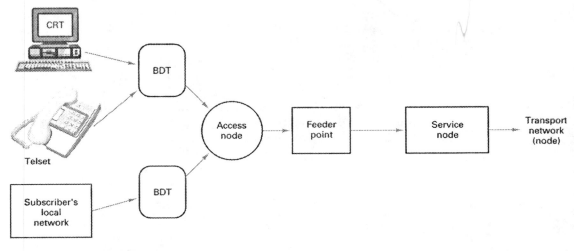

FIGURE 5-16 BISDN access

of information (excluding control signaling) between two subscribers or between a subscriber and a service provider. *Distribution services* are those in which information transfer is primarily from service provider to subscriber. On the other hand, *conversational services* will provide a means for bidirectional end-to-end data transmission, in real time, between two subscribers or between a subscriber and a service provider.

The authors of BISDN composed specifications that require the new services meet both existing ISDN interface specifications and the new BISDN needs. A standard ISDN terminal and a *broadband terminal interface* (BTI) will be serviced by the *subscriber's premise network* (SPN), which will multiplex incoming data and transfer them to the *broadband node*. The broadband node is called a *broadband network termination* (BNT), which codes the data information into smaller packets used by the BISDN network. Data transmission within the BISDN network can be asymmetric (i.e., access on to and off of the network may be accomplished at different transmission rates, depending on system requirements).

5-10-7-1 BISDN configuration.   Figure 5-16 shows how access to the BISDN network is accomplished. Each peripheral device is interfaced to the *access node* of a BISDN network through a *broadband distant terminal* (BDT). The BDT is responsible for the electrical-to-optical conversion, multiplexing of peripherals, and maintenance of the subscriber's local system. Access nodes concentrate several BDTs into high-speed optical fiber lines directed through a *feeder point* into a *service node*. Most of the control functions for system access are managed by the service node, such as call processing, administrative functions, and switching and maintenance functions. The functional modules are interconnected in a star configuration and include switching, administrative, gateway, and maintenance modules. The interconnection of the function modules is shown in Figure 5-17. The central control hub acts as the end user interface for control signaling and data traffic maintenance. In essence, it oversees the operation of the modules.

Subscriber terminals near the central office may bypass the access nodes entirely and be directly connected to the BISDN network through a service node. BISDN networks that use optical fiber cables can utilize much wider bandwidths and, consequently, have higher transmission rates and offer more channel-handling capacity than ISDN systems.

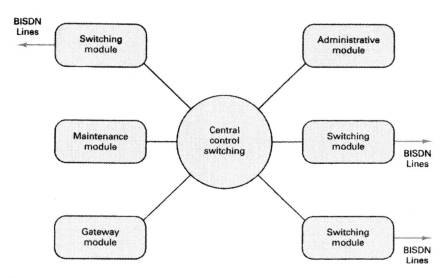

FIGURE 5-17   BISDN functional module interconnections

5-10-7-2 Broadband channel rates. The CCITT has published preliminary definitions of new broadband channel rates that will be added to the existing ISDN narrowband channel rates:

1. H21: 32.768 Mbps
2. H22: 43 Mbps to 45 Mbps
3. H4: 132 Mbps to 138.24 Mbps

The H21 and H22 data rates are intended to be used for full-motion video transmission for videoconferencing, video telephone, and video messaging. The H4 data rate is intended for bulk data transfer of text, facsimile, and enhanced video information. The H21 data rate is equivalent to 512 64-kbps channels. The H22 and H4 data rates must be multiples of the basic 64-kbps transmission rate.

5-11 ASYNCHRONOUS TRANSFER MODE

Asynchronous transfer mode (ATM) is a relatively new data communications technology that uses a high-speed form of packet switching network for the transmission media. ATM was developed in 1988 by the ITU-T as part of the BISDN. ATM is one means by which data can enter and exit the BISDN network in an asynchronous (time-independent) fashion. ATM is intended to be a carrier service that provides an integrated, high-speed communications network for corporate private networks. ATM can handle all kinds of communications traffic, including voice, data, image, video, high-quality music, and multimedia. In addition, ATM can be used in both LAN and WAN network environments, providing seamless internetworking between the two. Some experts claim that ATM may eventually replace both private leased T1 digital carrier systems and on-premise switching equipment.

Conventional electronic switching (ESS) machines currently utilize a central processor to establish switching paths and route traffic through a network. ATM switches, in contrast, will include self-routing procedures where individual cells (short, fixed-length packets of data) containing subscriber data will route their own way through the ATM switching

FIGURE 5-18   ATM cell structure

GFC—generic flow control field   PT —payload type identifier
VPI —virtual path identifier   CLP —cell loss priority
VCI —virtual channel identifier   HEC—header error control

FIGURE 5-19   ATM five-byte header field structure

network in real time using their own address instead of relying on an external process to establish the switching path.

ATM uses *virtual channels* (VCs) and *virtual paths* (VPs) to route cells through a network. In essence, a virtual channel is merely a connection between a source and a destination, which may entail establishing several ATM links between local switching centers. With ATM, all communications occur on the virtual channel, which preserves cell sequence. On the other hand, a virtual path is a group of virtual channels connected between two points that could compromise several ATM links.

ATM incorporates *labeled channels* that are transferable at fixed data rates anywhere from 16 kbps up to the maximum rate of the carrier system. Once data have entered the network, they are transferred into fixed time slots called *cells*. An ATM cell contains all the network information needed to relay individual cells from node to node over a preestablished ATM connection. Figure 5-18 shows the ATM cell structure, which is a fixed-length data packet only 53 bytes long, including a five-byte header and a 48-byte information field. Fixed-length cells provide the following advantages:

1. A uniform transmission time per cell ensures a more uniform transit-time characteristic for the network as a whole.
2. A short cell requires a shorter time to assemble and, thus, shorter delay characteristics for voice.
3. Short cells are easier to transfer over fixed-width processor buses, it is easier to buffer the data in link queues, and they require less processor logic.

5-11-1   ATM Header Field

Figure 5-19 shows the five-byte ATM header field, which includes the following fields: generic flow control field, virtual path identifier, virtual channel identifier, payload type identifier, cell loss priority, and header error control.

Generic flow control field (GFC). The GFC field uses the first four bits of the first byte of the header field. The GFC controls the flow of traffic across the user network interface (UNI) and into the network.

Virtual path identifier (*VPI*) *and virtual channel identifier* (*VCI*). The 24 bits immediately following the GFC are used for the ATM address.

Payload type identifier (*PT*). The first three bits of the second half of byte 4 specify the type of message (payload) in cell. With three bits, there are eight different types of payloads possible. At the present time, however, types 0 to 3 are used for identifying the type of user data, types 4 and 5 indicate management information, and types 6 and 7 are reserved for future use.

Cell loss priority (*CLP*). The last bit of byte 4 is used to indicate whether a cell is eligible to be discarded by the network during congested traffic periods. The CLP bit is set by the user or cleared by the user. If set, the network may discard the cell during times of heavy use.

Header error control (*HEC*). The last byte of the header field is for error control and is used to detect and correct single-bit errors that occur in the header field only; the HEC does not serve as an entire cell check character. The value placed in the HEC is computed from the four previous bytes of the header field. The HEC provides some protection against the delivery of cells to the wrong destination address.

5-11-1-1 ATM information field. The 48-byte information field is reserved for user data. Insertion of data into the information field of a cell is a function of the upper half of layer 2 of the ISO-OSI seven-layer protocol hierarchy. This layer is specifically called the ATM Adaptation Layer (AAL). The AAL gives ATM the versatility necessary to facilitate, in a single format, a wide variety of different types of services ranging from continuous processes signals, such as voice transmission, to messages carrying highly fragmented bursts of data such as those produced from LANs. Because most user data occupy more than 48 bytes, the AAL divides information into 48-byte segments and places them into a series of segments. The five types of AALs are the following:

1. *Constant bit rate* (*CBR*). CBR information fields are designed to accommodate PCM-TDM traffic, which allows the ATM network to emulate voice or DSN services.

2. *Variable bit rate (VBR) timing-sensitive services.* This type of AAL is currently undefined; however, it is reserved for future data services requiring transfer of timing information between terminal points as well as data (i.e., packet video).

3. *Connection-oriented VBR data transfer.* Type 3 information fields transfer VBR data such as impulsive data generated at irregular intervals between two subscribers over a preestablished data link. The data link is established by network signaling procedures that are very similar to those used by the public switched telephone network. This type of service is intended for large, long-duration data transfers, such as file transfers or file backups.

4. *Connectionless VBR data transfer.* This AAL type provides for transmission of VBR data that does not have a preestablished connection. Type 4 information fields are intended to be used for short, highly bursty types of transmissions, such as those generated from a LAN.

5-11-2 ATM Network Components

Figure 5-20 shows an ATM network, which is comprised of three primary components: ATM endpoints, ATM switches, and transmission paths.

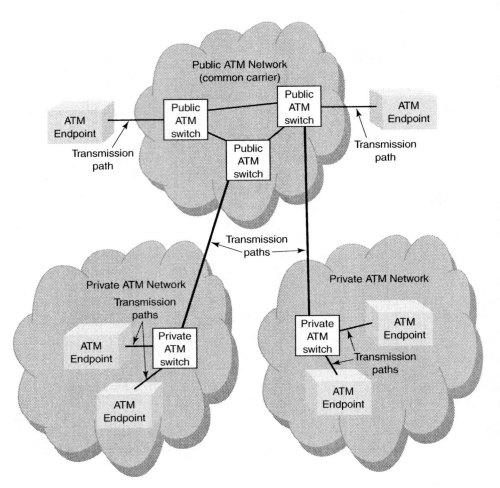

FIGURE 5-20   ATM network components

5-11-2-1 ATM endpoints.   *ATM endpoints* are shown in Figure 5-21. As shown in the figure, endpoints are the source and destination of subscriber data and, therefore, they are sometimes called *end systems.* Endpoints can be connected directly to either a public or a private ATM switch. An ATM endpoint can be as simple as an ordinary personal computer equipped with an ATM network interface card. An ATM endpoint could also be a special-purpose network component that services several ordinary personal computers, such as an Ethernet LAN.

5-11-2-2 ATM switches.   The primary function of an *ATM switch* is to route information from a source endpoint to a destination endpoint. ATM switches are sometimes called *intermediate systems,* as they are located between two endpoints. ATM switches fall into two general categories: public and private.

> *Public ATM switches.* A *public ATM switch* is simply a portion of a public service provider's switching system where the service provider could be a local telephone company or a long-distance carrier, such as AT&T. An ATM switch is sometimes called a *network node.*
> *Private ATM switches. Private ATM switches* are owned and maintained by a private company and sometimes called *customer premise nodes.* Private ATM switches are

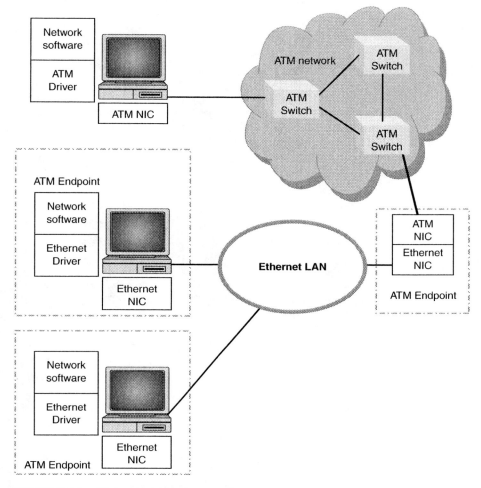

FIGURE 5-21   ATM endpoint implementations

sold to ATM customers by many of the same computer networking infrastructure vendors who provide ATM customers with network interface cards and connectivity devices, such as repeaters, hubs, bridges, switches, and routers.

5-11-2-3 Transmission paths. ATM switches and ATM endpoints are interconnected with physical communications paths called transmission paths. A transmission path can be any of the common transmission media, such as twisted-pair cable or optical fiber cable.

5-12   LOCAL AREA NETWORKS

Studies have indicated that most (80%) of the communications among data terminals and other data equipment occurs within a relatively small local environment. A *local area network* (LAN) provides the most economical and effective means of handling local data communication needs. A LAN is typically a privately owned data communications system in which the users share resources, including software. LANs provide two-way communications between a large variety of data communications terminals within a

FIGURE 5-22 Typical local area network component configuration

limited geographical area such as within the same room, building, or building complex. Most LANs link equipment that is within a few miles of each other.

Figure 5-22 shows several personal computers (PCs) connected to a LAN to share common resources such as a modem, printer, or server. The server may be a more powerful computer than the other PCs sharing the network, or it may simply have more disk storage space. The server "serves" information to the other PCs on the network in the form of software and data information files. A PC server is analogous to a mainframe computer except on a much smaller scale.

LANs allow for a room full or more of computers to share common resources such as printers and modems. The average PC uses these devices only a small percentage of the time, so there is no need to dedicate individual printers and modems to each PC. To print a document or file, a PC simply sends the information over the network to the server. The server organizes and prioritizes the documents and then sends them, one document at a time, to the common usage printer. Meanwhile, the PCs are free to continue performing other useful tasks. When a PC needs a modem, the network establishes a *virtual connection* between the modem and the PC. The network is transparent to the virtual connection, which allows the PC to communicate with the modem as if they were connected directly to each other.

LANS allow people to send and receive messages and documents through the network much quicker than they could be sent through a paper mail system. *Electronic mail* (e-mail) is a communications system that allows users to send messages to each other through their computers. E-mail enables any PC on the network to send or receive information from any other PC on the network as long as the PCs and the server use the same or compatible software. E-mail can also be used to interconnect users on different networks in different cities, states, countries, or even continents. To send an e-mail message, a user at one PC sends its address and message along with the destination address to the server. The server effectively "relays" the message to the destination PC if they are subscribers to the same network. If the destination PC is busy or not available for whatever reason, the server stores the message and resends it later. The server is the only computer that has to keep track of the location and address of all the other PCs on the network. To send e-mail to subscribers of other networks, the server relays the message to the server on the destination user's network, which in turn relays the mail to the destination PC. E-mail can be used to send text information (letters) as well as program files, graphics, audio, and even video. This is referred to as multimedia communications.

LANs are used extensively to interconnect a wide range of data services, including the following:

Data terminals	Data modems
Laser printers	Databases
Graphic plotters	Word processors
Large-volume disk and tape storage devices	Public switched telephone networks
Facsimile machines	Digital carrier systems (T carriers)
Personal computers	E-mail servers
Mainframe computers	

5-12-1 LAN System Considerations

The capabilities of a LAN are established primarily by three factors: *topology, transmission medium,* and *access control protocol.* Together these three factors determine the type of data, rate of transmission, efficiency, and applications that a network can effectively support.

5-12-1-1 LAN topologies.
The topology or physical architecture of a LAN identifies how the stations (terminals, printers, modems, and so on) are interconnected. The transmission media used with LANs include metallic *twisted-wire pairs, coaxial cable,* and *optical fiber cables.* Presently, most LANs use coaxial cable; however, optical fiber cable systems are being installed in many new networks. Fiber systems can operate at higher transmission bit rates and have a larger capacity to transfer information than coaxial cables.

The most common LAN topologies are the star, bus, bus tree, and ring, which are illustrated in Figure 5-23.

5-12-1-2 Star topology.
The preeminent feature of the star topology is that each station is radially linked to a *central node* through a direct point-to-point connection as shown in Figure 5-23a. With a star configuration, a transmission from one station enters the central node, where it is retransmitted on all the outgoing links. Therefore, although the circuit arrangement physically resembles a star, it is logically configured as a bus (i.e., transmissions from any station are received by all other stations).

Central nodes offer a convenient location for system or station troubleshooting because all traffic between outlying nodes must flow through the central node. The central node is sometimes referred to as *central control, star coupler,* or *central switch* and typically is a computer. The star configuration is best adapted to applications where most of the communications occur between the central node and outlying nodes. The star arrangement is also well suited to systems where there is a large demand to communicate with only a few of the remote terminals. Time-sharing systems are generally configured with a star topology. A star configuration is also well suited for word processing and database management applications.

Star couplers can be implemented either passively or actively. When passive couplers are used with a metallic transmission medium, transformers in the coupler provide an electromagnetic linkage through the coupler, which passes incoming signals on to outgoing links. If optical fiber cables are used for the transmission media, coupling can be achieved by fusing fibers together. With active couplers, digital circuitry in the central node acts as a repeater. Incoming data are simply regenerated and repeated on to all outgoing lines.

One disadvantage of a star topology is that the network is only as reliable as the central node. When the central node fails, the system fails. If one or more outlying nodes fail, however, the rest of the users can continue to use the remainder of the network. When failure of any single entity within a network is critical to the point that it will disrupt service on the entire network, that entity is referred to as a *critical resource.* Thus, the central node in a star configuration is a critical resource.

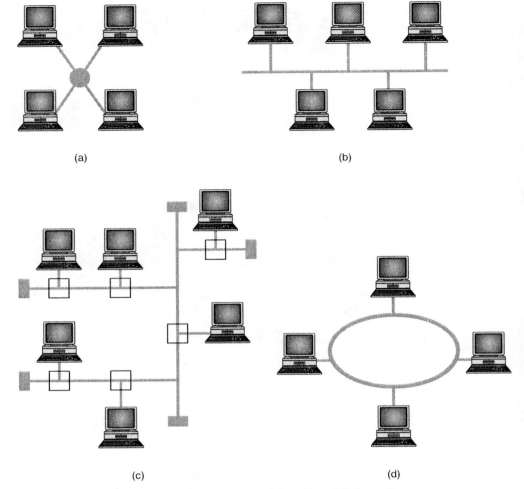

FIGURE 5-23 LAN Topologies: (a) star; (b) bus; (c) tree bus; (d) ring or loop

5-12-1-3 Bus topology. In essence, the bus topology is a multipoint or multidrop circuit configuration where individual nodes are interconnected by a common, shared communications channel as shown in Figure 5-5b. With the bus topology, all stations connect, using appropriate interfacing hardware, directly to a common linear transmission medium, generally referred to as a *bus*. In a bus configuration, network control is not centralized to a particular node. In fact, the most distinguishing feature of a bus LAN is that control is distributed among all the nodes connected to the LAN. Data transmissions on a bus network are usually in the form of small packets containing user addresses and data. When one station desires to transmit data to another station, it monitors the bus first to determine if it is currently being used. If no other stations are communicating over the network (i.e., the network is clear), the monitoring station can commence to transmit its data. When one station begins transmitting, all other stations become receivers. Each receiver must monitor all transmission on the network and determine which are intended for them. When a station identifies its address on a received data message, it acts on it or it ignores that transmission.

One advantage of a bus topology is that no special routing or circuit switching is required and, therefore, it is not necessary to store and retransmit messages intended for other nodes. This advantage eliminates a considerable amount of message identification overhead and processing time. However, with heavy-usage systems, there is a high likelihood that more than one station may desire to transmit at the same time. When transmissions from two or more stations occur simultaneously, a data collision occurs, disrupting data communications on the entire network. Obviously, a priority contention scheme is necessary to handle data collision. Such a priority scheme is called *carrier sense, multiple access with collision detect* (CSMA/CD), which is discussed in a later section of this chapter.

Because network control is not centralized in a bus configuration, a node failure will not disrupt data flow on the entire LAN. The critical resource in this case is not a node but instead the bus itself. A failure anywhere along the bus opens the network and, depending on the versatility of the communications channel, may disrupt communication on the entire network.

The addition of new nodes on a bus can sometimes be a problem because gaining access to the bus cable may be a cumbersome task, especially if it is enclosed within a wall, floor, or ceiling. One means of reducing installation problems is to add secondary buses to the primary communications channel. By branching off into other bases, a multiple bus structure called a *tree bus* is formed. Figure 5-23c shows a tree bus configuration.

5-12-1-4 Ring topology. With a ring topology, adjacent stations are interconnected by repeaters in a closed-loop configuration as shown in Figure 5-23d. Each node participates as a repeater between two adjacent links within the ring. The repeaters are relatively simple devices capable of receiving data from one link and retransmitting them on a second link. Messages, usually in packet form, are propagated in the simplex mode (one-way only) from node to node around the ring until it has circled the entire loop and returned to the originating node, where it is verified that the data in the returned message are identical to the data originally transmitted. Hence, the network configuration serves as an inherent error-detection mechanism. The destination station(s) can acknowledge reception of the data by setting or clearing appropriate bits within the control segment of the message packet. Packets contain both source and destination address fields as well as additional network control information and user data. Each node examines incoming data packets, copying packets designated for them and acting as a repeater for all data packets by retransmitting them (bit by bit) to the next down-line repeater. A repeater should neither alter the content of received packets nor change the transmission rate.

Virtually any physical transmission medium can be used with the ring topology. Twisted-wire pairs offer low cost but severely limited transmission rates. Coaxial cables provide greater capacity than twisted-wire pairs at practically the same cost. The highest data rates, however, are achieved with optical fiber cables, except at a substantially higher installation cost.

5-12-2 LAN Transmission Formats

Two transmission techniques or formats are used with LANs, baseband and broadband, to multiplex transmissions from a multitude of stations onto a single transmission medium.

5-12-2-1 Baseband transmission format. Baseband transmission formats are defined as transmission formats that use digital signaling. In addition, baseband formats use the transmission medium as a single-channel device. Only one station can transmit at a time, and all stations must transmit and receive the same types of signals (encoding schemes, bit rates, and so on). Baseband transmission formats time-division multiplex signals onto the transmission medium. All stations can use the media but only one at a time. The entire frequency spectrum (bandwidth) is used by (or at least made available to) whichever station is presently transmitting. With a baseband format, transmissions are bidirectional. A signal inserted at any point on the transmission medium propagates in both directions to the ends, where it is absorbed. Digital signaling requires a bus topology because digital signals cannot be easily propagated through the splitters and joiners necessary in a tree bus topology. Because of transmission line losses, baseband LANs are limited to a distance of no more than a couple miles.

5-12-2-2 Broadband transmission formats. Broadband transmission formats use the connecting media as a multichannel device. Each channel occupies a different frequency band within the total allocated bandwidth (i.e., frequency-division multiplexing). Consequently, each channel can contain different modulation and encoding schemes and operate at different transmission rates. A broadband network permits voice, digital data, and video to be transmitted simultaneously over the same transmission medium. However, broadband systems are unidirectional and require RF modems, amplifiers, and more complicated transceivers than baseband systems. For this reason, baseband systems are more prevalent. Circuit components used with broadband LANs easily facilitate splitting and joining operations; consequently, both bus and tree bus topologies are allowed. Broadband systems can span much greater distances than baseband systems. Distances of up to tens of miles are possible.

The layout for a baseband system is much less complex than a broadband system and, therefore, easier and less expensive to implement. The primary disadvantages of baseband are its limited capacity and length. Broadband systems can carry a wide variety of different kinds of signals on a number of channels. By incorporating amplifiers, broadband can span much greater distances than baseband. Table 5-8 summarizes baseband and broadband transmission formats.

5-12-3 LAN Access Control Methodologies

In a practical LAN, it is very likely that more than one user may wish to use the network media at any given time. For a medium to be shared by various users, a means of controlling access is necessary. Media-sharing methods are known as *access methodologies*. Network access methodologies describe how users access the communications channel in a LAN. The first LANs were developed by computer manufacturers; they were expensive and worked only with certain types of computers with a limited number of software programs. LANs also required a high degree of technical knowledge and expertise to install and maintain. In 1980, the IEEE, in an effort to resolve problems with LANs, formed the 802 Local Area Network Standards Committee. In 1983, the committee established several recommended standards for LANs. The two most prominent standards are IEEE Standard 802.3, which addresses an access method for bus topologies called *carrier sense, multiple access with collision detection* (CSMA/CD), and IEEE Standard 802.5, which describes an access method for ring topologies called *token passing.*

Table 5-8   Baseband versus Broadband Transmission Formats

Baseband	Broadband
Uses digital signaling	Analog signaling requiring RF modems and amplifiers
Entire bandwidth used by each transmission—no FDM	FDM possible, i.e., multiple data channels (video, audio, data, etc.)
Bidirectional	Unidirectional
Bus topology	Bus or tree bus topology
Maximum length approximately 1500 m	Maximum length up to tens of kilometers
Advantages	
Less expensive	High capacity
Simpler technology	Multiple traffic types
Easier and quicker to install	More flexible circuit configurations, larger area covered
Disadvantages	
Single channel	RF modem and amplifiers required
Limited capacity	Complex installation and maintenance
Grounding problems	Double propagation delay
Limited distance	

5-12-3-1 Carrier sense, multiple access with collision detection. CSMA/CD is an access method used primarily with LANs configured in a bus topology. CSMA/CD uses the basic philosophy that, "If you have something to say, say it. If there's a problem, we'll work it out later." With CSMA/CD, any station (node) can send a message to any other station (or stations) as long as the transmission medium is free of transmissions from other stations. Stations monitor (listen to) the line to determine if the line is busy. If a station has a message to transmit but the line is busy, it waits for an idle condition before transmitting its message. If two stations transmit at the same time, a *collision* occurs. When this happens, the station first sensing the collision sends a special jamming signal to all other stations on the network. All stations then cease transmitting (*back off*) and wait a random period of time before attempting a retransmission. The random delay time for each station is different and, therefore, allows for prioritizing the stations on the network. If successive collisions occur, the back-off period for each station is doubled.

With CSMA/CD, stations must contend for the network. A station is not guaranteed access to the network. To detect the occurrence of a collision, a station must be capable of transmitting and receiving simultaneously. CSMA/CD is used by most LANs configured in a bus topology. *Ethernet* is an example of a LAN that uses CSMA/CD and is described later in this chapter.

Another factor that could possibly cause collisions with CSMA/CD is *propagation delay*. Propagation delay is the time it takes a signal to travel from a source to a destination. Because of propagation delay, it is possible for the line to appear idle when, in fact, another station is transmitting a signal that has not yet reached the monitoring station.

5-12-3-2 Token passing. *Token passing* is a network access method used primarily with LANs configured in a ring topology using either baseband or broadband transmission formats. When using *token passing* access, nodes do not contend for the right to transmit data. With token passing, a specific packet of data, called a *token,* is circulated around the ring from station to station, always in the same direction. The token is generated by a designated station known as the *active monitor.* Before a station is allowed to transmit, it must first possess the token. Each station, in turn, acquires the token and examines the data frame to determine if it is carrying a packet addressed to it. If the frame contains a packet with the receiving station's address, it copies the packet into memory, appends any messages it has to send to the token, and then relinquishes the token by retransmitting all data packets and the token to the next node on the network. With token passing, each station has equal access to the transmission medium. As with CSMA/CD, each transmitted packet contains source and destination address fields. Successful delivery of a data frame is confirmed by the destination station by setting *frame status flags,* then forwarding the frame around the ring to the original transmitting station. The packet then is removed from the frame before transmitting the token. A token cannot be used twice, and there is a time limitation on how long a token can be held. This prevents one station from disrupting data transmissions on the network by holding the token until it has a packet to transmit. When a station does not possess the token, it can only receive and transfer other packets destined to other stations.

Some 16-Mbps token ring networks use a modified form of token passing methodology where the token is relinquished as soon as a data frame has been transmitted instead of waiting until the transmitted data frame has been returned. This is known as an *early token release mechanism.*

5-13 ETHERNET

Ethernet is a baseband transmission system designed in 1972 by Robert Metcalfe and David Boggs of the Xerox Palo Alto Research Center (PARC). Metcalfe, who later founded 3COM Corporation, and his colleagues at Xerox developed the first experimental Ethernet system to interconnect a Xerox Alto personal workstation to a graphical user interface. The first experimental Ethernet system was later used to link Altos workstations to each other and to link the workstations to servers and laser printers. The signal clock for the experimental Ethernet interface was derived from the Alto's system clock, which produced a data transmission rate of 2.94 Mbps.

Metcalfe's first Ethernet was called the Alto Aloha Network; however, in 1973 Metcalfe changed the name to Ethernet to emphasize the point that the system could support any computer, not just Altos, and to stress the fact that the capabilities of his new network had evolved well beyond the original Aloha system. Metcalfe chose the name based on the word *ether,* meaning "air," "atmosphere," or "heavens," as an indirect means of describing a vital feature of the system: the physical medium (i.e., a cable). The physical medium carries data bits to all stations in much the same way that *luminiferous ether* was once believed to transport electromagnetic waves through space.

In July 1976, Metcalfe and Boggs published a landmark paper titled "Ethernet: Distributed Packet Switching for Local Computer." On December 13, 1977, Xerox Corporation received patent number 4,063,220 titled "Multipoint Data Communications System with Collision Detection." In 1979, Xerox joined forces with Intel and Digital Equipment Corporation (DEC) in an attempt to make Ethernet an industry standard. In September 1980, the three companies jointly released the first version of the first Ethernet specification called the Ethernet Blue Book, DIX 1.0 (after the initials of the three companies), or Ethernet I.

Ethernet I was replaced in November 1982 by the second version, called Ethernet II (DIX 2.0), which remains the current standard. In 1983, the 802 Working Group of the IEEE released their first standard for Ethernet technology. The formal title of the standard was *IEEE 802.3 Carrier Sense Multiple Access with Collision Detection (CSMA/CD) Access Method and Physical Layer Specifications.* The IEEE subsequently reworked several sections of the original standard, especially in the area of the frame format definition, and in 1985 they released the 802.3a standard, which was called *thin Ethernet, cheapernet,* or *10Base-2 Ethernet.* In 1985, the IEEE also released the IEEE 802.3b 10Broad36 standard, which defined a transmission rate of 10 Mbps over a coaxial cable system.

In 1987, two additional standards were released: IEEE 802.3d and IEEE 802.3e. The 802.3d standard defined the *Fiber Optic Inter-Repeater Link* (FOIRL) that used two fiber optic cables to extend the maximum distance between 10 Mbps repeaters to 1000 meters. The IEEE 802.3e standard defined a 1-Mbps standard based on twisted-pair cable, which was never widely accepted. In 1990, the IEEE introduced a major advance in Ethernet standards: IEEE 802.3i. The 802.3i standard defined 10Base-T, which permitted a 10-Mbps transmission rate over simple category 3 unshielded twisted-pair (UTP) cable. The widespread use of UTP cabling in existing buildings created a high demand for 10Base-T technology. 10Base-T also facilitated a star topology, which made it much easier to install, manage, and troubleshoot. These advantages led to a vast expansion in the use of Ethernet.

In 1993, the IEEE released the 802.3j standard for 10Base-F (FP, FB, and FL), which permitted attachment over longer distances (2000 meters) through two optical fiber cables. This standard updated and expanded the earlier FOIRL standard. In 1995, the IEEE improved the performance of Ethernet technology by a factor of 10 when it released the 100-Mbps 802.3u 100Base-T standard. This version of Ethernet is commonly known as *fast Ethernet.* Fast Ethernet supported three media types: 100Base-TX, which operates over two pairs of category 5 twisted-pair cable; 100Base-T4, which operates over four pairs of category 3 twisted-pair cable; and 100Base-FX, which operates over two multimode fibers.

In 1997, the IEEE released the 802.3x standard, which defined full-duplex Ethernet operation. Full-duplex Ethernet bypasses the normal CSMA/CD protocol and allows two stations to communicate over a point-to-point link, which effectively doubles the transfer rate by allowing each station to simultaneously transmit and receive separate data streams. In 1997, the IEEE also released the IEEE 802.3y 100Base-T2 standard for 100-Mbps operation over two pairs of category 3 balanced transmission line.

In 1998, IEEE once again improved the performance of Ethernet technology by a factor of 10 when it released the 1-Gbps 802.3z 1000Base-X standard, which is commonly called *gigabit Ethernet*. Gigabit Ethernet supports three media types: 1000Base-SX, which operates with an 850-nm laser over multimode fiber; 1000Base-LX, which operates with a 1300-nm laser over single- and multimode fiber; and 1000Base-CX, which operates over short-haul copper-shielded twisted-pair (STP) cable. In 1998, the IEEE also released the 802.3ac standard, which defines extensions to support virtual LAN (VLAN) tagging on Ethernet networks. In 1999, the release of the 802.3ab 1000Base-T standard defined 1-Gbps operation over four pairs of category 5 UTP cabling.

The topology of choice for Ethernet LANs is either a linear bus or a star, and all Ethernet systems employ carrier sense, multiple access with collision detect (CSMA/CD) for the accessing method.

5-13-1 IEEE Ethernet Standard Notation

To distinguish the various implementations of Ethernet available, the IEEE 802.3 committee has developed a concise notation format that contains information about the Ethernet system, including such items as bit rate, transmission mode, transmission medium, and segment length. The IEEE 802.3 format is

<data rate in Mbps><transmission mode><maximum segment length in hundreds of meters>

or

<data rate in Mbps><transmission mode><transmission media>

The transmission rates specified for Ethernet are 10 Mbps, 100 Mbps, and 1 Gbps. There are only two transmission modes: baseband (base) or broadband (broad). The segment length can vary, depending on the type of transmission medium, which could be coaxial cable (no designation), twisted-pair cable (T), or optical fiber (F). For example, the notation 10Base-5 means 10-Mbps transmission rate, baseband mode of transmission, with a maximum segment length of 500 meters. The notation 100Base-T specifies 100-Mbps transmission rate, baseband mode of transmission, with a twisted-pair transmission medium. The notation 100Base-F means 100-Mbps transmission rate, baseband transmission mode, with an optical fiber transmission medium.

The IEEE currently supports nine 10-Mbps standards, six 100-Mbps standards, and five 1-Gbps standards. Table 5-9 lists several of the more common types of Ethernet, their cabling options, distances supported, and topology.

Table 5-9 Current IEEE Ethernet Standards

Transmission Rate	Ethernet System	Transmission Medium	Maximum Segment Length
10 Mbps	10Base-5	Coaxial cable (RG-8 or RG-11)	500 meters
	10Base-2	Coaxial cable (RG-58)	185 meters
	10Base-T	UTP/STP category 3 or better	100 meters
	10Broad-36	Coaxial cable (75 ohm)	Varies
	10Base-FL	Optical fiber	2000 meters
	10Base-FB	Optical fiber	2000 meters
	10Base-FP	Optical fiber	2000 meters
100 Mbps	100Base-T	UTP/STP category 5 or better	100 meters
	100Base-TX	UTP/STP category 5 or better	100 meters
	100Base-FX	Optical fiber	400–2000 meters
	100Base-T4	UTP/STP category 5 or better	100 meters
1000 Mbps	1000Base-LX	Long-wave optical fiber	Varies
	1000Base-SX	Short-wave optical fiber	Varies
	1000Base-CX	Short copper jumper	Varies
	1000Base-T	UTP/STP category 5 or better	Varies

FIGURE 5-24 10 Mbps 5-4-3 Ethernet configuration

5-13-2 10-Mbps Ethernet

Figure 5-24 shows the physical layout for a 10Base-5 Ethernet system. The maximum number of cable segments supported with 10Base-5 Ethernet is five, interconnected with four repeaters or hubs. However, only three of the segments can be populated with nodes (computers). This is called the *5-4-3 rule:* five segments joined by four repeaters, but only three segments can be populated. The maximum segment length for 10Base-5 is 500 meters. Imposing maximum segment lengths are required for the CSMA/CD to operate properly. The limitations take into account Ethernet frame size, velocity of propagation on a given transmission medium, and repeater delay time to ensure collisions that occur on the network are detected.

On 10Base-5 Ethernet, the maximum segment length is 500 meters with a maximum of five segments. Therefore, the maximum distance between any two nodes (computers) is $5 \times 500 = 2500$ meters. The worst-case scenario for collision detection is when the station at one end of the network completes a transmission at the same instant the station at the far end of the network begins a transmission. In this case, the station that transmitted first would not know that a collision had occurred. To prevent this from happening, minimum frame lengths are imposed on Ethernet.

The minimum frame length for 10Base-5 is computed as follows. The velocity of propagation along the cable is assumed to be approximately two-thirds the speed of light, or

$$v_p = \frac{2}{3} v_c$$

$$v_p = \left(\frac{2}{3}\right)(3 \times 10^8 \text{ m/s})$$

$$v_p = 2 \times 10^8 \text{ m/s}$$

Thus, the length of a bit along a cable for a bit rate of 10 Mbps is

$$\text{bit length} = \frac{2 \times 10^8 \text{ m/s}}{10 \text{ mbps}} = 20 \text{ meters/bit}$$

and the maximum number of bits on a cable with a maximum length of 2500 meters is

$$\frac{2500 \text{ m}}{20 \text{ m/b}} = 125 \text{ bits}$$

Therefore, the maximum time for a bit to propagate end to end is

$$\frac{2500 \text{ m}}{2 \times 10^8 \text{ m/s}} = 12.5 \text{ } \mu s$$

and the round-trip delay equals

$$2 \times 12.5 \text{ } \mu s = 25 \text{ } \mu s$$

Therefore, the minimum length of an Ethernet message for a 10-Mbps transmission rate is

$$\frac{\text{round-trip delay}}{\text{bit time}} = \frac{25 \text{ } \mu s}{0.1 \text{ } \mu s} = 250 \text{ bits}$$

where the time of a bit (t_b = 1/bit rate or 1/10 Mbps = 0.1 μs). However, the minimum number of bits is doubled and rounded up to 512 bits (64 eight-bit bytes).

10Base-5 is the original Ethernet that specifies a *thick* 50-Ω double-shielded RG-11 coaxial cable for the transmission medium. Hence, this version is sometimes called *thicknet* or *thick Ethernet*. Because of its inflexible nature, 10Base-5 is sometimes called *frozen yellow garden hose*. 10Base-5 Ethernet uses a bus topology with an external device called a *media access unit* (MAU) to connect terminals to the cable. The MAU is sometimes called a *vampire tap* because it connects to the cable by simply puncturing the cable with a sharp prong that extends into the cable until it makes contact with the center conductor. Each connection is called a *tap,* and the cable that connects the MAU to its terminal is called an *attachment unit interface* (AUI) or sometimes simply a *drop*. Within each MAU, a digital transceiver transfers electrical signals between the drop and the coaxial transmission medium. 10Base-5 supports a maximum of 100 nodes per segment. Repeaters are counted as nodes; therefore, the maximum capacity of a 10Base-5 Ethernet is 297 nodes. With 10Base-5, unused taps must be terminated in a 50-Ω resistive load. A drop left unterminated or any break in the cable will cause total LAN failure.

5-13-2-1 10Base-2 Ethernet. 10Base-5 Ethernet uses a 50-Ω RG-11 coaxial cable, which is thick enough to give it high noise immunity, thus making it well suited to laboratory and industrial applications. The RG-11 cable, however, is expensive to install. Consequently, the initial costs of implementing a 10Base-5 Ethernet system are too high for many small businesses. In an effort to reduce the cost, International Computer Ltd, Hewlett-Packard, and 3COM Corporation developed an Ethernet variation that uses thinner, less expensive 50-Ω RG-58 coaxial cable. RG-58 is less expensive to purchase and install than RG-11. In 1985, the IEEE 802.3 Standards Committee adopted a new version of Ethernet and gave it the name 10Base-2, which is sometimes called *cheapernet* or *thinwire* Ethernet.

10Base-2 Ethernet uses a bus topology and allows a maximum of five segments; however, only three can be populated. Each segment has a maximum length of 185 meters with no more than 30 nodes per segment. This limits the capacity of a 10Base-2 network to 96 nodes. 10Base-2 eliminates the MAU, as the digital transceiver is located inside the terminal and a simple BNC-T connector connects the network interface card (NIC) directly to the coaxial cable. This eliminates the expensive cable and the need to tap or drill into it.

With 10Base-2 Ethernet, unused taps must be terminated in a 50-Ω resistive load and a drop left unterminated, or any break in the cable will cause total LAN failure.

5-13-2-2 10Base-T Ethernet. 10Base-T Ethernet is the most popular 10-Mbps Ethernet commonly used with PC-based LAN environments utilizing a star topology. Because stations can be connected to a network hub through an internal transceiver, there is no need for an AUI. The "T" indicates unshielded twisted-pair cable. 10Base-T was developed to allow Ethernet to utilize existing voice-grade telephone wiring to carry Ethernet signals. Standard modular RJ-45 telephone jacks and four-pair UTP telephone wire are specified in the standard for interconnecting nodes directly to the LAN without an AUI. The RJ-45 connector plugs direction into the network interface card in the PC. 10Base-T operates at a transmission rate of 10 Mbps and uses CSMA/CD; however, it uses a multiport hub at the center of network to interconnect devices. This essentially converts each segment to a point-to-point connection into the LAN. The maximum segment length is 100 meters with no more than two nodes on each segment.

Nodes are added to the network through a port on the hub. When a node is turned on, its transceiver sends a DC current over the twisted-pair cable to the hub. The hub senses the current and enables the port, thus connecting the node to the network. The port remains connected as long as the node continues to supply DC current to the hub. If the node is turned off or if an open- or short-circuit condition occurs in the cable between the node and the hub, DC current stops flowing, and the hub disconnects the port from the network, allowing the remainder of the LAN to continue operating status quo. With 10Base-T Ethernet, a cable break affects only the nodes on that segment.

5-13-2-3 10Base-FL Ethernet. 10Base-FL (fiber link) is the most common 10-Mbps Ethernet that uses optical fiber for the transmission medium. 10Base-FL is arranged in a star topology where stations are connected to the network through an external AUI cable and an external transceiver called a fiber-optic MAU. The transceiver is connected to the hub with two pairs of optical fiber cable. The cable specified is graded-index multimode cable with a 62.5-μm-diameter core.

5-13-3   100-Mbps Ethernet

Over the past few years, it has become quite common for bandwidth-starved LANs to upgrade 10Base-T Ethernet LANs to 100Base-T (sometimes called fast Ethernet). The 100Base-T Ethernet includes a family of fast Ethernet standards offering 100-Mbps data transmission rates using CSMA/CD access methodology. 100-Mbps Ethernet installations do not have the same design rules as 10-Mbps Ethernet. 10-Mbps Ethernet allows several connections between hubs within the same segment (collision domain). 100-Mbps Ethernet does not allow this flexibility. Essentially, the hub must be connected to an internetworking device, such as a switch or a router. This is called the *2-1 rule*—two hubs minimum for each switch. The reason for this requirement is for collision detection within a domain. The transmission rate increased by a factor of 10; therefore, frame size, cable propagation, and hub delay are more critical.

IEEE standard 802.3u details operation of the 100Base-T network. There are three media-specific physical layer standards for 100Base-TX: 100Base-T, 100Base-T4, and 100Base-FX.

5-13-3-1 100Base-TX Ethernet. 100Base-TX Ethernet is the most common of the 100-Mbps Ethernet standards and the system with the most technology available. 100Base-TX specifies a 100-Mbps data transmission rate over two pairs of category 5 UTP or STP cables with a maximum segment length of 100 meters. 100Base-TX uses a physical star topology (half duplex) or bus (full duplex) with the same media access method (CSMA/CD) and frame structures as 10Base-T; however, 100Base-TX requires a hub port and NIC, both of which must be 100Base-TX compliant. 100Base-TX can operate full duplex in certain situations, such as from a switch to a server.

5-13-3-2 100Base-T4 Ethernet. 100Base-T4 is a physical layer standard specifying 100-Mbps data rates using two pairs of category 3, 4, or 5 UTP or STP cable. 100Base-T4 was devised to allow installations that do not comply with category 5 UTP cabling specifications. 100Base-T4 will operate using category 3 UTP installation or better; however, there are some significant differences in the signaling.

5-13-3-3 100Base-FX Ethernet. 100Base-FX is a physical layer standard specifying 100-Mbps data rates over two optical fiber cables using a physical star topology. The logical topology for 100Base-FX can be either a star or a bus. 100Base-FX is often used to interconnect 100Base-TX LANs to a switch or router. 100Base-FX uses a duplex optical fiber connection with multimode cable that supports a variety of distances, depending on circumstances.

5-13-4   1000-Mbps Ethernet

One-gigabit Ethernet (1 GbE) is the latest implementation of Ethernet that operates at a transmission rate of one billion bits per second and higher. The IEEE 802.3z Working Group is currently preparing standards for implementing gigabit Ethernet. Early deployments of gigabit Ethernet were used to interconnect 100-Mbps and gigabit Ethernet switches, and gigabit Ethernet is used to provide a *fat pipe* for high-density backbone connectivity. Gigabit Ethernet can use one of two approaches to medium access: half-duplex mode using CSMA/CD or full-duplex mode, where there is no need for multiple accessing.

Gigabit Ethernet can be generally categorized as either two-wire 1000Base-X or four-wire 1000Base-T. Two-wire gigabit Ethernet can be either 1000Base-SX for short-wave optical fiber, 1000Base-LX for long-wave optical fiber, or 1000Base-CX for short copper jumpers. The four-wire version of gigabit Ethernet is 1000Base-T. 1000Base-SX and 1000Base-LX use two optical fiber cables where the only difference between them is the wavelength (color) of the light waves propagated through the cable. 1000Base-T Ethernet was designed to be used with four twisted pairs of Category 5 UTP cables.

5-13-5   Ethernet Frame Formats

Over the years, four different Ethernet frame formats have emerged where network environment dictates which format is implemented for a particular configuration. The four formats are the following:

Ethernet II. The original format used with DIX.
IEEE 802.3. The first generation of the IEEE Standards Committee, often referred to as a raw IEEE 802.3 frame. Novell was the only software vendor to use this format.
IEEE 802.3 with 802.2 LLC. Provides support for IEEE 802.2 LLC.
IEEE 802.3 with SNAP similar to IEEE 802.3 but provides backward compatibility for 802.2 to Ethernet II formats and protocols.

Ethernet II and IEEE 802.3 are the two most popular frame formats used with Ethernet. Although they are sometimes thought of as the same thing, in actuality Ethernet II and IEEE 802.3 are not identical, although the term *Ethernet* is generally used to refer to any IEEE 802.3-compliant network. Ethernet II and IEEE 802.3 both specify that data be transmitted from one station to another in groups of data called *frames*.

5-13-5-1 Ethernet II frame format. The frame format for Ethernet II is shown in Figure 5-25 and is comprised of a preamble, start frame delimiter, destination address, source address, type field, data field, and frame check sequence field.

FIGURE 5-25   Ethernet II frame format

Preamble. The preamble consists of eight bytes (64 bits) of alternating 1s and 0s. The purpose of the preamble is to establish clock synchronization. The last two bits of the preamble are reserved for the start frame delimiter.

Start frame delimiter. The start frame delimiter is simply a series of two logic 1s appended to the end of the preamble, whose purpose is to mark the end of the preamble and the beginning of the data frame.

Destination address. The source and destination addresses and the field type make up the frame header. The destination address consists of six bytes (48 bits) and is the address of the node or nodes that have been designated to receive the frame. The address can be a unique, group, or broadcast address and is determined by the following bit combinations:

bit 0 = 0	If bit 0 is a 0, the address is interpreted as a unique address intended for only one station.
bit 0 = 1	If bit 0 is a 1, the address is interpreted as a multicast (group) address. All stations that have been preassigned with this group address will accept the frame.
bit 0–47	If all bits in the destination field are 1s, this identifies a broadcast address, and all nodes have been identified as receivers of this frame.

Source address. The source address consists of six bytes (48 bits) that correspond to the address of the station sending the frame.

Type field. Ethernet does not use the 16-bit type field. It is placed in the frame so it can be used for higher layers of the OSI protocol hierarchy.

Data field. The data field contains the information and can be between 46 bytes and 1500 bytes long. The data field is transparent. Data-link control characters and zero-bit stuffing are not used. Transparency is achieved by counting back from the FCS character.

Frame check sequence field. The CRC field contains 32 bits for error detection and is computed from the header and data fields.

5-13-5-2 IEEE 802.3 frame format.   The frame format for IEEE 802.3 is shown in Figure 5-26 and consists of the following:

Preamble. The preamble consists of seven bytes to establish clock synchronization. The last byte of the preamble is used for the start frame delimiter.

Start frame delimiter. The start frame delimiter is simply a series of two logic 1s appended to the end of the preamble, whose purpose is to mark the end of the preamble and the beginning of the data frame.

FIGURE 5-26   IEEE 802.3 frame format

Destination and source addresses. The destination and source addresses are defined the same as with Ethernet II.

Length field. The two-byte length field in the IEEE 802.3 frame replaces the type field in the Ethernet frame. The length field indicates the length of the variable-length logical link control (LLC) data field, which contains all upper-layered embedded protocols.

Logical link control (LLC). The LLC field contains the information and can be between 46 bytes and 1500 bytes long. The LLC field defined in IEEE 802.3 is identical to the LLC field defined for token ring networks.

Frame check sequence field. The CRC field is defined the same as with Ethernet II.

End-of-frame delimiter. The end-of-frame delimiter is a period of time (9.6 μs) in which no bits are transmitted. With Manchester encoding, a void in transitions longer than one-bit time indicates the end of the frame.

QUESTIONS

5-1. Define *data-link protocol.*

5-2. What is meant by a primary station? Secondary station?

5-3. What is a master station? Slave station?

5-4. List and describe the three data-link protocol functions.

5-5. Briefly describe the ENQ/ACK line discipline.

5-6. Briefly describe the poll/select line discipline.

5-7. Briefly describe the stop-and-wait method of flow control.

5-8. Briefly describe the sliding window method of flow control.

5-9. What is the difference between character- and bit-oriented protocols?

5-10. Describe the difference between asynchronous and synchronous protocols.

5-11. Briefly describe how the XMODEM protocol works.

5-12. Why is IBM's 3270 protocol called "bisync"?

5-13. Briefly describe the polling sequence for BSC, including the difference between a general and specific poll.

5-14. Briefly describe the selection sequence for BSC.

5-15. How does BSC achieve transparency?

5-16. What is the difference between a command and a response with SDLC?

5-17. What are the three transmission states used with SDLC?

5-18. What are the five fields used with SDLC?

5-19. What is the delimiting sequence used with SDLC?

5-20. What are the three frame formats used with SDLC?

5-21. What are the purposes of the *ns* and *nr* bit sequences?

5-22. What is the difference between P and F bits?

5-23. With SDLC, which frame types can contain an information field?

5-24. With SDLC, which frame types can be used for error correction?

5-25. What SDLC command/response is used for reporting procedural errors?

5-26. When is the configure command/response used with SDLC?

5-27. What is the go-ahead sequence? The turnaround sequence?

5-28. What is the transparency mechanism used with SDLC?

5-29. What supervisory condition exists with HDLC that is not included in SDLC?

5-30. What are the transparency mechanism and delimiting sequence for HDLC?

5-31. Briefly describe invert-on-zero encoding.

5-32. List and describe the HDLC operational modes.

5-33. Briefly describe the layout for a public switched data network.

5-34. What is a value-added network?

5-35. Briefly describe circuit, message, and packet switching.

5-36. What is a transactional switch? A transparent switch?

5-37. Explain the following terms: *permanent virtual circuit, virtual call,* and *datagram.*

5-38. Briefly describe an X.25 call request packet.

5-39. Briefly describe an X.25 data transfer packet.

5-40. Define *ISDN.*

5-41. List and describe the principles of ISDN.

5-42. List and describe the evolution of ISDN.

5-43. Describe the conceptual view of ISDN and what is meant by the term *digital pipe.*

5-44. List the objectives of ISDN.

5-45. Briefly describe the architecture of ISDN.

5-46. List and describe the ISDN system connections and interface units.

5-47. Briefly describe BISDN.

5-48. Briefly describe asynchronous transfer mode.

5-49. Describe the differences between virtual channels and virtual paths.

5-50. Briefly describe the ATM header field; ATM information field.

5-51. Describe the following ATM network components: ATM endpoints, ATM switches, ATM transmission paths.

5-52. Briefly describe a local area network.

5-53. List and describe the most common LAN topologies.

5-54. Describe the following LAN transmission formats: baseband and broadband.

5-55. Describe the two most common LAN access methodologies.

5-56. Briefly describe the history of Ethernet.

5-57. Describe the Ethernet standard notation.

5-58. List and briefly describe the 10-Mbps Ethernet systems.

5-59. List and briefly describe the 100-Mbps Ethernet systems.

5-60. List and briefly describe the 1000-Mbps Ethernet systems.

5-61. Describe the two most common Ethernet frame formats.

5-1. Determine the hex code for the control field in an SDLC frame for the following conditions: information frame, poll, transmitting frame 4, and confirming reception of frames 2, 3, and 4.

5-2. Determine the hex code for the control field in an SDLC frame for the following conditions: supervisory frame, ready to receive, final, and confirming reception of frames 6, 7, and 0.

5-3. Insert 0s into the following SDLC data stream:

111 001 000 011 111 111 100 111 110 100 111 101 011 111 111 111 001 011

5-4. Delete 0s from the following SDLC data stream:

010 111 110 100 011 011 111 011 101 110 101 111 101 011 100 011 111 00

5-5. Sketch the NRZI waveform for the following data stream (start with a high condition):

1 0 0   1 1 1   0 0 1   0 1 0

5-6. Determine the hex code for the control field in an SDLC frame for the following conditions: information frame, not a poll, transmitting frame number 5, and confirming the reception of frames 0, 1, 2, and 3.

5-7. Determine the hex code for the control field in an SDLC frame for the following conditions: supervisory frame, not ready to receive, not a final, and confirming reception of frames 7, 0, 1, and 2.

5-8. Insert 0s into the following SDLC data stream:

0110111111011000011110010111000101111111011111001

5-9. Delete 0s from the following SDLC data stream:

0010111100111110111110110001000111101110101000101

5-10. Sketch the NRZI levels for the following data stream (start with a high condition):

1 1 0 1 0 0 0 1 1 0 1

C H A P T E R   6

Digital Transmission

OBJECTIVES

- Define *digital transmission*
- List and describe the advantages and disadvantages of digital transmission
- Briefly describe pulse width modulation, pulse position modulation, and pulse amplitude modulation
- Define and describe pulse code modulation
- Explain flat-top and natural sampling
- Describe the Nyquist sampling theorem
- Describe folded binary codes
- Define and explain *dynamic range*
- Explain PCM coding efficiency
- Describe signal-to-quantization noise ratio
- Explain the difference between linear and nonlinear PCM codes
- Describe idle channel noise
- Explain several common coding methods
- Define *companding* and explain analog and digital companding
- Define *digital compression*

- Describe vocoders
- Explain how to determine PCM line speed
- Describe delta modulation PCM
- Describe adaptive delta modulation
- Define and describe differential pulse code modulation
- Describe the composition of digital pulses
- Explain intersymbol interference
- Explain eye patterns
- Explain the signal power distribution in binary digital signals

6-1 INTRODUCTION

As stated previously, *digital transmission* is the transmittal of digital signals between two or more points in a communications system. The signals can be binary or any other form of discrete-level digital pulses. The original source information may be in digital form, or it could be analog signals that have been converted to digital pulses prior to transmission and converted back to analog signals in the receiver. With digital transmission systems, a physical facility, such as a pair of wires, coaxial cable, or an optical fiber cable, is required to interconnect the various points within the system. The pulses are contained in and propagate down the cable. Digital pulses cannot be propagated through a wireless transmission system, such as Earth's atmosphere or free space (vacuum).

AT&T developed the first digital transmission system for the purpose of carrying digitally encoded analog signals, such as the human voice, over metallic wire cables between telephone offices. Today, digital transmission systems are used to carry not only digitally encoded voice and video signals but also digital source information directly between computers and computer networks. Digital transmission systems use both metallic and optical fiber cables for their transmission medium.

6-1-1 Advantages of Digital Transmission

The primary advantage of digital transmission over analog transmission is *noise immunity*. Digital signals are inherently less susceptible than analog signals to interference caused by noise because with digital signals it is not necessary to evaluate the precise amplitude, frequency, or phase to ascertain its logic condition. Instead, pulses are evaluated during a precise time interval, and a simple determination is made whether the pulse is above or below a prescribed reference level.

Digital signals are also better suited than analog signals for processing and combining using a technique called *multiplexing*. Digital signal processing (DSP) is the processing of analog signals using digital methods and includes bandlimiting the signal with filters, amplitude equalization, and phase shifting. It is much simpler to store digital signals than analog signals, and the transmission rate of digital signals can be easily changed to adapt to different environments and to interface with different types of equipment.

In addition, digital transmission systems are more resistant to analog systems to additive noise because they use signal *regeneration* rather than signal amplification. Noise produced in electronic circuits is additive (i.e., it accumulates); therefore, the signal-to-noise ratio deteriorates each time an analog signal is amplified. Consequently, the number of circuits the signal must pass through limits the total distance analog signals can be transported. However, digital regenerators sample noisy signals and then reproduce an entirely new digital signal with the same signal-to-noise ratio as the original transmitted signal. Therefore, digital signals can be transported longer distances than analog signals.

Finally, digital signals are simpler to measure and evaluate than analog signals. Therefore, it is easier to compare the error performance of one digital system to another digital system. Also, with digital signals, transmission errors can be detected and corrected more easily and more accurately than is possible with analog signals.

The transmission of digitally encoded analog signals requires significantly more bandwidth than simply transmitting the original analog signal. Bandwidth is one of the most important aspects of any communications system because it is costly and limited.

Also, analog signals must be converted to digital pulses prior to transmission and converted back to their original analog form at the receiver, thus necessitating additional encoding and decoding circuitry. In addition, digital transmission requires precise time synchronization between the clocks in the transmitters and receivers. Finally, digital transmission systems are incompatible with older analog transmission systems.

6-2   PULSE MODULATION

Pulse modulation consists essentially of sampling analog information signals and then converting those samples into discrete pulses and transporting the pulses from a source to a destination over a physical transmission medium. The four predominant methods of pulse modulation include *pulse width modulation* (PWM), *pulse position modulation* (PPM), *pulse amplitude modulation* (PAM), and *pulse code modulation* (PCM).

PWM is sometimes called *pulse duration modulation* (PDM) or *pulse length modulation* (PLM), as the width (active portion of the duty cycle) of a constant amplitude pulse is varied proportional to the amplitude of the analog signal at the time the signal is sampled. PWM is shown in Figure 6-1c. As the figure shows, the amplitude of sample 1 is lower than the amplitude of sample 2. Thus, pulse 1 is narrower than pulse 2. The maximum analog signal amplitude produces the widest pulse, and the minimum analog signal amplitude produces the narrowest pulse. Note, however, that all pulses have the same amplitude.

With PPM, the position of a constant-width pulse within a prescribed time slot is varied according to the amplitude of the sample of the analog signal. PPM is shown in Figure 6-1d. As the figure shows, the higher the amplitude of the sample, the farther to the right the pulse is positioned within the prescribed time slot. The highest amplitude sample produces a pulse to the far right, and the lowest amplitude sample produces a pulse to the far left.

With PAM, the amplitude of a constant width, constant-position pulse is varied according to the amplitude of the sample of the analog signal. PAM is shown in Figure 6-1e, where it can be seen that the amplitude of a pulse coincides with the amplitude of the analog signal. PAM waveforms resemble the original analog signal more than the waveforms for PWM or PPM.

With PCM, the analog signal is sampled and then converted to a serial n-bit binary code for transmission. Each code has the same number of bits and requires the same length of time for transmission. PCM is shown in Figure 6-1f.

PAM is used as an intermediate form of modulation with PSK, QAM, and PCM, although it is seldom used by itself. PWM and PPM are used in special-purpose communications systems mainly for the military but are seldom used for commercial digital transmission systems. PCM is by far the most prevalent form of pulse modulation and, consequently, will be discussed in more detail in subsequent sections of this chapter.

6-3   PCM

Alex H. Reeves is credited with inventing PCM in 1937 while working for AT&T at its Paris laboratories. Although the merits of PCM were recognized early in its development, it was not until the mid-1960s, with the advent of solid-state electronics, that PCM became prevalent. In the United States today, PCM is the preferred method of communications within the public switched telephone network because with PCM it is easy to combine digitized voice and digital data into a single, high-speed digital signal and propagate it over either metallic or optical fiber cables.

FIGURE 6-1   Pulse modulation: (a) analog signal; (b) sample pulse; (c) PWM; (d) PPM;
(e) PAM; (f) PCM

PCM is the only digitally encoded modulation technique shown in Figure 6-1 that is commonly used for digital transmission. The term *pulse code modulation* is somewhat of a misnomer, as it is not really a type of modulation but rather a form of digitally coding analog signals. With PCM, the pulses are of fixed length and fixed amplitude. PCM is a binary system where a pulse or lack of a pulse within a prescribed time slot represents either a logic 1 or a logic 0 condition. PWM, PPM, and PAM are digital but seldom binary, as a pulse does not represent a single binary digit (bit).

Figure 6-2 shows a simplified block diagram of a single-channel, simplex (one-way only) PCM system. The bandpass filter limits the frequency of the analog input signal to the standard voice-band frequency range of 300 Hz to 3000 Hz. The *sample-and-hold* cir-

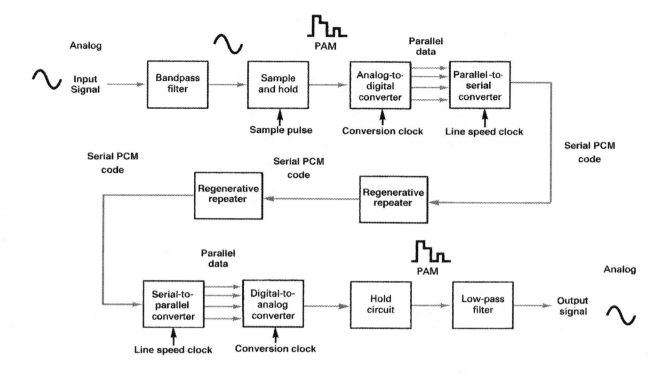

FIGURE 6-2   Simplified block diagram of a single-channel, simplex PCM transmission system

cuit periodically samples the analog input signal and converts those samples to a multilevel PAM signal. The *analog-to-digital converter* (ADC) converts the PAM samples to parallel PCM codes, which are converted to serial binary data in the *parallel-to-serial converter* and then outputted onto the transmission line as serial digital pulses. The transmission line *repeaters* are placed at prescribed distances to regenerate the digital pulses.

In the receiver, the *serial-to-parallel converter* converts serial pulses received from the transmission line to parallel PCM codes. The *digital-to-analog converter* (DAC) converts the parallel PCM codes to multilevel PAM signals. The hold circuit is basically a low-pass filter that converts the PAM signals back to its original analog form.

Figure 6-2 also shows several clock signals and sample pulses that will be explained in later sections of this chapter. An integrated circuit that performs the PCM encoding and decoding functions is called a codec (*co*der/*dec*oder), which is also described in a later section of this chapter.

6-4 PCM SAMPLING

The function of a sampling circuit in a PCM transmitter is to periodically sample the continually changing analog input voltage and convert those samples to a series of constant-amplitude pulses that can more easily be converted to binary PCM code. For the ADC to accurately convert a voltage to a binary code, the voltage must be relatively constant so that the ADC can complete the conversion before the voltage level changes. If not, the ADC would be continually attempting to follow the changes and may never stabilize on any PCM code.

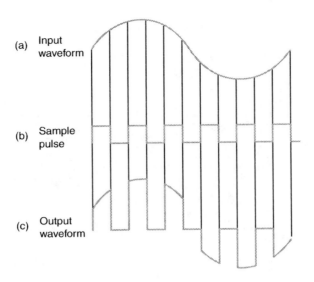

(a) Input waveform

(b) Sample pulse

(c) Output waveform

FIGURE 6-3   Natural sampling: (a) input analog signal; (b) sample pulse; (c) sampled output

Essentially, there are two basic techniques used to perform the sampling function: natural sampling and flat-top sampling. *Natural sampling* is shown in Figure 6-3. Natural sampling is when tops of the sample pulses retain their natural shape during the sample interval, making it difficult for an ADC to convert the sample to a PCM code. With natural sampling, the frequency spectrum of the sampled output is different from that of an ideal sample. The amplitude of the frequency components produced from narrow, finite-width sample pulses decreases for the higher harmonics in a $(\sin x)/x$ manner. This alters the information frequency spectrum requiring the use of frequency equalizers (compensation filters) before recovery by a low-pass filter.

The most common method used for sampling voice signals in PCM systems is *flat-top sampling*, which is accomplished in a *sample-and-hold circuit*. The purpose of a sample-and-hold circuit is to periodically sample the continually changing analog input voltage and convert those samples to a series of constant-amplitude PAM voltage levels. With flat-top sampling, the input voltage is sampled with a narrow pulse and then held relatively constant until the next sample is taken. Figure 6-4 shows flat-top sampling. As the figure shows, the sampling process alters the frequency spectrum and introduces an error called *aperture* error, which is when the amplitude of the sampled signal changes during the sample pulse time. This prevents the recovery circuit in the PCM receiver from exactly reproducing the original analog signal voltage. The magnitude of error depends on how much the analog signal voltage changes while the sample is being taken and the width (duration) of the sample pulse. Flat-top sampling, however, introduces less aperture distortion than natural sampling and can operate with a slower analog-to-digital converter.

Figure 6-5a shows the schematic diagram of a sample-and-hold circuit. The FET acts as a simple analog switch. When turned on, Q_1 provides a low-impedance path to deposit the analog sample voltage across capacitor C_1. The time that Q_1 is on is called the *aperture* or *acquisition time*. Essentially, C_1 is the hold circuit. When Q_1 is off, C_1 does not have a complete path to discharge through and, therefore, stores the sampled voltage. The *storage time* of the capacitor is called the A/D *conversion time* because it is during this time that the ADC converts the sample voltage to a PCM code. The acquisition time should be very short to ensure that a minimum change occurs in the analog signal while it is being deposited across C_1. If the input to the ADC is changing while it is performing the conversion, *aperture*

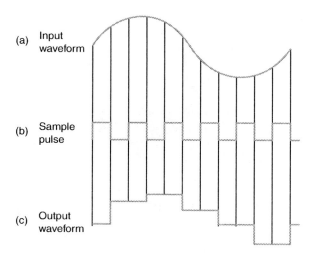

(a) Input waveform

(b) Sample pulse

(c) Output waveform

FIGURE 6-4 Flat-top sampling: (a) input analog signal; (b) sample pulse; (c) sampled output

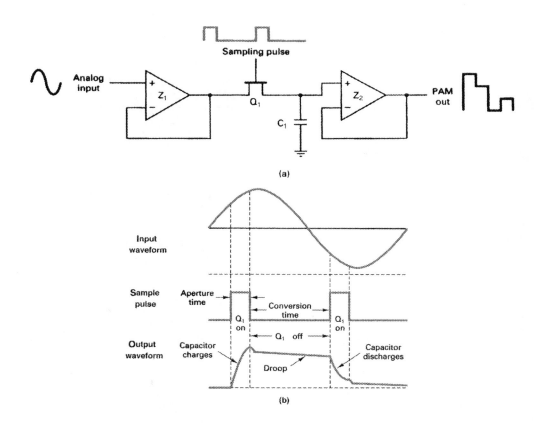

FIGURE 6-5 (a) Sample-and-hold circuit; (b) input and output waveforms

distortion results. Thus, by having a short aperture time and keeping the input to the ADC relatively constant, the sample-and-hold circuit can reduce aperture distortion. Flat-top sampling introduces less aperture distortion than natural sampling and requires a slower analog-to-digital converter.

Figure 6-5b shows the input analog signal, the sampling pulse, and the waveform developed across C_1. It is important that the output impedance of voltage follower Z_1 and the on resistance of Q_1 be as small as possible. This ensures that the RC charging time constant of the capacitor is kept very short, allowing the capacitor to charge or discharge rapidly during the short acquisition time. The rapid drop in the capacitor voltage immediately following each sample pulse is due to the redistribution of the charge across C_1. The interelectrode capacitance between the gate and drain of the FET is placed in series with C_1 when the FET is off, thus acting as a capacitive voltage-divider network. Also, note the gradual discharge across the capacitor during the conversion time. This is called *droop* and is caused by the capacitor discharging through its own leakage resistance and the input impedance of voltage follower Z_2. Therefore, it is important that the input impedance of Z_2 and the leakage resistance of C_1 be as high as possible. Essentially, voltage followers Z_1 and Z_2 isolate the sample-and-hold circuit (Q_1 and C_1) from the input and output circuitry.

Example 6-1

For the sample-and-hold circuit shown in Figure 6-5a, determine the largest-value capacitor that can be used. Use an output impedance for Z_1 of 10 Ω, an on resistance for Q_1 of 10 Ω, an acquisition time of 10 μs, a maximum peak-to-peak input voltage of 10 V, a maximum output current from Z_1 of 10 mA, and an accuracy of 1%.

Solution The expression for the current through a capacitor is

$$i = C\frac{dv}{dt}$$

Rearranging and solving for C yields

$$C = i\frac{dt}{dv}$$

where C = maximum capacitance (farads)
   i = maximum output current from Z_1, 10 mA
   dv = maximum change in voltage across C_1, which equals 10 V
   dt = charge time, which equals the aperture time, 10 μs

Therefore,

$$C_{max} = \frac{(10 \text{ mA})(10 \text{ μs})}{10 \text{ V}} = 10 \text{ nF}$$

The charge time constant for C when Q_1 is on is

$$\tau = RC$$

where τ = one charge time constant (seconds)
   R = output impedance of Z_1 plus the on resistance of Q_1 (ohms)
   C = capacitance value of C_1 (farads)

Rearranging and solving for C gives us

$$C_{max} = \frac{\tau}{R}$$

The charge time of capacitor C_1 is also dependent on the accuracy desired from the device. The percent accuracy and its required RC time constant are summarized as follows:

Accuracy (%)	Charge Time
10	2.3τ
1	4.6τ
0.1	6.9τ
0.01	9.2τ

For an accuracy of 1%,

$$C = \frac{10\ \mu s}{4.6(20)} = 108.7\ nF$$

To satisfy the output current limitations of Z_1, a maximum capacitance of 10 nF was required. To satisfy the accuracy requirements, 108.7 nF was required. To satisfy both requirements, the smaller-value capacitor must be used. Therefore, C_1 can be no larger than 10 nF.

6-4-1 Sampling Rate

The *Nyquist sampling theorem* establishes the *minimum sampling rate* (f_s) that can be used for a given PCM system. For a sample to be reproduced accurately in a PCM receiver, each cycle of the analog input signal (f_a) must be sampled at least twice. Consequently, the minimum sampling rate is equal to twice the highest audio input frequency. If f_s is less than two times f_a, an impairment called *alias* or *foldover distortion* occurs. Mathematically, the minimum Nyquist sampling rate is

$$f_s \geq 2f_a \tag{6-1}$$

where f_s = minimum Nyquist sample rate (hertz)
f_a = maximum analog input frequency (hertz)

A sample-and-hold circuit is a nonlinear device (mixer) with two inputs: the sampling pulse and the analog input signal. Consequently, nonlinear mixing (heterodyning) occurs between these two signals.

Figure 6-6a shows the frequency-domain representation of the output spectrum from a sample-and-hold circuit. The output includes the two original inputs (the audio and the fundamental frequency of the sampling pulse), their sum and difference frequencies ($f_s \pm f_a$), all the harmonics of f_s and f_a ($2f_s$, $2f_a$, $3f_s$, $3f_a$, and so on), and their associated cross products ($2f_s \pm f_a$, $3f_s \pm f_a$, and so on).

Because the sampling pulse is a repetitive waveform, it is made up of a series of harmonically related sine waves. Each of these sine waves is amplitude modulated by the analog signal and produces sum and difference frequencies symmetrical around each of the harmonics of f_s. Each sum and difference frequency generated is separated from its respective center frequency by f_a. As long as f_s is at least twice f_a, none of the side frequencies from one harmonic will spill into the sidebands of another harmonic, and aliasing does not

(a)

(b)

FIGURE 6-6 Output spectrum for a sample-and-hold circuit: (a) no aliasing; (b) aliasing distortion

FIGURE 6-7 Output spectrum for Example 15-2

occur. Figure 6-6b shows the results when an analog input frequency greater than $f_s/2$ modulates f_s. The side frequencies from one harmonic fold over into the sideband of another harmonic. The frequency that folds over is an alias of the input signal (hence the names "aliasing" or "foldover distortion"). If an alias side frequency from the first harmonic folds over into the audio spectrum, it cannot be removed through filtering or any other technique.

Example 6-2

For a PCM system with a maximum audio input frequency of 4 kHz, determine the minimum sample rate and the alias frequency produced if a 5-kHz audio signal were allowed to enter the sample-and-hold circuit.

Solution   Using Nyquist's sampling theorem (Equation 6-1), we have

$$f_s \geq 2f_a \quad \text{therefore,} \quad f_s \geq 8 \text{ kHz}$$

If a 5-kHz audio frequency entered the sample-and-hold circuit, the output spectrum shown in Figure 6-7 is produced. It can be seen that the 5-kHz signal produces an alias frequency of 3 kHz that has been introduced into the original audio spectrum.

The input bandpass filter shown in Figure 6-2 is called an *antialiasing* or *antifoldover filter*. Its upper cutoff frequency is chosen such that no frequency greater than one-half the sampling rate is allowed to enter the sample-and-hold circuit, thus eliminating the possibility of foldover distortion occurring.

With PCM, the analog input signal is sampled, then converted to a serial binary code. The binary code is transmitted to the receiver, where it is converted back to the original analog signal. The binary codes used for PCM are *n*-bit codes, where *n* may be any positive integer greater than 1. The codes currently used for PCM are *sign-magnitude codes,* where the *most significant bit* (MSB) is the sign bit and the remaining bits are used for magnitude. Table 6-1 shows an *n*-bit PCM code where *n* equals 3. The most significant bit is used to represent the sign of the sample (logic 1 = positive and logic 0 = negative). The two remaining bits represent the magnitude. With two magnitude bits, there are four codes possi-

Table 6-1   Three-Bit PCM Code

Sign	Magnitude	Decimal Value
1	1 1	+3
1	1 0	+2
1	0 1	+1
1	0 0	+0
0	0 0	−0
0	0 1	−1
0	1 0	−2
0	1 1	−3

ble for positive numbers and four codes possible for negative numbers. Consequently, there is a total of eight possible codes ($2^3 = 8$).

6-4-2 Quantization and the Folded Binary Code

Quantization is the process of converting an infinite number of possibilities to a finite number of conditions. Analog signals contain an infinite number of amplitude possibilities. Thus, converting an analog signal to a PCM code with a limited number of combinations requires quantization. In essence, quantization is the process of rounding off the amplitudes of flat-top samples to a manageable number of levels. For example, a sine wave with a peak amplitude of 5 V varies between +5 V and −5 V passing through every possible amplitude in between. A PCM code could have only eight bits, which equates to only 2^8, or 256 combinations. Obviously, to convert samples of a sine wave to PCM requires some rounding off.

With quantization, the total voltage range is subdivided into a smaller number of subranges, as shown in Table 6-2. The PCM code shown in Table 6-2 is a three-bit sign-magnitude code with eight possible combinations (four positive and four negative). The leftmost bit is the sign bit (1 = + and 0 = −), and the two rightmost bits represent magnitude. This type of code is called a *folded binary code* because the codes on the bottom half of the table are a mirror image of the codes on the top half, except for the sign bit. If the negative codes were folded over on top of the positive codes, they would match perfectly. With a folded binary code, each voltage level has one code assigned to it except zero volts, which has two codes, 100 (+0) and 000 (−0). The magnitude difference between adjacent steps is called the *quantization interval* or *quantum*. For the code shown in Table 6-2, the quantization interval is 1 V. Therefore, for this code, the maximum signal magnitude that can be encoded is +3 V (111) or −3 V (011), and the minimum signal magnitude is +1 V (101) or −1 V (001). If the magnitude of the sample exceeds the highest quantization interval, *overload distortion* (also called *peak limiting*) occurs.

Assigning PCM codes to absolute magnitudes is called quantizing. The magnitude of a quantum is also called the *resolution*. The resolution is equal to the voltage of the *minimum step size*, which is equal to the voltage of the *least significant bit* (V_{lsb}) of the PCM code. The resolution is the minimum voltage other than 0 V that can be decoded by the digital-to-analog converter in the receiver. The resolution for the PCM code shown in Table 6-2 is 1 V. The smaller the magnitude of a quantum, the better (smaller) the resolution and the more accurately the quantized signal will resemble the original analog sample.

In Table 6-2, each three-bit code has a range of input voltages that will be converted to that code. For example, any voltage between +0.5 and +1.5 will be converted to the code 101 (+1 V). Each code has a *quantization range* equal to + or − one-half the magnitude of a quantum except the codes for +0 and −0. The 0-V codes each have an input range equal to only one-half a quantum (0.5 V).

Table 6-2 Three-Bit PCM Code

	Sign	Magnitude		Decimal value	Quantization range
	1	1	1	+3	+2.5 V to +3.5 V
	1	1	0	+2	+1.5 V to +2.5 V
	1	0	1	+1	+0.5 V to +1.5 V
8 Sub ranges	1	0	0	+0	0 V to +0.5 V
	0	0	0	−0	0 V to −0.5 V
	0	0	1	−1	−0.5 V to −1.5 V
	0	1	0	−2	−1.5 V to −2.5 V
	0	1	1	−3	−2.5 V to −3.5 V

FIGURE 6-8 (a) Analog input signal; (b) sample pulse; (c) PAM signal; (d) PCM code

Figure 6-8 shows an analog input signal, the sampling pulse, the corresponding quantized signal (PAM), and the PCM code for each sample. The likelihood of a sample voltage being equal to one of the eight quantization levels is remote. Therefore, as shown in the figure, each sample voltage is rounded off (quantized) to the closest available level and then converted to its corresponding PCM code. The PAM signal in the transmitter is essentially the same PAM signal produced in the receiver. Therefore, any round-off errors in the transmitted signal are reproduced when the code is converted back to analog in the receiver. This error is called the *quantization error* (Q_e). The quantization error is equivalent to additive white noise as it alters the signal amplitude. Consequently, quantization error is also called *quantization noise* (Q_n). The maximum magnitude for the quantization error is equal to one-half a quantum (± 0.5 V for the code shown in Table 6-2).

The first sample shown in Figure 6-8 occurs at time t_1, when the input voltage is exactly +2 V. The PCM code that corresponds to +2 V is 110, and there is no quantization error. Sample 2 occurs at time t_2, when the input voltage is −1 V. The corresponding PCM code is 001, and again there is no quantization error. To determine the PCM code for a particular sample voltage, simply divide the voltage by the resolution, convert the quotient to an *n*-bit binary code, and then add the sign bit. For sample 3 in Figure 6-9, the voltage at t_3 is approximately +2.6 V. The folded PCM code is

$$\frac{\text{sample voltage}}{\text{resolution}} = \frac{2.6}{1} = 2.6$$

There is no PCM code for +2.6; therefore, the magnitude of the sample is rounded off to the nearest valid code, which is 111, or +3 V. The rounding-off process results in a quantization error of 0.4 V.

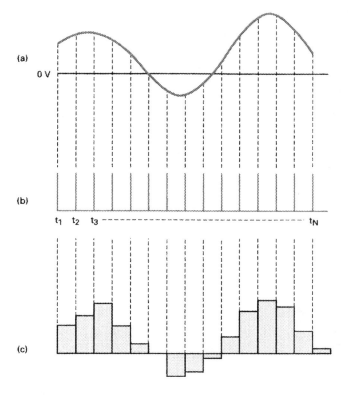

FIGURE 6-9 PAM: (a) input signal; (b) sample pulse; (c) PAM signal

The quantized signal shown in Figure 6-8c at best only roughly resembles the original analog input signal. This is because with a three-bit PCM code, the resolution is rather poor and also because there are only three samples taken of the analog signal. The quality of the PAM signal can be improved by using a PCM code with more bits, reducing the magnitude of a quantum and improving the resolution. The quality can also be improved by sampling the analog signal at a faster rate. Figure 6-9 shows the same analog input signal shown in Figure 6-8 except the signal is being sampled at a much higher rate. As the figure shows, the PAM signal resembles the analog input signal rather closely.

Figure 6-10 shows the input-versus-output transfer function for a linear analog-to-digital converter (sometimes called a linear quantizer). As the figure shows for a linear analog input signal (i.e., a ramp), the quantized signal is a staircase function. Thus, as shown in Figure 6-7c, the maximum quantization error is the same for any magnitude input signal.

Example 6-3

For the PCM coding scheme shown in Figure 6-8, determine the quantized voltage, quantization error (Q_e), and PCM code for the analog sample voltage of $+1.07$ V.

Solution   To determine the quantized level, simply divide the sample voltage by resolution and then round the answer off to the nearest quantization level:

$$\frac{+1.07 \ V}{1 \ V} = 1.07 = 1$$

The quantization error is the difference between the original sample voltage and the quantized level, or

$$Q_e = 1.07 - 1 = 0.07$$

From Table 6-2, the PCM code for $+1$ is 101.

(a)

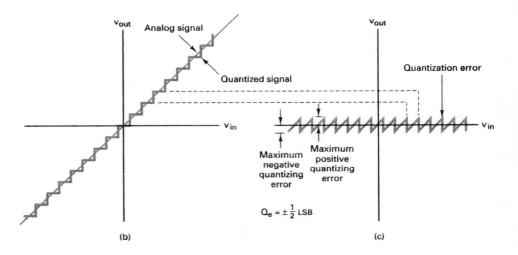

(b)

(c)

FIGURE 6-10   Linear input-versus-output transfer curve: (a) linear transfer function; (b) quantization; (c) Q_e

6-4-3   Dynamic Range

The number of PCM bits transmitted per sample is determined by several variables, including maximum allowable input amplitude, resolution, and dynamic range. *Dynamic range* (DR) is the ratio of the largest possible magnitude to the smallest possible magnitude (other than 0 V) that can be decoded by the digital-to-analog converter in the receiver. Mathematically, dynamic range is

$$DR = \frac{V_{max}}{V_{min}} \qquad\qquad (6\text{-}2)$$

where DR = dynamic range (unitless ratio)

V_{min} = the quantum value (resolution)

V_{max} = the maximum voltage magnitude that can be discerned by the DACs in the receiver

Equation 6-2 can be rewritten as

$$DR = \frac{V_{max}}{resolution} \qquad (6\text{-}3)$$

For the system shown in Table 6-2,

$$DR = \frac{3\,V}{1\,V} = 3$$

A dynamic range of 3 indicates that the ratio of the largest decoded voltage to the smallest decoded signal voltage is 3 to 1.

Dynamic range is generally expressed as a dB value; therefore,

$$DR = 20 \log \frac{V_{max}}{V_{min}} \qquad (6\text{-}4)$$

For the system shown in Table 6-2,

$$DR = 20 \log 3 = 9.54 \text{ dB}$$

The number of bits used for a PCM code depends on the dynamic range. The relationship between dynamic range and the number of bits in a PCM code is

$$2^n - 1 \geq DR \qquad (6\text{-}5\text{a})$$

and for a minimum number of bits

$$2^n - 1 = DR \qquad (6\text{-}5\text{b})$$

where n = number of bits in a PCM code, excluding the sign bit
DR = absolute value of dynamic range

Why $2^n - 1$? One positive and one negative PCM code is used for 0 V, which is not considered for dynamic range. Therefore,

$$2^n = DR + 1$$

To solve for the number of bits (n) necessary to produce a dynamic range of 3, convert to logs,

$$\log 2^n = \log(DR + 1)$$
$$n \log 2 = \log(DR + 1)$$
$$n = \frac{\log(3 + 1)}{\log 2} = \frac{0.602}{0.301} = 2$$

For a dynamic range of 3, a PCM code with two bits is required. Dynamic range can be expressed in decibels as

$$DR_{(dB)} = 20 \log\left(\frac{V_{max}}{V_{min}}\right)$$

or

$$DR_{(dB)} = 20 \log(2^n - 1) \qquad (6\text{-}6)$$

where n is the number of PCM bits. For values of $n > 4$, dynamic range is approximated as

$$DR_{(dB)} \approx 20 \log(2^n)$$
$$\approx 20n \log(2)$$
$$\approx 6n \qquad (6\text{-}7)$$

Table 6-3 Dynamic Range versus Number of PCM Magnitude Bits

Number of Bits in PCM Code (n)	Number of Levels Possible ($M = 2^n$)	Dynamic Range (dB)
1	2	6.02
2	4	12
3	8	18.1
4	16	24.1
5	32	30.1
6	64	36.1
7	128	42.1
8	256	48.2
9	512	54.2
10	1024	60.2
11	2048	66.2
12	4096	72.2
13	8192	78.3
14	16,384	84.3
15	32,768	90.3
16	65,536	96.3

Equation 6-7 indicates that there is approximately 6 dB dynamic range for each magnitude bit in a linear PCM code. Table 6-3 summarizes dynamic range for PCM codes with n bits for values of n up to 16.

Example 6-4

For a PCM system with the following parameters, determine (a) minimum sample rate, (b) minimum number of bits used in the PCM code, (c) resolution, and (d) quantization error.

> Maximum analog input frequency = 4 kHz
> Maximum decoded voltage at the receiver = ± 2.55 V
> Minimum dynamic range = 46 dB

Solution a. Substituting into Equation 6-1, the minimum sample rate is

$$f_s = 2f_{a-} = 2(4 \text{ kHz}) = 8 \text{ kHz}$$

b. To determine the absolute value for dynamic range, substitute into Equation 6-4:

$$46 \text{ dB} = 20 \log \frac{V_{max}}{V_{min}}$$

$$2.3 = \log \frac{V_{max}}{V_{min}}$$

$$10^{2.3} = \frac{V_{max}}{V_{min}}$$

$$199.5 = DR$$

The minimum number of bits is determined by rearranging Equation 6-5b and solving for n:

$$n = \frac{\log(199.5 + 1)}{\log 2} = 7.63$$

The closest whole number greater than 7.63 is 8; therefore, eight bits must be used for the magnitude.

Because the input amplitude range is ± 2.55, one additional bit, the sign bit, is required. Therefore, the total number of CM bits is nine, and the total number of PCM codes is $2^9 = 512$. (There are 255 positive codes, 255 negative codes, and 2 zero codes.)

To determine the actual dynamic range, substitute into Equation 6-6:

$$DR_{(dB)} = 20 \log(2^n - 1)$$
$$= 20(\log 256 - 1)$$
$$= 48.13 \text{ dB}$$

c. The resolution is determined by dividing the maximum positive or maximum negative voltage by the number of positive or negative nonzero PCM codes:

$$resolution = \frac{V_{max}}{2^n - 1} = \frac{2.55}{2^8 - 1} = \frac{2.55}{256 - 1} = 0.01 \text{ V}$$

The maximum quantization error is

$$Q_e = \frac{resolution}{2} = \frac{0.01 \text{ V}}{2} = 0.005 \text{ V}$$

6-4-4 Coding Efficiency

Coding efficiency is a numerical indication of how efficiently a PCM code is utilized. Coding efficiency is the ratio of the minimum number of bits required to achieve a certain dynamic range to the actual number of PCM bits used. Mathematically, coding efficiency is

$$coding \text{ } efficiency = \frac{minimum \text{ } number \text{ } of \text{ } bits \text{ } (including \text{ } sign \text{ } bit)}{actual \text{ } number \text{ } of \text{ } bits \text{ } (including \text{ } sign \text{ } bit)} \times 100 \qquad (6\text{-}8)$$

The coding efficiency for Example 6-4 is

$$coding \text{ } efficiency = \frac{8.63}{9} \times 100 = 95.89\%$$

6-5 SIGNAL-TO-QUANTIZATION NOISE RATIO

The three-bit PCM coding scheme shown in Figures 6-8 and 6-9 consists of *linear codes*, which means that the magnitude change between any two successive codes is the same. Consequently, the magnitude of their quantization error is also the same. The maximum quantization noise is half the resolution (quantum value). Therefore, the worst possible *signal voltage-to-quantization noise voltage ratio* (SQR) occurs when the input signal is at its minimum amplitude (101 or 001). Mathematically, the worst-case voltage SQR is

$$SQR = \frac{resolution}{Q_e} = \frac{V_{lsb}}{V_{lsb}/2} = 2$$

For the PCM code shown in Figure 6-8, the worst-case (minimum) SQR occurs for the lowest magnitude quantization voltage (± 1 V). Therefore, the minimum SQR is

$$SQR_{(min)} = \frac{1}{0.5} = 2$$

or in dB
$$= 20 \log(2)$$
$$= 6 \text{ dB}$$

For a maximum amplitude input signal of 3 V (either 111 or 011), the maximum quantization noise is also equal to the resolution divided by 2. Therefore, the SQR for a maximum input signal is

$$SQR_{(max)} = \frac{V_{max}}{Q_e} = \frac{3}{0.5/2} = 6$$

or in dB
$$= 20 \log 6$$
$$= 15.6 \text{ dB}$$

From the preceding example, it can be seen that even though the magnitude of the quantization error remains constant throughout the entire PCM code, the percentage error does not; it decreases as the magnitude of the sample increases.

The preceding expression for SQR is for voltage and presumes the maximum quantization error; therefore, it is of little practical use and is shown only for comparison purposes and to illustrate that the SQR is not constant throughout the entire range of sample amplitudes. In reality and as shown in Figure 6-9, the difference between the PAM waveform and the analog input waveform varies in magnitude. Therefore, the SQR is not constant. Generally, the quantization error or distortion caused by digitizing an analog sample is expressed as an average signal power-to-average noise power ratio. For linear PCM codes (all quantization intervals have equal magnitudes), the *signal power-to-quantizing noise power ratio* (also called *signal-to-distortion ratio* or *signal-to-noise ratio*) is determined by the following formula:

$$SQR_{(dB)} = 10 \log \frac{v^2/R}{(q^2/12)/R} \tag{6-9a}$$

where
$$R = \text{resistance (ohms)}$$
$$v = \text{rms signal voltage (volts)}$$
$$q = \text{quantization interval (volts)}$$
$$v^2/R = \text{average signal power (watts)}$$
$$(q^2/12)/R = \text{average quantization noise power (watts)}$$

If the resistances are assumed to be equal, Equation 6-8a reduces to

$$SQR = 10 \log \left[\frac{v^2}{q^2/12} \right]$$

$$= 10.8 = 20 \log \frac{v}{q} \tag{6-9b}$$

6-6 LINEAR VERSUS NONLINEAR PCM CODES

Early PCM systems used *linear codes* (i.e., the magnitude change between any two successive steps is uniform). With linear coding, the accuracy (resolution) for the higher-amplitude analog signals is the same as for the lower-amplitude signals, and the SQR for the lower-amplitude signals is less than for the higher-amplitude signals. With voice transmission, low-amplitude signals are more likely to occur than large-amplitude signals. Therefore, if there were more codes for the lower amplitudes, it would increase the accuracy where the accuracy is needed. As a result, there would be fewer codes available for the higher amplitudes, which would increase the quantization error for the larger-amplitude signals (thus decreasing the SQR). Such a coding technique is called *nonlinear* or *nonuniform encoding*. With nonlinear encoding, the step size increases with the amplitude of the input signal.

Figure 6-11 shows the step outputs from a linear and a nonlinear analog-to-digital converter. Note, with nonlinear encoding, there are more codes at the bottom of the scale than there are at the top, thus increasing the accuracy for the smaller-amplitude signals. Also note that the distance between successive codes is greater for the higher-amplitude signals, thus increasing the quantization error and reducing the SQR. Also, because the ratio of V_{max} to V_{min} is increased with nonlinear encoding, the dynamic range is larger than with a uniform linear code. It is evident that nonlinear encoding is a compromise; SQR is sacrificed for the higher-amplitude signals to achieve more accuracy for the lower-amplitude signals and to achieve a larger dynamic range. It is difficult to fabricate

FIGURE 6-11   (a) Linear versus (b) nonlinear encoding

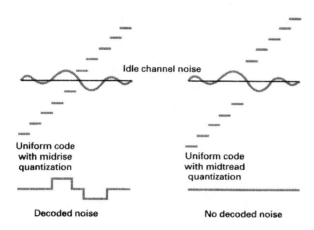

Idle channel noise

Uniform code
with midrise
quantization

Uniform code
with midtread
quantization

Decoded noise

No decoded noise

FIGURE 6-12   Idle channel noise

nonlinear analog-to-digital converters; consequently, alternative methods of achieving the same results have been devised.

6-7   IDLE CHANNEL NOISE

During times when there is no analog input signal, the only input to the PAM sampler is random, thermal noise. This noise is called *idle channel noise* and is converted to a PAM sample just as if it were a signal. Consequently, even input noise is quantized by the ADC. Figure 6-12 shows a way to reduce idle channel noise by a method called *midtread quantization*. With midtread quantizing, the first quantization interval is made larger in amplitude than the rest of the steps. Consequently, input noise can be quite large and still be quantized as a positive or negative zero code. As a result, the noise is suppressed during the encoding process.

In the PCM codes described thus far, the lowest-magnitude positive and negative codes have the same voltage range as all the other codes (+ or − one-half the resolution). This is called *midrise quantization*. Figure 6-12 contrasts the idle channel noise transmitted with a midrise PCM code to the idle channel noise transmitted when midtread quantization is used. The advantage of midtread quantization is less idle channel noise. The disadvantage is a larger possible magnitude for Q_e in the lowest quantization interval.

With a folded binary PCM code, residual noise that fluctuates slightly above and below 0 V is converted to either a + or − zero PCM code and, consequently, is eliminated. In systems that do not use the two 0-V assignments, the residual noise could cause the PCM encoder to alternate between the zero code and the minimum + or − code. Consequently, the decoder would reproduce the encoded noise. With a folded binary code, most of the residual noise is inherently eliminated by the encoder.

6-8 CODING METHODS

There are several coding methods used to quantize PAM signals into 2^n levels. These methods are classified according to whether the coding operation proceeds a level at a time, a digit at a time, or a word at a time.

6-8-1 Level-at-a-Time Coding

This type of coding compares the PAM signal to a ramp waveform while a binary counter is being advanced at a uniform rate. When the ramp waveform equals or exceeds the PAM sample, the counter contains the PCM code. This type of coding requires a very fast clock if the number of bits in the PCM code is large. Level-at-a-time coding also requires that 2^n sequential decisions be made for each PCM code generated. Therefore, level-at-a-time coding is generally limited to low-speed applications. Nonuniform coding is achieved by using a nonlinear function as the reference ramp.

6-8-2 Digit-at-a-Time Coding

This type of coding determines each digit of the PCM code sequentially. Digit-at-a-time coding is analogous to a balance where known reference weights are used to determine an unknown weight. Digit-at-a-time coders provide a compromise between speed and complexity. One common kind of digit-at-a-time coder, called a *feedback coder,* uses a successive approximation register (SAR). With this type of coder, the entire PCM code word is determined simultaneously.

6-8-3 Word-at-a-Time Coding

Word-at-a-time coders are flash encoders and are more complex; however, they are more suitable for high-speed applications. One common type of word-at-a-time coder uses multiple threshold circuits. Logic circuits sense the highest threshold circuit sensed by the PAM input signal and produce the approximate PCM code. This method is again impractical for large values of *n*.

6-9 COMPANDING

Companding is the process of *compressing* and then *expanding*. With companded systems, the higher-amplitude analog signals are compressed (amplified less than the lower-amplitude signals) prior to transmission and then expanded (amplified more than the lower-amplitude signals) in the receiver. Companding is a means of improving the dynamic range of a communications system.

Figure 6-13 illustrates the process of companding. An analog input signal with a dynamic range of 50 dB is compressed to 25 dB prior to transmission and then, in the receiver, expanded back to its original dynamic range of 50 dB. With PCM, companding may be accomplished using analog or digital techniques. Early PCM systems used analog companding, whereas more modern systems use digital companding.

6-9-1 Analog Companding

Historically, analog compression was implemented using specially designed diodes inserted in the analog signal path in a PCM transmitter prior to the sample-and-hold circuit.

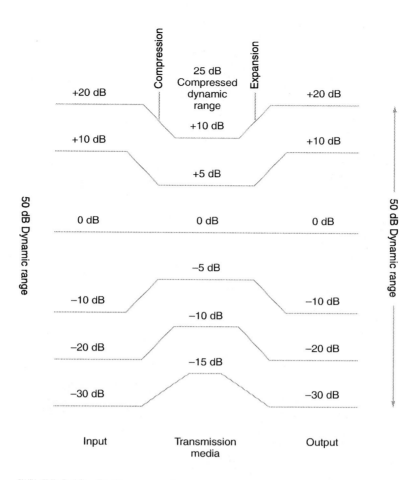

FIGURE 6-13   Basic companding process

Analog expansion was also implemented with diodes that were placed just after the low-pass filter in the PCM receiver.

Figure 6-14 shows the basic process of analog companding. In the transmitter, the dynamic range of the analog signal is compressed, sampled, and then converted to a linear PCM code. In the receiver, the PCM code is converted to a PAM signal, filtered, and then expanded back to its original dynamic range.

Different signal distributions require different companding characteristics. For instance, voice-quality telephone signals require a relatively constant SQR performance over a wide dynamic range, which means that the distortion must be proportional to signal amplitude for all input signal levels. This requires a logarithmic compression ratio, which requires an infinite dynamic range and an infinite number of PCM codes. Of course, this is impossible to achieve. However, there are two methods of analog companding currently being used that closely approximate a logarithmic function and are often called log-PCM codes. The two methods are μ-*law* and the *A-law* companding.

6-9-1-1 μ-Law companding.   In the United States and Japan, μ-*law* companding is used. The compression characteristics for μ-*law* is

$$V_{out} = \frac{V_{max} \ln(1 + \mu V_{in}/V_{max})}{\ln(1 + \mu)} \tag{6-10}$$

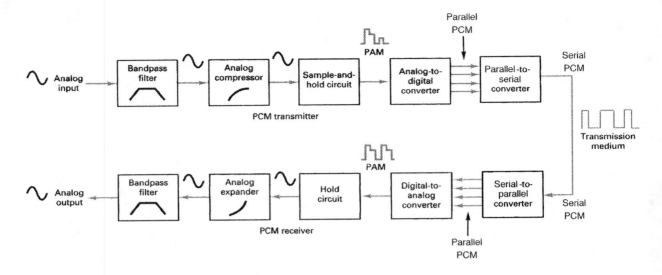

FIGURE 6-14   PCM system with analog companding

FIGURE 6-15   μ-law compression characteristics

where V_{max} = maximum uncompressed analog input amplitude (volts)
   V_{in} = amplitude of the input signal at a particular instant of time (volts)
   μ = parameter used to define the amount of compression (unitless)
   V_{out} = compressed output amplitude (volts)

Figure 6-15 shows the compression curves for several values of μ. Note that the higher the μ, the more compression. Also note that for μ = 0, the curve is linear (no compression).

The parameter μ determines the range of signal power in which the SQR is relatively constant. Voice transmission requires a minimum dynamic range of 40 dB and a seven-bit PCM code. For a relatively constant SQR and a 40-dB dynamic range, a μ ≥100 is required. The early Bell System PCM systems used a seven-bit code with a μ = 100. However, the most recent PCM systems use an eight-bit code and a μ = 255.

Example 6-5

For a compressor with a $\mu = 255$, determine

a. The voltage gain for the following relative values of V_{in}: V_{max}, 0.75 V_{max}, 0.5 V_{max}, and 0.25 V_{max}.
b. The compressed output voltage for a maximum input voltage of 4 V.
c. Input and output dynamic ranges and compression.

Solution a. Substituting into Equation 6-10, the following voltage gains are achieved for the given input magnitudes:

V_{in}	Compressed Voltage Gain
V_{max}	1.00
0.75 V_{max}	1.26
0.5 V_{max}	1.75
0.25 V_{max}	3.00

b. Using the compressed voltage gains determined in step (a), the output voltage is simply the input voltage times the compression gain:

V_{in}	Voltage Gain	V_{out}
$V_{max} = 4$ V	1.00	4.00 V
0.75 $V_{max} = 3$ V	1.26	3.78 V
0.50 $V_{max} = 2$ V	1.75	3.50 V
0.25 $V_{max} = 1$ V	3.00	3 00 V

c. Dynamic range is calculated by substituting into Equation 6-4:

$$\text{input dynamic range} = 20 \log \frac{4}{1} = 12 \text{ dB}$$

$$\text{output dynamic range} = 20 \log \frac{4}{3} = 2.5 \text{ dB}$$

$$\text{compression} = \text{input dynamic range minus output dynamic range}$$
$$= 12 \text{ dB} - 2.5 \text{ dB} = 9.5 \text{ dB}$$

To restore the signals to their original proportions in the receiver, the compressed voltages are expanded by passing them through an amplifier with gain characteristics that are the complement of those in the compressor. For the values given in Example 6-5, the voltage gains in the receiver are as follows:

V_{in}	Expanded Voltage Gain
V_{max}	1.00
0.75 V_{max}	0.79
0.5 V_{max}	0.57
0.25 V_{max}	0.33

The overall circuit gain is simply the product of the compression and expansion factors, which equals one for all input voltage levels. For the values given in Example 6-5,

$$V_{in} = V_{max} \qquad\qquad 1 \times 1 = 1$$
$$V_{in} = 0.75 \ V_{max} \qquad 1.26 \times 0.79 \cong 1$$
$$V_{in} = 0.5 \ V_{max} \qquad 1.75 \times 0.57 \cong 1$$
$$V_{in} = 0.25 \ V_{max} \qquad 3 \times 0.33 \cong 1$$

6-9-1-2 A-law companding. In Europe, the ITU-T has established *A-law* companding to be used to approximate true logarithmic companding. For an intended dynamic

FIGURE 6-16 Digitally companded PCM system

range, *A-law* companding has a slightly flatter SQR than μ-law. *A-law* companding, however, is inferior to μ-law in terms of small-signal quality (idle channel noise). The compression characteristic for *A-law* companding is

$$V_{out} = V_{max} \frac{AV_{in}/V_{max}}{1 + \ln A} \qquad 0 \le \frac{V_{in}}{V_{max}} \le \frac{1}{A} \qquad (6\text{-}11a)$$

$$= \frac{1 + \ln(AV_{in}/V_{max})}{1 + \ln A} \qquad \frac{1}{A} \le \frac{V_{in}}{V_{max}} \le 1 \qquad (6\text{-}11b)$$

6-9-2 Digital Companding

Digital companding involves compression in the transmitter after the input sample has been converted to a linear PCM code and then expansion in the receiver prior to PCM decoding. Figure 6-16 shows the block diagram for a digitally companded PCM system.

With digital companding, the analog signal is first sampled and converted to a linear PCM code and then the linear code is digitally compressed. In the receiver, the compressed PCM code is expanded and then decoded (i.e., converted back to analog). The most recent digitally compressed PCM systems use a 12-bit linear PCM code and an eight-bit compressed PCM code. The compression and expansion curves closely resemble the analog μ-*law* curves with a μ = 255 by approximating the curve with a set of eight straight-line segments (segments 0 through 7). The slope of each successive segment is exactly one-half that of the previous segment.

Figure 6-17 shows the 12-bit-to-8-bit digital compression curve for positive values only. The curve for negative values is identical except the inverse. Although there are 16 segments (eight positive and eight negative), this scheme is often called *13-segment compression* because the curve for segments +0, +1, −0, and −1 is a straight line with a constant slope and is considered as one segment.

The digital companding algorithm for a 12-bit linear-to-8-bit compressed code is actually quite simple. The eight-bit compressed code consists of a sign bit, a three-bit segment identifier, and a 10-bit magnitude code that specifies the quantization interval within the specified segment (see Figure 6-18a).

In the μ255-encoding table shown in Figure 6-18b, the bit positions designated with an X are truncated during compression and subsequently lost. Bits designated A, B, C, and

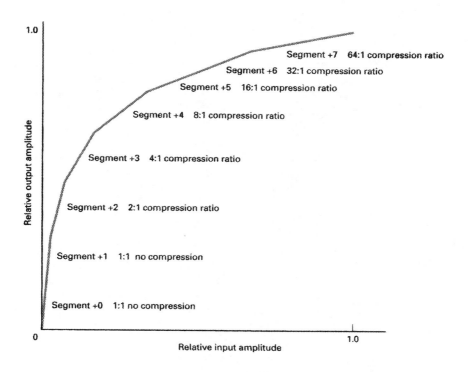

FIGURE 6-17   μ255 compression characteristics (positive values only)

Sign bit 1 = + 0 = −	3-Bit segment identifier	4-Bit quantization interval A B C D
	000 to 111	0000 to 1111

(a)

Transmission
media

Encoded
PCM

Decoded
PCM

Transmit   Receive

Segment	12-Bit linear code	8-Bit compressed code		8-Bit compressed code	12-Bit recovered code	Segment
0	s0000000ABCD	s000ABCD		s000ABCD	s0000000ABCD	0
1	s0000001ABCD	s001ABCD		s001ABCD	s0000001ABCD	1
2	s000001ABCDX	s010ABCD		s010ABCD	s000001ABCD1	2
3	s00001ABCDXX	s011ABCD		s011ABCD	s00001ABCD10	3
4	s0001ABCDXXX	s100ABCD		s100ABCD	s0001ABCD100	4
5	s001ABCDXXXX	s101ABCD		s101ABCD	s001ABCD1000	5
6	s01ABCDXXXXX	s110ABCD		s110ABCD	s01ABCD10000	6
7	s1ABCDXXXXXX	s111ABCD		s111ABCD	s1ABCD100000	7

(b)   (c)

FIGURE 6-18   12-bit-to-8-bit digital companding: (a) 8-bit μ255 compressed code format;
(b) μ255 encoding table; (c) μ255 decoding table

D are transmitted as is. The sign bit is also transmitted as is. Note that for segments 0 and 1, the encoded 12-bit PCM code is duplicated exactly at the output of the decoder (compare Figures 6-18b and c), whereas for segment 7, only the most significant six bits are duplicated. With 11 magnitude bits, there are 2048 possible codes, but they are not equally distributed among the eight segments. There are 16 codes in segment 0 and 16 codes in segment 1. In each subsequent segment, the number of codes doubles (i.e., segment 2 has 32 codes; segment 3 has 64 codes, and so on). However, in each of the eight segments, only 16 12-bit codes can be produced. Consequently, in segments 0 and 1, there is no compression (of the 16 possible codes, all 16 can be decoded). In segment 2, there is a compression ratio of 2:1 (of the 32 possible codes, only 16 can be decoded). In segment 3, there is a 4:1 compression ratio (64 codes to 16 codes). The compression ratio doubles with each successive segment. The compression ratio in segment 7 is 1024/16, or 64:1.

The compression process is as follows. The analog signal is sampled and converted to a linear 12-bit sign-magnitude code. The sign bit is transferred directly to an eight-bit compressed code. The segment number in the eight-bit code is determined by counting the number of leading 0s in the 11-bit magnitude portion of the linear code beginning with the most significant bit. Subtract the number of leading 0s (not to exceed 7) from 7. The result is the segment number, which is converted to a three-bit binary number and inserted into the eight-bit compressed code as the segment identifier. The four magnitude bits (A, B, C, and D) represent the quantization interval (i.e., subsegments) and are substituted into the least significant four bits of the 8-bit compressed code.

Essentially, segments 2 through 7 are subdivided into smaller subsegments. Each segment consists of 16 subsegments, which correspond to the 16 conditions possible for bits A, B, C, and D (0000 to 1111). In segment 2, there are two codes per subsegment. In segment 3, there are four. The number of codes per subsegment doubles with each subsequent segment. Consequently, in segment 7, each subsegment has 64 codes.

Figure 6-19 shows the breakdown of segments versus subsegments for segments 2, 5, and 7. Note that in each subsegment, all 12-bit codes, once compressed and expanded, yield a single 12-bit code. In the decoder, the most significant of the truncated bits is reinserted as a logic 1. The remaining truncated bits are reinserted as 0s. This ensures that the maximum magnitude of error introduced by the compression and expansion process is minimized. Essentially, the decoder guesses what the truncated bits were prior to encoding. The most logical guess is halfway between the minimum- and maximum-magnitude codes. For example, in segment 6, the five least significant bits are truncated during compression; therefore, in the receiver, the decoder must try to determine what those bits were. The possibilities include any code between 00000 and 11111. The logical guess is 10000, approximately half the maximum magnitude. Consequently, the maximum compression error is slightly more than one-half the maximum magnitude for that segment.

Example 6-6

Determine the 12-bit linear code, the eight-bit compressed code, the decoded 12-bit code, the quantization error, and the compression error for a resolution of 0.01 V and analog sample voltages of (a) +0.053 V, (b) −0.318 V, and (c) +10.234 V

Solution a. To determine the 12-bit linear code, simply divide the sample voltage by the resolution, round off the quotient, and then convert the result to a 12-bit sign-magnitude code:

$$\frac{+0.053 \text{ V}}{+0.01 \text{ V}} = +5.3, \text{ which is rounded off to 5 producing a quantization error}$$
$$Q_e = 0.3(0.01 \text{ V}) = 0.003 \text{ V}$$

$$\text{12-bit linear code} = \quad 1 \qquad \overset{\text{A B C D}}{0\ 0\ 0\ 0\ 0\ 0\ 0\ 0\ 1\ 0\ 1}$$

sign bit   11-bit magnitude bits 00000000101 = 5
(1 = +)

Segment	12-Bit linear code		12-Bit expanded code	Subsegment
7	s11111111111 .... s11111000000	} 64 : 1	s11111100000	15
7	s11110111111 .... s11110000000	} 64 : 1	s11110100000	14
7	s11101111111 .... s11101000000	} 64 : 1	s11101100000	13
7	s11100111111 .... s11100000000	} 64 : 1	s11100100000	12
7	s11011111111 .... s11011000000	} 64 : 1	s11011100000	11
7	s11010111111 .... s11010000000	} 64 : 1	s11010100000	10
7	s11001111111 .... s11001000000	} 64 : 1	s11001100000	9
7	s11000111111 .... s11000000000	} 64 : 1	s11000100000	8
7	s10111111111 .... s10111000000	} 64 : 1	s10111100000	7
7	s10110111111 .... s10110000000	} 64 : 1	s10110100000	6
7	s10101111111 .... s10101000000	} 64 : 1	s10101100000	5
7	s10100111111 .... s10100000000	} 64 : 1	s10100100000	4
7	s10011111111 .... s10011000000	} 64 : 1	s10011100000	3
7	s10010111111 .... s10010000000	} 64 : 1	s10010100000	2
7	s10001111111 .... s10001000000	} 64 : 1	s10001100000	1
7	s10000111111 .... s10000000000	} 64 : 1	s10000100000	0
	s1ABCD-------			

(a)

FIGURE 6-19 12-bit segments divided into subsegments: (a) segment 7; *(Continued)*

To determine the 8-bit compressed code,	1	0 0 0 0 0 0 0	0 1 0 1
	1	(7 − 7 = 0)	A B C D
	sign bit (+)	unit identifier (segment 0)	quantization interval (5)

8-bit compressed code	= 1	0 0 0	0 1 0 1
To determine the 12-bit recovered code, simply reverse the process:	1 s sign bit (+)	0 0 0 (000 = segment 0) segment 0 has seven leading 0s	0 1 0 1 A B C D quantization interval (0101 = 5)
12-bit recovered code	= 1	0 0 0 0 0 0	0 0 1 0 1 = +5
recovered voltage	= +5(0.01) = +0.05		

Segment	12-Bit linear code		12-Bit expanded code	Subsegment
5	s00111111111 . . . . s00111110000	16 : 1	s00111111000	15
5	s00111101111 . . . . s00111100000	16 : 1	s00111101000	14
5	s00111011111 . . . . s00111010000	16 : 1	s00111011000	13
5	s00111001111 . . . . s00111000000	16 : 1	s001110010000	12
5	s00110111111 . . . . s00110110000	16 : 1	s00110111000	11
5	s00110101111 . . . . s00110100000	16 : 1	s00110101000	10
5	s00110011111 . . . . s00110010000	16 : 1	s00110011000	9
5	s00110001111 . . . . s00110000000	16 : 1	s00110001000	8
5	s00101111111 . . . . s00101110000	16 : 1	s00101111000	7
5	s00101101111 . . . . s00101100000	16 : 1	s00101101000	6
5	s00101011111 . . . . s00101010000	16 : 1	s00101011000	5
5	s00101001111 . . . . s00101000000	16 : 1	s00101001000	4
5	s00100111111 . . . . s00100110000	16 : 1	s00100111000	3
5	s00100101111 . . . . s00100100000	16 : 1	s00100101000	2
5	s00100011111 . . . . s00100010000	16 : 1	s00100011000	1
5	s00100001111 . . . . s00100000000	16 : 1	s00100001000	0
	s001ABCD----			

(b)

FIGURE 6-19 *(Continued)* (b) segment 5

As Example 6-6 shows, the recovered 12-bit code (+5) is exactly the same as the original 12-bit linear code (+5). Therefore, the decoded voltage (+0.05 V) is the same as the original encoded voltage (+0.5). This is true for all codes in segments 0 and 1. Thus, there is no compression error in segments 0 and 1, and the only error produced is from the quantizing process (for this example, the quantization error $Q_e = 0.003$ V).

b. To determine the 12-bit linear code,

$$\frac{-0.318 \text{ V}}{+0.01 \text{ V}} = -31.8, \text{ which is rounded off to } -32, \text{ producing a}$$
$$\text{quantization error } Q_e = -0.2 \ (0.01 \text{ V}) = -0.002 \text{ V}$$

$$\begin{array}{ccc} & & \text{A B C D} \\ \text{12-bit linear code} = & 0 & 0\ 0\ 0\ 0\ 0\ 1\ 0\ 0\ 0\ 0\ 0 \\ & \downarrow & \longleftarrow \text{11-bit magnitude bits} \longrightarrow \\ & \text{sign bit} & \\ & (0 = -) & \end{array}$$

Segment	12-Bit linear code		12-Bit expanded code	Subsegment
2	s00000111111 .... s00000111110	2 : 1	s00000111111	15
2	s00000111101 .... s00000111100	2 : 1	s00000111101	14
2	s00000111011 .... s00000111010	2 : 1	s00000111011	13
2	s00000111001 .... s00000111000	2 : 1	s00000111001	12
2	s00000110111 .... s00000110110	2 : 1	s00000110111	11
2	s00000110101 .... s00000110100	2 : 1	s00000110101	10
2	s00000110011 .... s00000110010	2 : 1	s00000110011	9
2	s00000110001 .... s00000110000	2 : 1	s00000110001	8
2	s00000101111 .... s00000101110	2 : 1	s00000101111	7
2	s00000101101 .... s00000101100	2 : 1	s00000101101	6
2	s00000101011 .... s00000101010	2 : 1	s00000101011	5
2	s00000101001 .... s00000101000	2 : 1	s00000101001	4
2	s000000100111 .... s00000100110	2 : 1	s00000100111	3
2	s00000100101 .... s00000100100	2 : 1	s00000100101	2
2	s000000100011 .... s00000100010	2 : 1	s00000100011	1
2	s00000100001 .... s00000100000	2 : 1	s00000100001	0
	s000001ABCD-			

(c)

FIGURE 6-19 *(Continued)* (c) segment 2

To determine the 8-bit compressed code,

0	0 0 0 0 0	1	0 0 0 0	0
0	(7 − 5 = 2)		A B C D	X
sign bit (−)	unit identifier (segment 2)		quantization interval (0)	truncated

eight-bit compressed code = 0   0 1 0   0 0 0 0

Again, to determine the 12-bit recovered code, simply reverse the process:

0	0 1 0	0 0 0 0	
sign bit (−)	(7 − 2 = 5) segment 5 has five leading 0s	A B C D quantization interval (0000 = 0)	

                                    A B C D

12-bit recovered code = 0   0 0 0 0 0 1   0 0 0 0 1 = −33

        ↑s   inserted   inserted

decoded voltage = −33(0.1) = −0.33 V

Note the two inserted ones in the recovered 12-bit code. The least significant bit is determined from the decoding table shown in Figure 6-18c. As the figure shows, in the receiver the most significant of the truncated bits is always set (1), and all other truncated bits are cleared (0s). For segment 2 codes, there is only one truncated bit; thus, it is set in the receiver. The inserted 1 in bit position 6 was dropped during the 12-bit-to-8-bit conversion process, as transmission of this bit is redundant because if it were not a 1, the sample would not be in that segment. Consequently, for all segments except segments 0 and 1, a 1 is automatically inserted between the reinserted 0s and the ABCD bits.

For this example, there are two errors: the quantization error and the compression error. The quantization error is due to rounding off the sample voltage in the encoder to the closest PCM code, and the compression error is caused by forcing the truncated bit to be a 1 in the receiver. Keep in mind that the two errors are not always additive, as they could cause errors in the opposite direction and actually cancel each other. The worst-case scenario would be when the two errors were in the same direction and at their maximum values. For this example, the combined error was 0.33 V − 0.318 V = 0.012 V. The worst possible error in segments 0 and 1 is the maximum quantization error, or half the magnitude of the resolution. In segments 2 through 7, the worst possible error is the sum of the maximum quantization error plus the magnitude of the most significant of the truncated bits.

c. To determine the 12-bit linear code,

$$\frac{+10.234 \text{ V}}{+0.01 \text{ V}} = +1023.4, \text{ which is rounded off to 1023, producing a}$$

quantization error $Q_e = -0.4(0.01 \text{ V}) = -0.004 \text{ V}$

					A	B	C	D				
12-bit linear code =	1	0	1	1	1	1	1	1	1	1	1	1

sign bit
(1 = +)

←——— 11-bit magnitude bits ———→

To determine the 8-bit
compressed code,

				A	B	C	D	X	X	X	X	X
	1	0	1	1	1	1	1	1	1	1	1	1
	1											

truncated

8-bit compressed code	=	1	1	1	0	1	1	1	1

To determine the 12-bit
recovered code, simply

		1	1	1	0	1	1	1	1
		s	segment 6		A	B	C	D

12-bit recovered code = 1 0 1 1 1 1 1 1 0 0 0 0   +1008

s   inserted   A   B   C   D   inserted

decoded voltage = +1008(0.01) = +10.08 V

The difference between the original 12-bit code and the decoded 12-bit code is

10.23 − 10.08 = 0.15

or

$$\frac{\begin{array}{r} 1011\ 1111\ 1111 \\ 1011\ 1111\ 0000 \end{array}}{1111} = 15(0.01) = 0.15 \text{ V}$$

For this example, there are again two errors: a quantization error of 0.004 V and a compression error of 0.15 V. The combined error is 10.234 V − 10.08 V = 0.154 V.

6-9-3   Digital Compression Error

As seen in Example 6-6, the magnitude of the compression error is not the same for all samples. However, the maximum percentage error is the same in each segment (other than segments 0 and 1, where there is no compression error). For comparison purposes, the following formula is used for computing the percentage error introduced by digital compression:

$$\% \text{ error} = \frac{12\text{-bit encoded voltage} - 12\text{-bit decoded voltage}}{12\text{-bit decoded voltage}} \times 100 \qquad (6\text{-}12)$$

Example 6-7

The maximum percentage error will occur for the smallest number in the lowest subsegment within any given segment. Because there is no compression error in segments 0 and 1, for segment 3 the maximum percentage error is computed as follows:

transmit 12-bit code   s 0 0 0 0 1 0 0 0 0 0 0
receive 12-bit code   s 0 0 0 0 1 0 0 0 0 1 0
                         0 0 0 0 0 0 0 0 0 1 0

$$\% \text{ error} = \frac{|1000000 - 1000010|}{1000010} \times 100$$

$$= \frac{|64 - 66|}{66} \times 100 = 3.03\%$$

and for segment 7

transmit 12-bit code   s 1 0 0 0 0 0 0 0 0 0 0
receive 12-bit code   s 1 0 0 0 0 1 0 0 0 0 0
                         0 0 0 0 0 1 0 0 0 0 0

$$\% \text{ error} = \frac{|10000000000 - 10000100000|}{10000100000} \times 100$$

$$= \frac{|1024 - 1056|}{1056} \times 100 = 3.03\%$$

As Example 6-7 shows, the maximum magnitude of error is higher for segment 7; however, the maximum percentage error is the same for segments 2 through 7. Consequently, the maximum SQR degradation is the same for each segment.

Although there are several ways in which the 12-bit-to-8-bit compression and 8-bit-to-12-bit expansion can be accomplished with hardware, the simplest and most economical method is with a lookup table in ROM (read-only memory).

Essentially every function performed by a PCM encoder and decoder is now accomplished with a single integrated-circuit chip called a *codec*. Most of the more recently developed codecs are called *combo* chips, as they include an antialiasing (bandpass) filter, a sample-and-hold circuit, and an analog-to-digital converter in the transmit section and a digital-to-analog converter, a hold circuit, and a bandpass filter in the receive section.

6-10 VOCODERS

The PCM coding and decoding processes described in the preceding sections were concerned primarily with reproducing waveforms as accurately as possible. The precise nature of the waveform was unimportant as long as it occupied the voice-band frequency range. When digitizing speech signals only, special voice encoders/decoders called *vocoders* are often used. To achieve acceptable speech communications, the short-term power spectrum of the speech information is all that must be preserved. The human ear is relatively insensitive to the phase relationship between individual frequency components within a voice waveform. Therefore, vocoders are designed to reproduce only the short-term power spectrum, and the decoded time waveforms often only vaguely resemble the original input signal. Vocoders cannot be used in applications where analog signals other than voice are present, such as output signals from voice-band data modems. Vocoders typically produce *unnatural* sounding speech and, therefore, are generally used for recorded information, such as "wrong number" messages, encrypted voice for transmission over analog telephone circuits, computer output signals, and educational games.

The purpose of a vocoder is to encode the minimum amount of speech information necessary to reproduce a perceptible message with fewer bits than those needed by a conventional encoder/decoder. Vocoders are used primarily in limited bandwidth applications. Essentially, there are three vocoding techniques available: the *channel vocoder,* the *formant vocoder,* and the *linear predictive coder.*

6-10-1 Channel Vocoders

The first channel vocoder was developed by Homer Dudley in 1928. Dudley's vocoder compressed conventional speech waveforms into an analog signal with a total bandwidth of approximately 300 Hz. Present-day digital vocoders operate at less than 2 kbps. Digital channel vocoders use bandpass filters to separate the speech waveform into narrower *subbands.* Each subband is full-wave rectified, filtered, and then digitally encoded. The encoded signal is transmitted to the destination receiver, where it is decoded. Generally speaking, the quality of the signal at the output of a vocoder is quite poor. However, some of the more advanced channel vocoders operate at 2400 bps and can produce a highly intelligible, although slightly synthetic sounding speech.

6-10-2 Formant Vocoders

A formant vocoder takes advantage of the fact that the short-term spectral density of typical speech signals seldom distributes uniformly across the entire voice-band spectrum (300 Hz to 3000 Hz). Instead, the spectral power of most speech energy concentrates at three or four peak frequencies called *formants.* A formant vocoder simply determines the location of these peaks and encodes and transmits only the information with the most significant short-term components. Therefore, formant vocoders can operate at lower bit rates and, thus, require narrower bandwidths. Formant vocoders sometimes have trouble tracking changes in the formants. However, once the formants have been identified, a formant vocoder can transfer intelligible speech at less than 1000 bps.

6-10-3 Linear Predictive Coders

A linear predictive coder extracts the most significant portions of speech information directly from the time waveform rather than from the frequency spectrum as with the channel and formant vocoders. A linear predictive coder produces a time-varying model of the *vocal tract excitation* and transfer function directly from the speech waveform. At the receive end, a *synthesizer* reproduces the speech by passing the specified excitation through a mathematical model of the vocal tract. Linear predictive coders provide more natural sounding speech than either the channel or the formant vocoder. Linear predictive coders typically encode and transmit speech at between 1.2 kbps and 2.4 kbps.

6-11 PCM LINE SPEED

Line speed is simply the data rate at which serial PCM bits are clocked out of the PCM encoder onto the transmission line. Line speed is dependent on the sample rate and the number of bits in the compressed PCM code. Mathematically, line speed is

$$\text{line speed} = \frac{\text{samples}}{\text{second}} \times \frac{\text{bits}}{\text{sample}} \tag{6-13}$$

where
 line speed = the transmission rate in bits per second
 samples/second = sample rate (f_s)
 bits/sample = number of bits in the compressed PCM code

Example 6-8

For a single-channel PCM system with a sample rate $f_s = 6000$ samples per second and a seven-bit compressed PCM code, determine the line speed:

Solution
$$\text{line speed} = \frac{6000 \text{ samples}}{\text{second}} \times \frac{7 \text{ bits}}{\text{sample}}$$
$$= 42,000 \text{ bps}$$

6-12 DELTA MODULATION PCM

Delta modulation uses a single-bit PCM code to achieve digital transmission of analog signals. With conventional PCM, each code is a binary representation of both the sign and the magnitude of a particular sample. Therefore, multiple-bit codes are required to represent the many values that the sample can be. With delta modulation, rather than transmit a coded representation of the sample, only a single bit is transmitted, which simply indicates whether that sample is larger or smaller than the previous sample. The algorithm for a delta modulation system is quite simple. If the current sample is smaller than the previous sample, a logic 0 is transmitted. If the current sample is larger than the previous sample, a logic 1 is transmitted.

6-12-1 Delta Modulation Transmitter

Figure 6-20 shows a block diagram of a delta modulation transmitter. The input analog is sampled and converted to a PAM signal, which is compared with the output of the DAC. The output of the DAC is a voltage equal to the regenerated magnitude of the previous sample, which was stored in the up–down counter as a binary number. The up–down counter is incremented or decremented depending on whether the previous sample is larger or smaller than the current sample. The up–down counter is clocked at a rate equal to the sample rate. Therefore, the up–down counter is updated after each comparison.

Figure 6-21 shows the ideal operation of a delta modulation encoder. Initially, the up–down counter is zeroed, and the DAC is outputting 0 V. The first sample is taken, converted to a PAM signal, and compared with zero volts. The output of the comparator is a

FIGURE 6-20 Delta modulation transmitter

FIGURE 6-21   Ideal operation of a delta modulation encoder

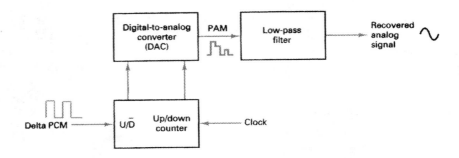

FIGURE 6-22   Delta modulation receiver

logic 1 condition (+V), indicating that the current sample is larger in amplitude than the previous sample. On the next clock pulse, the up–down counter is incremented to a count of 1. The DAC now outputs a voltage equal to the magnitude of the minimum step size (resolution). The steps change value at a rate equal to the clock frequency (sample rate). Consequently, with the input signal shown, the up–down counter follows the input analog signal up until the output of the DAC exceeds the analog sample; then the up–down counter will begin counting down until the output of the DAC drops below the sample amplitude. In the idealized situation (shown in Figure 6-21), the DAC output follows the input signal. Each time the up–down counter is incremented, a logic 1 is transmitted, and each time the up–down counter is decremented, a logic 0 is transmitted.

6-12-2   Delta Modulation Receiver

Figure 6-22 shows the block diagram of a delta modulation receiver. As you can see, the receiver is almost identical to the transmitter except for the comparator. As the logic 1s and 0s are received, the up–down counter is incremented or decremented accordingly. Consequently, the output of the DAC in the decoder is identical to the output of the DAC in the transmitter.

With delta modulation, each sample requires the transmission of only one bit; therefore, the bit rates associated with delta modulation are lower than conventional PCM systems. However, there are two problems associated with delta modulation that do not occur with conventional PCM: slope overload and granular noise.

6-12-2-1 Slope overload.   Figure 6-23 shows what happens when the analog input signal changes at a faster rate than the DAC can maintain. The slope of the analog signal is greater than the delta modulator can maintain and is called *slope overload.* Increasing the clock frequency reduces the probability of slope overload occurring. Another way to prevent slope overload is to increase the magnitude of the minimum step size.

FIGURE 6-23   Slope overload distortion

FIGURE 6-24   Granular noise

6-12-2-2 Granular noise.   Figure 6-24 contrasts the original and reconstructed signals associated with a delta modulation system. It can be seen that when the original analog input signal has a relatively constant amplitude, the reconstructed signal has variations that were not present in the original signal. This is called *granular noise*. Granular noise in delta modulation is analogous to quantization noise in conventional PCM.

Granular noise can be reduced by decreasing the step size. Therefore, to reduce the granular noise, a small resolution is needed, and to reduce the possibility of slope overload occurring, a large resolution is required. Obviously, a compromise is necessary.

Granular noise is more prevalent in analog signals that have gradual slopes and whose amplitudes vary only a small amount. Slope overload is more prevalent in analog signals that have steep slopes or whose amplitudes vary rapidly.

6-13   ADAPTIVE DELTA MODULATION PCM

Adaptive delta modulation is a delta modulation system where the step size of the DAC is automatically varied, depending on the amplitude characteristics of the analog input signal. Figure 6-25 shows how an adaptive delta modulator works. When the output of the transmitter is a string of consecutive 1s or 0s, this indicates that the slope of the DAC output is

FIGURE 6-25   Adaptive delta modulation

less than the slope of the analog signal in either the positive or the negative direction. Essentially, the DAC has lost track of exactly where the analog samples are, and the possibility of slope overload occurring is high. With an adaptive delta modulator, after a predetermined number of consecutive 1s or 0s, the step size is automatically increased. After the next sample, if the DAC output amplitude is still below the sample amplitude, the next step is increased even further until eventually the DAC catches up with the analog signal. When an alternative sequence of 1s and 0s is occurring, this indicates that the possibility of granular noise occurring is high. Consequently, the DAC will automatically revert to its minimum step size and, thus, reduce the magnitude of the noise error.

A common algorithm for an adaptive delta modulator is when three consecutive 1s or 0s occur, the step size of the DAC is increased or decreased by a factor of 1.5. Various other algorithms may be used for adaptive delta modulators, depending on particular system requirements.

6-14 DIFFERENTIAL PCM

In a typical PCM-encoded speech waveform, there are often successive samples taken in which there is little difference between the amplitudes of the two samples. This necessitates transmitting several identical PCM codes, which is redundant. Differential pulse code modulation (DPCM) is designed specifically to take advantage of the sample-to-sample redundancies in typical speech waveforms. With DPCM, the difference in the amplitude of two successive samples is transmitted rather than the actual sample. Because the range of sample differences is typically less than the range of individual samples, fewer bits are required for DPCM than conventional PCM.

Figure 6-26 shows a simplified block diagram of a DPCM transmitter. The analog input signal is bandlimited to one-half the sample rate, then compared with the preceding accumulated signal level in the differentiator. The output of the differentiation is the difference between the two signals. The difference is PCM encoded and transmitted. The ADC operates the same as in a conventional PCM system, except that it typically uses fewer bits per sample.

Figure 6-27 shows a simplified block diagram of a DPCM receiver. Each received sample is converted back to analog, stored, and then summed with the next sample received. In the receiver shown in Figure 6-27, the integration is performed on the analog signals, although it could also be performed digitally.

FIGURE 6-26   DPCM transmitter

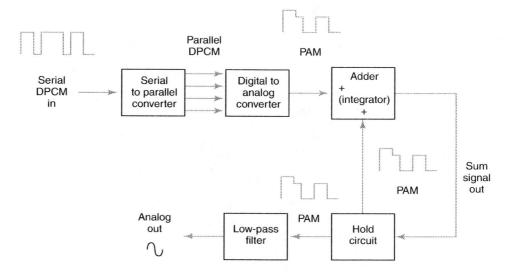

FIGURE 6-27 DPCM receiver

6-15 PULSE TRANSMISSION

All digital carrier systems involve the transmission of pulses through a medium with a finite bandwidth. A highly selective system would require a large number of filter sections, which is impractical. Therefore, practical digital systems generally utilize filters with bandwidths that are approximately 30% or more in excess of the ideal Nyquist bandwidth. Figure 6-28a shows the typical output waveform from a *bandlimited* communications channel when a narrow pulse is applied to its input. The figure shows that bandlimiting a pulse causes the energy from the pulse to be spread over a significantly longer time in the form of *secondary lobes*. The secondary lobes are called *ringing tails*. The output frequency spectrum corresponding to a rectangular pulse is referred to as a (sin *x*)/*x* response and is given as

$$f(\omega) = (T)\frac{\sin(\omega T/2)}{\omega T/2}$$

(6-14)

where $\omega = 2\pi f$ (radians)
    T = pulse width (seconds)

Figure 6-28b shows the distribution of the total spectrum power. It can be seen that approximately 90% of the signal power is contained within the first *spectral null* (i.e., $f = 1/T$). Therefore, the signal can be confined to a bandwidth $B = 1/T$ and still pass most of the energy from the original waveform. In theory, only the amplitude at the middle of each pulse interval needs to be preserved. Therefore, if the bandwidth is confined to $B = 1/2T$, the maximum signaling rate achievable through a low-pass filter with a specified bandwidth without causing excessive distortion is given as the Nyquist rate and is equal to twice the bandwidth. Mathematically, the Nyquist rate is

$$R = 2B$$

(6-15)

where R = signaling rate = $1/T$
    B = specified bandwidth

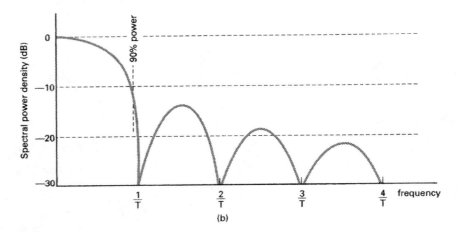

FIGURE 6-28 Pulse response: (a) typical pulse response of a bandlimited filter; (b) spectrum of square pulse with duration $1/T$

6-15-1 Intersymbol Interference

Figure 6-29 shows the input signal to an ideal minimum bandwidth, low-pass filter. The input signal is a random, binary nonreturn-to-zero (NRZ) sequence. Figure 6-29b shows the output of a low-pass filter that does not introduce any phase or amplitude distortion. Note that the output signal reaches its full value for each transmitted pulse at precisely the center of each sampling interval. However, if the low-pass filter is imperfect (which in reality it will be), the output response will more closely resemble that shown in Figure 6-29c. At the sampling instants (i.e., the center of the pulses), the signal does not always attain the maximum value. The ringing tails of several pulses have *overlapped*, thus interfering with the *major pulse lobe*. Assuming no time delays through the system, energy in the form of spurious responses from the third and fourth impulses from one pulse appears during the sampling instant ($T = 0$) of another pulse. This interference is commonly called *intersymbol interference*, or simply ISI. ISI is an important consideration in the transmission of pulses over circuits with a limited bandwidth and a nonlinear phase response. Simply stated, rectangular pulses will not remain rectangular in less than an infinite bandwidth. The narrower the bandwidth, the more rounded the pulses. If the phase distortion is excessive, the pulse will *tilt* and, consequently, affect the next pulse. When pulses from more than

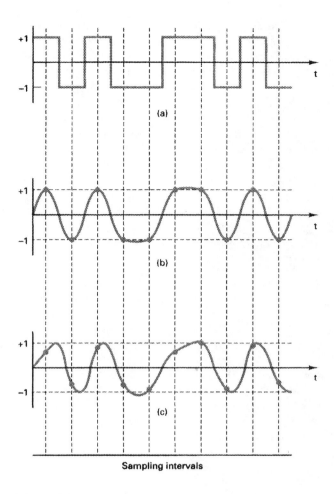

FIGURE 6-29 Pulse response: (a) NRZ input signal;
(b) output from a perfect filter; (c) output from an imperfect
filter

one source are multiplexed together, the amplitude, frequency, and phase responses become even more critical. ISI causes *crosstalk* between channels that occupy adjacent time slots in a time-division-multiplexed carrier system. Special filters called *equalizers* are inserted in the transmission path to "equalize" the distortion for all frequencies, creating a uniform transmission medium and reducing transmission impairments. The four primary causes of ISI are as follows:

1. *Timing inaccuracies.* In digital transmission systems, transmitter timing inaccuracies cause intersymbol interference if the rate of transmission does not conform to the *ringing frequency* designed into the communications channel. Generally, timing inaccuracies of this type are insignificant. Because receiver clocking information is derived from the received signals, which are contaminated with noise, inaccurate sample timing is more likely to occur in receivers than in transmitters.

2. *Insufficient bandwidth.* Timing errors are less likely to occur if the transmission rate is well below the channel bandwidth (i.e., the Nyquist bandwidth is significantly below the channel bandwidth). As the bandwidth of a communications channel is reduced, the ringing frequency is reduced, and intersymbol interference is more likely to occur.

3. *Amplitude distortion.* Filters are placed in a communications channel to bandlimit signals and reduce or eliminate predicted noise and interference. Filters are also used to produce a specific pulse response. However, the frequency response of a channel cannot always be predicted absolutely. When the frequency characteristics of a communications channel depart from the normal or expected values, *pulse distortion* results. Pulse distortion occurs when the peaks of pulses are reduced, causing improper ringing frequencies in the time domain. Compensation for such impairments is called *amplitude equalization.*

4. *Phase distortion.* A pulse is simply the superposition of a series of harmonically related sine waves with specific amplitude and phase relationships. Therefore, if the relative phase relations of the individual sine waves are altered, phase distortion occurs. Phase distortion occurs when frequency components undergo different amounts of time delay while propagating through the transmission medium. Special delay equalizers are placed in the transmission path to compensate for the varying delays, thus reducing the phase distortion. Phase equalizers can be manually adjusted or designed to automatically adjust themselves to varying transmission characteristics.

6-15-2 Eye Patterns

The performance of a digital transmission system depends, in part, on the ability of a repeater to regenerate the original pulses. Similarly, the quality of the regeneration process depends on the decision circuit within the repeater and the quality of the signal at the input to the decision circuit. Therefore, the performance of a digital transmission system can be measured by displaying the received signal on an oscilloscope and triggering the time base at the data rate. Thus, all waveform combinations are superimposed over adjacent signaling intervals. Such a display is called an *eye pattern* or *eye diagram*. An eye pattern is a convenient technique for determining the effects of the degradations introduced into the pulses as they travel to the regenerator. The test setup to display an eye pattern is shown in Figure 6-30. The received pulse stream is fed to the vertical input of the oscilloscope, and the symbol clock is fed to the external trigger input, while the sweep rate is set approximately equal to the symbol rate.

Figure 6-31 shows an eye pattern generated by a symmetrical waveform for *ternary* signals in which the individual pulses at the input to the regenerator have a cosine-squared shape. In an m-level system, there will be $m - 1$ separate eyes. The vertical lines labeled $+1$, 0, and -1 correspond to the ideal received amplitudes. The horizontal lines, separated by the signaling interval, T, correspond to the ideal *decision times*. The decision levels for the regenerator are represented by *crosshairs*. The vertical hairs represent the decision time, whereas the horizontal hairs represent the decision level. The eye pattern shows the quality of shaping and timing and discloses any noise and errors that might be present in the line equalization. The eye opening (the area in the middle of the eye pattern) defines a boundary within which no waveform *trajectories* can exist under any code-pattern condition. The eye

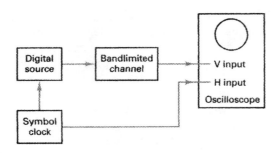

FIGURE 6-30 Eye diagram measurement setup

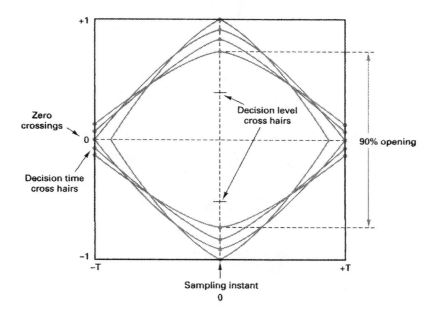

Zero crossings

Decision level cross hairs

90% opening

Decision time cross hairs

Sampling instant 0

FIGURE 6-31   Eye diagram

opening is a function of the number of code levels and the intersymbol interference caused by the ringing tails of any preceding or succeeding pulses. To regenerate the pulse sequence without error, the eye must be open (i.e., a decision area must exist), and the decision crosshairs must be within the open area. The effect of pulse degradation is a reduction in the size of the ideal eye. In Figure 6-31, it can be seen that at the center of the eye (i.e., the sampling instant) the opening is about 90%, indicating only minor ISI degradation due to filtering imperfections. The small degradation is due to the nonideal Nyquist amplitude and phase characteristics of the transmission system. Mathematically, the ISI degradation is

$$\text{ISI} = 20 \log \frac{h}{H} \qquad (6\text{-}16)$$

where H = ideal vertical opening (cm)
h = degraded vertical opening (cm)

For the eye diagram shown in Figure 6-31,

$$20 \log \frac{90}{100} = 0.915 \text{ dB (ISI degradation)}$$

In Figure 6-31, it can also be seen that the overlapping signal pattern does not cross the horizontal zero line at exact integer multiples of the symbol clock. This is an impairment known as *data transition jitter.* This jitter has an effect on the symbol timing (clock) recovery circuit and, if excessive, may significantly degrade the performance of cascaded regenerative sections.

6-16   SIGNAL POWER IN BINARY DIGITAL SIGNALS

Because binary digital signals can originate from literally scores of different types of data sources, it is impossible to predict which patterns or sequences of bits are most likely to occur over a given period of time in a given system. Thus, for signal analysis purposes, it is generally assumed that there is an equal probability of the occurrence of a 1 and a 0. Therefore,

FIGURE 6-32   Binary digital signals:
(a) $\tau/T < 0.5$; (b) $\tau/T = 0.5$

power can be averaged over an entire message duration, and the signal can be modeled as a continuous sequence of alternating 1s and 0s as shown in Figure 6-32. Figure 6-32a shows a stream of rectangularly shaped pulses with a pulse width-to-pulse duration ratio τ/T less than 0.5, and Figure 6-32b shows a stream of square wave pulses with a τ/T ratio of 0.5.

The normalized ($R - 1$) average power is derived for signal $f(t)$ from

$$\overline{P} = \lim_{T \to x} \frac{1}{T} \int_{-T/2}^{T/2} [f(t)]^2 \, dt \tag{6-17}$$

where T is the period of integration. If $f(t)$ is a periodic signal with period T_0, then Equation 6-17 reduces to

$$\overline{P} = \frac{1}{T_0} \int_{-T_0/2}^{T_0/2} [v(t)]^2 \, dt \tag{6-18}$$

If rectangular pulses of amplitude V with a τ/T ratio of 0.5 begin at $t = 0$, then

$$v(t) = \begin{cases} V & 0 \le t \le \tau \\ 0 & \tau < t \le T \end{cases} \tag{6-19}$$

Thus, from Equation 6-18,

$$\overline{P} = \frac{1}{T_0} \int_0^T (V)^2 \, dt = \frac{1}{T_0} V^2 t \big|_0^\tau$$

$$= \frac{\tau}{T_0} V^2 \tag{6-20}$$

and

$$\overline{P} = \left(\frac{\tau}{T}\right) \frac{V^2}{R}$$

Because the effective rms value of a periodic wave is found from $P = (V_{rms})^2/R$, the rms voltage for a rectangular pulse is

$$V_{rms} = \sqrt{\frac{\tau}{T}} (V) \tag{6-21}$$

Because $\overline{P} = (V_{rms})^2/R$, $\overline{P} = (\sqrt{\tau/T}V)^2/R = (\tau V^2)/(TR)$.

With the square wave shown in Figure 6-32, $\tau/T = 0.5$, therefore, $\overline{P} = V^2/2R$. Thus, the rms voltage for the square wave is the same as for sine waves, $V_{rms} = V/\sqrt{2}$.

QUESTIONS

6-1. Contrast the advantages and disadvantages of digital transmission.

6-2. What are the four most common methods of pulse modulation?

6-3. Which method listed in question 6-2 is the only form of pulse modulation that is used in a digital transmission system? Explain.

6-4. What is the purpose of the sample-and-hold circuit?

6-5. Define *aperture* and *acquisition time.*

6-6. What is the difference between natural and flat-top sampling?

6-7. Define *droop.* What causes it?

6-8. What is the Nyquist sampling rate?

6-9. Define and state the causes of foldover distortion.

6-10. Explain the difference between a magnitude-only code and a sign-magnitude code.

6-11. Explain overload distortion.

6-12. Explain quantizing.

6-13. What is quantization range? Quantization error?

6-14. Define *dynamic range.*

6-15. Explain the relationship between dynamic range, resolution, and the number of bits in a PCM code.

6-16. Explain coding efficiency.

6-17. What is SQR? What is the relationship between SQR, resolution, dynamic range, and the number of bits in a PCM code?

6-18. Contrast linear and nonlinear PCM codes.

6-19. Explain idle channel noise.

6-20. Contrast midtread and midrise quantization.

6-21. Define *companding.*

6-22. What does the parameter μ determine?

6-23. Briefly explain the process of digital companding.

6-24. What is the effect of digital compression on SQR, resolution, quantization interval, and quantization noise?

6-25. Contrast delta modulation PCM and standard PCM.

6-26. Define *slope overload* and *granular noise.*

6-27. What is the difference between adaptive delta modulation and conventional delta modulation?

6-28. Contrast differential and conventional PCM.

PROBLEMS

6-1. Determine the Nyquist sample rate for a maximum analog input frequency of
   a. 4 kHz.
   b. 10 kHz.

6-2. For the sample-and-hold circuit shown in Figure 6-5a, determine the largest-value capacitor that can be used. Use the following parameters: an output impedance for $Z_1 = 20\ \Omega$, an on resistance of Q_1 of 20 Ω, an acquisition time of 10 μs, a maximum output current from Z_1 of 20 mA, and an accuracy of 1%.

6-3. For a sample rate of 20 kHz, determine the maximum analog input frequency.

6-4. Determine the alias frequency for a 14-kHz sample rate and an analog input frequency of 8 kHz.

6-5. Determine the dynamic range for a 10-bit sign-magnitude PCM code.

6-6. Determine the minimum number of bits required in a PCM code for a dynamic range of 80 dB. What is the coding efficiency?

6-7. For a resolution of 0.04 V, determine the voltages for the following linear seven-bit sign-magnitude PCM codes:

a. 0 1 1 0 1 0 1
b. 0 0 0 0 0 1 1
c. 1 0 0 0 0 0 1
d. 0 1 1 1 1 1 1
e. 1 0 0 0 0 0 0

6-8. Determine the SQR for a 2-v_{rms} signal and a quantization interval of 0.2 V.

6-9. Determine the resolution and quantization error for an eight-bit linear sign-magnitude PCM code for a maximum decoded voltage of 1.27 V.

6-10. A 12-bit linear PCM code is digitally compressed into eight bits. The resolution = 0.03 V. Determine the following for an analog input voltage of 1.465 V:

a. 12-bit linear PCM code
b. eight-bit compressed code
c. Decoded 12-bit code
d. Decoded voltage
e. Percentage error

6-11. For a 12-bit linear PCM code with a resolution of 0.02 V, determine the voltage range that would be converted to the following PCM codes:

a. 1 0 0 0 0 0 0 0 0 0 0 1
b. 0 0 0 0 0 0 0 0 0 0 0 0
c. 1 1 0 0 0 0 0 0 0 0 0 0
d. 0 1 0 0 0 0 0 0 0 0 0 0
e. 1 0 0 1 0 0 0 0 0 0 0 1
f. 1 0 1 0 1 0 1 0 1 0 1 0

6-12. For each of the following 12-bit linear PCM codes, determine the eight-bit compressed code to which they would be converted:

a. 1 0 0 0 0 0 0 0 1 0 0 0
b. 1 0 0 0 0 0 0 0 1 0 0 1
c. 1 0 0 0 0 0 0 1 0 0 0 0
d. 0 0 0 0 0 0 1 0 0 0 0 0
e. 0 1 0 0 0 0 0 0 0 0 0 0
f. 0 1 0 0 0 0 1 0 0 0 0 0

6-13. Determine the Nyquist sampling rate for the following maximum analog input frequencies: 2 kHz, 5 kHz, 12 kHz, and 20 kHz.

6-14. For the sample-and-hold circuit shown in Figure 6-5a, determine the largest-value capacitor that can be used for the following parameters: Z_1 output impedance = 15 Ω, an on resistance of Q_1 of 15 Ω, an acquisition time of 12 μs, a maximum output current from Z_1 of 10 mA, an accuracy of 0.1%, and a maximum change in voltage dv = 10 V.

6-15. Determine the maximum analog input frequency for the following Nyquist sample rates: 2.5 kHz, 4 kHz, 9 kHz, and 11 kHz.

6-16. Determine the alias frequency for the following sample rates and analog input frequencies:

f_a (kHz)	f_s (kHz)
3	4
5	8
6	8
5	7

6-17. Determine the dynamic range in dB for the following n-bit linear sign-magnitude PCM codes: n = 7, 8, 12, and 14.

6-18. Determine the minimum number of bits required for PCM codes with the following dynamic ranges and determine the coding efficiencies: DR = 24 dB, 48 dB, and 72 dB.

6-19. For the following values of μ, V_{max}, and V_{in}, determine the compressor gain:

μ	V_{max} (V)	V_{in} (V)
255	1	0.75
100	1	0.75
255	2	0.5

6-20. For the following resolutions, determine the range of the eight-bit sign-magnitude PCM codes:

Code	Resolution (V)
10111000	0.1
00111000	0.1
11111111	0.05
00011100	0.02
00110101	0.02
11100000	0.02
00000111	0.02

6-21. Determine the SQR for the following input signal and quantization noise magnitudes:

V_s	V_n (V)
1 v_{rms}	0.01
2 v_{rms}	0.02
3 v_{rms}	0.01
4 v_{rms}	0.2

6-22. Determine the resolution and quantization noise for an eight-bit linear sign-magnitude PCM code for the following maximum decoded voltages: $V_{max} = 3.06$ V_p, 3.57 V_p, 4.08 V_p, and 4.59 V_p.

6-23. A 12-bit linear sign-magnitude PCM code is digitally compressed into 8 bits. For a resolution of 0.016 V, determine the following quantities for the indicated input voltages: 12-bit linear PCM code, eight-bit compressed code, decoded 12-bit code, decoded voltage, and percentage error. $V_{in} = -6.592$ V, $+12.992$ V, and -3.36 V.

6-24. For the 12-bit linear PCM codes given, determine the voltage range that would be converted to them:

12-Bit Linear Code	Resolution (V)
100011110010	0.12
000001000000	0.10
000111111000	0.14
111111110000	0.12

6-25. For the following 12-bit linear PCM codes, determine the eight-bit compressed code to which they would be converted:

12-Bit Linear Code
100011110010
000001000000
000111111000
111111110010
000000100000

6-26. For the following eight-bit compressed codes, determine the expanded 12-bit code.

Eight-Bit Code
11001010
00010010
10101010
01010101
11110000
11011011

C H A P T E R 7

Digital T-Carriers and Multiplexing

OBJECTIVES

- Define *multiplexing*
- Describe the frame format and operation of the T1 digital carrier system
- Describe the format of the North American Digital Hierarchy
- Define *line encoding*
- Define the following terms and describe how they affect line encoding: *duty cycle, bandwidth, clock recovery, error detection,* and *detecting* and *decoding*
- Describe the basic T carrier system formats
- Describe the European digital carrier system
- Describe several methods of achieving frame synchronization
- Describe the difference between bit and word interleaving
- Define *codecs* and *combo chips* and give a brief explanation of how they work
- Define *frequency-division multiplexing*
- Describe the format of the North American FDM Hierarchy
- Define and describe baseband and composite baseband signals
- Explain the formation of a mastergroup
- Describe wavelength-division multiplexing
- Explain the advantages and disadvantages of wavelength-division multiplexing

Multiplexing is the transmission of information (in any form) from one or more source to one or more destination over the same transmission medium (facility). Although transmissions occur on the same facility, they do not necessarily occur at the same time or occupy the same bandwidth. The transmission medium may be a metallic wire pair, a coaxial cable, a PCS mobile telephone, a terrestrial microwave radio system, a satellite microwave system, or an optical fiber cable.

There are several domains in which multiplexing can be accomplished, including space, phase, time, frequency, and wavelength.

Space-division multiplexing (SDM) is a rather unsophisticated form of multiplexing that simply constitutes propagating signals from different sources on different cables that are contained within the same trench. The trench is considered to be the transmission medium. QPSK is a form of *phase-division multiplexing* (PDM) where two data channels (the I and Q) modulate the same carrier frequency that has been shifted 90° in phase. Thus, the I-channel bits modulate a sine wave carrier, while the Q-channel bits modulate a cosine wave carrier. After modulation has occurred, the I- and Q-channel carriers are linearly combined and propagated at the same time over the same transmission medium, which can be a cable or free space.

The three most predominant methods of multiplexing signals are time-division multiplexing (TDM), frequency-division multiplexing (FDM), and the more recently developed wavelength-division multiplexing (WDM). The remainder of this chapter will be dedicated to time-, frequency-, and wavelength-division multiplexing.

7-2 TIME-DIVISION MULTIPLEXING

With *time division multiplexing* (TDM), transmissions from multiple sources occur on the same facility but not at the same time. Transmissions from various sources are *interleaved* in the time domain. PCM is the most prevalent encoding technique used for TDM digital signals. With a PCM-TDM system, two or more voice channels are sampled, converted to PCM codes, and then time-division multiplexed onto a single metallic or optical fiber cable.

The fundamental building block for most TDM systems in the United States begins with a DS-0 channel (digital signal level 0). Figure 7-1 shows the simplified block dia-

FIGURE 7-1   Single-channel (DS-0-level) PCM transmission system

gram for a DS-0 single-channel PCM system. As the figure shows, DS-0 channels use an 8-kHz sample rate and an eight-bit PCM code, which produces a 64-kbps PCM line speed:

$$\text{line speed} = \frac{8000 \text{ samples}}{\text{second}} \times \frac{8 \text{ bits}}{\text{sample}}$$

$$= 64,000 \text{ bps}$$

Figure 7-2a shows the simplified block diagram for a PCM carrier system comprised of two DS-0 channels that have been time-division multiplexed. Each channel's input is sampled at an 8-kHz rate and then converted to an eight-bit PCM code. While the PCM code for channel 1 is being transmitted, channel 2 is sampled and converted to a PCM code. While the PCM code from channel 2 is being transmitted, the next sample is taken from channel 1 and converted to a PCM code. This process continues, and samples are taken alternately from each channel, converted to PCM codes, and transmitted. The multiplexer is simply an electronically controlled digital switch with two inputs and one output. Channel 1 and channel 2 are alternately selected and connected to the transmission line through the multiplexer. One eight-bit PCM code from each channel (16 total bits) is called a TDM *frame,* and the time it takes to transmit one TDM frame is called the *frame time.* The frame time is equal to the reciprocal of the sample rate ($1/f_s$, or $1/8000 = 125$ µs). Figure 7-2b shows the TDM frame allocation for a two-channel PCM system with an 8-kHz sample rate.

The PCM code for each channel occupies a fixed time slot (epoch) within the total TDM frame. With a two-channel system, one sample is taken from each channel during each frame, and the time allocated to transmit the PCM bits from each channel is equal to one-half the total frame time. Therefore, eight bits from each channel must be transmitted during each frame (a total of 16 PCM bits per frame). Thus, the line speed at the output of the multiplexer is

$$\frac{2 \text{ channels}}{\text{frame}} \times \frac{8000 \text{ frames}}{\text{second}} \times \frac{8 \text{ bits}}{\text{channel}} = 128 \text{ kbps}$$

Although each channel is producing and transmitting only 64 kbps, the bits must be clocked out onto the line at a 128-kHz rate to allow eight bits from each channel to be transmitted in a 1211-µs time slot.

7-3 T1 DIGITAL CARRIER

A digital carrier system is a communications system that uses digital pulse rather than analog signals to encode information. Figure 7-3a shows the block diagram for AT&T's T1 digital carrier system, which has been the North American digital multiplexing standard since 1963 and recognized by the ITU-T as Recommendation G.733. T1 stands for *transmission one* and specifies a digital carrier system using PCM-encoded analog signals. A T1 carrier system time-division multiplexes PCM-encoded samples from 24 voice-band channels for transmission over a single metallic wire pair or optical fiber transmission line. Each voice-band channel has a bandwidth of approximately 300 Hz to 3000 Hz. Again, the multiplexer is simply a digital switch with 24 independent inputs and one time-division multiplexed output. The PCM output signals from the 24 voice-band channels are sequentially selected and connected through the multiplexer to the transmission line.

Simply, time-division multiplexing 24 voice-band channels does not in itself constitute a T1 carrier system. At this point, the output of the multiplexer is simply a multiplexed first-level digital signal (DS level 1). The system does not become a T1 carrier until it is line encoded and placed on special conditioned cables called *T1 lines.* Line encoding is described later in this chapter.

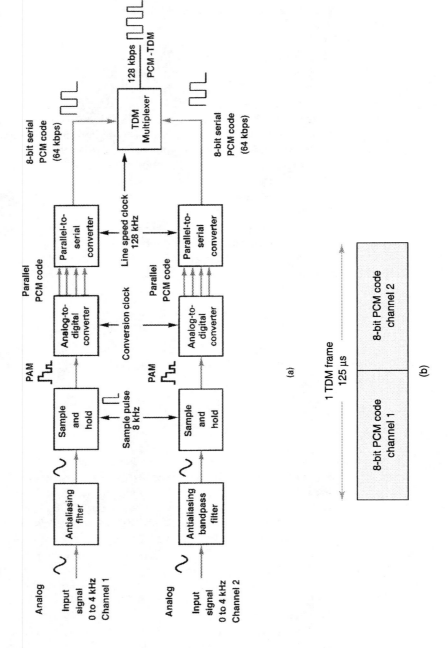

FIGURE 7-2 Two-channel PCM-TDM system: (a) block diagram; (b) TDM frame

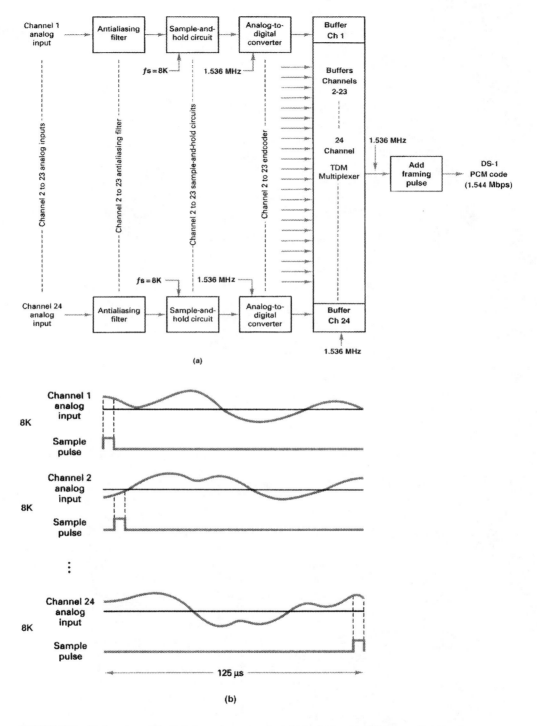

FIGURE 7-3 Bell system T1 digital carrier system: (a) block diagram; (b) sampling sequence

With a T1 carrier system, D-type (digital) channel banks perform the sampling, encoding, and multiplexing of 24 voice-band channels. Each channel contains an eight-bit PCM code and is sampled 8000 times a second. Each channel is sampled at the same rate but not necessarily at the same time. Figure 7-3b shows the channel sampling sequence for a 24-channel T1 digital carrier system. As the figure shows, each channel is sampled once each frame but not at the same time. Each channel's sample is offset from the previous channel's sample by 1/24 of the total frame time. Therefore, one 64-kbps PCM-encoded sample is transmitted for each voice-band channel during each frame (a frame time of $1/8000 = 125$ μs). The line speed is calculated as follows:

$$\frac{24 \text{ channels}}{\text{frame}} \times \frac{8 \text{ bits}}{\text{channel}} = 192 \text{ bits per frame}$$

thus

$$\frac{192 \text{ bits}}{\text{frame}} \times \frac{8000 \text{ frames}}{\text{second}} = 1.536 \text{ Mbps}$$

Later, an additional bit (called the *framing bit*) is added to each frame. The framing bit occurs once per frame (8000-bps rate) and is recovered in the receiver, where it is used to maintain frame and sample synchronization between the TDM transmitter and receiver. As a result, each frame contains 193 bits, and the line speed for a T1 digital carrier system is

$$\frac{193 \text{ bits}}{\text{frame}} \times \frac{8000 \text{ frames}}{\text{second}} = 1.544 \text{ Mbps}$$

7-3-1 D-Type Channel Banks

Early T1 carrier systems used D1 *digital channel banks* (PCM encoders and decoders) with a seven-bit magnitude-only PCM code, analog companding, and $\mu = 100$. A later version of the D1 digital channel bank added an eighth bit (the signaling bit) to each PCM code for performing interoffice *signaling* (supervision between telephone offices, such as on hook, off hook, dial pulsing, and so forth). Since a signaling bit was added to each sample in every frame, the signaling rate was 8 kbps. In the early digital channel banks, the framing bit sequence was simply an alternating 1/0 pattern. Figure 7-4 shows the frame and bit alignment for T1-carrier systems that used D1 channel banks.

Over the years, T1 carrier systems have generically progressed through D2, D3, D4, D5, and D6 channel banks. D4, D5, and D6 channel banks use digital companding and eight-bit sign-magnitude-compressed PCM codes with $\mu = 255$.

Because the early D1 channel banks used a magnitude-only PCM code, an error in the most significant bit of a PCM sample produced a decoded error equal to one-half the total quantization range. Newer version digital channel banks used sign-magnitude codes, and an error in the sign bit causes a decoded error equal to twice the sample magnitude ($+V$ to $-V$ or vice versa) with a worst-case error equal to twice the total quantization range. However, in practice, maximum amplitude samples occur rarely; therefore, most errors have a magnitude less than half the coding range. On average, performance with sign-magnitude PCM codes is much better than with magnitude-only codes.

7-3-2 Superframe TDM Format

The 8-kbps signaling rate used with the early digital channel banks was excessive for signaling on standard telephone voice circuits. Therefore, with modern channel banks, a signaling bit is substituted only into the least significant bit of every sixth frame. Hence, five of every six frames have eight-bit resolution, while one in every six frames (the signaling frame) has only seven-bit resolution. Consequently, the signaling rate on each channel is only 1.333 kbps (8000 bps/6), and the average number of bits per sample is actually $7^{5/6}$ bits.

Because only every sixth frame includes a signaling bit, it is necessary that all the frames be numbered so that the receiver knows when to extract the signaling bit. Also, because the signaling is accomplished with a two-bit binary word, it is necessary to identify the most and least significant bits of the signaling word. Consequently, the superframe format shown in

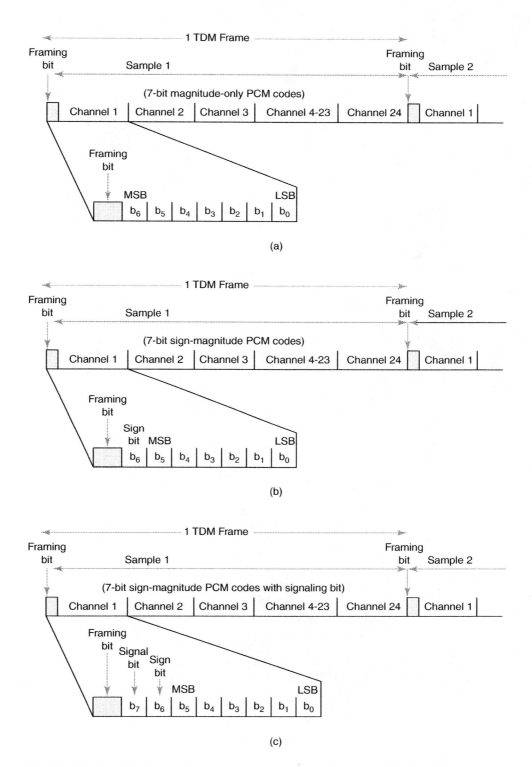

FIGURE 7-4 Early T1 Carrier system frame and sample alignment: (a) seven-bit magnitude-only PCM code; (b) seven-bit sign-magnitude code; (c) seven-bit sign-magnitude PCM code with signaling bit

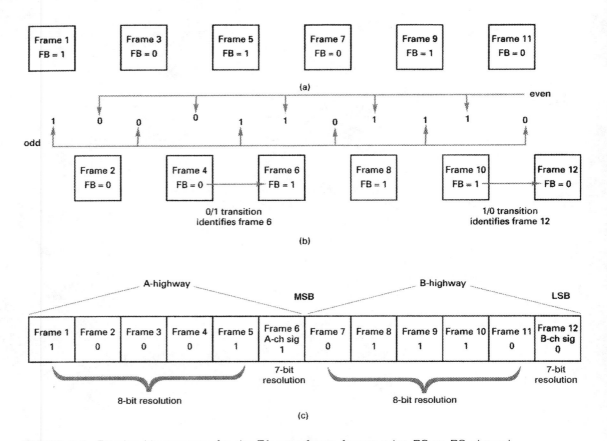

FIGURE 7-5 Framing bit sequence for the T1 superframe format using D2 or D3 channel banks: (a) frame synchronizing bits (odd-numbered frames); (b) signaling frame alignment bits (even-numbered frames); (c) composite frame alignment

Figure 7-5 was devised. Within each superframe, there are 12 consecutively numbered frames (1 to 12). The signaling bits are substituted in frames 6 and 12, the most significant bit into frame 6, and the least significant bit into frame 12. Frames 1 to 6 are called the A-highway, with frame 6 designated the A-channel signaling frame. Frames 7 to 12 are called the B-highway, with frame 12 designated the B-channel signaling frame. Therefore, in addition to identifying the signaling frames, the 6th and 12th frames must also be positively identified.

To identify frames 6 and 12, a different framing bit sequence is used for the odd- and even-numbered frames. The odd frames (frames 1, 3, 5, 7, 9, and 11) have an alternating 1/0 pattern, and the even frames (frames 2, 4, 6, 8, 10, and 12) have a 0 0 1 1 1 0 repetitive pattern. As a result, the combined framing bit pattern is 1 0 0 0 1 1 0 1 1 1 0 0. The odd-numbered frames are used for frame and sample synchronization, and the even-numbered frames are used to identify the A- and B-channel signaling frames (frames 6 and 12). Frame 6 is identified by a 0/1 transition in the framing bit between frames 4 and 6. Frame 12 is identified by a 1/0 transition in the framing bit between frames 10 and 12.

In addition to multiframe alignment bits and PCM sample bits, specific time slots are used to indicate alarm conditions. For example, in the case of a transmit power supply failure, a common equipment failure, or loss of multiframe alignment, the second bit in each channel is made a logic 0 until the alarm condition has cleared. Also, the framing bit in frame 12 is complemented whenever multiframe alignment is lost, which is assumed whenever frame alignment is lost. In addition, there are special framing conditions that must be avoided to maintain clock and bit synchronization in the receive demultiplexing equipment. Figure 7-6 shows the frame, sample, and signaling alignment for the T1 carrier system using D2 or D3 channel banks.

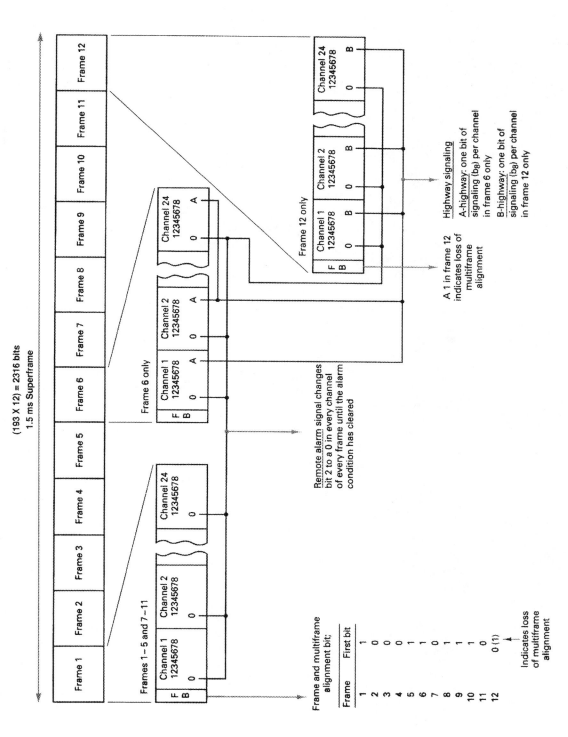

FIGURE 7-8 T1 carrier frame, sample, and signaling alignment for D2 and D3 channel banks

327

Figure 7-7a shows the framing bit circuitry for the 24-channel T1 carrier system using D2 or D3 channel banks. Note that the bit rate at the output of the TDM multiplexer is 1.536 Mbps and that the bit rate at the output of the 193-bit shift register is 1.544 Mbps. The 8-kHz difference is due to the addition of the framing bit.

D4 channel banks time-division multiplex 48 voice-band telephone channels and operate at a transmission rate of 3.152 Mbps. This is slightly more than twice the line speed for 24-channel D1, D2, or D3 channel banks because with D4 channel banks, rather than transmitting a single framing bit with each frame, a 10-bit frame synchronization pattern is used. Consequently, the total number of bits in a D4 (DS-1C) TDM frame is

$$\frac{8 \text{ bits}}{\text{channel}} \times \frac{48 \text{ channels}}{\text{frame}} = \frac{384 \text{ bits}}{\text{frame}} + \frac{10 \text{ framing bits}}{\text{frame}} = \frac{394 \text{ bits}}{\text{frame}}$$

and the line speed for DS-1C systems is

$$\frac{394 \text{ bits}}{\text{frame}} \times \frac{8000 \text{ frames}}{\text{second}} = 3.152 \text{ Mbps}$$

The framing for DS-1 (T1) PCM-TDM system or the framing pattern for the DS-1C (T1C) time-division multiplexed carrier system is added to the multiplexed digital signal at the output of the multiplexer. The framing bit circuitry used for the 48-channel DS-1C is shown in Figure 7-7b.

7-3-3 Extended Superframe Format

Another framing format recently developed for new designs of T1 carrier systems is the *extended superframe format*. The extended superframe format consists of 24 193-bit frames, totaling 4632 bits, of which 24 are framing bits. One extended superframe occupies 3 ms:

$$\left(\frac{1}{1.544 \text{ Mbits/s}}\right)\left(\frac{193 \text{ bits}}{\text{frame}}\right)(24 \text{ frames}) = 3 \text{ ms}$$

A framing bit occurs once every 193 bits; however, only 6 of the 24 framing bits are used for frame synchronization. Frame synchronization bits occur in frames 4, 8, 12, 16, 20, and 24 and have a bit sequence of 0 0 1 0 1 1. Six additional framing bits in frames 1, 5, 9, 13, 17, and 21 are used for an error detection code called CRC-6 (*cyclic redundancy checking*). The 12 remaining framing bits provide for a management channel called the *facilities data link* (FDL). FDL bits occur in frames 2, 3, 6, 7, 10, 11, 14, 15, 18, 19, 22, and 23.

The extended superframe format supports a four-bit signaling word with signaling bits provided in the second least significant bit of each channel during every sixth frame. The signaling bit in frame 6 is called the A bit, the signaling bit in frame 12 is called the B bit, the signaling bit in frame 18 is called the C bit, and the signaling bit in frame 24 is called the D bit. These signaling bit streams are sometimes called the A, B, C, and D *signaling channels* (or *signaling highways*). The extended superframe framing bit pattern is summarized in Table 7-1.

7-3-4 Fractional T Carrier Service

Fractional T carrier emerged because standard T1 carriers provide a higher capacity (i.e., higher bit rate) than most users require. Fractional T1 systems distribute the channels (i.e., bits) in a standard T1 system among more than one user, allowing several subscribers to share one T1 line. For example, several small businesses located in the same building can share one T1 line (both its capacity and its cost).

Bit rates offered with fractional T1 carrier systems are 64 kbps (1 channel), 128 kbps (2 channels), 256 kbps (4 channels), 384 kbps (6 channels), 512 kbps (8 channels), and 768 kbps (12 channels) with 384 kbps (1/4 T1) and 768 kbps (1/2 T1) being the most common. The minimum data rate necessary to propagate video information is 384 kbps.

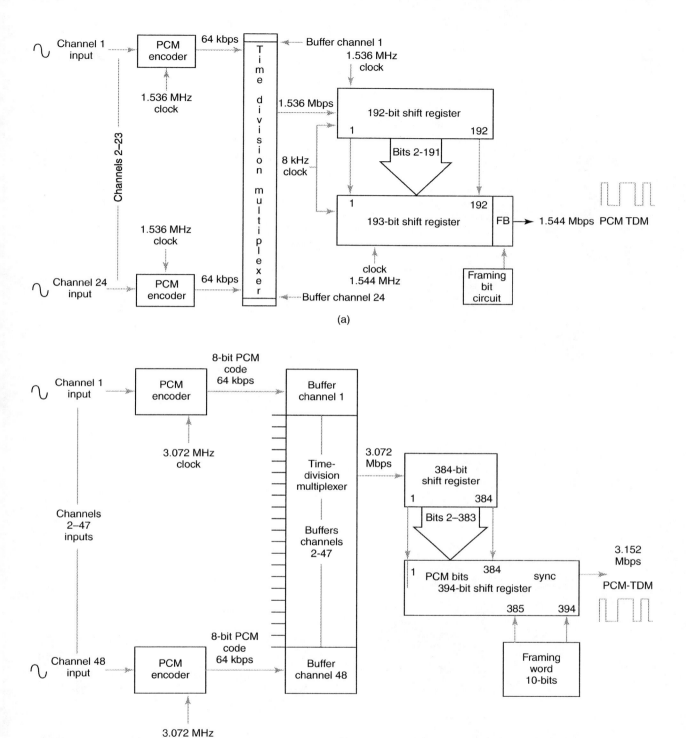

FIGURE 7-7 Framing bit circuitry T1 carrier system: (a) DS-1; (b) DS-1C

Table 7-1 Extended Superframe Format

Frame Number	Framing Bit	Frame Number	Framing Bit
1	C	13	C
2	F	14	F
3	F	15	F
4	S = 0	16	S = 0
5	C	17	C
6	F	18	F
7	F	19	F
8	S = 0	20	S = 1
9	C	21	C
10	F	22	F
11	F	23	F
12	S = 1	24	S = 1

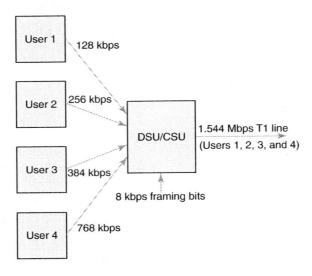

FIGURE 7-8 Fractional T1 carrier service

Fractional T3 is essentially the same as fractional T1 except with higher channel capacities, higher bit rates, and more customer options.

Figure 7-8 shows four subscribers combining their transmissions in a special unit called a *data service unit/channel service unit* (DSU/CSU). A DSU/CSU is a digital interface that provides the physical connection to a digital carrier network. User 1 is allocated 128 kbps, user 2 256 kbps, user 3 384 kbps, and user 4 768 kbps, for a total of 1.536 kbps (8 kbps is reserved for the framing bit).

7-4 NORTH AMERICAN DIGITAL HIERARCHY

Multiplexing signals in digital form lends itself easily to interconnecting digital transmission facilities with different transmission bit rates. Figure 7-9 shows the American Telephone and Telegraph Company (AT&T) North American Digital Hierarchy for multiplexing digital signals from multiple sources into a single higher-speed pulse stream suitable for transmission on the next higher level of the hierarchy. To upgrade from one level in the

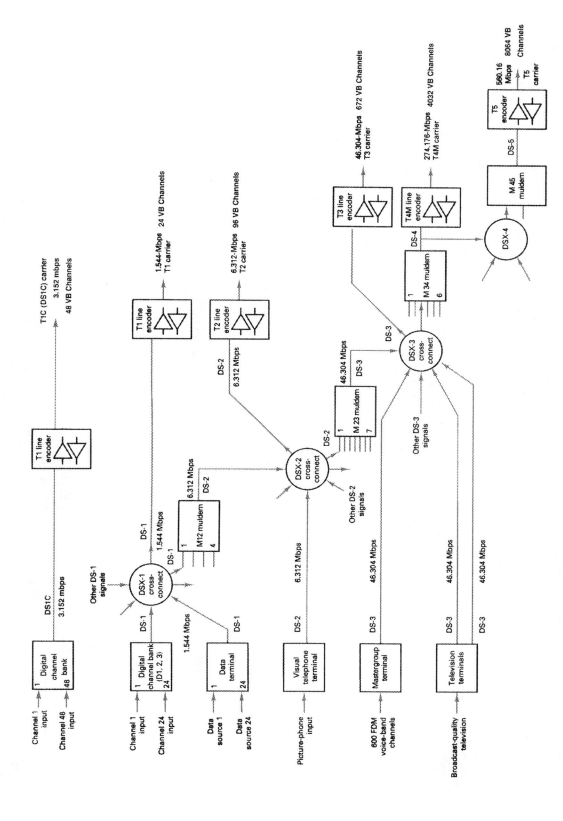

FIGURE 7.9 North American Digital Hierarchy

Table 7-2   North American Digital Hierarchy Summary

Line Type	Digital Signal	Bit Rate	Channel Capacities	Services Offered
T1	DS-1	1.544 Mbps	24	Voice-band telephone or data
Fractional T1	DS-1	64 kbps to 1.536 Mbps	24	Voice-band telephone or data
T1C	DS-1C	3.152 Mbps	48	Voice-band telephone or data
T2	DS-2	6.312 Mbps	96	Voice-band telephone, data, or picture phone
T3	DS-3	44.736 Mbps	672	Voice-band telephone, data, picture phone, and broadcast-quality television
Fractional T3	DS-3	64 kbps to 23.152 Mbps	672	Voice-band telephone, data, picture phone, and broadcast-quality television
T4M	DS-4	274.176 Mbps	4032	Same as T3 except more capacity
T5	DS-5	560.160 Mbps	8064	Same as T3 except more capacity

hierarchy to the next higher level, a special device called *muldem* (*mul*tiplexers/*dem*ultiplexer) is required. Muldems can handle bit-rate conversions in both directions. The muldem designations (M112, M23, and so on) identify the input and output digital signals associated with that muldem. For instance, an M12 muldem interfaces DS-1 and DS-2 digital signals. An M23 muldem interfaces DS-2 and DS-3 digital signals. As the figure shows, DS-1 signals may be further multiplexed or line encoded and placed on specially conditioned cables called T1 lines. DS-2, DS-3, DS-4, and DS-5 digital signals may be placed on T2, T3, T4M, or T5 lines, respectively.

Digital signals are routed at central locations called *digital cross-connects.* A digital cross-connect (DSX) provides a convenient place to make patchable interconnects and perform routine maintenance and troubleshooting. Each type of digital signal (DS-1, DS-2, and so on) has its own digital switch (DSX-1, DSX-2, and so on). The output from a digital switch may be upgraded to the next higher level of multiplexing or line encoded and placed on its respective T lines (T1, T2, and so on).

Table 7-2 lists the digital signals, their bit rates, channel capacities, and services offered for the line types included in the North American Digital Hierarchy.

7-4-1   Mastergroup and Commercial Television Terminals

Figure 7-10 shows the block diagram of a mastergroup and commercial television terminal. The mastergroup terminal receives voice-band channels that have already been frequency-division multiplexed (a topic covered later in this chapter) without requiring that each voice-band channel be demultiplexed to voice frequencies. The signal processor provides frequency shifting for the mastergroup signals (shifts it from a 564-kHz to 3084-kHz bandwidth to a 0-kHz to 2520-kHz bandwidth) and dc restoration for the television signal. By shifting the mastergroup band, it is possible to sample at a 5.1-MHz rate. Sampling of the commercial television signal is at twice that rate or 10.2 MHz.

When the bandwidth of the signals to be transmitted is such that after digital conversion it occupies the entire capacity of a digital transmission line, a single-channel terminal is provided. Examples of such single-channel terminals are mastergroup, commercial television, and picturephone terminals.

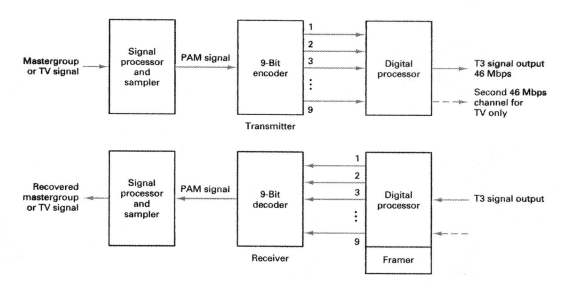

FIGURE 7-10 Block diagram of a mastergroup or commercial television digital terminal

To meet the transmission requirements, a nine-bit PCM code is used to digitize each sample of the mastergroup or television signal. The digital output from the terminal is, therefore, approximately 46 Mbps for the mastergroup and twice that much (92 Mbps) for the television signal.

The digital terminal shown in Figure 7-10 has three specific functions: (1) It converts the parallel data from the output of the encoder to serial data, (2) it inserts frame synchronizing bits, and (3) it converts the serial binary signal to a form more suitable for transmission. In addition, for the commercial television terminal, the 92-Mbps digital signal must be split into two 46-Mbps digital signals because there is no 92-Mbps line speed in the digital hierarchy.

7-4-2 Picturephone Terminal

Essentially, *picturephone* is a low-quality video transmission for use between nondedicated subscribers. For economic reasons, it is desirable to encode a picturephone signal into the T2 capacity of 6.312 Mbps, which is substantially less than that for commercial network broadcast signals. This substantially reduces the cost and makes the service affordable. At the same time, it permits the transmission of adequate detail and contrast resolution to satisfy the average picturephone subscriber. Picturephone service is ideally suited to a differential PCM code. Differential PCM is similar to conventional PCM except that the exact magnitude of a sample is not transmitted. Instead, only the difference between that sample and the previous sample is encoded and transmitted. To encode the difference between samples requires substantially fewer bits than encoding the actual sample.

7-4-3 Data Terminal

The portion of communications traffic that involves data (signals other than voice) is increasing exponentially. Also, in most cases the data rates generated by each individual subscriber are substantially less than the data rate capacities of digital lines. Therefore, it seems only logical that terminals be designed that transmit data signals from several sources over the same digital line.

Data signals could be sampled directly; however, this would require excessively high sample rates, resulting in excessively high transmission bit rates, especially for sequences

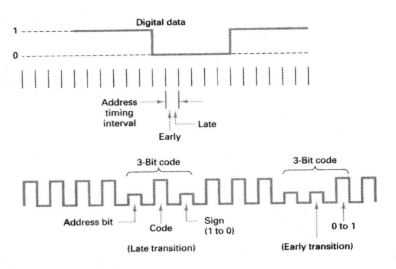

FIGURE 7-11   Data coding format

of data with few or no transitions. A more efficient method is one that codes the transition times. Such a method is shown in Figure 7-11. With the coding format shown, a three-bit code is used to identify when transitions occur in the data and whether that transition is from a 1 to a 0 or vice versa. The first bit of the code is called the address bit. When this bit is a logic 1, this indicates that no transition occurred; a logic 0 indicates that a transition did occur. The second bit indicates whether the transition occurred during the first half (0) or during the second half (1) of the sample interval. The third bit indicates the sign or direction of the transition; a 1 for this bit indicates a 0-to-1 transition, and a 0 indicates a 1-to-0 transition. Consequently, when there are no transitions in the data, a signal of all 1s is transmitted. Transmission of only the address bit would be sufficient; however, the sign bit provides a degree of error protection and limits error propagation (when one error leads to a second error and so on). The efficiency of this format is approximately 33%; there are three code bits for each data bit. The advantage of using a coded format rather than the original data is that coded data are more efficiently substituted for voice in analog systems. Without this coding format, transmitting a 250-kbps data signal requires the same bandwidth as would be required to transmit 60 voice channels with analog multiplexing. With this coded format, a 50-kbps data signal displaces three 64-kbps PCM-encoded channels, and a 250-kbps data stream displaces only 12 voice-band channels.

7-5   DIGITAL CARRIER LINE ENCODING

Digital line encoding involves converting standard logic levels (TTL, CMOS, and the like) to a form more suitable to telephone line transmission. Essentially, six primary factors must be considered when selecting a line-encoding format:

1. Transmission voltages and DC component
2. Duty cycle
3. Bandwidth considerations
4. Clock and framing bit recovery
5. Error detection
6. Ease of detection and decoding

Transmission voltages or levels can be categorized as being either *unipolar* (UP) or *bipolar* (BP). Unipolar transmission of binary data involves the transmission of only a single nonzero voltage level (e.g., either a positive or a negative voltage for a logic 1 and 0 V [ground] for a logic 0). In bipolar transmission, two nonzero voltages are involved (e.g., a positive voltage for a logic 1 and an equal-magnitude negative voltage for a logic 0 or vice versa).

Over a digital transmission line, it is more power efficient to encode binary data with voltages that are equal in magnitude but opposite in polarity and symmetrically balanced about 0 V. For example, assuming a 1-ohm resistance and a logic 1 level of $+5$ V and a logic 0 level of 0 V, the average power required is 12.5 W, assuming an equal probability of the occurrence of a logic 1 or a logic 0. With a logic 1 level of $+2.5$ V and a logic 0 level of -2.5 V, the average power is only 6.25 W. Thus, by using bipolar symmetrical voltages, the average power is reduced by a factor of 50%.

7-5-2 Duty Cycle

The *duty cycle* of a binary pulse can be used to categorize the type of transmission. If the binary pulse is maintained for the entire bit time, this is called *nonreturn to zero* (NRZ). If the active time of the binary pulse is less than 100% of the bit time, this is called *return to zero* (RZ).

Unipolar and bipolar transmission voltages can be combined with either RZ or NRZ in several ways to achieve a particular line-encoding scheme. Figure 7-12 shows five line-encoding possibilities.

In Figure 7-12a, there is only one nonzero voltage level ($+V =$ logic 1); a zero voltage indicates a logic 0. Also, each logic 1 condition maintains the positive voltage for the entire bit time (100% duty cycle). Consequently, Figure 7-12a represents a unipolar nonreturn-to-zero signal (UPNRZ). Assuming an equal number of 1s and 0s, the average dc voltage of a UPNRZ waveform is equal to half the nonzero voltage (V/2).

In Figure 7-12b, there are two nonzero voltages ($+V =$ logic 1 and $-V =$ logic 0) and a 100% duty cycle is used. Therefore, Figure 7-12b represents a bipolar nonreturn-to-zero signal (BPNRZ). When equal-magnitude voltages are used for logic 1s and logic 0s, and assuming an equal probability of logic 1s and logic 0s occurring, the average dc voltage of a BPNRZ waveform is 0 V.

In Figure 7-12c, only one nonzero voltage is used, but each pulse is active for only 50% of a bit time ($t_b/2$). Consequently, the waveform shown in Figure 7-12c represents a unipolar return-to-zero signal (UPRZ). Assuming an equal probability of 1s and 0s occurring, the average dc voltage of a UPRZ waveform is one-fourth the nonzero voltage (V/4).

Figure 7-12d shows a waveform where there are two nonzero voltages ($+V =$ logic 1 and $-V =$ logic 0). Also, each pulse is active only 50% of a bit time. Consequently, the waveform shown in Figure 7-8d represents a bipolar return-to-zero (BPRZ) signal. Assuming equal-magnitude voltages for logic 1s and logic 0s and an equal probability of 1s and 0s occurring, the average dc voltage of a BPRZ waveform is 0 V.

In Figure 7-12e, there are again two nonzero voltage levels ($-V$ and $+V$), but now both polarities represent logic 1s, and 0 V represents a logic 0. This method of line encoding is called *alternate mark inversion* (AMI). With AMI transmissions, successive logic 1s are inverted in polarity from the previous logic 1. Because return to zero is used, the encoding technique is called *bipolar-return-to-zero alternate mark inversion* (BPRZ-AMI). The average dc voltage of a BPRZ-AMI waveform is approximately 0 V regardless of the bit sequence.

With NRZ encoding, a long string of either logic 1s or logic 0s produces a condition in which a receive may lose its amplitude reference for optimum discrimination between received 1s and 0s. This condition is called *dc wandering*. The problem may also arise when there is a significant imbalance in the number of 1s and 0s transmitted. Figure 7-13 shows how dc wandering is produced from a long string of successive logic 1s. It can be seen that after a long string of 1s, 1-to-0 errors are more likely than 0-to-1 errors. Similarly, long strings of logic 0s increase the probability of 0-to-1 errors.

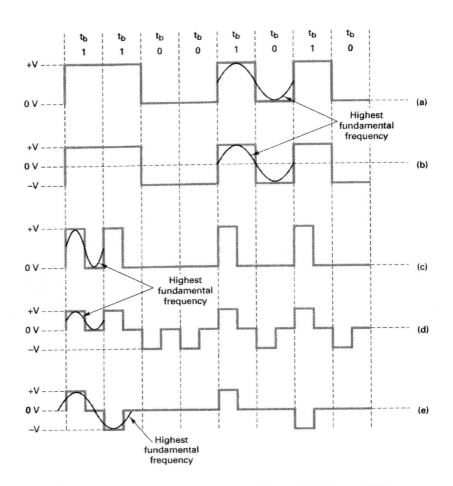

FIGURE 7-12 Line-encoding formats: (a) UPNRZ; (b) BPNRZ; (c) UPRZ; (d) BPRZ; (e) BPRZ-AMI

FIGURE 7-13 DC wandering

The method of line encoding used determines the minimum bandwidth required for transmission, how easily a clock may be extracted from it, how easily it may be decoded, the average dc voltage level, and whether it offers a convenient means of detecting errors.

7-5-3 Bandwidth Requirements

To determine the minimum bandwidth required to propagate a line-encoded digital signal, you must determine the highest fundamental frequency associated with the signal (see Figure 7-12). The highest fundamental frequency is determined from the worst-case (fastest transition) binary bit sequence. With UPNRZ, the worst-case condition is an alternating 1/0 sequence; the period of the highest fundamental frequency takes the time of two bits and, therefore, is equal to one-half the bit rate ($f_b/2$). With BPNRZ, again the worst-case condition is an alternating 1/0 sequence, and the highest fundamental frequency is one-half the bit rate ($f_b/2$). With UPRZ, the worst-case condition occurs when two successive logic 1s occur. Therefore, the minimum bandwidth is equal to the bit rate (f_b). With BPRZ encoding, the worst-case condition occurs for successive logic 1s or successive logic 0s, and the minimum bandwidth is again equal to the bit rate (f_b). With BPRZ-AMI, the worst-case condition is two or more consecutive logic 1s, and the minimum bandwidth is equal to one-half the bit rate ($f_b/2$).

7-5-4 Clock and Framing Bit Recovery

To recover and maintain clock and framing bit synchronization from the received data, there must be sufficient transitions in the data waveform. With UPNRZ and BPNRZ encoding, a long string of 1s or 0s generates a data signal void of transitions and, therefore, is inadequate for clock recovery. With UPRZ and BPRZ-AMI encoding, a long string of 0s also generates a data signal void of transitions. With BPRZ, a transition occurs in each bit position regardless of whether the bit is a 1 or a 0. Thus, BPRZ is the best encoding scheme for clock recovery. If long sequences of 0s are prevented from occurring, BPRZ-AMI encoding provides sufficient transitions to ensure clock synchronization.

7-5-5 Error Detection

With UPNRZ, BPNRZ, UPRZ, and BPRZ encoding, there is no way to determine if the received data have errors. However, with BPRZ-AMI encoding, an error in any bit will cause a bipolar violation (BPV, or the reception of two or more consecutive logic 1s with the same polarity). Therefore, BPRZ-AMI has a built-in error-detection mechanism. T carriers use BPRZ-AMI with $+3$ V and -3 V representing a logic 1 and 0 V representing a logic 0.

Table 7-3 summarizes the bandwidth, average voltage, clock recovery, and error-detection capabilities of the line-encoding formats shown in Figure 7-12. From Table 7-3, it can be seen that BPRZ-AMI encoding has the best overall characteristics and is, therefore, the most commonly used encoding format.

7-5-6 Digital Biphase

Digital biphase (sometimes called the *Manchester code* or *diphase*) is a popular type of line encoding that produces a strong timing component for clock recovery and does not cause dc wandering. Biphase is a form of BPRZ encoding that uses one cycle of a square wave at $0°$ phase to represent a logic 1 and one cycle of a square wave at $180°$ phase to represent a logic 0. Digital biphase encoding is shown in Figure 7-14. Note that a transition occurs in the center of every signaling element regardless of its logic condition or phase. Thus, biphase produces a strong timing component for clock recovery. In addition, assuming an equal probability of 1s and 0s, the average dc voltage is 0 V, and there is no dc wandering. A disadvantage of biphase is that it contains no means of error detection.

Biphase encoding schemes have several variations, including *biphase M, biphase L,* and *biphase S.* Biphase M is used for encoding SMPTE (Society of Motion Picture and Television Engineers) time-code data for recording on videotapes. Biphase M is well suited for this application because it has no dc component, and the code is self-synchronizing (self-clocking). Self-synchronization is an import feature because it allows clock recovery from the

Table 7-3   Line-Encoding Summary

Encoding Format	Minimum BW	Average DC	Clock Recovery	Error Detection
UPNRZ	$f_b/2$*	$+V/2$	Poor	No
BPNRZ	$f_b/2$*	0 V*	Poor	No
UPRZ	f_b	$+V/4$	Good	No
BPRZ	f_b	0 V*	Best*	No
BPRZ-AMI	$f_b/2$*	0 V*	Good	Yes*

*Denotes best performance or quality.

FIGURE 7-14   Digital biphase

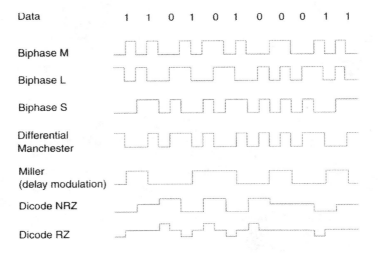

FIGURE 7-15   Biphase, Miller, and dicode encoding formats

data stream even when the speed varies with tape speed, such as when searching through a tape in either the fast or the slow mode. Biphase L is commonly called the Manchester code. Biphase L is specified in IEEE standard 802.3 for Ethernet local area networks (see Chapter 23).

Miller codes are forms of *delay-modulated codes* where a logic 1 condition produces a transition in the middle of the clock pulse, and a logic 0 produces no transition at the end of the clock intervals unless followed by another logic 0.

Dicodes are multilevel binary codes that use more than two voltage levels to represent the data. Bipolar RZ and RZ-AMI are two dicode encoding formats already discussed. Dicode NRZ and dicode RZ are two more commonly used dicode formats.

Figure 7-15 shows several variations of biphase, Miller, and dicode encoding, and Table 7-4 summarizes their characteristics.

7-6   T CARRIER SYSTEMS

T carriers are used for the transmission of PCM-encoded time-division multiplexed digital signals. In addition, T carriers utilize special line-encoded signals and metallic cables that have been conditioned to meet the relatively high bandwidths required for high-speed digital transmission. Digital signals deteriorate as they propagate along a cable because of power losses in the metallic conductors and the low-pass filtering inherent in parallel-wire transmission lines. Consequently, *regenerative repeaters* must be placed at periodic intervals. The distance between repeaters depends on the transmission bit rate and the line-encoding technique used.

Table 7-4   Summary of Biphase, Miller, and Dicode Encoding Formats

Biphase M (biphase-mark)
  1 (hi)—transition in the middle of the clock interval
  0 (low)—no transition in the middle of the clock interval
  Note: There is always a transition at the beginning of the clock interval.
Biphase L (biphase-level/Manchester)
  1 (hi)—transition from high to low in the middle of the clock interval
  0 (low)—transition from low to high in the middle of the clock interval
Biphase S (biphase-space)
  1 (hi)—no transition in the middle of the clock interval
  0 (low)—transition in the middle of the clock interval
  Note: There is always a transition at the beginning of the clock interval.
Differential Manchester
  1 (hi)—transition in the middle of the clock interval
  0 (low)—transition at the beginning of the clock interval
Miller/delay modulation
  1 (hi)—transition in the middle of the clock interval
  0 (low)—no transition at the end of the clock interval unless followed by a zero
Dicode NRZ
  One-to-zero and zero-to-one data transitions change the signal polarity. If the data remain constant,
  then a zero-voltage level is output.
Dicode RZ
  One-to-zero and zero-to-one data transitions change the signal polarity in half-step voltage increments. If
  the data do not change, then a zero-voltage level is output.

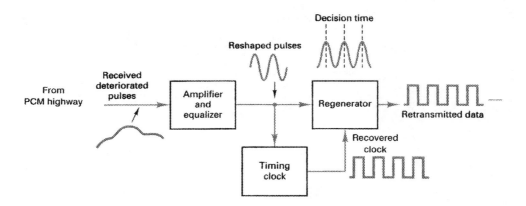

FIGURE 7-16   Regenerative repeater block diagram

Figure 7-16 shows the block diagram for a regenerative repeater. Essentially, there are three functional blocks: an *amplifier/equalizer,* a *timing clock recovery circuit,* and the *regenerator* itself. The amplifier/equalizer filters and shapes the incoming digital signal and raises its power level so that the regenerator circuit can make a pulse–no pulse decision. The timing clock recovery circuit reproduces the clocking information from the received data and provides the proper timing information to the regenerator so that samples can be made at the optimum time, minimizing the chance of an error occurring. A regenerative repeater is simply a threshold detector that compares the sampled voltage received to a reference level and determines whether the bit is a logic 1 or a logic 0.

Spacing of repeaters is designed to maintain an adequate signal-to-noise ratio for error-free performance. The signal-to-noise ratio at the output of a regenerative repeater is exactly what it was at the output of the transmit terminal or at the output of the previous regenerator (i.e., the signal-to-noise ratio does not deteriorate as a digital signal propagates through a regenerator; in fact, a regenerator reconstructs the original pulses with the original signal-to-noise ratio).

7-6-1   T1 Carrier Systems

T1 carrier systems were designed to combine PCM and TDM techniques for short-haul transmission of 24 64-kbps channels with each channel capable of carrying digitally encoded voice-band telephone signals or data. The transmission bit rate (*line speed*) for a T1 carrier is 1.544 Mbps, including an 8-kbps framing bit. The lengths of T1 carrier systems typically range from about 1 mile to over 50 miles.

T1 carriers use BPRZ-AMI encoding with regenerative repeaters placed every 3000, 6000, or 9000 feet. These distances were selected because they were the distances between telephone company manholes where regenerative repeaters are placed. The transmission medium for T1 carriers is generally 19- to 22-gauge twisted-pair metallic cable.

Because T1 carriers use BPRZ-AMI encoding, they are susceptible to losing clock synchronization on long strings of consecutive logic 0s. With a folded binary PCM code, the possibility of generating a long string of contiguous logic 0s is high. When a channel is idle, it generates a 0-V code, which is either seven or eight consecutive logic zeros. Therefore, whenever two or more adjacent channels are idle, there is a high likelihood that a long string of consecutive logic 0s will be transmitted. To reduce the possibility of transmitting a long string of consecutive logic 0s, the PCM data were complemented prior to transmission and then complemented again in the receiver before decoding. Consequently, the only time a long string of consecutive logic 0s are transmitted is when two or more adjacent channels each encode the maximum possible positive sample voltage, which is unlikely to happen.

Ensuring that sufficient transitions occur in the data stream is sometimes called *ones density*. Early T1 and T1C carrier systems provided measures to ensure that no single eight-bit byte was transmitted without at least one bit being a logic 1 or that 15 or more consecutive logic 0s were not transmitted. The transmissions from each frame are monitored for the presence of either 15 consecutive logic 0s or any one PCM sample (eight bits) without at least one nonzero bit. If either of these conditions occurred, a logic 1 is substituted into the appropriate bit position. The worst-case conditions were

	MSB		LSB MSB		LSB	
Original DS-1 signal	1000	0000	0000	0001	14 consecutive 0s (no substitution)

	MSB		LSB MSB		LSB	
Original DS-1 signal	1000	0000	0000	0000	15 consecutive 0s
Substituted DS-1 signal	1000	0000	0000	0010	

Substituted
bit

A 1 is substituted into the second least significant bit, which introduces an encoding error equal to twice the amplitude resolution. This bit is selected rather than the least significant bit because, with the superframe format, during every sixth frame the LSB is the signaling bit, and to alter it would alter the signaling word.

If at any time 32 consecutive logic 0s are received, it is assumed that the system is not generating pulses and is, therefore, out of service.

With modern T1 carriers, a technique called *binary eight zero substitution* (B8ZS) is used to ensure that sufficient transitions occur in the data to maintain clock synchronization. With

	MSB		LSB MSB		LSB MSB		LSB
Original DS-1 signal	1010	1000	0000	0000	0000	0001	
Substituted DS-1 signal	1010	1000	0000	0010	0000	0001	

Substituted bit

B8ZS, whenever eight consecutive 0s are encountered, one of two special patterns is substituted for the eight 0s, either $+ - 0 - + 0\,0\,0$ or $- + 0 + - 0\,0\,0$. The + (plus) and − (minus) represent bipolar logic 1 conditions, and a 0 (zero) indicates a logic 0 condition. The eight-bit pattern substituted for the eight consecutive 0s is the one that purposely induces bipolar violations in the fourth and seventh bit positions. Ideally, the receiver will detect the bipolar violations and the substituted pattern and then substitute the eight 0s back into the data signal. During periods of low usage, eight logic 1s are substituted into idle channels. Two examples of

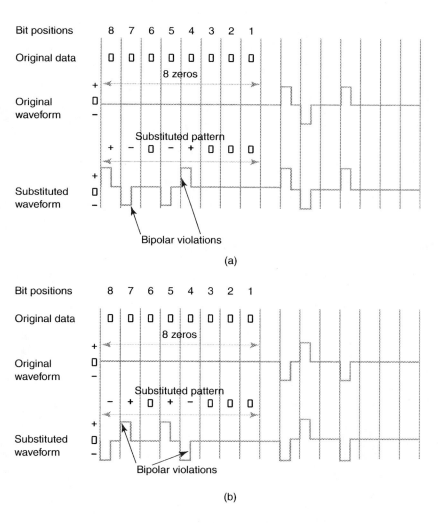

FIGURE 7-17 Waveforms for B8ZS example: (a) substitution pattern 1; (b) substitution pattern 2

B8ZS are illustrated here and their corresponding waveforms shown in Figures 7-17a and b, respectively:

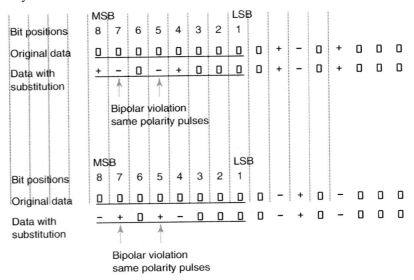

7-6-2　T2 Carrier System

T2 carriers time-division multiplex 96 64-kbps voice or data channels into a single 6.312-Mbps data signal for transmission over twisted-pair copper wire up to 500 miles over a special LOCAP (low capacitance) metallic cable. T2 carriers also use BPRZ-AMI encoding; however, because of the higher transmission rate, clock synchronization is even more critical than with a T1 carrier. A sequence of six consecutive logic 0s could be sufficient to cause loss of clock synchronization. Therefore, T2 carrier systems use an alternative method of ensuring that ample transitions occur in the data. This method is called *binary six zero substitution* (B6ZS).

With B6ZS, whenever six consecutive logic 0s occur, one of the following binary codes is substituted in its place: $0 - + 0 + -$ or $0 + - 0 - +$. Again + and − represent logic 1s, and 0 represents a logic 0. The six-bit code substituted for the six consecutive 0s is selected to purposely cause a bipolar violation. If the violation is detected in the receiver, the original six 0s can be substituted back into the data signal. The substituted patterns produce bipolar violations (i.e., consecutive pulses with the same polarity) in the second and fourth bits of the substituted patterns. If DS-2 signals are multiplexed to form DS-3 signals, the B6ZS code must be detected and removed from the DS-2 signal prior to DS-3 multiplexing. An example of B6ZS is illustrated here and its corresponding waveform shown in Figure 7-18.

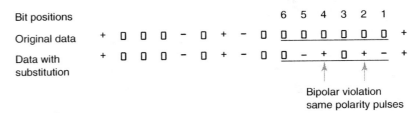

7-6-3　T3 Carrier System

T3 carriers time-division multiplex 672 64-kbps voice or data channels for transmission over a single 3A-RDS coaxial cable. The transmission bit rate for T3 signals is 44.736 Mbps. The coding technique used with T3 carriers is *binary three zero substitution* (B3ZS).

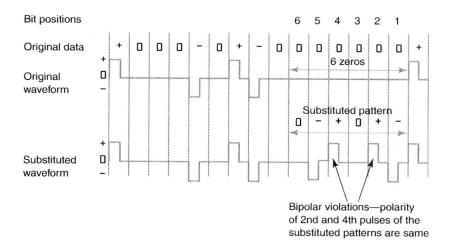

Bit positions ... 6 5 4 3 2 1

Bipolar violations—polarity
of 2nd and 4th pulses of the
substituted patterns are same

FIGURE 7-18   Waveform for B6ZS example

Substitutions are made for any occurrence of three consecutive 0s. There are four substitution patterns used: $00-$, $-0-$, $00+$, and $+0+$. The pattern chosen should cause a bipolar error in the third substituted bit. An example of B3ZS is shown here:

7-6-4   T4M and T5 Carrier Systems

T4M carriers time-division multiplex 4032 64-kbps voice or data channels for transmission over a single T4M coaxial cable up to 500 miles. The transmission rate is sufficiently high that substitute patterns are impractical. Instead, T4M carriers transmit scrambled unipolar NRZ digital signals; the scrambling and descrambling functions are performed in the subscriber's terminal equipment.

T5 carriers time-division multiplex 8064 64-kbps voice or data channels and transmit them at a 560.16 Mbps rate over a single coaxial cable.

7-7   EUROPEAN DIGITAL CARRIER SYSTEM

In Europe, a different version of T carrier lines is used, called *E-lines*. Although the two systems are conceptually the same, they have different capabilities. Figure 7-19 shows the frame alignment for the E1 European standard PCM-TDM system. With the basic E1 system, a 125-μs frame is divided into 32 equal time slots. Time slot 0 is used for a frame alignment pattern and for an alarm channel. Time slot 17 is used for a *common signaling channel* (CSC). The signaling for all 30 voice-band channels is accomplished on the common signaling channel. Consequently, 30 voice-band channels are time-division multiplexed into each E1 frame.

Time slot 0	Time slot 1	Time slots 2–16	Time slot 17	Time slots 18–30	Time slot 31
Framing and alarm channel	Voice channel 1	Voice channels 2–15	Common signaling channel	Voice channels 16–29	Voice channel 30
8 bits	8 bits	112 bits	8 bits	112 bits	8 bits

(a)

Time slot 17

	Bits	
Frame	1234	5678
0	0000	xyxx
1	ch 1	ch 16
2	ch 2	ch 17
3	ch 3	ch 18
4	ch 4	ch 19
5	ch 5	ch 20
6	ch 6	ch 21
7	ch 7	ch 22
8	ch 8	ch 23
9	ch 9	ch 24
10	ch 10	ch 25
11	ch 11	ch 26
12	ch 12	ch 27
13	ch 13	ch 28
14	ch 14	ch 29
15	ch 15	ch 30

16 frames equal one multiframe; 500 multiframes are transmitted each second

x = spare
y = loss of multiframe alignment if a 1

4 bits per channel are transmitted once every 16 frames, resulting in a 500 words per second (2000 bps) signaling rate for each channel

(b)

FIGURE 7-19   CCITT TDM frame alignment and common signaling channel alignment: (a) CCITT TDM frame (125 μs, 256 bits, 2.048 Mbps); (b) common signaling channel

Table 7–5   European Transmission Rates and Capacities

Line	Transmission Bit Rate (Mbps)	Channel Capacity
E1	2.048	30
E2	8.448	120
E3	34.368	480
E4	139.264	1920

With the European E1 standard, each time slot has eight bits. Consequently, the total number of bits per frame is

$$\frac{8 \text{ bits}}{\text{time slot}} \times \frac{32 \text{ time slots}}{\text{frame}} = \frac{256 \text{ bits}}{\text{frame}}$$

and the line speed for an E-1 TDM system is

$$\frac{256 \text{ bits}}{\text{frame}} \times \frac{8000 \text{ frames}}{\text{second}} = 2.048 \text{ Mbps}$$

The European digital transmission system has a TDM multiplexing hierarchy similar to the North American hierarchy except the European system is based on the 32-time-slot (30-voice-channel) E1 system. The *European Digital Multiplexing Hierarchy* is shown in Table 7-5. Interconnecting T carriers with E carriers is not generally a problem because most multiplexers and demultiplexers are designed to perform the necessary bit rate conversions.

With TDM systems, it is imperative not only that a frame be identified but also that individual time slots (samples) within the frame be identified. To acquire frame synchronization, a certain amount of overhead must be added to the transmission. There are several methods used to establish and maintain frame synchronization, including added-digit, robbed-digit, added-channel, statistical, and unique-line code framing.

7-8-1 Added-Digit Framing

T1 carriers using D1, D2, or D3 channel banks use *added-digit framing*. A special *framing digit* (framing pulse) is added to each frame. Consequently, for an 8-kHz sample rate, 8000 digits are added each second. With T1 carriers, an alternating 1/0 frame-synchronizing pattern is used.

To acquire frame synchronization, the digital terminal in the receiver searches through the incoming data until it finds the framing bit pattern. This encompasses testing a bit, counting off 193 more bits, and then testing again for the opposite logic condition. This process continues until a repetitive alternating 1/0 pattern is found. Initial frame synchronization depends on the total frame time, the number of bits per frame, and the period of each bit. Searching through all possible bit positions requires N tests, where N is the number of bit positions in the frame. On average, the receiving terminal dwells at a false framing position for two frame periods during a search; therefore, the maximum average synchronization time is

$$\text{synchronization time} = 2NT = 2N^2 t_b \qquad (7\text{-}1)$$

where N = number of bits per frame
$\quad\quad\ T$ = frame period of Nt_b
$\quad\quad\ t_b$ = bit time

For the T1 carrier, $N = 193$, $T = 125$ μs, and $t_b = 0.648$ μs; therefore, a maximum of 74,498 bits must be tested, and the maximum average synchronization time is 48.25 ms.

7-8-2 Robbed-Digit Framing

When a short frame is used, added-digit framing is inefficient. This occurs with single-channel PCM systems. An alternative solution is to replace the least significant bit of every nth frame with a framing bit. This process is called *robbed-digit framing*. The parameter n is chosen as a compromise between reframe time and signal impairment. For $n = 10$, the SQR is impaired by only 1 dB. Robbed-digit framing does not interrupt transmission but instead periodically replaces information bits with forced data errors to maintain frame synchronization.

7-8-3 Added-Channel Framing

Essentially, *added-channel framing* is the same as added-digit framing except that digits are added in groups or words instead of as individual bits. The European time-division multiplexing scheme previously discussed uses added-channel framing. One of the 32 time slots in each frame is dedicated to a unique synchronizing bit sequence. The average number of bits to acquire frame synchronization using added-channel framing is

$$\frac{N^2}{2(2^K - 1)} \qquad (7\text{-}2)$$

where N = number of bits per frame
$\quad\quad\ K$ = number of bits in the synchronizing word

For the European E1 32-channel system, $N = 256$ and $K = 8$. Therefore, the average number of bits needed to acquire frame synchronization is 128.5. At 2.048 Mbps, the synchronization time is approximately 62.7 μs.

7-8-4 Statistical Framing

With *statistical framing,* it is not necessary to either rob or add digits. With the gray code, the second bit is a logic 1 in the central half of the code range and a logic 0 at the extremes. Therefore, a signal that has a centrally peaked amplitude distribution generates a high probability of a logic 1 in the second digit. Hence, the second digit of a given channel can be used for the framing bit.

7-8-5 Unique-Line Code Framing

With *unique-line code framing,* some property of the framing bit is different from the data bits. The framing bit is made either higher or lower in amplitude or with a different time duration. The earliest PCM-TDM systems used unique-line code framing. D1 channel banks used framing pulses that were twice the amplitude of normal data bits. With unique-line code framing, either added-digit or added-word framing can be used, or specified data bits can be used to simultaneously convey information and carry synchronizing signals. The advantage of unique-line code framing is that synchronization is immediate and automatic. The disadvantage is the additional processing requirements necessary to generate and recognize the unique bit.

7-9 BIT VERSUS WORD INTERLEAVING

When time-division multiplexing two or more PCM systems, it is necessary to interleave the transmissions from the various terminals in the time domain. Figure 7-20 shows two methods of interleaving PCM transmissions: *bit interleaving* and *word interleaving.*

T1 carrier systems use word interleaving; eight-bit samples from each channel are interleaved into a single 24-channel TDM frame. Higher-speed TDM systems and delta mod-

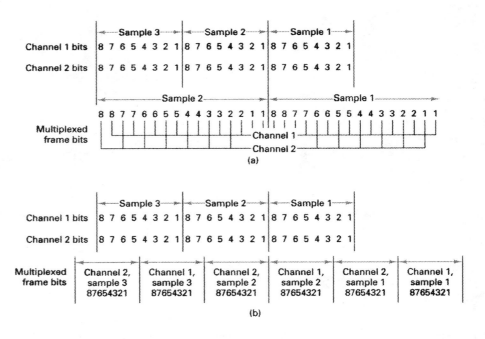

FIGURE 7-20 Interleaving: (a) bit; (b) word

ulation systems use bit interleaving. The decision as to which type of interleaving to use is usually determined by the nature of the signals to be multiplexed.

7-10 STATISTICAL TIME-DIVISION MULTIPLEXING

Digital transmissions over a synchronous TDM system often contain an abundance of time slots within each frame that contain no information (i.e., at any given instant, several of the channels may be idle). For example, TDM is commonly used to link remote data terminals or PCs to a common server or mainframe computer. A majority of the time, however, there are no data being transferred in either direction, even if all the terminals are active. The same is true for PCM-TDM systems carrying digital-encoded voice-grade telephone conversations. Normal telephone conversations generally involve information being transferred in only one direction at a time with significant pauses embedded in typical speech patterns. Consequently, there is a lot of time wasted within each TDM frame. There is an efficient alternative to synchronous TDM called *statistical time-division multiplexing*. Statistical time division multiplexing is generally not used for carrying standard telephone circuits but are used more often for the transmission of data when they are called *asynchronous* TDM, *intelligent* TDM, or simply *stat muxs*.

A statistical TDM multiplexer exploits the natural breaks in transmissions by dynamically allocating time slots on a demand basis. Just as with the multiplexer in a synchronous TDM system, a statistical multiplexer has a finite number of low-speed data input lines with one high-speed multiplexed data output line, and each input line has its own digital encoder and buffer. With the statistical multiplexer, there are n input lines but only k time slots available within the TDM frame (where $k > n$). The multiplexer scans the input buffers, collecting data until a frame is filled, at which time the frame is transmitted. On the receive end, the same holds true, as there are more output lines than time slots within the TDM frame. The demultiplexer removes the data from the time slots and distributes them to their appropriate output buffers.

Statistical TDM takes advantage of the fact that the devices attached to the inputs and outputs are not all transmitting or receiving all the time and that the data rate on the multiplexed line is lower than the combined data rates of the attached devices. In other words, statistical TDM multiplexers require a lower data rate than synchronous multiplexers need to support the same number of inputs. Alternately, a statistical TDM multiplexer operating at the same transmission rate as a synchronous TDM multiplexer can support more users.

Figure 7-21 shows a comparison between statistical and synchronous TDM. Four data sources (A, B, C, and D) and four time slots, or epochs (t_1, t_2, t_3, and t_4). The synchronous multiplexer has an output data rate equal to four times the data rate of each of the input channels. During each sample time, data are collected from all four sources and transmitted regardless of whether there is any input. As the figure shows, during sample time t_1, channels C and D have no input data, resulting in a transmitted TDM frame void of information in time slots C_1 and D_1. With a statistical multiplexer, however, the empty time slots are not transmitted. A disadvantage of the statistical format, however, is that the length of a frame varies and the positional significance of each time slot is lost. There is no way of knowing beforehand which channel's data will be in which time slot or how many time slots are included in each frame. Because data arrive and are distributed to receive buffers unpredictably, address information is required to ensure proper delivery. This necessitates more overhead per time slot for statistical TDM because each slot must carry an address as well as data.

The frame format used by a statistical TDM multiplexer has a direct impact on system performance. Obviously, it is desirable to minimize overhead to improve data throughput. Normally, a statistical TDM system will use a synchronous protocol such as HDLC (described in detail in a later chapter). With statistical multiplexing, control bits must be included

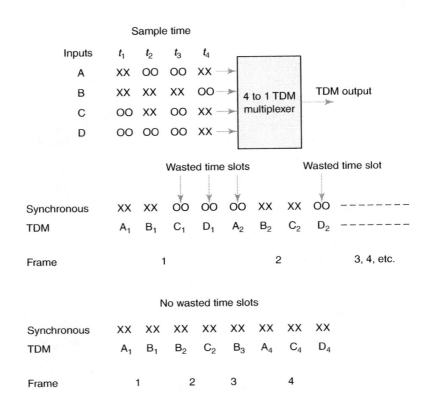

Sample time

Inputs	t_1	t_2	t_3	t_4
A	XX	OO	OO	XX ----➤
B	XX	XX	XX	OO ----➤
C	OO	XX	OO	XX ----➤
D	OO	OO	OO	XX ----➤

4 to 1 TDM multiplexer   TDM output

Wasted time slots   Wasted time slot

Synchronous   XX XX OO OO OO XX XX OO ---------
TDM A_1 B_1 C_1 D_1 A_2 B_2 C_2 D_2 ---------

Frame   1   2   3, 4, etc.

No wasted time slots

Synchronous   XX XX XX XX XX XX XX XX
TDM A_1 B_1 B_2 C_2 B_3 A_4 C_4 D_4

Frame   1   2   3   4

XX denotes data present
OO denotes no data present

FIGURE 7-21   Comparison between synchronous and statistical TDM

Beginning flag	Address field	Control field	Statistical TDM subframe	FCS field	Ending flag

(a)

Address field	Data field

(b)

Address field	Length field	Data field	...	Address field	Length field	Data field

(c)

FIGURE 7-22   Statistical TDM frame format: (a) overall statistical TDM frame; (b) one-source per frame; (c) multiple sources per frame

within the frame. Figure 7-22a shows the overall frame format for a statistical TDM multiplexer. The frame includes beginning and ending flags that indicate the beginning and end of the frame, an address field that identifies the transmitting device, a control field, a statistical TDM subframe, and a frame check sequence field (FCS) that provides error detection.

Figure 7-22b shows the frame when only one data source is transmitting. The transmitting device is identified in the address field. The data field length is variable and limited only by the maximum length of the frame. Such a scheme works well in times of light loads but rather inefficiently under heavy loads. Figure 7-14c shows one way to improve the efficiency by allowing more than one data source to be included within a single frame. With multiple sources, however, some means is necessary to specify the length of the data stream from each source. Hence, the statistical frame consists of sequences of data fields labeled with an address and a bit count. There are several techniques that can be used to further improve efficiency. The address field can be shortened by using relative addressing where each address specifies the position of the current source relative to the previously transmitted source and the total number of sources. With relative addressing, an eight-bit address field can be replaced with a four-bit address field.

Another method of refining the frame is to use a two-bit label with the length field. The binary values 01, 10, and 11 correspond to a data field of 1, 2, or 3 bytes, respectively, and no length field necessary is indicated by the code 00.

7-11 CODECS AND COMBO CHIPS

7-11-1 Codec

A *codec* is a large-scale integration (LSI) chip designed for use in the telecommunications industry for private branch exchanges (PBXs), central office switches, digital handsets, voice store-and-forward systems, and digital echo suppressors. Essentially, the codec is applicable for any purpose that requires the digitizing of analog signals, such as in a PCM-TDM carrier system.

Codec is a generic term that refers to the coding functions performed by a device that converts analog signals to digital codes and digital codes to analog signals. Recently developed codecs are called *combo* chips because they combine codec and filter functions in the same LSI package. The input/output filter performs the following functions: bandlimiting, noise rejection, antialiasing, and reconstruction of analog audio waveforms after decoding. The codec performs the following functions: analog sampling, encoding/decoding (analog-to-digital and digital-to-analog conversions), and digital companding.

7-11-2 Combo Chips

A combo chip can provide the analog-to-digital and the digital-to-analog conversions and the transmit and receive filtering necessary to interface a full-duplex (four-wire) voice telephone circuit to the PCM highway of a TDM carrier system. Essentially, a combo chip replaces the older codec and filter chip combination.

Table 7-6 lists several of the combo chips available and their prominent features.

Table 7-6   Features of Several Codec/Filter Combo Chips

2916 (16-Pin)	2917 (16-Pin)	2913 (20-Pin)	2914 (24-Pin)
μ-law companding only	A-law companding only	μ/A-law companding	μ/A-law companding
Master clock, 2.048 MHz only	Master clock, 2.048 MHz only	Master clock, 1.536 MHz, 1.544 MHz, or 2.048 MHz	Master clock, 1.536 MHz, 1.544 MHz, or 2.048 MHz
Fixed data rate	Fixed data rate	Fixed data rate	Fixed data rate
Variable data rate, 64 kbps–2.048 Mbps	Variable data rate, 64 kbps–4.096 Mbps	Variable data rate, 64 kbps–4.096 Mbps	Variable data rate, 64 kbps–4.096 Mbps
78-dB dynamic range	78-dB dynamic range	78-dB dynamic range	78-dB dynamic range
ATT D3/4 compatible	ATT D3/4 compatible	ATT D3/4 compatible	ATT D3/4 compatible
Single-ended input	Single-ended input	Differential input	Differential input
Single-ended output	Single-ended output	Differential output	Differential output
Gain adjust transmit only	Gain adjust transmit only	Gain adjust transmit and receive	Gain adjust transmit and receive
Synchronous clocks	Synchronous clocks	Synchronous clocks	Synchronous clocks
			Asynchronous clocks
			Analog loopback
			Signaling

7-11-2-1 General operation. The following major functions are provided by a combo chip:

1. Bandpass filtering of the analog signals prior to encoding and after decoding
2. Encoding and decoding of voice and call progress signals
3. Encoding and decoding of signaling and supervision information
4. Digital companding

Figure 7-23a shows the block diagram of a typical combo chip. Figure 7-23b shows the frequency response curve for the transmit bandpass filter, and Figure 7-23c shows the frequency response for the receive low-pass filter.

7-11-2-2 Fixed-data-rate mode. In the *fixed-data-rate mode,* the master *transmit* and *receive clocks* on a combo chip (CLKX and CLKR) perform the following functions:

1. Provide the master clock for the on-board switched capacitor filter
2. Provide the clock for the analog-to-digital and digital-to-analog converters
3. Determine the input and output data rates between the codec and the PCM highway

Therefore, in the fixed-data-rate mode, the transmit and receive data rates must be either 1.536 Mbps, 1.544 Mbps, or 2.048 Mbps—the same as the master clock rate.

Transmit and receive frame synchronizing pulses (FSX and FSR) are 8-kHz inputs that set the transmit and receive sampling rates and distinguish between *signaling* and *nonsignaling* frames. $\overline{\text{TSX}}$ is a *time-slot strobe buffer enable* output that is used to gate the PCM word onto the PCM highway when an external buffer is used to drive the line. $\overline{\text{TSX}}$ is also used as an external gating pulse for a time-division multiplexer (see Figure 7-24a).

Data are transmitted to the PCM highway from DX on the first eight positive transitions of CLKX following the rising edge of FSX. On the receive channel, data are received from the PCM highway from DR on the first eight falling edges of CLKR after the occurrence of FSR. Therefore, the occurrence of FSX and FSR must be synchronized between codecs in a multiple-channel system to ensure that only one codec is transmitting to or receiving from the PCM highway at any given time.

Figures 7-24a and b show the block diagram and timing sequence for a single-channel PCM system using a combo chip in the fixed-data-rate mode and operating with a master clock frequency of 1.536 MHz. In the fixed-data-rate mode, data are input and output for a single channel in short bursts. (This mode of operation is sometimes called the *burst mode.*) With only a single channel, the PCM highway is active only 1/24 of the total frame time. Additional channels can be added to the system provided that their transmissions are synchronized so that they do not occur at the same time as transmissions from any other channel.

From Figure 7-24, the following observations can be made:

1. The input and output bit rates from the codec are equal to the master clock frequency, 1.536 Mbps.
2. The codec inputs and outputs 64,000 PCM bits per second.
3. The data output (DX) and data input (DR) are enabled only 1/24 of the total frame time (125 μs).

To add channels to the system shown in Figure 7-24, the occurrence of the FSX, FSR, and $\overline{\text{TSX}}$ signals for each additional channel must be synchronized so that they follow a timely sequence and do not allow more than one codec to transmit or receive at the same

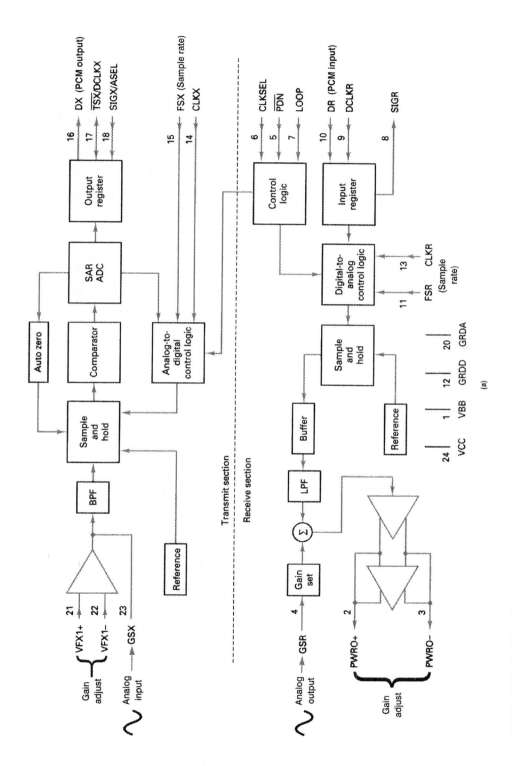

FIGURE 7-23 Combo chip: (a) block diagram; (b) transmit BPF response curve; (c) receive LPF response curve (*Continued*)

FIGURE 7-23 (*Continued*) Combo chip: (b) transmit BPF response curve; (c) receive LPF response curve

FIGURE 7-24 Single-channel PCM system using a combo chip in the fixed-data-rate mode: (a) block diagram; (*Continued*)

time. Figures 7-25a and b show the block diagram and timing sequence for a 24-channel PCM-TDM system operating with a master clock frequency of 1.536 MHz.

7-11-2-3 Variable-data-rate mode. The *variable-data-rate mode* allows for a flexible data input and output clock frequency. It provides the ability to vary the frequency of the transmit and receive bit clocks. In the variable-data-rate mode, a master clock frequency of 1.536 MHz, 1.544 MHz, or 2.048 MHz is still required for proper operation of the onboard bandpass filters and the analog-to-digital and digital-to-analog converters. However, in the variable-data-rate mode, DCLKR and DCLKX become the data clocks for the receive and transmit PCM highways, respectively. When FSX is high, data are transmitted onto the PCM highway on the next eight consecutive positive transitions of DCLKX. Similarly, while FSR is high, data from the PCM highway are clocked into the codec on the next eight consecutive negative transitions of DCLKR. This mode of operation is sometimes called the *shift register mode*.

On the transmit channel, the last transmitted PCM word is repeated in all remaining time slots in the 125-μs frame as long as DCLKX is pulsed and FSX is held active high.

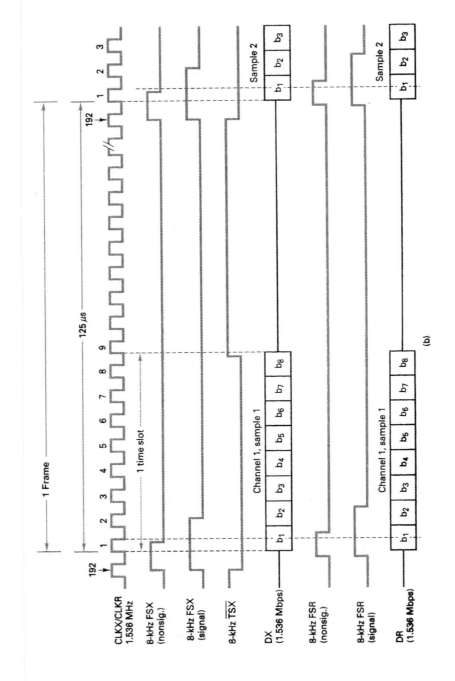

FIGURE 7.24 (Continued) (b) timing sequence

FIGURE 7-25 Twenty-four channel PCM-TDM system using a combo chip in the fixed-data-rate mode and operating with a master clock frequency of 1.536 MHz: (a) block diagram; (Continued)

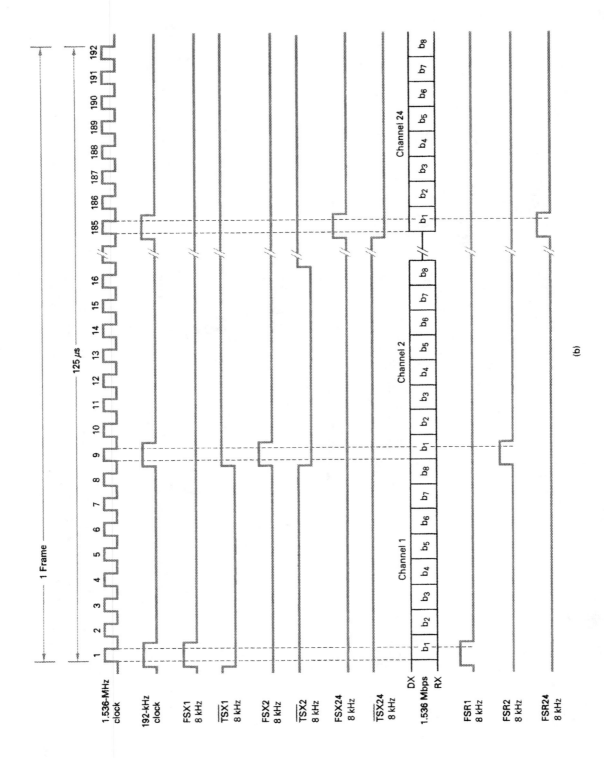

FIGURE 7-25 (Continued) (b) timing diagram

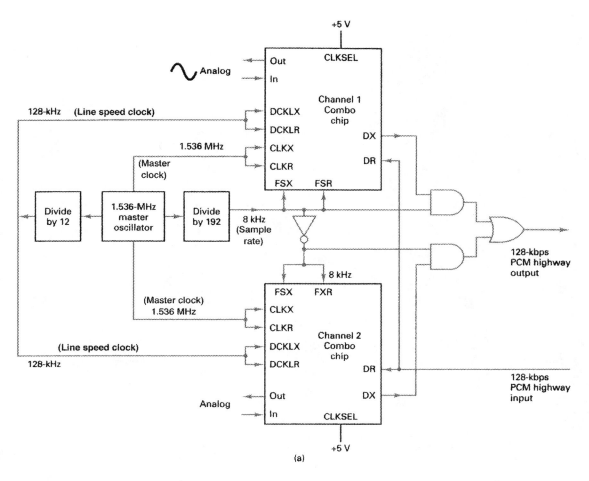

FIGURE 7-26 Two-channel PCM-TDM system using a combo chip in the variable-data-rate mode with a master clock frequency of 1.536 MHz: (a) block diagram; (*Continued*)

This feature allows the PCM word to be transmitted to the PCM highway more than once per frame. Signaling is not allowed in the variable-data-rate mode because this mode provides no means to specify a signaling frame.

Figures 7-26a and b shows the block diagram and timing sequence for a two-channel PCM-TDM system using a combo chip in the variable-data-rate mode with a master clock frequency of 1.536 MHz, a sample rate of 8 kHz, and a transmit and receive data rate of 128 kbps.

With a sample rate of 8 kHz, the frame time is 125 μs. Therefore, one eight-bit PCM word from each channel is transmitted and/or received during each 125-μs frame. For 16 bits to occur in 125 μs, a 128-kHz transmit and receive data clock is required:

$$t_b = \frac{1 \text{ channel}}{8 \text{ bits}} \times \frac{1 \text{ frame}}{2 \text{ channels}} \times \frac{125 \text{ μs}}{\text{frame}} = \frac{125 \text{ μs}}{16 \text{ bits}} = \frac{7.8125 \text{ μs}}{\text{bit}}$$

$$\text{bit rate} = \frac{1}{t_b} = \frac{1}{7.8125 \text{ μs}} = 128 \text{ kbps}$$

or

$$\frac{8 \text{ bits}}{\text{channel}} \times \frac{2 \text{ channels}}{\text{frame}} \times \frac{8000 \text{ frames}}{\text{second}} = 128 \text{ kbps}$$

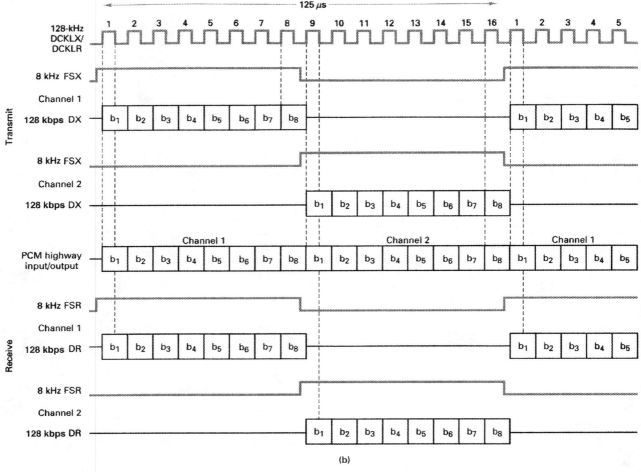

FIGURE 7-26 (*Continued*) (b) timing diagram

The transmit and receive enable signals (FSX and FSR) for each codec are active for one-half of the total frame time. Consequently, 8-kHz, 50% duty cycle transmit and receive data enable signals (FSX and FXR) are fed directly to one codec and fed to the other codec 180° out of phase (inverted), thereby enabling only one codec at a time.

To expand to a four-channel system, simply increase the transmit and receive data clock rates to 256 kHz and change the enable signals to 8-kHz, 25% duty cycle pulses.

7-11-2-4 Supervisory signaling. With a combo chip, *supervisory signaling* can be used only in the fixed-data-rate mode. A transmit signaling frame is identified by making the FSX and FSR pulses twice their normal width. During a transmit signaling frame, the signal present on input SIGX is substituted into the least significant bit position (b_1) of the encoded PCM word. At the receive end, the signaling bit is extracted from the PCM word prior to decoding and placed on output SIGR until updated by reception of another signaling frame.

Asynchronous operation occurs when the master transmit and receive clocks are derived from separate independent sources. A combo chip can be operated in either the synchronous or the asynchronous mode using separate digital-to-analog converters and voltage references in the transmit and receive channels, which allows them to be operated completely independent of each other. With either synchronous or asynchronous operation, the master clock, data clock, and time-slot strobe must be synchronized at the beginning of each frame. In the variable-data-rate mode, CLKX and DCLKX must be synchronized once per frame but may be different frequencies.

7-12 FREQUENCY-DIVISION MULTIPLEXING

With *frequency-division multiplexing* (FDM), multiple sources that originally occupied the same frequency spectrum are each converted to a different frequency band and transmitted simultaneously over a single transmission medium, which can be a physical cable or the Earth's atmosphere (i.e., wireless). Thus, many relatively narrow-bandwidth channels can be transmitted over a single wide-bandwidth transmission system without interfering with each other. FDM is used for combining many relatively narrowband sources into a single wideband channel, such as in public telephone systems. Essentially, FDM is taking a given bandwidth and subdividing it into narrower segments with each segment carrying different information.

FDM is an analog multiplexing scheme; the information entering an FDM system must be analog, and it remains analog throughout transmission. If the original source information is digital, it must be converted to analog before being frequency-division multiplexed.

A familiar example of FDM is the commercial AM broadcast band, which occupies a frequency spectrum from 535 kHz to 1605 kHz. Each broadcast station carries an information signal (voice and music) that occupies a bandwidth between 0 Hz and 5 kHz. If the information from each station were transmitted with the original frequency spectrum, it would be impossible to differentiate or separate one station's transmissions from another. Instead, each station amplitude modulates a different carrier frequency and produces a 10-kHz signal. Because the carrier frequencies of adjacent stations are separated by 10 kHz, the total commercial AM broadcast band is divided into 107 10-kHz frequency slots stacked next to each other in the frequency domain. To receive a particular station, a receiver is simply tuned to the frequency band associated with that station's transmissions. Figure 7-27 shows how commercial AM broadcast station signals are frequency-division multiplexed and transmitted over a common transmission medium (Earth's atmosphere).

With FDM, each narrowband channel is converted to a different location in the total frequency spectrum. The channels are stacked on top of one another in the frequency domain. Figure 7-28a shows a simple FDM system where four 5-kHz channels are frequency-division multiplexed into a single 20-kHz combined channel. As the figure shows,

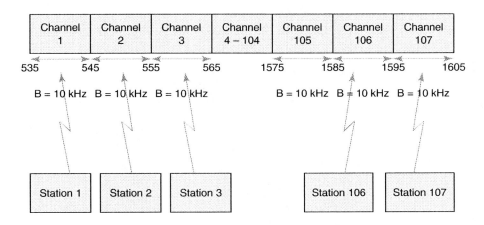

FIGURE 7-27 Frequency-division multiplexing of the commercial AM broadcast band

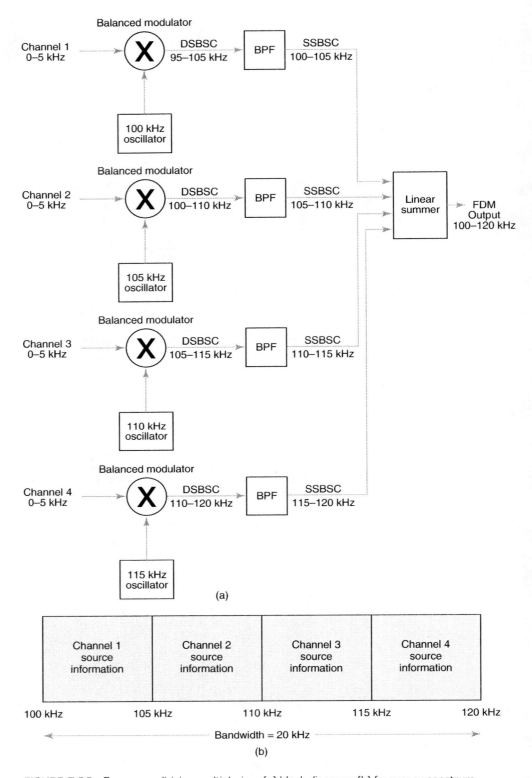

FIGURE 7-28 Frequency-division multiplexing: (a) block diagram; (b) frequency spectrum

channel 1 signals amplitude modulate a 100-kHz carrier in a balanced modulator, which inherently suppresses the 100-kHz carrier. The output of the balanced modulator is a double-sideband suppressed-carrier waveform with a bandwidth of 10 kHz. The double sideband waveform passes through a bandpass filter (BPF) where it is converted to a single sideband signal. For this example, the lower sideband is blocked; thus, the output of the BPF occupies the frequency band between 100 kHz and 105 kHz (a bandwidth of 5 kHz).

Channel 2 signals amplitude modulate a 105-kHz carrier in a balanced modulator, again producing a double sideband signal that is converted to single sideband by passing it through a bandpass filter tuned to pass only the upper sideband. Thus, the output from the BPF occupies a frequency band between 105 kHz and 110 kHz. The same process is used to convert signals from channels 3 and 4 to the frequency bands 110 kHz to 115 kHz and 115 kHz to 120 kHz, respectively. The combined frequency spectrum produced by combining the outputs from the four bandpass filters is shown in Figure 7-28b. As the figure shows, the total combined bandwidth is equal to 20 kHz, and each channel occupies a different 5-kHz portion of the total 20-kHz bandwidth.

There are many other applications for FDM, such as commercial FM and television broadcasting, high-volume telephone and data communications systems, and cable television and data distribution networks. Within any of the commercial broadcast frequency bands, each station's transmissions are independent of all the other stations' transmissions. Consequently, the multiplexing (stacking) process is accomplished without synchronization between stations. With a high-volume telephone communications system, many voice-band telephone channels may originate from a common source and terminate in a common destination. The source and destination terminal equipment is most likely a high-capacity electronic switching system (ESS). Because of the possibility of a large number of narrowband channels originating and terminating at the same location, all multiplexing and demultiplexing operations must be synchronized.

7-13 AT&T'S FDM HIERARCHY

Although AT&T is no longer the only long-distance common carrier in the United States, it still provides the vast majority of the long-distance services and, if for no other reason than its overwhelming size, has essentially become the standards organization for the telephone industry in North America.

AT&T's nationwide communications network is subdivided into two classifications: *short haul* (short distance) and *long haul* (long distance). The T1 carrier explained earlier in this chapter is an example of a short-haul communications system.

Figure 7-29 shows AT&T's long-haul FDM hierarchy. Only the transmit terminal is shown, although a complete set of inverse functions must be performed at the receiving terminal. As the figure shows, voice channels are combined to form groups, groups are combined to form supergroups, and supergroups are combined to form mastergroups.

7-13-1 Message Channel

The *message channel* is the basic building block of the FDM hierarchy. The basic message channel was originally intended for the analog voice transmission, although it now includes any transmissions that utilize voice-band frequencies (0 kHz to 4 kHz), such as data transmission using voice-band data modems. The basic voice-band (VB) circuit is called a basic 3002 channel and is actually bandlimited to approximately a 300-Hz to 3000-Hz frequency band, although for practical design considerations it is considered a 4-kHz channel. The basic 3002 channel can be subdivided and frequency-division multiplexed into 24 narrower-band 3001 (telegraph) channels.

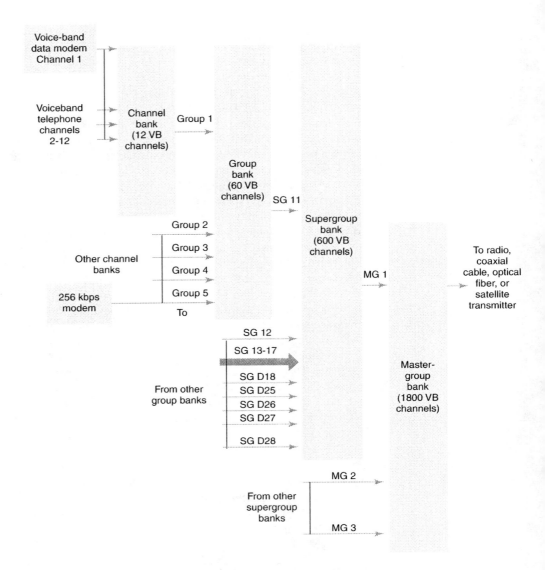

FIGURE 7-29 American Telephone & Telegraph Company's FDM hierarchy

7-13-2 Basic Group

A *group* is the next higher level in the FDM hierarchy above the basic message channel and, consequently, is the first multiplexing step for combining message channels. A basic group consists of 12 voice-band message channels multiplexed together by stacking them next to each other in the frequency domain. Twelve 4-kHz voice-band channels occupy a combined bandwidth of 48 kHz (4 × 12). The 12-channel modulating block is called an A-type (analog) channel bank. The 12-channel group output from an A-type channel bank is the standard building block for most long-haul broadband telecommunications systems.

7-13-3 Basic Supergroup

The next higher level in the FDM hierarchy shown in Figure 7-29 is the *supergroup*, which is formed by frequency-division multiplexing five groups containing 12 channels each for a combined bandwidth of 240 kHz (5 groups × 48 kHz/group or 5 groups × 12 channels/group × 4 kHz/channel).

7-13-4 Basic Mastergroup

The next highest level of multiplexing shown in Figure 7-29 is the *mastergroup*, which is formed by frequency-division multiplexing 10 supergroups together for a combined capacity of 600 voice-band message channels occupying a bandwidth of 2.4 MHz (600 channels × 4 kHz/channel or 5 groups × 12/channels/group × 10 groups/supergroup). Typically, three mastergroups are frequency-division multiplexed together and placed on a single microwave or satellite radio channel. The capacity is 1800 VB channels (3 mastergroups × 600 channels/mastergroup) utilizing a combined bandwidth of 7.2 MHz.

7-13-5 Larger Groupings

Mastergroups can be further multiplexed in mastergroup banks to form *jumbogroups* (3600 VB channels), *multijumbogroups* (7200 VB channels), and *superjumbogroups* (10,800 VB channels).

7-14 COMPOSITE BASEBAND SIGNAL

Baseband describes the modulating signal (intelligence) in a communications system. A single message channel is baseband. A group, supergroup, or mastergroup is also baseband. The composite baseband signal is the total intelligence signal prior to modulation of the final carrier. In Figure 7-29, the output of a channel bank is baseband. Also, the output of a group or supergroup bank is baseband. The final output of the FDM multiplexer is the *composite* (total) baseband. The formation of the composite baseband signal can include channel, group, supergroup, and mastergroup banks, depending on the capacity of the system.

7-14-1 Formation of Groups and Supergroups

Figure 7-30 shows how a group is formed with an A-type channel bank. Each voice-band channel is bandlimited with an antialiasing filter prior to modulating the channel carrier. FDM uses single-sideband suppressed-carrier (SSBSC) modulation. The combination of the balanced modulator and the bandpass filter makes up the SSBSC modulator. A balanced modulator is a double-sideband suppressed-carrier modulator, and the bandpass filter is tuned to the difference between the carrier and the input voice-band frequencies (LSB). The ideal input frequency range for a single voice-band channel is 0 kHz to 4 kHz. The carrier frequencies for the channel banks are determined from the following expression:

$$f_c = 112 - 4n \text{ kHz} \tag{7-3}$$

where n is the channel number. Table 7-7 lists the carrier frequencies for channels 1 through 12. Therefore, for channel 1, a 0-kHz to 4-kHz band of frequencies modulates a 108-kHz carrier. Mathematically, the output of a channel bandpass filter is

$$f_{\text{out}} = (f_c - 4 \text{ kHz}) \text{ to } f_c \tag{7-4}$$

where f_c = channel carrier frequency ($112 - 4n$ kHz) and each voice-band channel has a 4-kHz bandwidth.

> For channel 1, $f_{\text{out}} = 108 \text{ kHz} - 4 \text{ kHz} = 104 \text{ kHz to } 108 \text{ kHz}$
> For channel 2, $f_{\text{out}} = 104 \text{ kHz} - 4 \text{ kHz} = 100 \text{ kHz to } 104 \text{ kHz}$
> For channel 12, $f_{\text{out}} = 64 \text{ kHz} - 4 \text{ kHz} = 60 \text{ kHz to } 64 \text{ kHz}$

The outputs from the 12 A-type channel modulators are summed in the *linear* combiner to produce the total group spectrum shown in Figure 7-30b (60 kHz to 108 kHz). Note that the total group bandwidth is equal to 48 kHz (12 channels × 4 kHz).

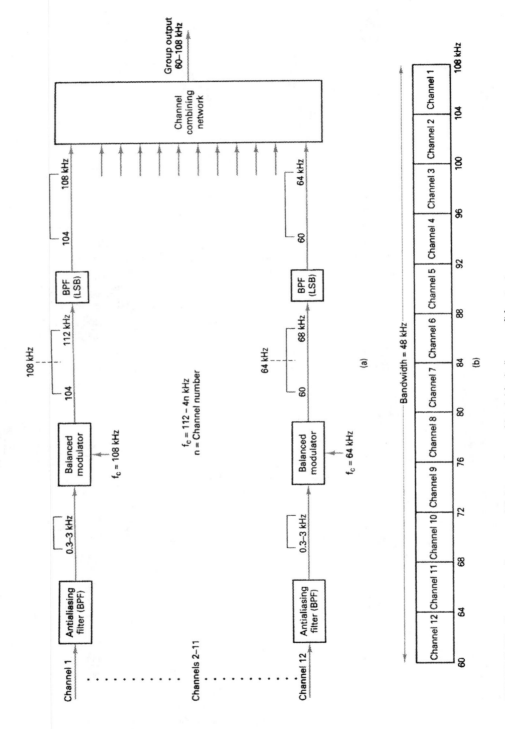

FIGURE 7-30 Formation of a group: (a) A-type channel bank block diagram; (b) output spectrum

Table 7-7 Channel Carrier Frequencies			Table 7-8 Group Carrier Frequencies	
Channel	Carrier Frequency (kHz)		Group	Carrier Frequency (kHz)
1	108		1	420
2	104		2	468
3	100		3	516
4	96		4	564
5	92		5	612
6	88			
7	84			
8	80			
9	76			
10	72			
11	68			
12	64			

Figure 7-31a shows how a supergroup is formed with a group bank and combining network. Five groups are combined to form a supergroup. The frequency spectrum for each group is 60 kHz to 108 kHz. Each group is mixed with a different group carrier frequency in a balanced modulator and then bandlimited with a bandpass filter tuned to the difference frequency band (LSB) to produce a SSBSC signal. The group carrier frequencies are derived from the following expression:

$$f_c = 372 + 48n \text{ kHz}$$

where n is the group number. Table 7-8 lists the carrier frequencies for groups 1 through 5. For group 1, a 60-kHz to 80-kHz group signal modulates a 420-kHz group carrier frequency. Mathematically, the output of a group bandpass filter is

$$f_{out} = (f_c - 108 \text{ kHz}) \text{ to } (f_c - 60 \text{ kHz})$$

where f_c = group carrier frequency (372 + 48n kHz) and for a group frequency spectrum of 60 KHz to 108 KHz

Group 1, f_{out} = 420 kHz − (60 kHz to 108 kHz) = 312 kHz to 360 kHz
Group 2, f_{out} = 468 kHz − (60 kHz to 108 kHz) = 360 kHz to 408 kHz
Group 5, f_{out} = 612 kHz − (60 kHz to 108 kHz) = 504 kHz to 552 kHz

The outputs from the five group modulators are summed in the linear combiner to produce the total supergroup spectrum shown in Figure 7-31b (312 kHz to 552 kHz). Note that the total supergroup bandwidth is equal to 240 kHz (60 channels × 4 kHz).

7-15 FORMATION OF A MASTERGROUP

There are two types of mastergroups: L600 and U600 types. The L600 mastergroup is used for low-capacity microwave systems, and the U600 mastergroup may be further multiplexed and used for higher-capacity microwave radio systems.

7-15-1 U600 Mastergroup

Figure 7-32a shows how a U600 mastergroup is formed with a supergroup bank and combining network. Ten supergroups are combined to form a mastergroup. The frequency spectrum for each supergroup is 312 kHz to 552 kHz. Each supergroup is mixed with a different supergroup carrier frequency in a balanced modulator. The output is then bandlimited to the difference frequency band (LSB) to form a SSBSC signal. The 10 supergroup carrier

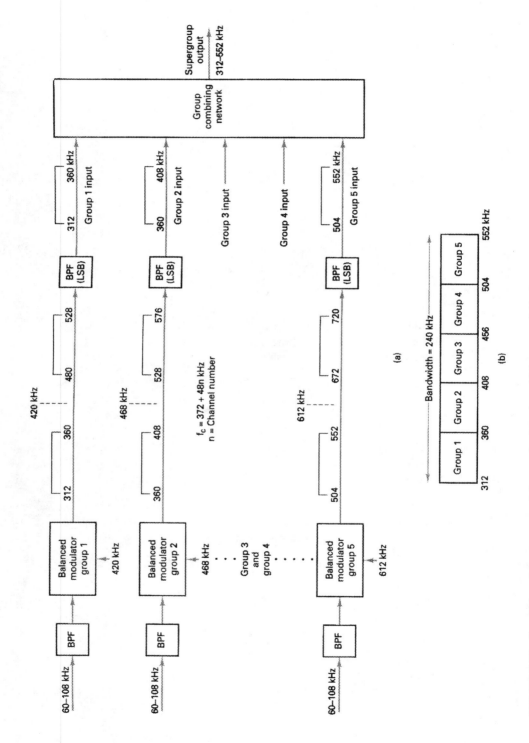

FIGURE 7-31 Formation of a supergroup: (a) group bank and combining network block diagram; (b) output spectrum

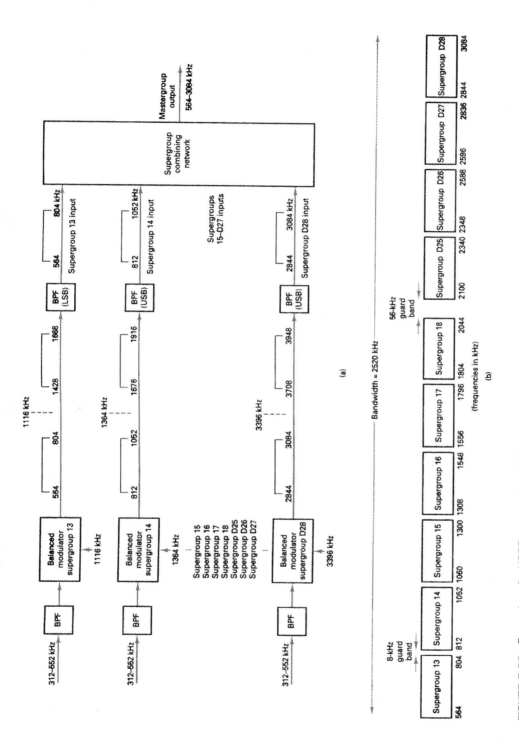

FIGURE 7-32 Formation of a U600 mastergroup: (a) supergroup bank and combining network block diagram; (b) output spectrum

Table 7-9 Supergroup Carrier
Frequencies for a U600
Mastergroup

Supergroup	Carrier Frequency (kHz)
13	1116
14	1364
15	1612
16	1860
17	2108
18	2356
D25	2652
D26	2900
D27	3148
D28	3396

frequencies are listed in Table 7-9. For supergroup 13, a 312-kHz to 552-kHz supergroup band of frequencies modulates a 1116-kHz carrier frequency. Mathematically, the output from a supergroup bandpass filter is

$$f_{out} = f_c - f_s \text{ to } f_c$$

where f_c = supergroup carrier frequency
f_s = supergroup frequency spectrum (312 kHz to 552 kHz)

For supergroup 13, $f_{out} = 1116 \text{ kHz} - (312 \text{ kHz to } 552 \text{ kHz}) = 564 \text{ kHz to } 804 \text{ kHz}$
For supergroup 14, $f_{out} = 1364 \text{ kHz} - (312 \text{ kHz to } 552 \text{ kHz}) = 812 \text{ kHz to } 1052 \text{ kHz}$
For supergroup D28, $f_{out} = 3396 \text{ kHz} - (312 \text{ kHz to } 552 \text{ kHz}) = 2844 \text{ kHz to } 3084 \text{ kHz}$

The outputs from the 10 supergroup modulators are summed in the linear summer to produce the total mastergroup spectrum shown in Figure 7-32b (564 kHz to 3084 kHz). Note that between any two adjacent supergroups, there is a void band of frequencies that is not included within any supergroup band. These voids are called *guard bands*. The guard bands are necessary because the demultiplexing process is accomplished through filtering and down-converting. Without the guard bands, it would be difficult to separate one supergroup from an adjacent supergroup. The guard bands reduce the *quality factor* (*Q*) required to perform the necessary filtering. The guard band is 8 kHz between all supergroups except 18 and D25, where it is 56 kHz. Consequently, the bandwidth of a U600 mastergroup is 2520 kHz (564 kHz to 3084 kHz), which is greater than is necessary to stack 600 voice-band channels (600 × 4 kHz = 2400 kHz).

Guard bands were not necessary between adjacent groups because the group frequencies are sufficiently low, and it is relatively easy to build bandpass filters to separate one group from another.

In the channel bank, the antialiasing filter at the channel input passes a 0.3-kHz to 3-kHz band. The separation between adjacent channel carrier frequencies is 4 kHz. Therefore, there is a 1300-Hz guard band between adjacent channels. This is shown in Figure 7-33.

7-15-2 L600 Mastergroup
With an L600 mastergroup, 10 supergroups are combined as with the U600 mastergroup, except that the supergroup carrier frequencies are lower. Table 7-10 lists the supergroup carrier frequencies for an L600 mastergroup. With an L600 mastergroup, the composite baseband spectrum occupies a lower-frequency band than the U-type mastergroup (Figure 7-34). An L600 mastergroup is not further multiplexed. Therefore, the maximum channel capacity for a microwave or coaxial cable system using a single L600 mastergroup is 600 voice-band channels.

FIGURE 7-33 Channel guard bands

Table 7-10 Supergroup Carrier
Frequencies for a L600 Mastergroup

Supergroup	Carrier Frequency (kHz)
1	612
2	Direct
3	1116
4	1364
5	1612
6	1860
7	2108
8	2356
9	2724
10	3100

FIGURE 7-34 L600 mastergroup

7-15-3 Formation of a Radio Channel

A *radio channel* comprises either a single L600 mastergroup or up to three U600 master-groups (1800 voice-band channels). Figure 7-35a shows how an 1800-channel composite FDM baseband signal is formed for transmission over a single microwave radio channel. Mastergroup 1 is transmitted directly as is, while mastergroups 2 and 3 undergo an additional multiplexing step. The three mastergroups are summed in a mastergroup combining network to produce the output spectrum shown in Figure 7-35b. Note the 80-kHz guard band between adjacent mastergroups.

The system shown in Figure 7-35 can be increased from 1800 voice-band channels to 1860 by adding an additional supergroup (supergroup 12) directly to mastergroup 1. The additional 312-kHz to 552-kHz supergroup extends the composite output spectrum from 312 kHz to 8284 kHz.

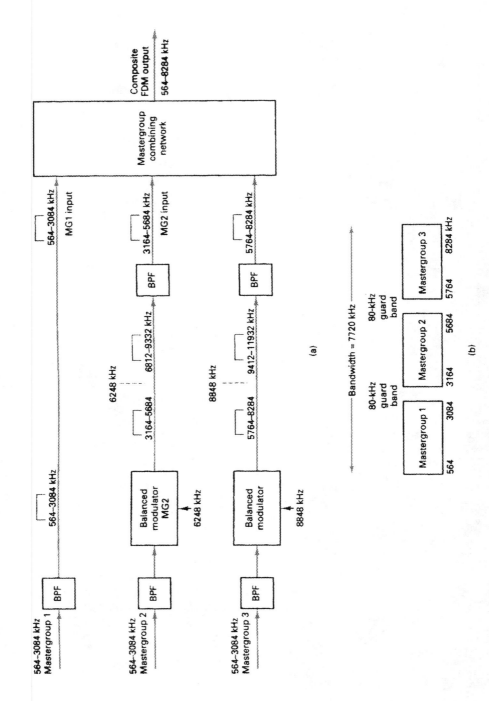

FIGURE 7-35 Three-mastergroup radio channel: (a) block diagram; (b) output spectrum

During the last two decades of the 20th century, the telecommunications industry witnessed an unprecedented growth in data traffic and the need for computer networking. The possibility of using *wavelength-division multiplexing* (WDM) as a networking mechanism for telecommunications routing, switching, and selection based on wavelength begins a new era in optical communications.

WDM promises to vastly increase the bandwidth capacity of optical transmission media. The basic principle behind WDM involves the transmission of multiple digital signals using several wavelengths without their interfering with one another. Digital transmission equipment currently being deployed utilizes optical fibers to carry only one digital signal per fiber per propagation direction. WDM is a technology that enables many optical signals to be transmitted simultaneously by a single fiber cable.

WDM is sometimes referred to as simply *wave-division multiplexing.* Since wavelength and frequency are closely related, WDM is similar to frequency-division multiplexing (FDM) in that the idea is to send information signals that originally occupied the same band of frequencies through the same fiber at the same time without their interfering with each other. This is accomplished by modulating injection laser diodes that are transmitting highly concentrated light waves at different wavelengths (i.e., at different optical frequencies). Therefore, WDM is coupling light at two or more discrete wavelengths into and out of an optical fiber. Each wavelength is capable of carrying vast amounts of information in either analog or digital form, and the information can already be time- or frequency-division multiplexed. Although the information used with lasers is almost always time-division multiplexed digital signals, the wavelength separation used with WDM is analogous to analog radio channels operating at different carrier frequencies. However, the carrier with WDM is in essence a wavelength rather than a frequency.

7-16-1 WDM versus FDM

The basic principle of WDM is essentially the same as FDM, where several signals are transmitted using different carriers, occupying nonoverlapping bands of a frequency or wavelength spectrum. In the case of WDM, the wavelength spectrum used is in the region of 1300 or 1500 nm, which are the two wavelength bands at which optical fibers have the least amount of signal loss. In the past, each window transmitted a signal digital signal. With the advance of optical components, each transmitting window can be used to propagate several optical signals, each occupying a small fraction of the total wavelength window. The number of optical signals multiplexed with a window is limited only by the precision of the components used. Current technology allows over 100 optical channels to be multiplexed into a single optical fiber.

Although FDM and WDM share similar principles, they are not the same. The most obvious difference is that optical frequencies (in THz) are much higher than radio frequencies (in MHz and GHz). Probably the most significant difference, however, is in the way the two signals propagate through their respective transmission media. With FDM, signals propagate at the same time and through the same medium and follow the same transmission path. The basic principle of WDM, however, is somewhat different. Different wavelengths in a light pulse travel through an optical fiber at different speeds (e.g., blue light propagates slower than red light). In standard optical fiber communications systems, as the light propagates down the cable, wavelength dispersion causes the light waves to spread out and distribute their energy over a longer period of time. Thus, in standard optical fiber systems, wavelength dispersion creates problems, imposing limitations on the system's performance. With WDM, however, wavelength dispersion is the essence of how the system operates.

With WDM, information signals from multiple sources modulate lasers operating at different wavelengths. Hence, the signals enter the fiber at the same time and travel through the same medium. However, they do not take the same path down the fiber. Since each

(a)

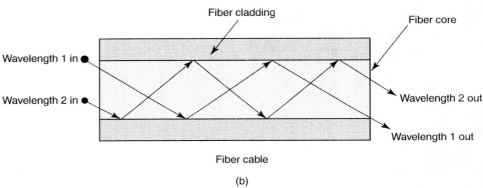

Fiber cable

(b)

FIGURE 7-36 (a) Frequency-division multiplexing; (b) wave-length-division multiplexing

wavelength takes a different transmission path, they each arrive at the receive end at slightly different times. The result is a series of rainbows made of different colors (wavelengths) each about 20 billionths of a second long, simultaneously propagating down the cable.

Figure 7-36 illustrates the basic principles of FDM and WDM signals propagating through their respective transmission media. As shown in Figure 7-36a, FDM channels all propagate at the same time and over the same transmission medium and take the same transmission path, but they occupy different bandwidths. In Figure 7-36b, it can be seen that with WDM, each channel propagates down the same transmission medium at the same time, but each channel occupies a different bandwidth (wavelength), and each wavelength takes a different transmission path.

7-16-2 Dense-Wave-Division Multiplexing, Wavelengths, and Wavelength Channels

WDM is generally accomplished at approximate wavelengths of 1550 nm (1.55 μm) with successive frequencies spaced in multiples of 100 GHz (e.g., 100 GHz, 200 GHz, 300 GHz, and so on). At 1550-nm and 100-GHz frequency separation, the wavelength separation is approximately 0.8 nm. For example, three adjacent wavelengths each separated by 100 GHz correspond to wavelengths of 1550.0 nm, 1549.2 nm, and 1548.4 nm. Using a multiplexing technique called dense-wave-division multiplexing (D-WDM), the spacing between adjacent frequencies is considerably less. Unfortunately, there does not seem to be a standard definition of exactly what D-WDM means. Generally, optical systems carrying multiple optical signals spaced more than 200 GHz or 1.6 nm apart in the vicinity of 1550 nm are considered standard WDM. WDM systems carrying multiple optical signals in the vicinity of 1550 nm with less than 200-GHz separation are considered D-WDM. Obviously, the more wavelengths used in a WDM system, the closer they are to each other and the denser the wavelength spectrum.

Light waves are comprised of many frequencies (wavelengths), and each frequency corresponds to a different color. Transmitters and receivers for optical fiber systems have been developed that transmit and receive only a specific color (i.e., a specific wavelength at a specific frequency with a fixed bandwidth). WDM is a process in which different sources of information (channels) are propagated down an optical fiber on different wavelengths where the different wavelengths do not interfere with each other. In essence, each wavelength adds an optical lane to the transmission superhighway, and the more lanes there are, the more traffic (voice, data, video, and so on) can be carried on a single optical fiber cable. In contrast, conventional optical fiber systems have only one channel per cable, which is used to carry information over a relatively narrow bandwidth. A Bell Laboratories research team recently constructed a D-WDM transmitter using a single femtosecond, erbium-doped fiber-ring laser that can simultaneously carry 206 digitally modulated wavelengths of color over a single optical fiber cable. Each wavelength (channel) has a bit rate of 36.7 Mbps with a channel spacing of approximately 36 GHz.

Figure 7-37a shows the wavelength spectrum for a WDM system using six wavelengths, each modulated with equal-bandwidth information signals. Figure 7-37b shows how the output wavelengths from six lasers are combined (multiplexed) and then propagated over a single optical cable before being separated (demultiplexed) at the receiver with wavelength selective couplers. Although it has been proven that a single, ultrafast light source can generate hundreds of individual communications channels, standard WDM communications systems are generally limited to between 2 and 16 channels.

WDM enhances optical fiber performance by adding channels to existing cables. Each wavelength added corresponds to adding a different channel with its own information source and transmission bit rate. Thus, WDM can extend the information-carrying capacity of a fiber to hundreds of gigabits per second or higher.

7-16-3 Advantages and Disadvantages of WDM

An obvious advantage of WDM is enhanced capacity and, with WDM, full-duplex transmission is also possible with a single fiber. In addition, optical communications networks use optical components that are simpler, more reliable, and often less costly than their electronic counterparts. WDM has the advantage of being inherently easier to reconfigure (i.e., adding or removing channels). For example, WDM local area networks have been constructed that allow users to access the network simply by tuning to a certain wavelength.

There are also limitations to WDM. Signals cannot be placed so close in the wavelength spectrum that they interfere with each other. Their proximity depends on system design parameters, such as whether optical amplification is used and what optical technique is used to combine and separate signals at different wavelengths. The International Telecommunications Union adopted a standard frequency grid for D-WDM with a spacing of 100 GHz or integer multiples of 100 GHz, which at 1550 nm corresponds to a wavelength spacing of approximately 0.8 nm.

With WDM, the overall signal strength should be approximately the same for each wavelength. Signal strength is affected by fiber attenuation characteristics and the degree of amplification, both of which are wavelength dependent. Under normal conditions, the

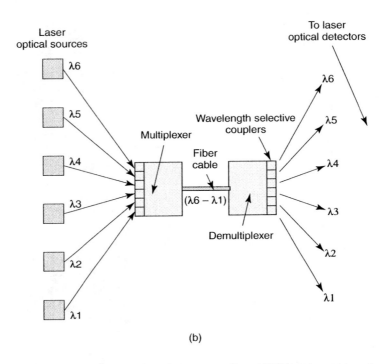

FIGURE 7-37 (a) Wavelength spectrum for a WDM system using six wavelengths; (b) multiplexing and demultiplexing six lasers

wavelengths chosen for a system are spaced so close to one another that attenuation differs very little among them.

One difference between FDM and WDM is that WDM multiplexing is performed at extremely high optical frequencies, whereas FDM is performed at relatively low radio and baseband frequencies. Therefore, radio signals carrying FDM are not limited to propagating through a contained physical transmission medium, such as an optical cable. Radio signals can be propagated through virtually any transmission medium, including free space. Therefore, radio signals can be transmitted simultaneously to many destinations, whereas light waves carrying WDM are limited to a two-point circuit or a combination of many two-point circuits that can go only where the cable goes.

The information capacity of a single optical cable can be increased n-fold, where n represents how many different wavelengths the fiber is propagating at the same time. Each wavelength in a WDM system is modulated by information signals from different sources. Therefore, an optical communications system using a single optical cable propagating n separate wavelengths must utilize n modulators and n demodulators.

The circuit components used with WDM are similar to those used with conventional radio-wave and metallic-wire transmission systems; however, some of the names used for WDM couplers are sometimes confusing.

7-16-4-1 Wavelength-division multiplexers and demultiplexers. *Multiplexers* or *combiners* mix or combine optical signals with different wavelengths in a way that allows them to all pass through a single optical fiber without interfering with one another. *Demultiplexers* or *splitters* separate signals with different wavelengths in a manner similar to the way filters separate electrical signals of different frequencies. Wavelength demultiplexers have as many outputs as there are wavelengths, with each output (wavelength) going to a different destination. Multiplexers and demultiplexers are at the terminal ends of optical fiber communications systems.

7-16-4-2 Wavelength-division add/drop multiplexer/demultiplexers. *Add/drop multiplexer/demultiplexers* are similar to regular multiplexers and demultiplexers except they are located at intermediate points in the system. Add/drop multiplexers and demultiplexers are devices that separate a wavelength from a fiber cable and reroute it on a different fiber going in a different direction. Once a wavelength has been removed, it can be replaced with a new signal at the same wavelength. In essence, add/drop multiplexers and demultiplexers are used to reconfigure optical fiber cables.

7-16-4-3 Wavelength-division routers. WDM *routers* direct signals of a particular wavelength to a specific destination while not separating all the wavelengths present on the cable. Thus, a router can be used to direct or redirect a particular wavelength (or wavelengths) in a different direction from that followed by the other wavelengths on the fiber.

7-16-4-4 Wavelength-division couplers. WDM *couplers* enable more efficient utilization of the transmission capabilities of optical fibers by permitting different wavelengths to be combined and separated. There are three basic types of WDM couplers: *diffraction grating, prism,* and *dichroic filter.* With diffraction gratings or prisms, specific wavelengths are separated from the other optic signal by reflecting them at different angles. Once a wavelength has been separated, it can be coupled into a different fiber. A dichroic filter is a mirror with a surface that has been coated with a material that permits light of only one wavelength to pass through while reflecting all other wavelengths. Therefore, the dichroic filter can allow two wavelengths to be coupled in different optical fibers.

7-16-4-5 WDM and the synchronous optical network. The *synchronous optical network* (SONET) is a multiplexing system similar to conventional time-division multiplexing except SONET was developed to be used with optical fibers. The initial SONET standard is OC-1. This level is referred to as *synchronous transport level 1* (STS-1). STS-1 has a 51.84-Mbps synchronous frame structure made of 28 DS-1 signals. Each DS-1 signal is equivalent to a single 24-channel T1 digital carrier system. Thus, one STS-1 system can carry 672 individual voice channels (24 × 28). With STS-1, it is possible to extract or add individual DS-1 signals without completely disassembling the entire frame.

OC-48 is the second level of SONET multiplexing. It combines 48 OC-1 systems for a total capacity of 32,256 voice channels. OC-48 has a transmission bit rate of 2.48332 Gbps (2.48332 billion bits per second). A single optical fiber can carry an OC-48 system. As many as 16 OC-48 systems can be combined using wave-division multiplexing. The light spectrum is divided into 16 different wavelengths with an OC-48 system attached to each transmitter for a combined capacity of 516,096 voice channels (16 × 32,256).

7-1. Define *multiplexing.*

7-2. Describe time-division multiplexing.

7-3. Describe the Bell System T1 carrier system.

7-4. What is the purpose of the signaling bit?

7-5. What is frame synchronization? How is it achieved in a PCM-TDM system?

7-6. Describe the superframe format. Why is it used?

7-7. What is a codec? A combo chip?

7-8. What is a fixed-data-rate mode?

7-9. What is a variable-data-rate mode?

7-10. What is a DSX? What is it used for?

7-11. Explain *line coding.*

7-12. Briefly explain unipolar and bipolar transmission.

7-13. Briefly explain return-to-zero and nonreturn-to-zero transmission.

7-14. Contrast the bandwidth considerations of return-to-zero and nonreturn-to-zero transmission.

7-15. Contrast the clock recovery capabilities with return-to-zero and nonreturn-to-zero transmission.

7-16. Contrast the error detection and decoding capabilities of return-to-zero and nonreturn-to-zero transmission.

7-17. What is a regenerative repeater?

7-18. Explain B6ZS and B3ZS. When or why would you use one rather than the other?

7-19. Briefly explain the following framing techniques: added-digit framing, robbed-digit framing, added-channel framing, statistical framing, and unique-line code framing.

7-20. Contrast *bit* and *word interleaving.*

7-21. Describe frequency-division multiplexing.

7-22. Describe a message channel.

7-23. Describe the formation of a group, a supergroup, and a mastergroup.

7-24. Define *baseband* and *composite baseband.*

7-25. What is a guard band? When is a guard band used?

7-26. Describe the basic concepts of wave-division multiplexing.

7-27. What is the difference between WDM and D-WDM?

7-28. List the advantages and disadvantages of WDM.

7-29. Give a brief description of the following components: wavelength-division multiplexer/demultiplexers, wavelength-division add/drop multiplexers, and wavelength-division routers.

7-30. Describe the three types of wavelength-division couplers.

7-31. Briefly describe the SONET standard, including OC-1 and OC-48 levels.

7-1. A PCM-TDM system multiplexes 24 voice-band channels. Each sample is encoded into seven bits, and a framing bit is added to each frame. The sampling rate is 9000 samples per second. BPRZ-AMI encoding is the line format. Determine

   a. Line speed in bits per second.
   b. Minimum Nyquist bandwidth.

7-2. A PCM-TDM system multiplexes 32 voice-band channels each with a bandwidth of 0 kHz to 4 kHz. Each sample is encoded with an 8-bit PCM code. UPNRZ encoding is used. Determine

   a. Minimum sample rate.
   b. Line speed in bits per second.
   c. Minimum Nyquist bandwidth.

7-3. For the following bit sequence, draw the timing diagram for UPRZ, UPNRZ, BPRZ, BPNRZ, and BPRZ-AMI encoding:

bit stream: **1 1 1 0 0 1 0 1 0 1 1 0 0**

7-4. Encode the following BPRZ-AMI data stream with B6ZS and B3ZS:

$$+-0000+-+0-00000+-00+$$

7-5. Calculate the 12 channel carrier frequencies for the U600 FDM system.

7-6. Calculate the five group carrier frequencies for the U600 FDM system.

7-7. A PCM-TDM system multiplexes 20 voice-band channels. Each sample is encoded into eight bits, and a framing bit is added to each frame. The sampling rate is 10,000 samples per second. BPRZ-AMI encoding is the line format. Determine

 a. The maximum analog input frequency.
 b. The line speed in bps.
 c. The minimum Nyquist bandwidth.

7-8. A PCM-TDM system multiplexes 30 voice-band channels each with a bandwidth of 0 kHz to 3 kHz. Each sample is encoded with a nine-bit PCM code. UPNRZ encoding is used. Determine

 a. The minimum sample rate.
 b. The line speed in bps.
 c. The minimum Nyquist bandwidth.

7-9. For the following bit sequence, draw the timing diagram for UPRZ, UPNRZ, BPRZ, BPNRZ, and BPRZ-AMI encoding:

bit stream: **1 1 0 0 0 1 0 1 0 1**

7-10. Encode the following BPRZ-AMI data stream with B6ZS and B3ZS:

$$-+000000+-000+00-$$

7-11. Calculate the frequency range for a single FDM channel at the output of the channel, group, supergroup, and mastergroup combining networks for the following assignments:

CH	GP	SG	MG
2	2	13	1
6	3	18	2
4	5	D25	2
9	4	D28	3

7-12. Determine the frequency that a single 1-kHz test tone will translate to at the output of the channel, group, supergroup, and mastergroup combining networks for the following assignments:

CH	GP	SG	MG
4	4	13	2
6	4	16	1
1	2	17	3
11	5	D26	3

7-13. Calculate the frequency range at the output of the mastergroup combining network for the following assignments:

GP	SG	MG
3	13	2
5	D25	3
1	15	1
2	17	2

7-14. Calculate the frequency range at the output of the mastergroup combining network for the following assignments:

SG	MG
18	2
13	3
D26	1
14	1

C H A P T E R 8

Telephone Instruments and Signals

OBJECTIVES

- Define *communications* and *telecommunications*
- Define and describe *subscriber loop*
- Describe the operation and basic functions of a standard telephone set
- Explain the relationship among telephone sets, local loops, and central office switching machines
- Describe the block diagram of a telephone set
- Explain the function and basic operation of the following telephone set components: ringer circuit, on/off-hook circuit, equalizer circuit, speaker, microphone, hybrid network, and dialing circuit
- Describe basic telephone call procedures
- Define *call progress tones* and *signals*
- Describe the following terms: *dial tone, dual-tone multifrequency, multifrequency, dial pulses, station busy, equipment busy, ringing, ring back,* and *receiver on/off hook*
- Describe the basic operation of a cordless telephone
- Define and explain the basic format of caller ID
- Describe the operation of electronic telephones
- Describe the basic principles of paging systems

Communications is the process of conveying information from one place to another. Communications requires a source of information, a transmitter, a receiver, a destination, and some form of transmission medium (connecting path) between the transmitter and the receiver. The transmission path may be quite short, as when two people are talking face to face with each other or when a computer is outputting information to a printer located in the same room. *Telecommunications* is long-distance communications (from the Greek word *tele* meaning "distant" or "afar"). Although the word "long" is an arbitrary term, it generally indicates that communications is taking place between a transmitter and a receiver that are too far apart to communicate effectively using only sound waves.

Although often taken for granted, the telephone is one of the most remarkable devices ever invented. To talk to someone, you simply pick up the phone and dial a few digits, and you are almost instantly connected with them. The telephone is one of the simplest devices ever developed, and the telephone connection has not changed in nearly a century. Therefore, a telephone manufactured in the 1920s will still work with today's intricate telephone system.

Although telephone systems were originally developed for conveying human speech information (voice), they are now also used extensively to transport data. This is accomplished using modems that operate within the same frequency band as human voice. Anyone who uses a telephone or a data modem on a telephone circuit is part of a global communications network called the *public telephone network* (PTN). Because the PTN interconnects subscribers through one or more switches, it is sometimes called the *public switched telephone network* (PSTN). The PTN is comprised of several very large corporations and hundreds of smaller independent companies jointly referred to as *Telco*.

The telephone system as we know it today began as an unlikely collaboration of two men with widely disparate personalities: Alexander Graham Bell and Thomas A. Watson. Bell, born in 1847 in Edinburgh, Scotland, emigrated to Ontario, Canada, in 1870, where he lived for only six months before moving to Boston, Massachusetts. Watson was born in a livery stable owned by his father in Salem, Massachusetts. The two met characteristically in 1874 and invented the telephone in 1876. On March 10, 1876, one week after his patent was allowed, Bell first succeeded in transmitting speech in his lab at 5 Exeter Place in Boston. At the time, Bell was 29 years old and Watson only 22. Bell's patent, number 174,465, has been called the most valuable ever issued.

The telephone system developed rapidly. In 1877, there were only six telephones in the world. By 1881, 3,000 telephones were producing revenues, and in 1883, there were over 133,000 telephones in the United States alone. Bell and Watson left the telephone business in 1881, as Watson put it, "in better hands." This proved to be a financial mistake, as the telephone company they left evolved into the telecommunications giant known officially as the American Telephone and Telegraph Company (AT&T). Because at one time AT&T owned most of the local operating companies, it was often referred to as the *Bell Telephone System* and sometimes simply as "*Ma Bell.*" By 1982, the Bell System grew to an unbelievable $155 billion in assets ($256 billion in today's dollars), with over one million employees and 100,000 vehicles. By comparison, in 1998, Microsoft's assets were approximately $10 billion.

AT&T once described the Bell System as "the world's most complicated machine." A telephone call could be made from any telephone in the United States to virtually any other telephone in the world using this machine. Although AT&T officially divested the Bell System on January 1, 1983, the telecommunications industry continued to grow at an unbelievable rate. Some estimate that more than 1.5 billion telephone sets are operating in the world today.

The simplest and most straightforward form of telephone service is called *plain old telephone service* (POTS), which involves subscribers accessing the public telephone network through a pair of wires called the *local subscriber loop* (or simply *local loop*). The local loop is the most fundamental component of a telephone circuit. A local loop is simply an unshielded twisted-pair transmission line (cable pair), consisting of two insulated conductors twisted together. The insulating material is generally a polyethylene plastic coating, and the conductor is most likely a pair of 116- to 26-gauge copper wire. A subscriber loop is generally comprised of several lengths of copper wire interconnected at junction and cross-connect boxes located in manholes, back alleys, or telephone equipment rooms within large buildings and building complexes.

The subscriber loop provides the means to connect a telephone set at a subscriber's location to the closest telephone office, which is commonly called an *end office, local exchange office,* or *central office.* Once in the central office, the subscriber loop is connected to an *electronic switching system* (ESS), which enables the subscriber to access the public telephone network. The local subscriber loop is described in greater detail in Chapter 17.

8-3 STANDARD TELEPHONE SET

The word *telephone* comes from the Greek words *tele,* meaning "from afar," and *phone,* meaning "sound," "voice," or "voiced sound." The standard dictionary defines a telephone as follows:

> *An apparatus for reproducing sound, especially that of the human voice (speech), at a great distance, by means of electricity; consisting of transmitting and receiving instruments connected by a line or wire which conveys the electric current.*

In essence, *speech* is sound in motion. However, sound waves are acoustic waves and have no electrical component. The basic telephone set is a simple analog transceiver designed with the primary purpose of converting speech or acoustical signals to electrical signals. However, in recent years, new features such as multiple-line selection, hold, caller ID, and speakerphone have been incorporated into telephone sets, creating a more elaborate and complicated device. However, their primary purpose is still the same, and the basic functions they perform are accomplished in much the same way as they have always been.

The first telephone set that combined a transmitter and receiver into a single handheld unit was introduced in 1878 and called the Butterstamp telephone. You talked into one end and then turned the instrument around and listened with the other end. In 1951, Western Electric Company introduced a telephone set that was the industry standard for nearly four decades (the rotary dial telephone used by your grandparents). This telephone set is called the Bell System 500-type telephone and is shown in Figure 8-1a. The 500-type telephone set replaced the earlier 302-type telephone set (the telephone with the hand-crank magneto, fixed microphone, hand-held earphone, and no dialing mechanism). Although there are very few 500-type telephone sets in use in the United States today, the basic functions and operation of modern telephones are essentially the same. In modern-day telephone sets, the rotary dial mechanism is replaced with a Touch-Tone keypad. The modern Touch-Tone telephone is called a 2500-type telephone set and is shown in Figure 8-1b.

The quality of transmission over a telephone connection depends on the received volume, the relative frequency response of the telephone circuit, and the degree of interference. In a typical connection, the ratio of the acoustic pressure at the transmitter input to the corresponding pressure at the receiver depends on the following:

The translation of acoustic pressure into an electrical signal

The losses of the two customer local loops, the central telephone office equipment, and the cables between central telephone offices

(a)

(b)

FIGURE 8-1   (a) 500-type telephone set; (b) 2500-type telephone set

The translation of the electrical signal at the receiving telephone set to acoustic pressure at the speaker output

8-3-1   Functions of the Telephone Set

The basic functions of a telephone set are as follows:

1. Notify the subscriber when there is an incoming call with an audible signal, such as a bell, or with a visible signal, such as a flashing light. This signal is analogous to an interrupt signal on a microprocessor, as its intent is to interrupt what you are doing. These signals are purposely made annoying enough to make people want to answer the telephone as soon as possible.

2. Provide a signal to the telephone network verifying when the incoming call has been acknowledged and answered (i.e., the receiver is lifted off hook).

3. Convert speech (acoustical) energy to electrical energy in the transmitter and vice versa in the receiver. Actually, the microphone converts the acoustical energy to mechanical energy, which is then converted to electrical energy. The speaker performs the opposite conversions.

4. Incorporate some method of inputting and sending destination telephone numbers (either mechanically or electrically) from the telephone set to the central office switch over the local loop. This is accomplished using either rotary dialers (pulses) or Touch-Tone pads (frequency tones).

5. Regulate the amplitude of the speech signal the calling person outputs onto the telephone line. This prevents speakers from producing signals high enough in amplitude to interfere with other people's conversations taking place on nearby cable pairs (crosstalk).

6. Incorporate some means of notifying the telephone office when a subscriber wishes to place an outgoing call (i.e., handset lifted off hook). Subscribers cannot dial out until they receive a dial tone from the switching machine.

7. Ensure that a small amount of the transmit signal is fed back to the speaker, enabling talkers to hear themselves speaking. This feedback signal is sometimes called *sidetone* or *talkback*. Sidetone helps prevent the speaker from talking too loudly.

8. Provide an open circuit (idle condition) to the local loop when the telephone is not in use (i.e., on hook) and a closed circuit (busy condition) to the local loop when the telephone is in use (off hook).

9. Provide a means of transmitting and receiving call progress signals between the central office switch and the subscriber, such as on and off hook, busy, ringing, dial pulses, Touch-Tone signals, and dial tone.

(a)

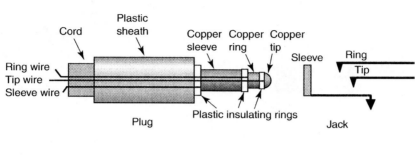

(b)

FIGURE 8-2 (a) Simplified two-wire loop showing telephone set hookup to a local switching machine; (b) plug and jack configurations showing tip, ring, and sleeve

FIGURE 8-3 RJ-11 Connector

8-3-2 Telephone Set, Local Loop, and Central Office Switching Machines

Figure 8-2a shows how a telephone set is connected to a central office switching machine (local switch). As shown in the figure, a basic telephone set requires only two wires (one pair) from the telephone company to operate. Again, the pair of wires connecting a subscriber to the closest telephone office is called the *local loop*. One wire on the local loop is called the *tip*, and the other is called the *ring*. The names *tip* and *ring* come from the ¼-inch-diameter two-conductor phone plugs and patch cords used at telephone company switchboards to interconnect and test circuits. The tip and ring for a standard plug and jack are shown in Figure 8-2b. When a third wire is used, it is called the *sleeve*.

Since the 1960s, phone plugs and jacks have gradually been replaced in the home with a miniaturized plastic plug known as RJ-11 and a matching plastic receptacle (shown in Figure 8-3). *RJ* stands for *registered jacks* and is sometimes described as RJ-XX. RJ is a series of telephone connection interfaces (receptacle and plug) that are registered with the U.S. Federal Communications Commission (FCC). The term *jack* sometimes describes both the receptacle and the plug and sometimes specifies only the receptacle. RJ-11 is the most common telephone jack in use today and can have up to six conductors. Although an RJ-11 plug is capable of holding six wires in a ³⁄₁₆-inch-by-³⁄₁₆-inch body, only two wires (one pair) are necessary for a standard telephone circuit to operate. The other four wires can be used for a second telephone line and/or for some other special function.

As shown in Figure 8-2a, the switching machine outputs −48 Vdc on the ring and connects the tip to ground. A dc voltage was used rather than an ac voltage for several reasons: (1) to prevent power supply hum, (2) to allow service to continue in the event of a power outage, and (3) because people were afraid of ac. Minus 48 volts was selected to minimize electrolytic corrosion on the loop wires. The −48 Vdc is used for supervisory signaling and to provide talk battery for the microphone in the telephone set. On-hook, off-hook, and dial pulsing are examples of supervisory signals and are described in a later section of this chapter. It should be noted that −48 Vdc is the only voltage required for the operation of a standard telephone. However, most modern telephones are equipped with nonstandard (and often nonessential) features and enhancements and may require an additional source of ac power.

8-3-3 Block Diagram of a Telephone Set

A standard telephone set is comprised of a transmitter, a receiver, an electrical network for equalization, associated circuitry to control sidetone levels and to regulate signal power, and necessary signaling circuitry. In essence, a telephone set is an apparatus that creates an exact likeness of sound waves with an electric current. Figure 8-4 shows the functional block diagram of a *telephone set*. The essential components of a telephone set are the ringer circuit, on/off hook circuit, equalizer circuit, hybrid circuit, speaker, microphone, and a dialing circuit.

8-3-3-1 Ringer circuit. The telephone *ringer* has been around since August 1, 1878, when Thomas Watson filed for the first ringer patent. The *ringer circuit,* which was originally an electromagnetic bell, is placed directly across the tip and ring of the local loop. The purpose of the ringer is to alert the destination party of incoming calls. The audible tone from the ringer must be loud enough to be heard from a reasonable distance and offensive enough to make a person want to answer the telephone as soon as possible. In modern telephones, the bell has been replaced with an electronic oscillator connected to the speaker. Today, ringing signals can be any imaginable sound, including buzzing, a beeping, a chiming, or your favorite melody.

8-3-3-2 On/off hook circuit. The *on/off hook circuit* (sometimes called a *switch hook*) is nothing more than a simple single-throw, double-pole (STDP) switch placed across

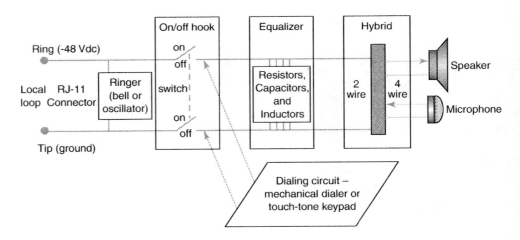

FIGURE 8-4 Functional block diagram of a standard telephone set

the tip and ring. The switch is mechanically connected to the telephone handset so that when the telephone is idle (on hook), the switch is open. When the telephone is in use (off hook), the switch is closed completing an electrical path through the microphone between the tip and ring of the local loop.

8-3-3-3 Equalizer circuit. *Equalizers* are combinations of passive components (resistors, capacitors, and so on) that are used to regulate the amplitude and frequency response of the voice signals. The equalizer helps solve an important transmission problem in telephone set design, namely, the interdependence of the transmitting and receiving efficiencies and the wide range of transmitter currents caused by a variety of local loop cables with different dc resistances.

8-3-3-4 Speaker. In essence, the *speaker* is the receiver for the telephone. The speaker converts electrical signals received from the local loop to acoustical signals (sound waves) that can be heard and understood by a human being. The speaker is connected to the local loop through the hybrid network. The speaker is typically enclosed in the *handset* of the telephone along with the microphone.

8-3-3-5 Microphone. For all practical purposes, the *microphone* is the transmitter for the telephone. The microphone converts acoustical signals in the form of sound pressure waves from the caller to electrical signals that are transmitted into the telephone network through the local subscriber loop. The microphone is also connected to the local loop through the hybrid network. Both the microphone and the speaker are transducers, as they convert one form of energy into another form of energy. A microphone converts acoustical energy first to mechanical energy and then to electrical energy, while the speaker performs the exact opposite sequence of conversions.

8-3-3-6 Hybrid network. The *hybrid network* (sometimes called a *hybrid coil* or *duplex coil*) in a telephone set is a special balanced transformer used to convert a two-wire circuit (the local loop) into a four-wire circuit (the telephone set) and vice versa, thus enabling full duplex operation over a two-wire circuit. In essence, the hybrid network separates the transmitted signals from the received signals. Outgoing voice signals are typically in the 1-V to 2-V range, while incoming voice signals are typically half that value. Another function of the hybrid network is to allow a small portion of the transmit signal to be returned to the receiver in the form of a *sidetone*. Insufficient sidetone causes the speaker to raise his voice, making the telephone conversation seem unnatural. Too much sidetone causes the speaker to talk too softly, thereby reducing the volume that the listener receives.

8-3-3-7 Dialing circuit. The *dialing circuit* enables the subscriber to output signals representing digits, and this enables the caller to enter the destination telephone number. The dialing circuit could be a rotary dialer, which is nothing more than a switch connected to a mechanical rotating mechanism that controls the number and duration of the on/off condition of the switch. However, more than likely, the dialing circuit is either an electronic dial-pulsing circuit or a Touch-Tone keypad, which sends various combinations of tones representing the called digits.

8-4 BASIC TELEPHONE CALL PROCEDURES

Figure 8-5 shows a simplified diagram illustrating how two telephone sets (subscribers) are interconnected through a central office dial switch. Each subscriber is connected to the switch through a local loop. The switch is most likely some sort of an electronic switching system (*ESS machine*). The local loops are terminated at the calling and called stations in telephone sets and at the central office ends to switching machines.

Called party's house

Called party's
telephone set

Called party's
2-Wire Local Loop

RJ-11 Connector

T (gnd)   R (-48 Vdc)

Local Telephone
Office
Switching Machine

T (gnd)   R (-48 Vdc)

Calling party's
2-Wire Local Loop

RJ-11 Connector

Calling party's house

Calling party's
telephone set

FIGURE 8-5   Telephone call procedures

When the calling party's telephone set goes off hook (i.e., lifting the handset off the cradle), the switch hook in the telephone set is released, completing a dc path between the tip and the ring of the loop through the microphone. The ESS machine senses a dc current in the loop and recognizes this as an off-hook condition. This procedure is referred to as *loop start operation* since the loop is completed through the telephone set. The amount of dc current produced depends on the wire resistance, which varies with loop length, wire gauge, type of wire, and the impedance of the subscriber's telephone. Typical loop resistance ranges from a few ohms up to approximately 1300 ohms, and typical telephone set impedances range from 500 ohms to 1000 ohms.

Completing a local telephone call between two subscribers connected to the same telephone switch is accomplished through a standard set of procedures that includes the 10 steps listed next. Accessing the telephone system in this manner is known as POTS (plain old telephone service):

Step 1   Calling station goes off hook.

Step 2   After detecting a dc current flow on the loop, the switching machine returns an audible dial tone to the calling station, acknowledging that the caller has access to the switching machine.

Step 3   The caller dials the destination telephone number using one of two methods: mechanical dial pulsing or, more likely, electronic dual-tone multifrequency (Touch-Tone) signals.

Step 4   When the switching machine detects the first dialed number, it removes the dial tone from the loop.

Step 5   The switch interprets the telephone number and then locates the local loop for the destination telephone number.

Step 6   Before ringing the destination telephone, the switching machine tests the destination loop for dc current to see if it is idle (on hook) or in use (off hook). At the same time, the switching machine locates a signal path through the switch between the two local loops.

Step 7a   If the destination telephone is off hook, the switching machine sends a station busy signal back to the calling station.

Step 7b   If the destination telephone is on hook, the switching machine sends a ringing signal to the destination telephone on the local loop and at the same time sends a ring back signal to the calling station to give the caller some assurance that something is happening.

Step 8   When the destination answers the telephone, it completes the loop, causing dc current to flow.

Step 9   The switch recognizes the dc current as the station answering the telephone. At this time, the switch removes the ringing and ring-back signals and completes the path through the switch, allowing the calling and called parties to begin their conversation.

Step 10   When either end goes on hook, the switching machine detects an open circuit on that loop and then drops the connections through the switch.

Placing telephone calls between parties connected to different switching machines or between parties separated by long distances is somewhat more complicated and is described in Chapter 17.

8-5   CALL PROGRESS TONES AND SIGNALS

Call progress tones and *call progress signals* are acknowledgment and status signals that ensure the processes necessary to set up and terminate a telephone call are completed in an orderly and timely manner. Call progress tones and signals can be sent from machines to machines, machines to people, and people to machines. The people are the subscribers (i.e., the calling and the called party), and the machines are the electronic switching systems in the telephone offices and the telephone sets themselves. When a switching machine outputs a call progress tone to a subscriber, it must be audible and clearly identifiable.

Signaling can be broadly divided into two major categories: *station signaling* and *interoffice signaling.* Station signaling is the exchange of signaling messages over local loops between stations (telephones) and telephone company switching machines. On the other hand, interoffice signaling is the exchange of signaling messages between switching machines. Signaling messages can be subdivided further into one of four categories: *alerting, supervising, controlling,* and *addressing.* Alerting signals indicate a request for service, such as going off hook or ringing the destination telephone. Supervising signals provide call status information, such as busy or ring-back signals. Controlling signals provide information in the form of announcements, such as number changed to another number, a number no longer in service, and so on. Addressing signals provide the routing information, such as calling and called numbers.

Examples of essential call progress signals are dial tone, dual tone multifrequency tones, multifrequency tones, dial pulses, station busy, equipment busy, ringing, ring-back, receiver on hook, and receiver off hook. Tables 8-1 and 8-2 summarize the most important call progress tones and their direction of propagation, respectively.

8-5-1 Dial Tone

Siemens Company first introduced *dial tone* to the public switched telephone network in Germany in 1908. However, it took several decades before being accepted in the United

Table 8-1   Call Progress Tone Summary

Tone or Signal	Frequency	Duration/Range
Dial tone	350 Hz plus 440 Hz	Continuous
DTMF	697 Hz, 770 Hz, 852 Hz, 941 Hz, 1209 Hz, 1336 Hz, 1477 Hz, 1633 Hz	Two of eight tones On, 50-ms minimum Off, 45-ms minimum, 3-s maximum
MF	700 Hz, 900 Hz, 1100 Hz, 1300 Hz, 1500 Hz, 1700 Hz	Two of six tones On, 90-ms minimum, 120-ms maximum
Dial pulses	Open/closed switch	On, 39 ms Off, 61 ms
Station busy	480 Hz plus 620 Hz	On, 0.5 s Off, 0.5 s
Equipment busy	480 Hz plus 620 Hz	On, 0.2 s Off, 0.3 s
Ringing	20 Hz, 90 vrms (nominal)	On, 2 s Off, 4 s
Ring-back	440 Hz plus 480 Hz	On, 2 s Off, 4 s
Receiver on hook	Open loop	Indefinite
Receiver off hook	dc current	20-mA minimum, 80-mA maximum,
Receiver-left-off-hook alert	1440 Hz, 2060 Hz, 2450 Hz, 2600 Hz	On, 0.1 s Off, 0.1 s

Table 8-2   Call Progress Tone Direction of Propagation

Tone or Signal	Direction
Dial tone	Telephone office to calling station
DTMF	Calling station to telephone office
MF	Telephone office to telephone office
Dial pulses	Calling station to telephone office
Station busy	Telephone office to calling subscriber
Equipment busy	Telephone office to calling subscriber
Ringing	Telephone office to called subscriber
Ring-back	Telephone office to calling subscriber
Receiver on hook	Calling subscriber to telephone office
Receiver off hook	Calling subscriber to telephone office
Receiver-left-off-hook alert	Telephone office to calling subscriber

States. Dial tone is an audible signal comprised of two frequencies: 350 Hz and 440 Hz. The two tones are linearly combined and transmitted simultaneously from the central office switching machine to the subscriber in response to the subscriber going off hook. In essence, dial tone informs subscribers that they have acquired access to the electronic switching machine and can now dial or use Touch-Tone in a destination telephone number. After a subscriber hears the dial tone and begins dialing, the dial tone is removed from the line (this is called *breaking dial tone*). On rare occasions, a subscriber may go off hook and not receive dial tone. This condition is appropriately called *no dial tone* and occurs when there are more subscribers requesting access to the switching machine than the switching machine can handle at one time.

8-5-2 Dual-Tone MultiFrequency

Dual-tone multifrequency (DTMF) was first introduced in 1963 with 10 buttons in Western Electric 1500-type telephones. DTMF was originally called *Touch-Tone*. DTMF is a more efficient means than dial pulsing for transferring telephone numbers from a subscriber's location to the central office switching machine. DTMF is a simple two-of-eight encoding scheme where each digit is represented by the linear addition of two frequencies. DTMF is strictly for signaling between a subscriber's location and the nearest telephone office or message switching center. DTMF is sometimes confused with another two-tone signaling system called *multifrequency signaling* (MF), which is a two-of-six code designed to be used only to convey information between two electronic switching machines.

Figure 8-6 shows the four-row-by-four-column keypad matrix used with a DTMF keypad. As the figure shows, the keypad is comprised of 16 keys and eight frequencies. Most household telephones, however, are not equipped with the special-purpose keys located in the fourth column (i.e., the A, B, C, and D keys). Therefore, most household telephones actually use two-of-seven tone encoding scheme. The four vertical frequencies (called the *low group frequencies*) are 697 Hz, 770 Hz, 852 Hz, and 941 Hz, and the four horizontal frequencies (called the *high group frequencies*) are 1209 Hz, 1336 Hz, 1477 Hz, and 1633 Hz. The frequency tolerance of the oscillators is ±.5%. As shown in Figure 8-6, the digits 2 through 9 can also be used to represent 24 of the 26 letters (Q and Z are omitted). The letters were originally used to identify one local telephone exchange from another,

FIGURE 8-6   DTMF keypad layout and frequency allocation

Table 8-3 DTMF Specifications

Transmitter (Subscriber)	Parameter	Receiver (Local Office)
−10 dBm	Minimum power level (single frequency)	−25 dBm
+2 dBm	Maximum power level (two tones)	0 dBm
+4 dB	Maximum power difference between two tones	+4 dB
50 ms	Minimum digit duration	40 ms
45 ms	Minimum interdigit duration	40 ms
3 s	Maximum interdigit time period	3 s
Maximum echo level relative to transmit frequency level (−10 dB)		
Maximum echo delay (<20 ms)		

such as BR for Bronx, MA for Manhattan, and so on. Today, the letters are used to personalize telephone numbers. For example; 1-800-UPS-MAIL equates to the telephone number 1-800-877-6245. When a digit (or letter) is selected, two of the eight frequencies (or seven for most home telephones) are transmitted (one from the low group and one from the high group). For example, when the digit 5 is depressed, 770 Hz and 1336 Hz are transmitted simultaneously. The eight frequencies were purposely chosen so that there is absolutely no harmonic relationship between any of them, thus eliminating the possibility of one frequency producing a harmonic that might be misinterpreted as another frequency.

The major advantages for the subscriber in using Touch-Tone signaling over dial pulsing is speed and control. With Touch-Tone signaling, all digits (and thus telephone numbers) take the same length of time to produce and transmit. Touch-Tone signaling also eliminates the impulse noise produced from the mechanical switches necessary to produce dial pulses. Probably the most important advantage of DTMF over dial pulsing is the way in which the telephone company processes them. Dial pulses cannot pass through a central office exchange (local switching machine), whereas DTMF tones will pass through an exchange to the switching system attached to the called number.

Table 8-3 lists the specifications for DTME. The transmit specifications are at the subscriber's location, and the receive specifications are at the local switch. Minimum power levels are given for a single frequency, and maximum power levels are given for two tones. The minimum duration is the minimum time two tones from a given digit must remain on. The interdigit time specifies the minimum and maximum time between the transmissions of any two successive digits. An echo occurs when a pair of tones is not totally absorbed by the local switch and a portion of the power is returned to the subscriber. The maximum power level of an echo is 10 dB below the level transmitted by the subscriber and must be delayed less than 20 ms.

8-5-3 Multifrequency

Multifrequency tones (codes) are similar to DTMF signals in that they involve the simultaneous transmission of two tones. MF tones are used to transfer digits and control signals between switching machines, whereas DTMF signals are used to transfer digits and control signals between telephone sets and local switching machines. MF tones are combinations of two frequencies that fall within the normal speech bandwidth so that they can be propagated over the same circuits as voice. This is called *in-band signaling*. In-band signaling is rapidly being replaced by *out-of-band signaling,* which is discussed in Chapter 17.

MF codes are used to send information between the control equipment that sets up connections through a switch when more than one switch is involved in completing a call. MF codes are also used to transmit the calling and called numbers from the originating telephone office to the destination telephone office. The calling number is sent first, followed by the called number.

Table 8-4 lists the two-tone MF combinations and the digits or control information they represent. As the table shows, MF tones involve the transmission of two-of-six possi-

Table 8-4 Multifrequency Codes

Frequencies (Hz)	Digit or Control
700 + 900	1
700 + 1100	2
700 + 1300	4
700 + 1500	7
900 + 1100	3
900 + 1300	5
900 + 1500	8
1100 + 1300	6
1100 + 1500	9
1100 + 1700	Key pulse (KP)
1300 + 1500	0
1500 + 1700	Start (ST)
2600 Hz	IDLE

FIGURE 8-7 Dial pulsing sequence

ble frequencies representing the 10 digits plus two control signals. The six frequencies are 700 Hz, 900 Hz, 1100 Hz, 1300 Hz, 1500 Hz, and 1700 Hz. Digits are transmitted at a rate of seven per second, and each digit is transmitted as a 68-ms burst. The *key pulse* (KP) signal is a multifrequency control tone comprised of 1100 Hz plus 1700 Hz, ranging from 90 ms to 120 ms. The KP signal is used to indicate the beginning of a sequence of MF digits. The *start* (ST) signal is a multifrequency control tone used to indicate the end of a sequence of dialed digits. From the perspective of the telephone circuit, the ST control signal indicates the beginning of the processing of the signal. The IDLE signal is a 2600-Hz single-frequency tone placed on a circuit to indicate the circuit is not currently in use. For example, KP 3 1 5 7 3 6 1 0 5 3 ST is the sequence transmitted for the telephone number 315-736-1053.

8-5-4 Dial Pulses

Dial pulsing (sometimes called *rotary dial pulsing*) is the method originally used to transfer digits from a telephone set to the local switch. Pulsing digits from a rotary switch began soon after the invention of the automatic switching machine. The concept of dial pulsing is quite simple and is depicted in Figure 8-7. The process begins when the telephone set is lifted off hook, completing a path for current through the local loop. When the switching machine detects the off-hook condition, it responds with dial tone. After hearing the dial tone, the subscriber begins dial pulsing digits by rotating a mechanical dialing mechanism and then letting it return to its rest position. As the rotary switch returns to its rest position, it outputs a series of dial pulses corresponding to the digit dialed.

When a digit is dialed, the loop circuit alternately opens (breaks) and closes (makes) a prescribed number of times. The number of switch make/break sequences corresponds to the digit dialed (i.e., the digit 3 produces three switch openings and three switch closures). Dial pulses occur at 10 make/break cycles per second (i.e., a period of 100 ms per pulse cycle). For example, the digit 5 corresponds to five make/break cycles lasting a total of 500 ms. The switching machine senses and counts the number of make/break pairs in the sequence. The break time is nominally 61 ms, and the make time is nominally 39 ms. Digits are separated by an idle period of 300 ms called the *interdigit time*. It is essential that the switching machine recognize the interdigit time so that it can separate the pulses from successive digits. The central office switch incorporates a special *time-out circuit* to ensure that the break part of the dialing pulse is not misinterpreted as the phone being returned to its on-hook (idle) condition.

All digits do not take the same length of time to dial. For example, the digit 1 requires only one make/break cycle, whereas the digit 0 requires 10 cycles. Therefore, all telephone numbers do not require the same amount of time to dial or to transmit. The minimum time to dial pulse out the seven-digit telephone number 987-1234 is as follows:

digit	9	ID	8	ID	7	ID	1	ID	2	ID	3	ID	4
time (ms)	900	300	800	300	700	300	100	300	200	300	300	300	400

where ID is the interdigit time (300 ms) and the total minimum time is 5200 ms, or 5.2 seconds.

8-5-5 Station Busy

In telephone terminology, a *station* is a telephone set. A *station busy signal* is sent from the switching machine back to the calling station whenever the called telephone number is off hook (i.e., the station is in use). The station busy signal is a two-tone signal comprised of 480 Hz and 620 Hz. The two tones are on for 0.5 seconds, then off for 0.5 seconds. Thus, a busy signal repeats at a 60-pulse-per-minute (ppm) rate.

8-5-6 Equipment Busy

The *equipment busy signal* is sometimes called a *congestion tone* or a *no-circuits-available tone*. The equipment busy signal is sent from the switching machine back to the calling station whenever the system cannot complete the call because of equipment unavailability (i.e., all the circuits, switches, or switching paths are already in use). This condition is called *blocking* and occurs whenever the system is overloaded and more calls are being placed than can be completed. The equipment busy signal uses the same two frequencies as the station busy signal, except the equipment busy signal is on for 0.2 seconds and off for 0.3 seconds (120 ppm). Because an equipment busy signal repeats at twice the rate as a station busy signal, an equipment busy is sometimes called a *fast busy,* and a station busy is sometimes called a *slow busy.* The telephone company refers to an equipment busy condition as a *can't complete.*

8-5-7 Ringing

The *ringing signal* is sent from a central office to a subscriber whenever there is an incoming call. The purpose of the ringing signal is to ring the bell in the telephone set to alert the subscriber that there is an incoming call. If there is no bell in the telephone set, the ringing signal is used to trigger another audible mechanism, which is usually a tone oscillator circuit. The ringing signal is nominally a 20-Hz, 90-Vrms signal that is on for 2 seconds and then off for 4 seconds. The ringing signal should not be confused with the actual ringing sound the bell makes. The audible ring produced by the bell was originally made as annoying as possible so that the called end would answer the telephone as soon as possible, thus tying up common usage telephone equipment in the central office for the minimum length of time.

8-5-8 Ring-Back

The *ring-back signal* is sent back to the calling party at the same time the ringing signal is sent to the called party. However, the ring and ring-back signals are two distinctively different signals. The purpose of the ring-back signal is to give some assurance to the calling party that the destination telephone number has been accepted, processed, and is being rung. The ring-back signal is an audible combination of two tones at 440 Hz and 480 Hz that are on for 2 seconds and then off for 4 seconds.

8-5-9 Receiver On/Off Hook

When a telephone is *on hook,* it is not being used, and the circuit is in the *idle* (or *open*) *state.* The term *on hook* was derived in the early days of telephone when the telephone handset was literally placed on a hook (the hook eventually evolved into a cradle). When the telephone set is on hook, the local loop is open, and there is no current flowing on the loop. An on-hook signal is also used to terminate a call and initiate a disconnect.

When the telephone set is taken *off hook,* a switch closes in the telephone that completes a dc path between the two wires of the local loop. The switch closure causes a dc current to flow on the loop (nominally between 20 mA and 80 mA, depending on loop length and wire gauge). The switching machine in the central office detects the dc current and recognizes it as a receiver off-hook condition (sometimes called a *seizure* or *request for service*). The receiver off-hook condition is the first step to completing a telephone call. The switching machine will respond to the off-hook condition by placing an audible dial tone on the loop. The off-hook signal is also used at the destination end as an *answer signal* to indicate that the called party has answered the telephone. This is sometimes referred to as a *ring trip* because when the switching machine detects the off-hook condition, it removes (or trips) the ringing signal.

8-5-10 Other Nonessential Signaling and Call Progress Tones

There are numerous additional signals relating to initiating, establishing, completing, and terminating a telephone call that are nonessential, such as *call waiting tones, caller waiting tones, calling card service tones, comfort tones, hold tones, intrusion tones, stutter dial tone* (for voice mail), and *receiver off-hook tones* (also called *howler tones*).

8-6 CORDLESS TELEPHONES

Cordless telephones are simply telephones that operate without cords attached to the handset. Cordless telephones originated around 1980 and were quite primitive by today's standards. They originally occupied a narrow band of frequencies near 1.7 MHz, just above the AM broadcast band, and used the 117-vac, 60-Hz household power line for an antenna. These early units used frequency modulation (FM) and were poor quality and susceptible to interference from fluorescent lights and automobile ignition systems. In 1984, the FCC reallocated cordless telephone service to the 46-MHz to 49-MHz band. In 1990, the FCC extended cordless telephone service to the 902-MHz to 928-MHz band, which appreciated a superior signal-to-noise ratio. Cordless telephone sets transmit and receive over narrowband FM (NBFM) channels spaced 30 kHz to 100 kHz apart, depending on the modulation and frequency band used. In 1998, the FCC expanded service again to the 2.4-GHz band. Adaptive differential pulse code modulation and spread spectrum technology (SST) are used exclusively in the 2.4-GHz band, while FM and SST digital modulation are used in the 902-MHz to 928-MHz band. Digitally modulated SST telephones offer higher quality and more security than FM telephones.

In essence, a cordless telephone is a full-duplex, battery-operated, portable radio transceiver that communicates directly with a stationary transceiver located somewhere in

FIGURE 8-8   Cordless telephone system

the subscriber's home or office. The basic layout for a cordless telephone is shown in Figure 8-8. The base station is an ac-powered stationary radio transceiver (transmitter and receiver) connected to the local loop through a cord and telephone company interface unit. The interface unit functions in much the same way as a standard telephone set in that its primary function is to interface the cordless telephone with the local loop while being transparent to the user. Therefore, the base station is capable of transmitting and receiving both supervisory and voice signals over the subscriber loop in the same manner as a standard telephone. The base station must also be capable of relaying voice and control signals to and from the portable telephone set through the wireless transceiver. In essence, the portable telephone set is a battery-powered, two-way radio capable of operating in the full-duplex mode.

Because a portable telephone must be capable of communicating with the base station in the full-duplex mode, it must transmit and receive at different frequencies. In 1984, the FCC allocated 10 full-duplex channels for 46-MHz to 49-MHz units. In 1995 to help relieve congestion, the FCC added 15 additional full-duplex channels and extended the frequency band to include frequencies in the 43-MHz to 44-MHz band. Base stations transmit on high-band frequencies and receive on low-band frequencies, while the portable unit transmits on low-band frequencies and receives on high-band frequencies. The frequency assignments are listed in Table 8-5. Channels 16 through 25 are the original 10 full-duplex carrier frequencies. The maximum transmit power for both the portable unit and the base station is 500 mW. This stipulation limits the useful range of a cordless telephone to within 100 feet or less of the base station.

Table 8-5   43-MHz- to 49-MHz-Band Cordless Telephone Frequencies

	Portable Unit	
Channel	Transmit Frequency (MHz)	Receive Frequency (MHz)
1	43.720	48.760
2	43.740	48.840
3	43.820	48.860
4	43.840	48.920
5	43.920	49.920
6	43.960	49.080
7	44.120	49.100
8	44.160	49.160
9	44.180	49.200
10	44.200	49.240
11	44.320	49.280
12	44.360	49.360
13	44.400	49.400
14	44.460	49.460
15	44.480	49.500
16	46.610	49.670
17	46.630	49.845
18	46.670	49.860
19	46.710	49.770
20	46.730	49.875
21	46.770	49.830
22	46.830	49.890
23	46.870	49.930
24	46.930	49.970
25	46.970	49.990

Note. Base stations transmit on the 49-MHz band and receive on the 46-MHz band.

Cordless telephones using the 2.4-GHz band offer excellent sound quality utilizing digital modulation and twin-band transmission to extend their range. With twin-band transmission, base stations transmit in the 2.4-GHz band, while portable units transmit in the 902-MHz to 928-MHz band.

8-7   CALLER ID

Caller ID (identification) is a service originally envisioned by AT&T in the early 1970s, although local telephone companies have only recently offered it. The basic concept of caller ID is quite simple. Caller ID enables the destination station of a telephone call to display the name and telephone number of the calling party before the telephone is answered (i.e., while the telephone is ringing). This allows subscribers to screen incoming calls and decide whether they want to answer the telephone.

The caller ID message is a simplex transmission sent from the central office switch over the local loop to a caller ID display unit at the destination station (no response is provided). The caller ID information is transmitted and received using Bell System 202-compatible modems (ITU V.23 standard). This standard specifies a 1200-bps FSK (frequency shift keying) signal with a 1200-Hz mark frequency (f_m) and a 2200-Hz space frequency (f_m). The FSK signal is transmitted in a burst between the first and second 20-Hz, 90-Vrms ringing signals, as shown in Figure 8-9a. Therefore, to ensure detection of the caller ID signal, the telephone must ring at least twice before being answering. The caller ID signal does not begin until 500 ms after the end of the first ring and must end 500 ms before the beginning of the second ring. Therefore, the caller ID signal has a 3-second window in which it must be transmitted.

(a)

	Caller ID Signal					
Channel Seizure 200 ms Alternating 1/0 Sequence (55H or AAH)	Conditioning Signal 130 ms all 1s	Message Type 8.33 ms	Message Length 8.33 ms	Caller ID Data Field	Check Sum 6.67 ms
240 bits	156 bits	10 bits (8 data bits, one start bit, and one stop bit)	10 bits	Variable length	8 bits

Variable Length

66.7 ms

Month 10 bits	Month 10 bits	Day 10 bits	Day 10 bits	Hour 10 bits	Hour 10 bits	Minute 10 bits	Minute 10 bits	Caller's Name and Telephone Number

(8 ASCII data bits, one start bit, and one stop bit) — (ASCII characters)

(b)

FIGURE 8-9   Caller ID: (a) ringing cycle; (b) frame format

The format for a caller ID signal is shown in Figure 8-9b. The 500-ms delay after the first ringing signal is immediately followed by the *channel seizure field,* which is a 200-ms-long sequence of alternating logic 1s and logic 0s (240 bits comprised of 120 pairs of alternating 1/0 bits, either 55 hex or AA hex). A *conditioning signal field* immediately follows the channel seizure field. The conditioning signal is a continuous 1200-Hz tone lasting for 130 ms, which equates to 156 consecutive logic 1 bits.

The protocol used for the next three fields—*message type field, message length field,* and *caller ID data field*—specifies asynchronous transmission of 16-bit characters (without parity) framed by one start bit (logic 0) and one stop bit (logic 1) for a total of 10 bits per character. The message type field is comprised of a 16-bit hex code, indicating the type of service and capability of the data message. There is only one message type field currently used with caller ID (04 hex). The message type field is followed by a 16-bit message length field, which specifies the total number of characters (in binary) included in the caller ID data field. For example, a message length code of 15 hex (0001 0101) equates to the number 21 in decimal. Therefore, a message length code of 15 hex specifies 21 characters in the caller ID data field.

The caller ID data field uses extended ASCII coded characters to represent a month code (01 through 12), a two-character day code (01 through 31), a two-character hour code in local military time (00 through 23), a two-character minute code (00 through 59), and a variable-length code, representing the caller's name and telephone number. ASCII coded digits are comprised of two independent hex characters (eight bits each). The first hex character is always 3 (0011 binary), and the second hex character represents a digit between 0 and 9 (0000 to 1001 binary). For example, 30 hex (0011 0000 binary) equates to the digit 0, 31 hex (0011 0001 binary) equates to the digit 1, 39 hex (0011 1001) equates to the digit

9, and so on. The caller ID data field is followed by a checksum for error detection, which is the 2's complement of the module 256 sum of the other words in the data message (message type, message length, and data words).

Example 8-1

Interpret the following hex code for a caller ID message (start and stop bits are not included in the hex codes):

04 12 31 31 32 37 31 35 35 37 33 31 35 37 33 36 31 30 35 33 xx

Solution 04—message type word
12—18 decimal (18 characters in the caller ID data field)
31, 31—ASCII code for 11 (the month of November)
32, 37—ASCII code for 27 (the 27th day of the month)
31, 35—ASCII code for 15 (the 15th hour—3:00 P.M.)
35, 37—ASCII code for 57 (57 minutes after the hour—3:57 P.M.)
33, 31, 35, 37, 33, 36, 31, 30, 35, 33—10-digit ASCII-coded telephone number
(315 736–1053)

xx—checksum (00 hex to FF hex)

8-8 ELECTRONIC TELEPHONES

Although 500- and 2500-type telephone sets still work with the public telephone network, they are becoming increasingly more difficult to find. Most modern-day telephones have replaced many of the mechanical functions performed in the old telephone sets with electronic circuits. Electronic telephones use integrated-circuit technology to perform many of the basic telephone functions as well as a myriad of new and, and in many cases, nonessential functions. The refinement of microprocessors has also led to the development of multiple-line, full-feature telephones that permit automatic control of the telephone set's features, including telephone number storage, automatic dialing, redialing, and caller ID. However, no matter how many new gadgets are included in the new telephone sets, they still have to interface with the telephone network in much the same manner as telephones did a century ago.

Figure 8-10 shows the block diagram for a typical electronic telephone comprised of one multifunctional integrated-circuit chip, a microprocessor chip, a Touch-Tone keypad, a speaker, a microphone, and a handful of discrete devices. The major components included in the multifunctional integrated circuit chip are DTMF tone generator, MPU (microprocessor unit) interface circuitry, random access memory (RAM), tone ringer circuit, speech network, and a line voltage regulator.

The Touch-Tone keyboard provides a means for the operator of the telephone to access the DTMF tone generator inside the multifunction integrated-circuit chip. The external crystal provides a stable and accurate frequency reference for producing the dual-tone multifrequency signaling tones.

The tone ringer circuit is activated by the reception of a 20-Hz ringing signal. Once the ringing signal is detected, the tone ringer drives a piezoelectric sound element that produces an electronic ring (without a bell).

The voltage regulator converts the dc voltage received from the local loop and converts it to a constant-level dc supply voltage to operate the electronic components in the telephone. The internal speech network contains several amplifiers and associated components that perform the same functions as the hybrid did in a standard telephone.

The microprocessor interface circuit interfaces the MPU to the multifunction chip. The MPU, with its internal RAM, controls many of the functions of the telephone, such as

FIGURE 8-10 Electronic telephone set

number storage, speed dialing, redialing, and autodialing. The bridge rectifier protects the telephone from the relatively high-voltage ac ringing signal, and the switch hook is a mechanical switch that performs the same functions as the switch hook on a standard telephone set.

8-9 PAGING SYSTEMS

Most *paging system*s are simplex wireless communications system designed to alert subscribers of awaiting messages. Paging transmitters relay radio signals and messages from wire-line and cellular telephones to subscribers carrying portable receivers. The simplified block diagram of a paging system is shown in Figure 8-11. The infrastructure used with paging systems is somewhat different than the one used for cellular telephone system. This is because standard paging systems are one way, with signals transmitted from the paging system to portable pager and never in the reverse direction. There are narrow-, mid-, and wide-area pagers (sometimes called local, regional, and national). Narrow-area paging systems operate only within a building or building complex, mid-area pagers cover an area of several square miles, and wide-area pagers operate worldwide. Most pagers are mid-area where one centrally located high-power transmitter can cover a relatively large geographic area, typically between 6 and 10 miles in diameter.

To contact a person carrying a pager, simply dial the telephone number assigned that person's portable pager. The paging company receives the call and responds with a query requesting the telephone number you wish the paged person to call. After the number is entered, a *terminating signal* is appended to the number, which is usually the # sign. The caller then hangs up. The paging system converts the telephone number to a digital code and transmits it in the form of a digitally encoded signal over a wireless communications system. The signal may be simultaneously sent from more than one radio transmitter (sometimes called *simulcasting* or *broadcasting*), as is necessary in a wide-area paging system. If the paged person is within range of a broadcast transmitter, the targeted pager will receive the message. The message includes a notification signal, which either produces an audible beep or causes the pager to vibrate and the number the paged unit should call shown on an alphanumeric display. Some newer paging units are also capable of displaying messages as well as the telephone number of the paging party.

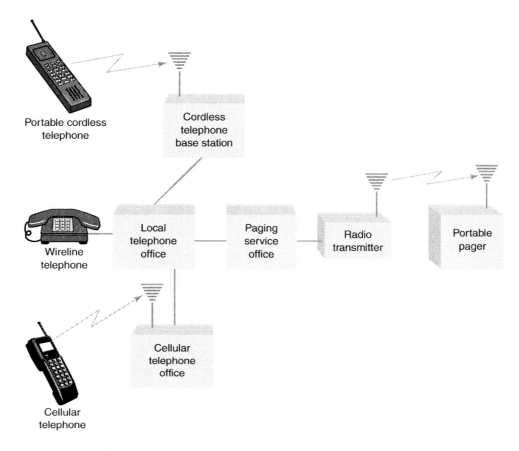

FIGURE 8-11   Simplified block diagram of a standard simplex paging system

Early paging systems used FM; however, most modern paging systems use FSK or PSK. Pagers typically transmit bit rates between 200 bps and 6400 bps with the following carrier frequency bands: 138 MHz to 175 MHz, 267 MHz to 284 MHz, 310 MHz to 330 MHz, 420 MHz to 470 MHz, and several frequency slots within the 900-MHz band.

Each portable pager is assigned a special code, called a *cap code,* which includes a sequence of digits or a combination of digits and letters. The cap code is broadcasted along with the paging party's telephone number. If the portable paging unit is within range of the broadcasting transmitter, it will receive the signal, demodulate it, and recognize its cap code. Once the portable pager recognizes its code, the callback number and perhaps a message will be displayed on the unit. Alphanumeric messages are generally limited to between 20 and 40 characters in length.

Early paging systems, such as one developed by the British Post Office called Post Office Code Standardization Advisory Group (POCSAG), transmitted a two-level FSK signal. POCSAG used an asynchronous protocol, which required a long preamble for synchronization. The preamble begins with a long *dotting sequence* (sometimes called a *dotting comma*) to establish clock synchronization. Data rates for POCSAG are 512 bps, 1200 bps, and 2400 bps. With POCSAG, portable pagers must operate in the *always-on mode* all the time, which means the pager wastes much of its power resources on nondata preamble bits.

In the early 1980s, the European Telecommunications Standards Institute (ETSI) developed the ERMES protocol. ERMES transmitted data at a 6250 bps rate using four-level FSK (3125 baud). ERMES is a synchronous protocol, which requires less time to synchronize. ERMES supports 16 25-kHz paging channels in each of its frequency bands.

The most recent paging protocol, FLEX, was developed in the 1990s. FLEX is designed to minimize power consumption in the portable pager by using a synchronous time-slotted protocol to transmit messages in precise time slots. With FLEX, each frame is comprised of 128 data frames, which are transmitted only once during a 4-minute period. Each frame lasts for 1.875 seconds and includes two synchronizing sequences, a header containing frame information and pager identification addresses, and 11 discrete data blocks. Each portable pager is assigned a specific frame (called a *home frame*) within the frame cycle that it checks for transmitted messages. Thus, a pager operates in the high-power standby condition for only a few seconds every 4 minutes (this is called the *wakeup time*). The rest of the time, the pager is in an ultra-low power standby condition. When a pager is in the wakeup mode, it synchronizes to the frame header and then adjusts itself to the bit rate of the received signal. When the pager determines that there is no message waiting, it puts itself back to sleep, leaving only the timer circuit active.

QUESTIONS

8-1. Define the terms *communications* and *telecommunications*.

8-2. Define *plain old telephone service*.

8-3. Describe a *local subscriber loop*.

8-4. Where in a telephone system is the *local loop?*

8-5. Briefly describe the basic functions of a standard *telephone set*.

8-6. What is the purpose of the *RJ-11 connector?*

8-7. What is meant by the terms *tip* and *ring?*

8-8. List and briefly describe the essential components of a standard telephone set.

8-9. Briefly describe the steps involved in completing a local telephone call.

8-10. Explain the basic purpose of *call progress tones* and *signals*.

8-11. List and describe the two primary categories of *signaling*.

8-12. Describe the following signaling messages: *alerting, supervising, controlling,* and *addressing*.

8-13. What is the purpose of *dial tone,* and when is it applied to a telephone circuit?

8-14. Briefly describe *dual-tone multifrequency* and *multifrequency* signaling and tell where they are used.

8-15. Describe *dial pulsing*.

8-16. What is the difference between a *station busy* signal and an *equipment busy* signal?

8-17. What is the difference between a *ringing* and a *ring-back* signal?

8-18. Briefly describe what happens when a telephone set is taken *off hook*.

8-19. Describe the differences between the operation of a *cordless telephone* and a *standard telephone*.

8-20. Explain how *caller ID* operates and when it is used.

8-21. Briefly describe how a paging system operates.

C H A P T E R 9

The Telephone Circuit

OBJECTIVES

- Define *telephone circuit, message,* and *message channel*
- Describe the transmission characteristics a local subscriber loop
- Describe loading coils and bridge taps
- Describe loop resistance and how it is calculated
- Explain telephone message–channel noise and C-message noise weighting
- Describe the following units of power measurement: db, dBm, dBmO, rn, dBrn, dBrnc, dBrn 3-kHz flat, and dBrncO
- Define *psophometric noise weighting*
- Define and describe transmission parameters
- Define *private-line circuit*
- Explain bandwidth, interface, and facilities parameters
- Define *line conditioning* and describe C- and D-type conditioning
- Describe two-wire and four-wire circuit arrangements
- Explain hybrids, echo suppressors, and echo cancelers
- Define *crosstalk*
- Describe nonlinear, transmittance, and coupling crosstalk

A *telephone circuit* is comprised of two or more facilities, interconnected in tandem, to provide a transmission path between a source and a destination. The interconnected facilities may be temporary, as in a standard telephone call, or permanent, as in a dedicated private-line telephone circuit. The facilities may be metallic cable pairs, optical fibers, or wireless carrier systems. The information transferred is called the *message,* and the circuit used is called the *message channel.*

Telephone companies offer a wide assortment of message channels ranging from a basic 4-kHz voice-band circuit to wideband microwave, satellite, or optical fiber transmission systems capable of transferring high-resolution video or wideband data. The following discussion is limited to basic voice-band circuits. In telephone terminology, the word *message* originally denoted speech information. However, this definition has been extended to include any signal that occupies the same bandwidth as a standard voice channel. Thus, a message channel may include the transmission of ordinary speech, supervisory signals, or data in the form of digitally modulated carriers (FSK, PSK, QAM, and so on). The network bandwidth for a standard voice-band message channel is 4 kHz; however, a portion of that bandwidth is used for *guard bands* and signaling. Guard bands are unused frequency bands located between information signals. Consequently, the effective channel bandwidth for a voice-band message signal (whether it be voice or data) is approximately 300 Hz to 3000 Hz.

9-2   THE LOCAL SUBSCRIBER LOOP

The *local subscriber loop* is the only facility required by all voice-band circuits, as it is the means by which subscriber locations are connected to the local telephone company. In essence, the sole purpose of a local loop is to provide subscribers access to the public telephone network. The local loop is a metallic transmission line comprised of two insulated copper wires (a pair) twisted together. The local loop is the primary cause of *attenuation* and *phase distortion* on a telephone circuit. Attenuation is an actual loss of signal strength, and phase distortion occurs when two or more frequencies undergo different amounts of phase shift.

The *transmission characteristics* of a cable pair depend on the wire diameter, conductor spacing, dielectric constant of the insulator separating the wires, and the conductivity of the wire. These physical properties, in turn, determine the inductance, resistance, capacitance, and conductance of the cable. The resistance and inductance are distributed along the length of the wire, whereas the conductance and capacitance exist between the two wires. When the insulation is sufficient, the effects of conductance are generally negligible. Figure 9-1a shows the electrical model for a copper-wire transmission line.

The electrical characteristics of a cable (such as inductance, capacitance, and resistance) are uniformly distributed along its length and are appropriately referred to as *distributed parameters.* Because it is cumbersome working with distributed parameters, it is common practice to lump them into discrete values per unit length (i.e., millihenrys per mile, microfarads per kilometer, or ohms per 1000 feet). The amount of attenuation and phase delay experienced by a signal propagating down a metallic transmission line is a function of the frequency of the signal and the electrical characteristics of the cable pair.

There are seven main component parts that make up a traditional local loop:

Feeder cable (F1). The largest cable used in a local loop, usually 3600 pair of copper wire placed underground or in conduit.

Serving area interface (SAI). A cross-connect point used to distribute the larger feeder cable into smaller distribution cables.

C = capacitance – two conductors separated
     by an insulator
R = resistance – opposition to current flow
L = self inductance
1/G = leakage resistance of dielectric
R_s = shunt leakage resistance

(a)

(b)

FIGURE 9-1 (a) Electrical model of a copper-wire transmission
line, (b) frequency-versus-attenuation characteristics for unloaded
and loaded cables

Distribution cable (F2). A smaller version of a feeder cable containing less wire pairs.

Subscriber or standard network interface (SNI). A device that serves as the demarcation point between local telephone company responsibility and subscriber responsibility for telephone service.

Drop wire. The final length of cable pair that terminates at the SNI.

Aerial. That portion of the local loop that is strung between poles.

Distribution cable and drop-wire cross-connect point. The location where individual cable pairs within a distribution cable are separated and extended to the subscriber's location on a drop wire.

Two components often found on local loops are loading coils and bridge taps.

9-2-1 Loading Coils

Figure 9-1b shows the effect of frequency on attenuation for a 12,000-foot length of 26-gauge copper cable. As the figure shows, a 3000-Hz signal experiences 6 dB more attenuation than a 500-Hz signal on the same cable. In essence, the cable acts like a low-pass filter. Extensive studies of attenuation on cable pairs have shown that a substantial reduction in attenuation is achieved by increasing the inductance value of the cable. Minimum attenuation requires a value of inductance nearly 100 times the value obtained in ordinary twisted-wire cable. Achieving such values on a uniformly distributed basis is impractical. Instead, the desired effect can be obtained by adding inductors periodically in series with the wire. This practice is called *loading,* and the inductors are called *loading coils.* Loading coils placed in a cable decrease the attenuation, increase the line impedance, and improve transmission levels for circuits longer than 18,000 feet. Loading coils allowed local loops to extend three to four times their previous length. A loading coil is simply a passive conductor wrapped around a core and placed in series with a cable creating a small electromagnet. Loading coils can be placed on telephone poles, in manholes, or on cross-connect boxes. Loading coils increase the effective distance that a signal must travel between two locations and cancels the capacitance that inherently builds up between wires with distance. Loading coils first came into use in 1900.

Loaded cables are specified by the addition of the letter codes A, B, C, D, E, F, H, X, or Y, which designate the distance between loading coils and by numbers, which indicate the inductance value of the wire gauge. The letters indicate that loading coils are separated by 700, 3000, 929, 4500, 5575, 2787, 6000, 680, or 2130 feet, respectively. B-, D-, and H-type loading coils are the most common because their separations are representative of the distances between manholes. The amount of series inductance added is generally 44 mH, 88 mH, or 135 mH. Thus, a cable pair designated 26H88 is made from 26-gauge wire with 88 mH of series inductance added every 6000 feet. The loss-versus-frequency characteristics for a loaded cable are relatively flat up to approximately 2000 Hz, as shown in Figure 9-1b. From the figure, it can be seen that a 3000-Hz signal will suffer only 1.5 dB more loss than a 500-Hz signal on 26-gauge wire when 88-mH loading coils are spaced every 6000 feet.

Loading coils cause a sharp drop in frequency response at approximately 3400 Hz, which is undesirable for high-speed data transmission. Therefore, for high-performance data transmission, loading coils should be removed from the cables. The low-pass characteristics of a cable also affect the phase distortion-versus-frequency characteristics of a signal. The amount of *phase distortion* is proportional to the length and gauge of the wire. Loading a cable also affects the phase characteristics of a cable. The telephone company must often add gain and delay equalizers to a circuit to achieve the minimum requirements. Equalizers introduce discontinuities or ripples in the bandpass characteristics of a circuit. Automatic equalizers in data modems are sensitive to this condition, and very often an overequalized circuit causes as many problems to a data signal as an underequalized circuit.

9-2-2 Bridge Taps

A *bridge tap* is an irregularity frequently found in cables serving subscriber locations. Bridge taps are unused sections of cable that are connected in shunt to a working cable pair, such as a local loop. Bridge taps can be placed at any point along a cable's length. Bridge taps were used for party lines to connect more than one subscriber to the same local loop. Bridge taps also increase the flexibility of a local loop by allowing the cable to go to more than one junction box, although it is unlikely that more than one of the cable pairs leaving a bridging point will be used at any given time. Bridge taps may or may not be used at some future time, depending on service demands. Bridge taps increase the flexibility of a cable by making it easier to reassign a cable to a different subscriber without requiring a person working in the field to cross connect sections of cable.

Bridge taps introduce a loss called *bridging loss.* They also allow signals to split and propagate down more than one wire. Signals that propagate down unterminated (open-circuited) cables reflect back from the open end of the cable, often causing interference with the original signal. Bridge taps that are short and closer to the originating or terminating ends often produce the most interference.

Bridge taps and loading coils are not generally harmful to voice transmissions, but if improperly used, they can literally destroy the integrity of a data signal. Therefore, bridge taps and loading coils should be removed from a cable pair that is used for data transmission. This can be a problem because it is sometimes difficult to locate a bridge tap. It is estimated that the average local loop can have as many as 16 bridge taps.

9-2-3 Loop Resistance

The dc resistance of a local loop depends primarily on the type of wire and wire size. Most local loops use 18- to 26-gauge, twisted-pair copper wire. The lower the wire gauge, the larger the diameter, the less resistance, and the lower the attenuation. For example, 26-gauge unloaded copper wire has an attenuation of 2.67 dB per mile, whereas the same length of 19-gauge copper wire has only 1.12 dB per mile. Therefore, the maximum length of a local loop using 19-gauge wire is twice as long as a local loop using 26-gauge wire.

The total attenuation of a local loop is generally limited to a maximum value of 7.5 dB with a maximum dc resistance of 1300 Ω, which includes the resistance of the telephone (approximately 120 Ω). The dc resistance of 26-gauge copper wire is approximately 41 Ω per 1000 feet, which limits the round-trip loop length to approximately 5.6 miles. The maximum distance for lower-gauge wire is longer of course.

The dc loop resistance for copper conductors is approximated by

$$R_{dc} = \frac{0.1095}{d^2}$$

(9-1)

where R_{dc} = dc loop resistance (ohms per mile)
    d = wire diameter (inches)

9-3 TELEPHONE MESSAGE–CHANNEL NOISE AND NOISE WEIGHTING

The *noise* that reaches a listener's ears affects the degree of annoyance to the listener and, to some extent, the intelligibility of the received speech. The total noise is comprised of room *background noise* and noise introduced in the circuit. Room background noise on the listening subscriber's premises reaches the ear directly through leakage around the receiver and indirectly by way of the sidetone path through the telephone set. Room noise from the talking subscriber's premises also reaches the listener over the communications channel. Circuit noise is comprised mainly of thermal noise, nonlinear distortion, and impulse noise, which are described in a later section of this chapter.

The measurement of interference (noise), like the measurement of volume, is an effort to characterize a complex signal. Noise measurements on a telephone message channel are characterized by how annoying the noise is to the subscriber rather than by the absolute magnitude of the average noise power. Noise interference is comprised of two components: annoyance and the effect of noise on intelligibility, both of which are functions of frequency. Noise signals with equal interfering effects are assigned equal magnitudes. To accomplish this effect, the American Telephone and Telegraph Company (AT&T) developed a weighting network called *C-message* weighting.

When designing the C-message weighting network, groups of observers were asked to adjust the loudness of 14 different frequencies between 180 Hz and 3500 Hz until the sound of each tone was judged to be equally annoying as a 1000-Hz reference tone in the absence of speech. A 1000-Hz tone was selected for the reference because empirical data indicated that 1000 Hz is the most annoying frequency (i.e., the best frequency response)

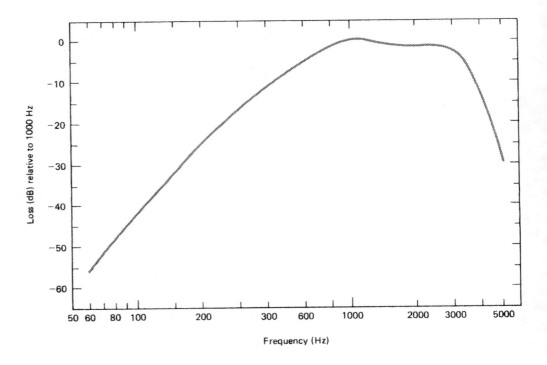

FIGURE 9-2 C-message weighting curve

to humans. The same people were then asked to adjust the amplitude of the tones in the presence of speech until the effect of noise on articulation (annoyance) was equal to that of the 1000-Hz reference tone. The results of the two experiments were combined, smoothed, and plotted, resulting in the C-message weighting curve shown in Figure 9-2. A 500-type telephone set was used for these tests; therefore, the C-message weighting curve includes the frequency response characteristics of a standard telephone set receiver as well as the hearing response of an average listener.

The significance of the C-message weighting curve is best illustrated with an example. From Figure 9-2, it can be seen that a 200-Hz test tone of a given power is 25 dB less disturbing than a 1000-Hz test tone of the same power. Therefore, the C-message weighting network will introduce 25 dB more loss for 200 Hz than it will for 1000 Hz.

When designing the C-message network, it was found that the additive effect of several noise sources combine on a root-sum-square (RSS) basis. From these design considerations, it was determined that a telephone message–channel noise measuring set should be a voltmeter with the following characteristics:

Readings should take into consideration that the interfering effect of noise is a function of frequency as well as magnitude.

When dissimilar noise signals are present simultaneously, the meter should combine them to properly measure the overall interfering effect.

It should have a transient response resembling that of the human ear. For sounds shorter than 200 ms, the human ear does not fully appreciate the true power of the sound. Therefore, noise-measuring sets are designed to give full-power indication only for bursts of noise lasting 200 ms or longer.

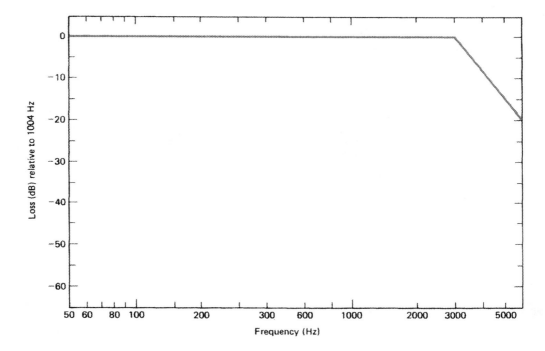

FIGURE 9-3   3-kHz flat response curve

When different types of noise cause equal interference as determined in subjective tests, use of the meter should give equal readings.

The reference established for performing message-channel noise measurements is -90 dBm (10^{-12} watts). The power level of -90 dBm was selected because, at the time, power levels could not measure levels below -90 dBm and, therefore, it would not be necessary to deal with negative values when reading noise levels. Thus, a 1000-Hz tone with a power level of -90 dBm is equal to a noise reading of 0 dBrn. Conversely, a 1000-Hz tone with a power level of 0 dBm is equal to a noise reading of 90 dBrn, and a 1000-Hz tone with a power level of -40 dBm is equal to a noise reading of 50 dBrn.

When appropriate, other weighting networks can be substituted for C-message. For example, a *3-kHz flat* network is used to measure power density of white noise. This network has a nominal low-pass frequency response down 3 dB at 3 kHz and rolls off at 12 dB per octave. A 3-kHz flat network is often used for measuring high levels of low-frequency noise, such as power supply hum. The frequency response for a 3-kHz flat network is shown in Figure 9-3.

9-4   UNITS OF POWER MEASUREMENT

9-4-1   dB and dBm

To specify the amplitudes of signals and interference, it is often convenient to define them at some reference point in the system. The amplitudes at any other physical location can then be related to this reference point if the loss or gain between the two points is known. For example, sea level is generally used as the reference point when comparing elevations. By referencing two mountains to sea level, we can compare the two elevations, regardless of where the mountains are located. A mountain peak in Colorado 12,000 feet above sea level is 4000 feet higher than a mountain peak in France 8000 feet above sea level.

The decibel (dB) is the basic yardstick used for making power measurements in communications. The unit dB is simply a logarithmic expression representing the ratio of one power level to another and expressed mathematically as

$$dB = 10 \log\left(\frac{P_1}{P_2}\right) \qquad (9\text{-}2)$$

where P_1 and P_2 are power levels at two different points in a transmission system.

From Equation 9-2, it can be seen when $P_1 = P_2$, the power ratio is 0 dB; when $P_1 > P_2$, the power ratio in dB is positive; and when $P_1 < P_2$, the power ratio in dB is negative. In telephone and telecommunications circuits, power levels are given in dBm and differences between power levels in dB.

Equation 9-2 is essentially dimensionless since neither power is referenced to a base. The unit dBm is often used to reference the power level at a given point to 1 milliwatt. One milliwatt is the level from which all dBm measurements are referenced. The unit dBm is an indirect measure of absolute power and expressed mathematically as

$$dBm = 10 \log\left(\frac{P}{1 \text{ mW}}\right) \qquad (9\text{-}3)$$

where P is the power at any point in a transmission system. From Equation 9-3, it can be seen that a power level of 1 mW equates to 0 dBm, power levels above 1 mW have positive dBm values, and power levels less than 1 mW have negative dBm values.

Example 9-1

Determine
a. The power levels in dBm for signal levels of 10 mW and 0.5 mW.
b. The difference between the two power levels in dB.

Solution   a. The power levels in dBm are determined by substituting into Equation 9-3:

$$dBm = 10 \log\left(\frac{10 \text{ mW}}{1 \text{ mW}}\right) = 10 \text{ dBm}$$

$$dBm = 10 \log\left(\frac{0.5 \text{ mW}}{1 \text{ mW}}\right) = -3 \text{ dBm}$$

b. The difference between the two power levels in dB is determined by substituting into Equation 9-2:

$$dB = 10 \log\left(\frac{10 \text{ mW}}{0.5 \text{ mW}}\right) = 13 \text{ dB}$$

or $10 \text{ dBm} - (-3 \text{ dBm}) = 13 \text{ dB}$

The 10-mW power level is 13 dB higher than a 0.5-mW power level.

Experiments indicate that a listener cannot give a reliable estimate of the loudness of a sound but can distinguish the difference in loudness between two sounds. The ear's sensitivity to a change in sound power follows a logarithmic rather than a linear scale, and the dB has become the unit of this change.

9-4-2   Transmission Level Point, Transmission Level, and Data Level Point

Transmission level point (TLP) is defined as the optimum level of a test tone on a channel at some point in a communications system. The numerical value of the TLP does not describe the total signal power present at that point—it merely defines what the ideal level should be. The *transmission level* (TL) at any point in a transmission system is the ratio in dB of the power of a signal at that point to the power the same signal would be at a 0-dBm transmission level point. For example, a signal at a particular point in a transmission system measures −13 dBm. Is this good or bad? This could be answered only if it is known what the signal strength should be at that point. TLP does just that. The reference for TLP is 0 dBm. A −15-dBm TLP indicates that, at this specific point in the transmission system, the signal should measure −15 dBm. Therefore, the transmission level for a signal that measures −13 dBm at a −15-dBm point is −2 dB. A 0 TLP is a TLP where the signal power should be 0 dBm. TLP says nothing about the actual signal level itself.

Data level point (DLP) is a parameter equivalent to TLP except TLP is used for voice circuits, whereas DLP is used as a reference for data transmission. The DLP is always 13 dB below the voice level for the same point. If the TLP is −15 dBm, the DLP at the same point is −28 dBm. Because a data signal is more sensitive to nonlinear distortion (harmonic and intermodulation distortion), data signals are transmitted at a lower level than voice signals.

9-4-3 Units of Measurement
Common units for signal and noise power measurements in the telephone industry include dBmO, rn, dBrn, dBrnc, dBrn 3-kHz flat, and dBrncO.

9-4-3-1 dBmO. *dBmO* is dBm referenced to a zero transmission level point (0 TLP). dBmO is a power measurement adjusted to 0 dBm that indicates what the power would be if the signal were measured at a 0 TLP. dBmO compares the actual signal level at a point with what that signal level should be at that point. For example, a signal measuring −17 dBm at a −16-dBm transmission level point is −1 dBmO (i.e., the signal is 1 dB below what it should be, or if it were measured at a 0 TLP, it would measure −1 dBm).

9-4-3-2 rn (reference noise). *rn* is the dB value used as the reference for noise readings. Reference noise equals −90 dBm or 1 pW (1×10^{-12} W). This value was selected for two reasons: (1) Early noise measuring sets could not accurately measure noise levels lower than −90 dBm, and (2) noise readings are typically higher than −90 dBm, resulting in positive dB readings in respect to reference noise.

9-4-3-3 dBrn. *dBrn* is the dB level of noise with respect to reference noise (−90 dBm). dBrn is seldom used by itself since it does not specify a weighting. A noise reading of −50 dBm equates to 40 dBrn, which is 40 dB above reference noise (−50 − [− 90]) = 40 dBrn.

9-4-3-4 dBrnc. *dBrnc* is similar to dBrn except dBrnc is the dB value of noise with respect to reference noise using C-message weighting. Noise measurements obtained with a C-message filter are meaningful, as they relate the noise measured to the combined frequency response of a standard telephone and the human ear.

9-4-3-5 dBrn 3-kHz flat. *dBrn 3-kHz flat* noise measurements are noise readings taken with a filter that has a flat frequency response from 30 Hz to 3 kHz. Noise readings taken with a 3-kHz flat filter are especially useful for detecting low-frequency noise, such as power supply hum. dBrn 3-kHz flat readings are typically 1.5 dB higher than dBrnc readings for equal noise power levels.

9-4-3-6 dBrncO. *dBrncO* is the amount of noise in dBrnc corrected to a 0 TLP. A noise reading of 34 dBrnc at a +7-dBm TLP equates to 27 dBrncO. dBrncO relates noise power readings (dBrnc) to a 0 TLP. This unit establishes a common reference point throughout the transmission system.

dBm		dBrnc
0	————————	90
-5	————————	85
-10	————————	80
-15	————————	75
-20	————————	70
-25	————————	65
-30	————————	60
-35	————————	55
-40	————————	50
-45	————————	45
-50	————————	40
-55	————————	35
-60	————————	30
-65	————————	25
-70	————————	20
-75	————————	15
-80	————————	10
-85	————————	5
-90	————————	0

TLP
S (-42 dBm)
(-2 dBmO)

S/N = 32 dB

N (-74 dBm)

S (48 dBrnc)

S/N = 32 dB

N (16 dBrnc)
(16 dB above rn)

Reference noise (rn)

FIGURE 9-4 Figure for Example 9-2

Example 9-2

For a signal measurement of −42 dBm, a noise measurement of 16 dBrnc, and a −40-dBm TLP, determine

a. Signal level in dBrnc.
b. Noise level in dBm.
c. Signal level in dBmO.
d. signal-to-noise ratio in dB. (For the solutions, refer to Figure 9-4.)

Solution a. The signal level in dBrnc can be read directly from the chart shown in Figure 9-4 as 48 dBrnc. The signal level in dBrnc can also be computed mathematically as follows:

$$-42 \text{ dBm} - (-90 \text{ dBrn}) = 48 \text{ dBrnc}$$

b. The noise level in dBm can be read directly from the chart shown in Figure 9-4 as −74 dBm. The noise level in dBm can also be calculated as follows:

$$-90 + 16 = -74 \text{ dBm}$$

c. The signal level in dBmO is simply the difference between the actual signal level in dBm and the TLP or 2 dBmO as shown in Figure 9-4. The signal level in dBmO can also be computed mathematically as follows:

$$-42 \text{ dBm} - (-40 \text{ dBm}) = -2 \text{ dBmO}$$

d. The signal-to-noise ratio is simply the difference in the signal power in dBm and the noise power in dBm or the signal level in dBrnc and the noise power in dBrnc as shown in Figure 9-4 as 32 dB. The signal-to-noise ratio is computed mathematically as

$$-42 \text{ dBm} - (-74 \text{ dBm}) = 32 \text{ dB}$$

or

$$48 \text{ dBrnc} - 16 \text{ dBrnc} = 32 \text{ dB}$$

9-4-4 Psophometric Noise Weighting

Psophometric noise weighting is used primarily in Europe. Psophometric weighting assumes a perfect receiver; therefore, its weighting curve corresponds to the frequency response of the human ear only. The difference between C-message weighting and psophometric weighting is so small that the same conversion factor may be used for both.

9-5 TRANSMISSION PARAMETERS AND PRIVATE-LINE CIRCUITS

Transmission parameters apply to dedicated *private-line data circuits* that utilize the private sector of the public telephone network—circuits with bandwidths comparable to those of standard voice-grade telephone channels that do not utilize the public switched telephone network. Private-line circuits are direct connections between two or more locations. On private-line circuits, transmission facilities and other telephone company–provided equipment are hardwired and available only to a specific subscriber. Most private-line data circuits use four-wire, full-duplex facilities. Signal paths established through switched lines are inconsistent and may differ greatly from one call to another. In addition, telephone lines provided through the public switched telephone network are two wire, which limits high-speed data transmission to half-duplex operation. Private-line data circuits have several advantages over using the switched public telephone network:

Transmission characteristics are more consistent because the same facilities are used with every transmission.

The facilities are less prone to noise produced in telephone company switches.

Line conditioning is available only on private-line facilities.

Higher transmission bit rates and better performance is appreciated with private-line data circuits.

Private-line data circuits are more economical for high-volume circuits.

Transmission parameters are divided into three broad categories: bandwidth parameters, which include attenuation distortion and envelope delay distortion; interface parameters, which include terminal impedance, in-band and out-of-band signal power, test signal power, and ground isolation; and facility parameters, which include noise measurements, frequency distortion, phase distortion, amplitude distortion, and nonlinear distortion.

9-5-1 Bandwidth Parameters

The only transmission parameters with limits specified by the FCC are attenuation distortion and envelope delay distortion. *Attenuation distortion* is the difference in circuit gain experienced at a particular frequency with respect to the circuit gain of a reference frequency. This characteristic is sometimes referred to as *frequency response, differential gain, and 1004-Hz deviation. Envelope delay distortion* is an indirect method of evaluating the phase delay characteristics of a circuit. FCC tariffs specify the limits for attenuation distortion and envelope delay distortion. To reduce attenuation and envelope delay distortion and improve the performance of data modems operating over standard message channels, it is often necessary to improve the quality of the channel. The process used to improve a basic telephone channel is called *line conditioning.* Line conditioning improves the high-frequency response of a message channel and reduces power loss.

The attenuation and delay characteristics of a circuit are artificially altered to meet limits prescribed by the *line conditioning* requirements. Line conditioning is available only to private-line subscribers at an additional charge. The *basic voice-band channel* (sometimes called a *basic 3002 channel*) satisfies the minimum line conditioning requirements. Telephone companies offer two types of special line conditioning for subscriber loops: C-type and D-type.

9-5-1-1 C-type line conditioning. *C-type conditioning* specifies the maximum limits for attenuation distortion and envelope delay distortion. C-type conditioning pertains to line impairments for which compensation can be made with filters and equalizers. This is accomplished with telephone company–provided equipment. When a circuit is initially turned up for service with a specific C-type conditioning, it must meet the requirements for that type of conditioning. The subscriber may include devices within the station equipment that compensate for minor long-term variations in the bandwidth requirements.

There are five classifications or levels of C-type conditioning available. The grade of conditioning a subscriber selects depends on the bit rate, modulation technique, and desired performance of the data modems used on the line. The five classifications of C-type conditioning are the following:

C1 and C2 conditioning pertain to two-point and multipoint circuits.

C3 conditioning is for access lines and trunk circuits associated with private switched networks.

C4 conditioning pertains to two-point and multipoint circuits with a maximum of four stations.

C5 conditioning pertains only to two-point circuits.

Private switched networks are telephone systems provided by local telephone companies dedicated to a single customer, usually with a large number of stations. An example is a large corporation with offices and complexes at two or more geographical locations, sometimes separated by great distances. Each location generally has an on-premise *private branch exchange* (PBX). A PBX is a relatively low-capacity switching machine where the subscribers are generally limited to stations within the same building or building complex. *Common-usage access lines* and *trunk circuits* are required to interconnect two or more PBXs. They are common only to the subscribers of the private network and not to the general public telephone network. Table 9-1 lists the limits prescribed by C-type conditioning for attenuation distortion. As the table shows, the higher the classification of conditioning imposed on a circuit, the flatter the frequency response and, therefore, a better-quality circuit.

Attenuation distortion is simply the frequency response of a transmission medium referenced to a 1004-Hz test tone. The attenuation for voice-band frequencies on a typical cable pair is directly proportional to the square root of the frequency. From Table 9-1, the attenuation distortion limits for a basic (unconditioned) circuit specify the circuit gain at any frequency between 500 Hz and 2500 Hz to be not more than 2 dB more than the circuit gain at 1004 Hz and not more than 3 dB below the circuit gain at 1004 Hz. For attenuation distortion, the circuit gain for 1004 Hz is always the reference. Also, within the frequency bands from 300 Hz and 499 Hz and from 2501 Hz to 3000 Hz, the circuit gain cannot be

Table 9-1 Basic and C-Type Conditioning Requirements

Channel Conditioning	Attenuation Distortion (Frequency Response Relative to 1004 Hz)		Envelope Delay Distortion	
	Frequency Range (Hz)	Variation (dB)	Frequency Range (Hz)	Variation (μs)
Basic	300–499	+3 to −12	800–2600	1750
	500–2500	+2 to −8		
	2501–3000	+3 to −12		
C1	300–999	+2 to −6	800–999	1750
	1000–2400	+1 to −3	1000–2400	1000
	2401–2700	+3 to −6	2401–2600	1750
	2701–3000	+3 to −12		
C2	300–499	+2 to −6	500–600	3000
	500–2800	+1 to −3	601–999	1500
	2801–3000	+2 to −6	1000–2600	500
			2601–2800	3000
C3 (access line)	300–499	+0.8 to −3	500–599	650
	500–2800	+0.5 to −1.5	600–999	300
	2801–3000	+0.8 to −3	1000–2600	110
			2601–2800	650
C3 (trunk)	300–499	+0.8 to −2	500–599	500
	500–2800	+0.5 to −1	600–999	260
	2801–3000	+0.8 to −2	1000–2600	80
			2601–3000	500
C4	300–499	+2 to −6	500–599	3000
	500–3000	+2 to −3	600–799	1500
	3001–3200	+2 to −6	800–999	500
			1000–2600	300
			2601–2800	500
			2801–3000	1500
C5	300–499	+1 to −3	500–599	600
	500–2800	+0.5 to −1.5	600–999	300
	2801–3000	+1 to −3	1000–2600	100
			2601–2800	600

greater than 3 dB above or more than 12 dB below the gain at 1004 Hz. Figure 9-5 shows a graphical presentation of basic line conditioning requirements.

Figure 9-6 shows a graphical presentation of the attenuation distortion requirements specified in Table 9-1 for C2 conditioning, and Figure 9-7 shows the graph for C2 conditioning superimposed over the graph for basic conditioning. From Figure 9-7, it can be seen that the requirements for C2 conditioning are much more stringent than those for a basic circuit.

Example 9-3

A 1004 Hz test tone is transmitted over a telephone circuit at 0 dBm and received at −16 dBm. Determine

a. The 1004-Hz circuit gain.
b. The attenuation distortion requirements for a basic circuit.
c. The attenuation distortion requirements for a C2 conditioned circuit.

Solution a. The circuit gain is determined mathematically as

$$0 \text{ dBm} - (-16 \text{ dB}) = -16 \text{ dB (which equates to a loss of 16 dB)}$$

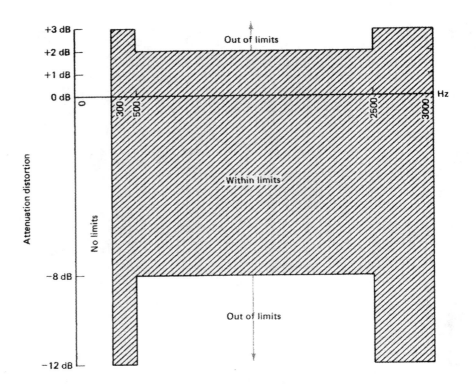

FIGURE 9-5 Graphical presentation of the limits for attenuation distortion for a basic 3002 telephone circuit

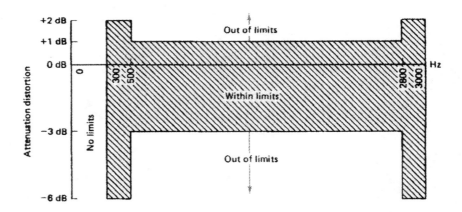

FIGURE 9-6 Graphical presentation of the limits for attenuation distortion for a C2 conditioned telephone circuit

b. Circuit gain requirements for a basic circuit can be determined from Table 9-1:

Frequency Band	Requirements	Minimum Level	Maximum Level
500 Hz and 2500 Hz	+2 dB and −8 dB	−24 dBm	−14 dBm
300 Hz and 499 Hz	+3 dB and −12 dB	−28 dBm	−13 dBm
2501 Hz and 3000 Hz	+3 dB and −12 dB	−28 dBm	−13 dBm

FIGURE 9-7 Overlay of Figure 9-5 over Figure 9-6 to demonstrate the more stringent requirements imposed by C2 conditioning compared to a basic (unconditioned) circuit

c. Circuit gain requirements for a C2 conditioned circuit can be determined from Table 9-1:

Frequency Band	Requirements	Minimum Level	Maximum Level
500 Hz and 2500 Hz	+1 dB and −3 dB	−19 dBm	−15 dBm
300 Hz and 499 Hz	+2 dB and −6 dB	−22 dBm	−14 dBm
2801 Hz and 3000 Hz	+2 dB and −6 dB	−22 dBm	−14 dBm

A linear phase-versus-frequency relationship is a requirement for error-free data transmission—signals are delayed more at some frequencies than others. Delay distortion is the difference in phase shifts with respect to frequency that signals experience as they propagate through a transmission medium. This relationship is difficult to measure because of the difficulty in establishing a phase (time) reference. Envelope delay is an alternate method of evaluating the phase-versus-frequency relationship of a circuit.

The time delay encountered by a signal as it propagates from a source to a destination is called *propagation time,* and the delay measured in angular units, such as degrees or radians, is called *phase delay.* All frequencies in the usable voice band (300 Hz to 3000 Hz) do not experience the same time delay in a circuit. Therefore, a complex waveform, such as the output of a data modem, does not possess the same phase-versus-frequency relationship when received as it possessed when it was transmitted. This condition represents a possible impairment to a data signal. The *absolute phase delay* is the actual time required for a particular frequency to propagate from a source to a destination through a communications channel. The difference between the absolute delays of all the frequencies is phase distortion. A graph of phase delay-versus-frequency for a typical circuit is nonlinear.

By definition, envelope delay is the first derivative (slope) of phase with respect to frequency:

$$\text{envelope delay} = \frac{d\theta(\omega)}{d\omega} \tag{9-4}$$

In actuality, envelope delay only closely approximates $d\theta(\omega)/d\omega$. Envelope delay measurements evaluate not the true phase-versus-frequency characteristics but rather the phase of a wave that is the result of a narrow band of frequencies. It is a common misconception to confuse true phase distortion (also called delay distortion) with envelope delay distortion (EDD). *Envelope delay* is the time required to propagate a change in an AM envelope (the actual information-bearing part of the signal) through a transmission medium. To measure envelope delay, a narrowband amplitude-modulated carrier, whose frequency is varied over the usable voice band, is transmitted (the amplitude-modulated rate is typically between 25 Hz and 100 Hz). At the receiver, phase variations of the low-frequency envelope are measured. The phase difference at the different carrier frequencies is *envelope delay distortion*. The carrier frequency that produces the minimum envelope delay is established as the reference and is normalized to zero. Therefore, EDD measurements are typically given in microseconds and yield only positive values. EDD indicates the relative envelope delays of the various carrier frequencies with respect to the reference frequency. The reference frequency of a typical voice-band circuit is typically around 1800 Hz.

EDD measurements do not yield true phase delays, nor do they determine the relative relationships between true phase delays. EDD measurements are used to determine a close approximation of the relative phase delay characteristics of a circuit. Propagation time cannot be increased. Therefore, to correct delay distortion, equalizers are placed in a circuit to slow down the frequencies that travel the fastest more than frequencies that travel the slowest. This reduces the difference between the fastest and slowest frequencies, reducing the phase distortion.

The EDD limits for basic and conditioned telephone channels are listed in Table 9-1. Figure 9-8 shows a graphical representation of the EDD limits for a basic telephone chan-

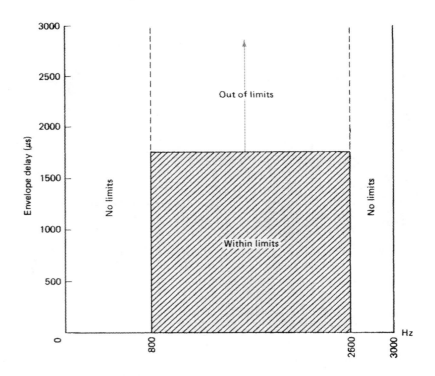

FIGURE 9-8 Graphical presentation of the limits for envelope delay in a basic telephone channel

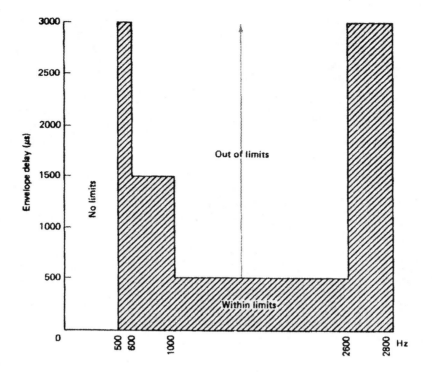

FIGURE 9-9 Graphical presentation of the limits for envelope delay in a telephone channel with C2 conditioning

nel, and Figure 9-9 shows a graphical representation of the EDD limits for a channel meeting the requirements for C2 conditioning. From Table 9-1, the EDD limit of a basic telephone channel is 1750 μs between 800 Hz and 2600 Hz. This indicates that the maximum difference in envelope delay between any two carrier frequencies (the fastest and slowest frequencies) within this range cannot exceed 1750 μs.

Example 9-4

An EDD test on a basic telephone channel indicated that an 1800-Hz carrier experienced the minimum absolute delay of 400 μs. Therefore, it is the reference frequency. Determine the maximum absolute envelope delay that any frequency within the 800-Hz to 2600-Hz range can experience.

Solution   The maximum envelope delay for a basic telephone channel is 1750 μs within the frequency range of 800 Hz to 2600 Hz. Therefore, the maximum envelope delay is 2150 μs (400 μs + 1750 μs).

The absolute time delay encountered by a signal between any two points in the continental United States should never exceed 100 ms, which is not sufficient to cause any problems. Consequently, relative rather than absolute values of envelope delay are measured. For the previous example, as long as EDD tests yield relative values less than +1750 μs, the circuit is within limits.

9-5-1-2 D-type line conditioning.   D-type conditioning neither reduces the noise on a circuit nor improves the signal-to-noise ratio. It simply sets the minimum requirements for *signal-to-noise* (S/N) *ratio* and *nonlinear distortion*. If a subscriber requests D-type conditioning and the facilities assigned to the circuit do not meet the requirements, a different facility is assigned. D-type conditioning is simply a requirement and does not add anything to the circuit, and it cannot be used to improve a circuit. It simply places higher requirements on circuits used for high-speed data transmission. Only circuits that meet D-type conditioning requirements can be used for high-speed data transmission. D-type conditioning is sometimes referred to as *high-performance conditioning* and can be applied to private-line data circuits in addition to either basic or C-conditioned requirements. There are two categories for D-type conditioning: D1 and D2. Limits imposed by D1 and D2 are virtually identical. The only difference between the two categories is the circuit arrangement to which they apply. D1 conditioning specifies requirements for two-point circuits, and D2 conditioning specifies requirements for multipoint circuits.

D-type conditioning is mandatory when the data transmission rate is 9600 bps because without D-type conditioning, it is highly unlikely that the circuit can meet the minimum performance requirements guaranteed by the telephone company. When a telephone company assigns a circuit to a subscriber for use as a 9600-bps data circuit and the circuit does not meet the minimum requirements of D-type conditioning, a new circuit is assigned. This is because a circuit cannot generally be upgraded to meet D-type conditioning specifications by simply adding corrective devices, such as equalizers and amplifiers. Telephone companies do not guarantee the performance of data modems operating at bit rates above 9600 bps over standard voice-grade circuits.

D-type conditioned circuits must meet the following specifications:

Signal-to-C-notched noise ratio: ≥ 28 dB

Nonlinear distortion

Signal-to-second order distortion: ≥ 35 dB

Signal-to-third order distortion: ≥ 40 dB

The signal-to-notched noise ratio requirement for standard circuits is only 24 dB, and they have no requirements for nonlinear distortion.

Nonlinear distortion is an example of correlated noise and is produced from nonlinear amplification. When an amplifier is driven into a nonlinear operating region, the signal is distorted, producing multiples and sums and differences (cross products) the original signal frequencies. The noise caused by nonlinear distortion is in the form of additional frequencies produced from nonlinear amplification of a signal. In other words, no signal, no noise. Nonlinear distortion produces distorted waveforms that are detrimental to digitally modulated carriers used with voice-band data modems, such as FSK, PSK, and QAM. Two classifications of nonlinear distortion are *harmonic distortion* (unwanted multiples of the transmitted frequencies) and *intermodulation distortion* (cross products [sums and differences] of the transmitted frequencies, sometimes called *fluctuation noise* or *cross-modulation noise*). Harmonic and intermodulation distortion, if of sufficient magnitude, can destroy the integrity of a data signal. The degree of circuit nonlinearity can be measured using either harmonic or intermodulation distortion tests.

Harmonic distortion is measured by applying a single-frequency test tone to a telephone channel. At the receive end, the power of the fundamental, second, and third harmonic frequencies is measured. Harmonic distortion is classified as second, third, *n*th order, or as total harmonic distortion. The actual amount of nonlinearity in a circuit is determined by comparing the power of the fundamental with the combined powers of the second and third harmonics. Harmonic distortion tests use a single-frequency (704-Hz) source (see Figure 9-10); therefore, no cross-product frequencies are produced.

Although simple harmonic distortion tests provide an accurate measurement of the nonlinear characteristics of analog telephone channel, they are inadequate for digital (T carrier) facilities. For this reason, a more refined method was developed that uses a multifrequency test-tone signal. Four test frequencies are used (see Figure 9-11): two designated

$$\frac{V_2}{V_1} \times 100 = \text{2nd order harmonic distortion}$$

$$\frac{V_3}{V_1} \times 100 = \text{3rd order harmonic distortion}$$

$$\frac{\sqrt{V_2^2 + V_3^2}}{V_1} \times 100 = \text{total harmonic distortion (THD)}$$

FIGURE 9-10   Harmonic distortion

FIGURE 9-11   Intermodulation distortion

the A band (A1 = 856 Hz, A2 = 863 Hz) and two designated the B band (B1 = 1374 Hz and B2 = 1385 Hz). The four frequencies are transmitted with equal power levels, and the total combined power is equal to that of a normal data signal. The nonlinear amplification of the circuit produces multiples of each frequency (harmonics) and their cross-product frequencies (sum and difference frequencies). For reasons beyond the scope of this text, the following second- and third-order products were selected for measurement: B + A, B − A, and 2B − A. The combined signal power of the four A and B band frequencies is compared with the second-order cross products and then compared with the third-order cross products. The results are converted to dB values and then compared to the requirements of D-type conditioning.

Harmonic and intermodulation distortion tests do not directly determine the amount of interference caused by nonlinear circuit gain. They serve as a figure of merit only when evaluating circuit parameters.

9-5-2   Interface Parameters

The two primary considerations of the interface parameters are electrical protection of the telephone network and its personnel and standardization of design arrangements. The interface parameters include the following:

Station equipment impedances should be 600 Ω resistive over the usable voice band.

Station equipment should be isolated from ground by a minimum of 20 MΩ dc and 50 kΩ ac.

The basic voice-grade telephone circuit is a 3002 channel; it has an ideal bandwidth of 0 Hz to 4 kHz and a usable bandwidth of 300 Hz to 3000 Hz.

The circuit gain at 3000 Hz is 3 dB below the specified in-band signal power.

The gain at 4 kHz must be at least 15 dB below the gain at 3 kHz.

The maximum transmitted signal power for a private-line circuit is 0 dBm.

The transmitted signal power for dial-up circuits using the public switched telephone network is established for each loop so that the signal is received at the telephone central office at −12 dBm.

Table 9-2 summarizes interface parameter limits.

Table 9-2   Interface Parameter Limits

Parameter	Limit
1. Recommended impedance of terminal equipment	600 Ω resistive ± 10%
2. Recommended isolation to ground of terminal equipment	At least 20 MΩ dc
	At least 50 kΩ ac
	At least 1500 V rms breakdown voltage at 60 Hz
3. Data transmit signal power	0 dBm (3-s average)
4. In-band transmitted signal power	2450-Hz to 2750-Hz band should not exceed signal power in 800-Hz to 2450-Hz band
5. Out-of-band transmitted signal power	
Above voice band:	
(a) 3995 Hz–4005 Hz	At least 18 dB below maximum allowed in-band signal power
(b) 4-kHz–10-kHz band	Less than −16 dBm
(c) 10-kHz–25-kHz band	Less than −24 dBm
(d) 25-kHz–40-kHz band	Less than −36 dBm
(e) Above 40 kHz	Less than −50 dBm

Below voice band:

(f) rms current per conductor as specified by Telco but never greater than 0.35 A.

(g) Magnitude of peak conductor-to-ground voltage not to exceed 70 V.

(h) Conductor-to-conductor voltage shall be such that conductor-to-ground voltage is not exceeded. For an underground signal source, the conductor-to-conductor limit is the same as the conductor-to-ground limit.

(i) Total weighted rms voltage in band from 50 Hz to 300 Hz, not to exceed 100 V. Weighting factors for each frequency component (f) are $f^2/10^4$ for f between 50 Hz and 100 Hz and $f^{3.3}/10^{6.6}$ for f between 101 Hz and 300 Hz.

6. Maximum test signal power: same as transmitted data power.

9-5-3   Facility Parameters

Facility parameters represent potential impairments to a data signal. These impairments are caused by telephone company equipment and the limits specified pertain to all private-line data circuits using voice-band facilities, regardless of line conditioning. Facility parameters include 1004-Hz variation, C-message noise, impulse noise, gain hits and dropouts, phase hits, phase jitter, single-frequency interference, frequency shift, phase intercept distortion, and peak-to-average ratio.

9-5-3-1 1004-Hz variation.   The telephone industry has established 1004 Hz as the standard test-tone frequency; 1000 Hz was originally selected because of its relative location in the passband of a standard voice-band circuit. The frequency was changed to 1004 Hz with the advent of digital carriers because 1000 Hz is an exact submultiple of the 8-kHz sample rate used with T carriers. Sampling a continuous 1000-Hz signal at an 8000-Hz rate produced repetitive patterns in the PCM codes, which could cause the system to lose frame synchronization.

The purpose of the 1004-Hz test tone is to simulate the combined signal power of a standard voice-band data transmission. The 1004-Hz channel loss for a private-line data circuit is typically 16 dB. A 1004-Hz test tone applied at the transmit end of a circuit should be received at the output of the circuit at −16 dBm. Long-term variations in the gain of the transmission facility are called *1004-Hz variation* and should not exceed ±4 dB. Thus, the received signal power must be within the limits of −12 dBm to −20 dBm.

9-5-3-2 C-message noise.   C-message noise measurements determine the average weighted rms noise power. Unwanted electrical signals are produced from the random movement of electrons in conductors. This type of noise is commonly called *thermal noise* because its magnitude is directly proportional to temperature. Because the electron movement is completely random and travels in all directions, thermal noise is also called *random noise,* and because it contains all frequencies, it is sometimes referred to as *white noise.* Thermal noise is inherently present in a circuit because of its electrical makeup. Because thermal noise is additive, its magnitude is dependent, in part, on the electrical length of the circuit.

C-message noise measurements are the terminated rms power readings at the receive end of a circuit with the transmit end terminated in the characteristic impedance of the telephone line. Figure 9-12 shows the test setup for conducting terminated C-message noise readings. As shown in the figure, a C-message filter is placed between the circuit and the power meter in the noise measuring set so that the noise measurement evaluates the noise with a response similar to that of a human listening to the noise through a standard telephone set speaker.

There is a disadvantage to measuring noise this way. The overall circuit characteristics, in the absence of a signal, are not necessarily the same as when a signal is present. Using compressors, expanders, and automatic gain devices in a circuit causes this difference. For this reason, *C-notched noise* measurements were developed. C-notched noise measurements differ from standard C-message noise measurements only in the fact that a *holding tone* (usually 1004 Hz or 2804 Hz) is applied to the transmit end of the circuit while the noise measurement is taken. The holding tone ensures that the circuit operation simulates a loaded voice or data transmission. *Loaded* is a communications term that indicates the presence of a signal power comparable to the power of an actual message transmission. A narrowband notch filter removes the holding tone before the noise power is measured. The test setup for making C-notched noise measurements is shown in Figure 9-13. As the figure shows, the notch filter is placed in front of the C-message filter, thus blocking the holding tone from reaching the power meter.

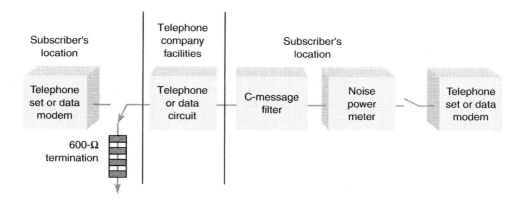

FIGURE 9-12   Terminated C-message noise test setup

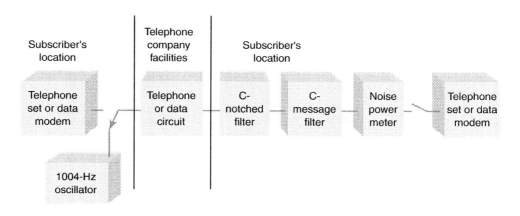

FIGURE 9-13   C-notched noise test setup

FIGURE 9-14   C-notched noise and impulse noise

The physical makeup of a private-line data circuit may require using several carrier facilities and cable arrangements in tandem. Each facility may be analog, digital, or some combination of analog and digital. Telephone companies have established realistic C-notched noise requirements for each type of facility for various circuit lengths. Telephone companies guarantee standard private-line data circuits a minimum signal-to-C-notched noise ratio of 24 dB. A standard circuit is one operating at less than 9600 bps. Data circuits operating at 9600 bps require D-type conditioning, which guarantees a minimum signal-to-C-notched noise ratio of 28 dB. C-notched noise is shown in Figure 9-14. Telephone companies do not guarantee the performance of voice-band circuits operating at bit rates in excess of 9600 bps.

9-5-3-3 Impulse noise.   *Impulse noise* is characterized by high-amplitude peaks (impulses) of short duration having an approximately flat frequency spectrum. Impulse noise can saturate a message channel. Impulse noise is the primary source of transmission errors in data circuits. There are numerous sources of impulse noise—some are controllable, but most are not. The primary cause of impulse noise is man-made sources, such as interference from ac power lines, transients from switching machines, motors, solenoids, relays, electric trains, and so on. Impulse noise can also result from lightning and other adverse atmospheric conditions.

The significance of impulse noise hits on data transmission has been a controversial topic. Telephone companies have accepted the fact that the absolute magnitude of the impulse hit is not as significant as the magnitude of the hit relative to the signal amplitude. Empirically, it has been determined that an impulse hit will not produce transmission errors in a data signal unless it comes within 6 dB of the signal level as shown in Figure 9-14. Impulse hit counters are designed to register a maximum of seven counts per second. This leaves a 143-ms lapse called a *dead time* between counts when additional impulse hits are not registered. Contemporary high-speed data formats transfer data in a block or frame format, and whether one hit or many hits occur during a single transmission is unimportant, as any error within a message generally necessitates retransmission of the entire message. It has been determined that counting additional impulses during the time of a single transmission does not correlate well with data transmission performance.

FIGURE 9-15   Gain hits and dropouts

Impulse noise objectives are based primarily on the error susceptibility of data signals, which depends on the type of modem used and the characteristics of the transmission medium. It is impractical to measure the exact peak amplitudes of each noise pulse or to count the number that occur. Studies have shown that expected error rates in the absence of other impairments are approximately proportional to the number of impulse hits that exceed the rms signal power level by approximately 2 dB. When impulse noise tests are performed, a 2802-Hz holding tone is placed on a circuit to ensure loaded circuit conditions. The counter records the number of hits in a prescribed time interval (usually 15 minutes). An impulse hit is typically less than 4 ms in duration and never more than 10 ms. Telephone company limits for recordable impulse hits is 15 hits within a 15-minute time interval. This does not limit the number of hits to one per minute but, rather, the average occurrence to one per minute.

9-5-3-4 Gain hits and dropouts.   A *gain hit* is a sudden, random change in the gain of a circuit resulting in a temporary change in the signal level. Gain hits are classified as temporary variations in circuit gain exceeding ±3 dB, lasting more than 4 ms, and returning to the original value within 200 ms. The primary cause of gain hits is noise transients (impulses) on transmission facilities during the normal course of a day.

A *dropout* is a decrease in circuit gain (i.e., signal level) of more than 12 dB lasting longer than 4 ms. Dropouts are characteristics of temporary open-circuit conditions and are generally caused by deep fades on radio facilities or by switching delays. Gain hits and dropouts are depicted in Figure 9-15.

9-5-3-5 Phase hits.   *Phase hits* (slips) are sudden, random changes in the phase of a signal. Phase hits are classified as temporary variations in the phase of a signal lasting longer than 4 ms. Generally, phase hits are not recorded unless they exceed ±20C° peak. Phase hits, like gain hits, are caused by transients produced when transmission facilities are switched. Phase hits are shown in Figure 9-16.

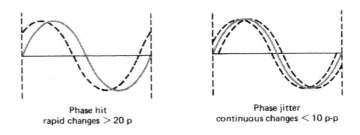

Phase hit
rapid changes > 20 p

Phase jitter
continuous changes < 10 p-p

FIGURE 9-16   Phase hits and phase jitter

FIGURE 9-17   Single-frequency interference (spurious tone)

9-5-3-6 Phase jitter. *Phase jitter* is a form of incidental phase modulation—a continuous, uncontrolled variation in the zero crossings of a signal. Generally, phase jitter occurs at a 300-Hz rate or lower, and its primary cause is low-frequency ac ripple in power supplies. The number of power supplies required in a circuit is directly proportional to the number of transmission facilities and telephone offices that make up the message channel. Each facility has a separate phase jitter requirement; however, the maximum acceptable end-to-end phase jitter is 10° peak to peak regardless of how many transmission facilities or telephone offices are used in the circuit. Phase jitter is shown in Figure 9-16.

9-5-3-7 Single-frequency interference. *Single-frequency interference* is the presence of one or more continuous, unwanted tones within a message channel. The tones are called *spurious tones* and are often caused by crosstalk or cross modulation between adjacent channels in a transmission system due to system nonlinearities. Spurious tones are measured by terminating the transmit end of a circuit and then observing the channel frequency band. Spurious tones can cause the same undesired circuit behavior as thermal noise. Single-frequency interference is shown in Figure 9-17.

9-5-3-8 Frequency shift. *Frequency shift* is when the frequency of a signal changes during transmission. For example, a tone transmitted at 1004 Hz is received at 1005 Hz. Analog transmission systems used by telephone companies operate single-sideband suppressed carrier (SSBSC) and, therefore, require coherent demodulation. With coherent demodulation, carriers must be synchronous—the frequency must be reproduced exactly in the receiver. If this is not accomplished, the demodulated signal will be offset in frequency by the difference between transmit and receive carrier frequencies. The longer a circuit, the more analog transmission systems and the more likely frequency shift will occur. Frequency shift is shown in Figure 9-18.

Input 1004 Hz
test signal

101,004 Hz sum frequency
(100,000 Hz + 1004 Hz)

Output difference frequency
(101,004 Hz – 99,998 Hz)

Input 1004 Hz — Modulator — Communications channel — Demodulator — Output 1006 Hz

100,000 Hz carrier oscillator

99,998-Hz carrier oscillator

FIGURE 9-18   Frequency shift

9-5-3-9 Phase intercept distortion.   *Phase intercept distortion* occurs in coherent SSBSC systems, such as those using frequency-division multiplexing when the received carrier is not reinserted with the exact phase relationship to the received signal as the transmit carrier possessed. This impairment causes a constant phase shift to all frequencies, which is of little concern for data modems using FSK, PSK, or QAM. Because these are practically the only techniques used today with voice-band data modems, no limits have been set for phase intercept distortion.

9-5-3-10 Peak-to-average ratio.   The difficulties encountered in measuring true phase distortion or envelope delay distortion led to the development of peak-to-average ratio (PAR) tests. A signal containing a series of distinctly shaped pulses with a high peak voltage-to-average voltage ratio is transmitted. Differential delay distortion in a circuit has a tendency to spread the pulses, thus reducing the peak voltage-to-average voltage ratio. Low peak-to-average ratios indicate the presence of differential delay distortion. PAR measurements are less sensitive to attenuation distortion than EDD tests and are easier to perform.

9-5-3-11 Facility parameter summary.   Table 9-3 summarizes facility parameter limits.

9-6   VOICE-FREQUENCY CIRCUIT ARRANGEMENTS

Electronic communications circuits can be configured in several ways. Telephone instruments and the voice-frequency facilities to which they are connected may be either *two wire* or *four wire*. Two-wire circuits have an obvious economic advantage, as they use only half as much copper wire. This is why most local subscriber loops connected to the public switched telephone network are two wire. However, most private-line data circuits are configured four wire.

9-6-1   Two-Wire Voice-Frequency Circuits

As the name implies, *two-wire transmission* involves two wires (one for the signal and one for a reference or ground) or a circuit configuration that is equivalent to using only two wires. Two-wire circuits are ideally suited to simplex transmission, although they are often used for half- and full-duplex transmission.

Figure 9-19 shows the block diagrams for four possible two-wire circuit configurations. Figure 9-19a shows the simplest two-wire configuration, which is a passive circuit consisting of two copper wires connecting a telephone or voice-band modem at one station through a telephone company interface to a telephone or voice-band modem at the

Table 9-3 Facility Parameter Limits

Parameter	Limit	
1. 1004-Hz loss variation	Not more than ±4 dB long term	
2. C-message noise	Maximum rms noise at modem receiver (nominal − 16 dBm point)	
Facility miles	*dBm*	*dBrncO*
0–50	−61	32
51–100	−59	34
101–400	−58	35
401–1000	−55	38
1001–1500	−54	39
1501–2500	−52	41
2501–4000	−50	43
4001–8000	−47	46
8001–16,000	−44	49
3. C-notched noise	(minimum values)	
(a) Standard voice-band channel	24-dB signal to C-notched noise	
(b) High-performance line	28-dB signal to C-notched noise	
4. Single-frequency interference	At least 3 dB below C-message noise limits	
5. Impulse noise		
Threshold with respect to	*Maximum counts above threshold*	
1004-Hz holding tone	*allowed in 15 minutes*	
0 dB	15	
+4 dB	9	
+8 dB	5	
6. Frequency shift	±5 Hz end to end	
7. Phase intercept distortion	No limits	
8. Phase jitter	No more than 10° peak to peak (end-to-end requirement)	
9. Nonlinear distortion		
(D-conditioned circuits only)		
Signal to second order	At least 35 dB	
Signal to third order	At least 40 dB	
10. Peak-to-average ratio	Reading of 50 minimum end to end with standard PAR meter	
11. Phase hits	8 or less in any 15-minute period greater than ±20 peak	
12. Gain hits	8 or less in any 15-minute period greater than ±3 dB	
13. Dropouts	2 or less in any 15-minute period greater than 12 dB	

destination station. The modem, telephone, and circuit configuration are capable of two-way transmission in either the half- or the full-duplex mode.

Figure 9-19b shows an active two-wire transmission system (i.e., one that provides gain). The only difference between this circuit and the one shown in Figure 9-19a is the addition of an amplifier to compensate for transmission line losses. The amplifier is unidirectional and, thus, limits transmission to one direction only (simplex).

Figure 9-19c shows a two-wire circuit using a digital T carrier for the transmission medium. This circuit requires a T carrier transmitter at one end and a T carrier receiver at the other end. The digital T carrier transmission line is capable of two-way transmission; however, the transmitter and receiver in the T carrier are not. The transmitter encodes the analog voice or modem signals into a PCM code, and the decoder in the receiver performs the opposite operation, converting PCM codes back to analog. The digital transmission medium is a pair of copper wire.

Figures 9-19a, b, and c are examples of *physical two-wire circuits,* as the two stations are physically interconnected with a two-wire metallic transmission line. Figure 9-19d shows an *equivalent two-wire circuit.* The transmission medium is Earth's atmosphere, and

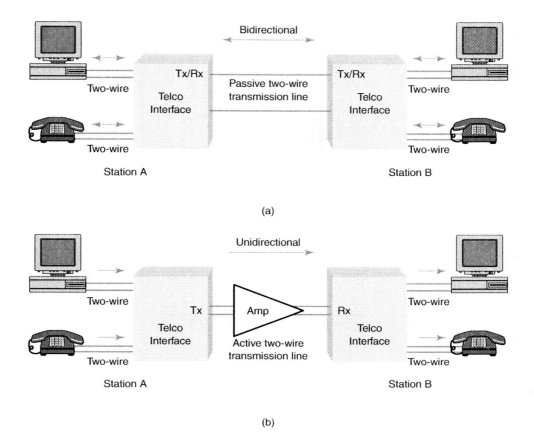

FIGURE 9-19   Two-wire configurations: (a) passive cable circuit; (b) active cable circuit
(*Continued*)

there are no copper wires between the two stations. Although Earth's atmosphere is capable of two-way simultaneous transmission, the radio transmitter and receiver are not. Therefore, this is considered an equivalent two-wire circuit.

9-6-2   Four-Wire Voice-Frequency Circuits

As the name implies, *four-wire transmission* involves four wires (two for each direction—a signal and a reference) or a circuit configuration that is equivalent to using four wires. Four-wire circuits are ideally suited to full-duplex transmission, although they can (and very often do) operate in the half-duplex mode. As with two-wire transmission, there are two forms of four-wire transmission systems: *physical four wire* and *equivalent four wire.*

Figure 9-20 shows the block diagrams for four possible four-wire circuit configurations. As the figures show, a four-wire circuit is equivalent to two two-wire circuits, one for each direction of transmission. The circuits shown in Figures 9-20a, b, and c are physical four-wire circuits, as the transmitter at one station is hardwired to the receiver at the other station. Therefore, each two-wire pair is unidirectional (simplex), but the combined four-wire circuit is bidirectional (full duplex).

The circuit shown in Figure 9-20d is an equivalent four-wire circuit that uses Earth's atmosphere for the transmission medium. Station A transmits on one frequency (f_1) and receives on a different frequency (f_2), while station B transmits on frequency f_2 and receives on frequency f_1. Therefore, the two radio signals do not interfere with one another, and simultaneous bidirectional transmission is possible.

FIGURE 9-19 (Continued) (c) digital T-carrier system; (d) wireless radio carrier system

9-6-3 Two Wire versus Four Wire

There are several inherent advantages of four-wire circuits over two-wire circuits. For instance, four-wire circuits are considerably less noisy, have less crosstalk, and provide more isolation between the two directions of transmission when operating in either the half- or the full-duplex mode. However, two-wire circuits require less wire, less circuitry and, thus, less money than their four-wire counterparts.

Providing amplification is another disadvantage of four-wire operation. Telephone or modem signals propagated more than a few miles require amplification. A bidirectional amplifier on a two-wire circuit is not practical. It is much easier to separate the two directions of propagation with a four-wire circuit and install separate amplifiers in each direction.

9-6-4 Hybrids, Echo Suppressors, and Echo Cancelers

When a two-wire circuit is connected to a four-wire circuit, as in a long-distance telephone call, an interface circuit called a *hybrid*, or *terminating, set* is used to affect the interface. The hybrid set is used to match impedances and to provide isolation between the two directions of signal flow. The hybrid circuit used to convert two-wire circuits to four-wire circuits is similar to the hybrid coil found in standard telephone sets.

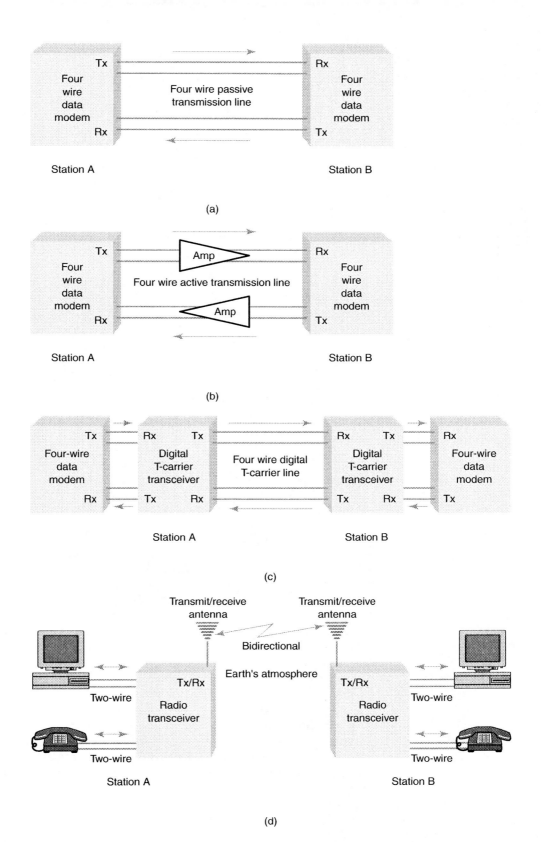

FIGURE 9-20 Four-wire configurations: (a) passive cable circuit; (b) active cable circuit; (c) digital T-carrier system; (d) wireless radio carrier system

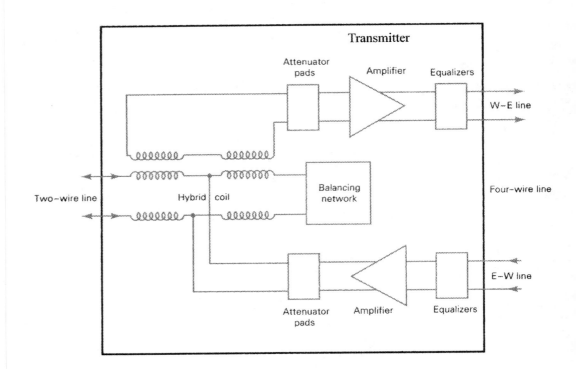

FIGURE 9-21 Hybrid (terminating) sets

Figure 9-21 shows the block diagram for a two-wire to four-wire hybrid network. The hybrid coil compensates for impedance variations in the two-wire portion of the circuit. The amplifiers and attenuators adjust the signal power to required levels, and the equalizers compensate for impairments in the transmission line that affect the frequency response of the transmitted signal, such as line inductance, capacitance, and resistance. Signals traveling west to east (W-E) enter the terminating set from the two-wire line, where they are inductively coupled into the west-to-east transmitter section of the four-wire circuit. Signals received from the four-wire side of the hybrid propagate through the receiver in the east-to-west (E-W) section of the four-wire circuit, where they are applied to the center taps of the hybrid coils. If the impedances of the two-wire line and the balancing network are properly matched, all currents produced in the upper half of the hybrid by the E-W signals will be equal in magnitude but opposite in polarity. Therefore, the voltages induced in the secondaries will be 180° out of phase with each other and, thus, cancel. This prevents any of the signals from being retransmitted to the sender as an echo.

If the impedances of the two-wire line and the balancing network are not matched, voltages induced in the secondaries of the hybrid coil will not completely cancel. This imbalance causes a portion of the received signal to be returned to the sender on the W-E portion of the four-wire circuit. Balancing networks can never completely match a hybrid to the subscriber loop because of long-term temperature variations and degradation of transmission lines. The talker hears the returned portion of the signal as an echo, and if the round-trip delay exceeds approximately 45 ms, the echo can become quite annoying. To eliminate this echo, devices called *echo suppressors* are inserted at one end of the four-wire circuit.

Figure 9-22 shows a simplified block diagram of an echo suppressor. The speech detector senses the presence and direction of the signal. It then enables the amplifier in the appropriate direction and disables the amplifier in the opposite direction, thus preventing the echo

FIGURE 9-22   Echo suppressor

from returning to the speaker. A typical echo suppressor suppresses the returned echo by as much as 60 dB. If the conversation is changing direction rapidly, the people listening may be able to hear the echo suppressors turning on and off (every time an echo suppressor detects speech and is activated, the first instant of sound is removed from the message, giving the speech a choppy sound). If both parties talk at the same time, neither person is heard by the other.

With an echo suppressor in the circuit, transmissions cannot occur in both directions at the same time, thus limiting the circuit to half-duplex operation. Long-distance carriers, such as AT&T, generally place echo suppressors in four-wire circuits that exceed 1500 electrical miles in length (the longer the circuit, the longer the round-trip delay time). Echo suppressors are automatically disabled when they receive a tone between 2020 Hz and 2240 Hz, thus allowing full-duplex data transmission over a circuit with an echo suppressor. Full-duplex operation can also be achieved by replacing the echo suppressors with *echo cancelers*. Echo cancelers eliminate the echo by electrically subtracting it from the original signal rather than disabling the amplifier in the return circuit.

9-7   CROSSTALK

Crosstalk can be defined as any disturbance created in a communications channel by signals in other communications channels (i.e., unwanted coupling from one signal path into another). Crosstalk is a potential problem whenever two metallic conductors carrying different signals are located in close proximity to each other. Crosstalk can originate in telephone offices, at a subscriber's location, or on the facilities used to interconnect subscriber locations to telephone offices. Crosstalk is a subdivision of the general subject of interference. The term *crosstalk* was originally coined to indicate the presence of unwanted speech sounds in a telephone receiver caused by conversations on another telephone circuit.

The nature of crosstalk is often described as either *intelligible* or *unintelligible*. Intelligible (or near intelligible) crosstalk is particularly annoying and objectionable because the listener senses a real or fancied loss of privacy. Unintelligible crosstalk does not violate privacy, although it can still be annoying. Crosstalk between unlike channels, such as different types of carrier facilities, is usually unintelligible because of frequency inversion, frequency displacement, or digital encoding. However, such crosstalk often retains the syllabic pattern of speech and is more annoying than steady-state noise (such as thermal noise) with the same average power. Intermodulation noise, such as that found in multichannel frequency-division-multiplexed telephone systems, is a form of interchannel crosstalk that is usually unintelligible. Unintelligible crosstalk is generally grouped with other types of noise interferences.

The use of the words *intelligible* and *unintelligible* can also be applied to non-voice circuits. The methods developed for quantitatively computing and measuring crosstalk between voice circuits are also useful when studying interference between voice circuits and data circuits and between two data circuits.

There are three primary types of crosstalk in telephone systems: nonlinear crosstalk, transmittance crosstalk, and coupling crosstalk.

9-7-1 Nonlinear Crosstalk

Nonlinear crosstalk is a direct result of nonlinear amplification (hence the name) in analog communications systems. Nonlinear amplification produces harmonics and cross products (sum and difference frequencies). If the nonlinear frequency components fall into the passband of another channel, they are considered crosstalk. Nonlinear crosstalk can be distinguished from other types of crosstalk because the ratio of the signal power in the disturbing channel to the interference power in the disturbed channel is a function of the signal level in the disturbing channel.

9-7-2 Transmittance Crosstalk

Crosstalk can also be caused by inadequate control of the frequency response of a transmission system, poor filter design, or poor filter performance. This type of crosstalk is most prevalent when filters do not adequately reject undesired products from other channels. Because this type of interference is caused by inadequate control of the transfer characteristics or transmittance of networks, it is called *transmittance crosstalk*.

9-7-3 Coupling Crosstalk

Electromagnetic coupling between two or more physically isolated transmission media is called *coupling crosstalk*. The most common coupling is due to the effects of near-field mutual induction between cables from physically isolated circuits (i.e., when energy radiates from a wire in one circuit to a wire in a different circuit). To reduce coupling crosstalk due to mutual induction, wires are twisted together (hence the name *twisted pair*). Twisting the wires causes a canceling effect that helps eliminate crosstalk. Standard telephone cable pairs have 20 twists per foot, whereas data circuits generally require more twists per foot. Direct capacitive coupling between adjacent cables is another means in which signals from one cable can be coupled into another cable. The probability of coupling crosstalk occurring increases with cable length, signal power, and frequency.

There are two types of coupling crosstalk: near end and far end. *Near-end crosstalk* (NEXT) is crosstalk that occurs at the transmit end of a circuit and travels in the opposite direction as the signal in the disturbing channel. *Far-end crosstalk* (FEXT) occurs at the far-end receiver and is energy that travels in the same direction as the signal in the disturbing channel.

9-7-4 Unit of Measurement

Crosstalk interference is often expressed in its own special decibel unit of measurement, dBx. Unlike dBm, where the reference is a fixed power level, dBx is referenced to the level on the cable that is being interfered with (whatever the level may be). Mathematically, dBx is

$$dBx = 90 - (\text{crosstalk loss in decibels}) \tag{9-5}$$

where 90 dB is considered the ideal isolation between adjacent lines. For example, the magnitude of the crosstalk on a circuit is 70 dB lower than the power of the signal on the same circuit. The crosstalk is then 90 dB − 70 dBx = 20 dBx.

9-1. Briefly describe a *local subscriber loop*.

9-2. Explain what *loading coils* and *bridge taps* are and when they can be detrimental to the performance of a telephone circuit.

9-3. What are the designations used with *loading coils*?

9-4. What is meant by the term *loop resistance*?

9-5. Briefly describe *C-message noise weighting* and state its significance.

9-6. What is the difference between dB and dBm?

9-7. What is the difference between a TLP and a DLP?

9-8. What is meant by the following terms: dBmO, rn, dBrn, dBrnc, and dBrncO?

9-9. What is the difference between *psophometric noise weighting* and C-message weighting?

9-10. What are the three categories of *transmission parameters*?

9-11. Describe *attenuation distortion; envelope delay distortion.*

9-12. What is the reference frequency for attenuation distortion? Envelope delay distortion?

9-13. What is meant by *line conditioning*? What types of line conditioning are available?

9-14. What kind of circuits can have C-type line conditioning; D-type line conditioning?

9-15. When is D-type conditioning mandatory?

9-16. What limitations are imposed with D-type conditioning?

9-17. What is meant by *nonlinear distortion*? What are two kinds of nonlinear distortion?

9-18. What considerations are addressed by the *interface parameters*?

9-19. What considerations are addressed by *facility parameters*?

9-20. Briefly describe the following parameters: 1004-Hz variation, C-message noise, impulse noise, gain hits and dropouts, phase hits, phase jitter, single-frequency interference, frequency shift, phase intercept distortion, and peak-to-average ratio.

9-21. Describe what is meant by a *two-wire circuit; four-wire circuit*?

9-22. Briefly describe the function of a two-wire-to-four-wire *hybrid set*.

9-23. What is the purpose of an *echo suppressor; echo canceler*?

9-24. Briefly describe *crosstalk*.

9-25. What is the difference between *intelligible* and *unintelligible* crosstalk?

9-26. List and describe three types of crosstalk.

9-27. What is meant by near-end crosstalk; far-end crosstalk?

9-1. Describe what the following loading coil designations mean:
   a. 22B44
   b. 19H88
   c. 24B44
   d. 16B135

9-2. Frequencies of 250 Hz and 1 kHz are applied to the input of a C-message filter. Would their difference in amplitude be (greater, the same, or less) at the output of the filter?

9-3. A C-message noise measurement taken at a -22-dBm TLP indicates -72 dBm of noise. A test tone is measured at the same TLP at -25 dBm. Determine the following levels:
   a. Signal power relative to TLP (dBmO)
   b. C-message noise relative to reference noise (dBrn)
   c. C-message noise relative to reference noise adjusted to a 0 TLP (dBrncO)
   d. Signal-to-noise ratio

9-4. A C-message noise measurement taken at a -20-dBm TLP indicates a corrected noise reading of 43 dBrncO. A test tone at data level (0 DLP) is used to determine a signal-to-noise ratio of 30 dB. Determine the following levels:

a. Signal power relative to TLP (dBmO)
b. C-message noise relative to reference noise (dBrnc)
c. Actual test-tone signal power (dBm)
d. Actual C-message noise (dBm)

9-5. A test-tone signal power of -62 dBm is measured at a -61-dBm TLP. The C-message noise is measured at the same TLP at -10 dBrnc. Determine the following levels:

a. C-message noise relative to reference noise at a O TLP (dBrncO)
b. Actual C-message noise power level (dBm)
c. Signal power level relative to TLP (dBmO)
d. Signal-to-noise ratio (dB)

9-6. Sketch the graph for attenuation distortion and envelope delay distortion for a channel with C4 conditioning.

9-7. An EDD test on a basic telephone channel indicated that a 1600-Hz carrier experienced the minimum absolute delay of 550 μs. Determine the maximum absolute envelope delay that any frequency within the range of 800 Hz to 2600 Hz can experience.

9-8. The magnitude of the crosstalk on a circuit is 66 dB lower than the power of the signal on the same circuit. Determine the crosstalk in dBx.

CHAPTER 10

The Public Telephone Network

OBJECTIVES

- Define *public telephone company*
- Explain the differences between the public and private sectors of the public telephone network
- Define *telephone instruments, local loops, trunk circuits,* and *exchanges*
- Describe the necessity for central office telephone exchanges
- Briefly describe the history of the telephone industry
- Describe operator-assisted local exchanges
- Describe automated central office switches and exchanges and their advantages over operator-assisted local exchanges
- Define *circuits, circuit switches,* and *circuit switching*
- Describe the relationship between local telephone exchanges and exchange areas
- Define *interoffice trunks, tandem trunks,* and *tandem switches*
- Define *toll-connecting trunks, intertoll trunks,* and *toll offices*
- Describe the North American Telephone Numbering Plan Areas
- Describe the predivestiture North American Telephone Switching Hierarchy
- Define the five classes of telephone switching centers
- Explain switching routes

- Describe the postdivestiture North American Telephone Switching Hierarchy
- Define *Common Channel Signaling System No. 7 (SS7)*
- Describe the basic functions of SS7
- Define and describe SS7 signaling points

10-1 INTRODUCTION

The telecommunications industry is the largest industry in the world. There are over 1400 independent telephone companies in the United States, jointly referred to as the *public telephone network* (PTN). The PTN uses the largest computer network in the world to interconnect millions of subscribers in such a way that the myriad of companies function as a single entity. The mere size of the PTN makes it unique and truly a modern-day wonder of the world. Virtually any subscriber to the network can be connected to virtually any other subscriber to the network within a few seconds by simply dialing a telephone number. One characteristic of the PTN that makes it unique from other industries is that every piece of equipment, technique, or procedure, new or old, is capable of working with the rest of the system. In addition, using the PTN does not require any special skills or knowledge.

10-2 TELEPHONE TRANSMISSION SYSTEM ENVIRONMENT

In its simplest form, a telephone transmission system is a pair of wires connecting two telephones or data modems together. A more practical transmission system is comprised of a complex aggregate of electronic equipment and associated transmission medium, which together provide a multiplicity of channels over which many subscriber's messages and control signals are propagated.

In general, a telephone call between two points is handled by interconnecting a number of different transmission systems in tandem to form an overall *transmission path (connection)* between the two points. The manner in which transmission systems are chosen and interconnected has a strong bearing on the characteristics required of each system because each element in the connection degrades the message to some extent. Consequently, the relationship between the performance and the cost of a transmission system cannot be considered only in terms of that system. Instead, a transmission system must be viewed with respect to its relationship to the complete system.

To provide a service that permits people or data modems to talk to each other at a distance, the communications system (telephone network) must supply the means and facilities for connecting the subscribers at the beginning of a call and disconnecting them at the completion of the call. Therefore, switching, signaling, and transmission functions must be involved in the service. The *switching function* identifies and connects the subscribers to a suitable transmission path. *Signaling functions* supply and interpret control and supervisory signals needed to perform the operation. Finally, transmission functions involve the actual transmission of a subscriber's messages and any necessary control signals. New transmission systems are inhibited by the fact that they must be compatible with an existing multi-trillion-dollar infrastructure.

10-3 THE PUBLIC TELEPHONE NETWORK

The public telephone network (PTN) accommodates two types of subscribers: *public* and *private.* Subscribers to the private sector are customers who lease equipment, transmission media (*facilities*), and services from telephone companies on a permanent basis. The leased circuits are designed and configured for their use only and are often referred to as *private-line* circuits or *dedicated* circuits. For example, large banks do not wish to share their communications network with other users, but it is not cost effective for them to construct their own networks. Therefore, banks lease equipment and facilities from public telephone companies and essentially operate a private telephone or data network within the PTN. The public telephone companies are sometimes called *service providers,* as they lease equipment and provide services to other private companies, organizations, and government agencies. Most metropolitan area networks (MANs) and wide area networks (WANs) utilize private-line data circuits and one or more service provider.

Subscribers to the public sector of the PTN share equipment and facilities that are available to all the public subscribers to the network. This equipment is appropriately called *common usage equipment,* which includes transmission facilities and telephone switches. Anyone with a telephone number is a subscriber to the public sector of the PTN. Since subscribers to the public network are interconnected only temporarily through switches, the network is often appropriately called the *public switched telephone network* (PSTN) and sometimes simply as the *dial-up network.* It is possible to interconnect telephones and modems with one another over great distances in fractions of a second by means of an elaborate network comprised of central offices, switches, cables (optical and metallic), and wireless radio systems that are connected by routing *nodes* (a node is a *switching point*). When someone talks about the public switched telephone network, they are referring to the combination of lines and switches that form a system of electrical routes through the network.

In its simplest form, data communications is the transmittal of digital information between two pieces of digital equipment, which includes computers. Several thousand miles may separate the equipment, which necessitates using some form of transmission medium to interconnect them. There is an insufficient number of transmission media capable of carrying digital information in digital form. Therefore, the most convenient (and least expensive) alternative to constructing an all-new all-digital network is to use the existing PTN for the transmission medium. Unfortunately, much of the PTN was designed (and much of it constructed) before the advent of large-scale data communications. The PTN was intended for transferring voice, not digital data. Therefore, to use the PTN for data communications, it is necessary to use a modem to convert the data to a form more suitable for transmission over the wireless carrier systems and conventional transmission media so prevalent in the PTN.

There are as many network configurations as there are subscribers in the private sector of the PTN, making it impossible to describe them all. Therefore, the intent of this chapter is to describe the public sector of the PTN (i.e., the public switched telephone network). Private-line data networks are described in later chapters of this book.

10-4 INSTRUMENTS, LOCAL LOOPS, TRUNK CIRCUITS, AND EXCHANGES

Telephone network equipment can be broadly divided into four primary classifications: instruments, local loops, exchanges, and trunk circuits.

10-4-1 Instruments

An *instrument* is any device used to originate and terminate calls and to transmit and receive signals into and out of the telephone network, such as a 2500-type telephone set, a cordless telephone, or a data modem. The instrument is often referred to as *station equipment* and the location of the instrument as the *station.* A *subscriber* is the operator or user of the instrument. If you have a home telephone, you are a subscriber.

10-4-2 Local Loops

As described in Chapters 8 and 9, the *local loop* is simply the dedicated cable facility used to connect an instrument at a subscriber's station to the closest telephone office. In the United States alone, there are several hundred million miles of cable used for local subscriber loops. Everyone who subscribes to the PTN is connected to the closest telephone office through a local loop. Local loops connected to the public switched telephone network are two-wire metallic cable pairs. However, local loops used with private-line data circuits are generally four-wire configurations.

10-4-3 Trunk Circuits

A *trunk circuit* is similar to a local loop except trunk circuits are used to interconnect two telephone offices. The primary difference between a local loop and a trunk is that a local loop is permanently associated with a particular station, whereas a trunk is a common-usage connection. A trunk circuit can be as simple as a pair of copper wires twisted together or as sophisticated as an optical fiber cable. A trunk circuit could also be a wireless communications channel. Although all trunk circuits perform the same basic function, there are different names given to them, depending on what types of telephone offices they interconnect and for what reason. Trunk circuits can be two wire or four wire, depending on what type of facility is used. Trunks are described in more detail in a later section of this chapter.

10-4-4 Exchanges

An *exchange* is a central location where subscribers are interconnected, either temporarily or on a permanent basis. Telephone company switching machines are located in exchanges. Switching machines are programmable matrices that provide temporary signal paths between two subscribers. Telephone sets and data modems are connected through local loops to switching machines located in exchanges. Exchanges connected directly to local loops are often called *local exchanges* or sometimes *dial switches* or *local dial switches*. The first telephone exchange was installed in 1878, only two years after the invention of the telephone. A central exchange is also called a *central telephone exchange, central office* (CO), *central wire center, central exchange, central office exchange,* or simply *central.*

    The purpose of a telephone exchange is to provide a path for a call to be completed between two parties. To process a call, a switch must provide three primary functions:

       Identify the subscribers

       Set up or establish a communications path

       Supervise the calling processes

10-5 LOCAL CENTRAL OFFICE TELEPHONE EXCHANGES

The first telephone sets were self-contained, as they were equipped with their own battery, microphone, speaker, bell, and ringing circuit. Telephone sets were originally connected directly to each other with heavy-gauge iron wire strung between poles, requiring a dedicated cable pair and telephone set for each subscriber you wished to be connected to. Figure 10-1a shows two telephones interconnected with a single cable pair. This is simple enough; however, if more than a few subscribers wished to be directly connected together, it became cumbersome, expensive, and very impractical. For example, to interconnect one subscriber to five other subscribers, five telephone sets and five cable pairs are needed, as shown in Figure 10-1b. To completely interconnect four subscribers, it would require six cable pairs, and each subscriber would need three telephone sets. This is shown in Figure 10-1c.

Telephone 1   Telephone 2
(a)

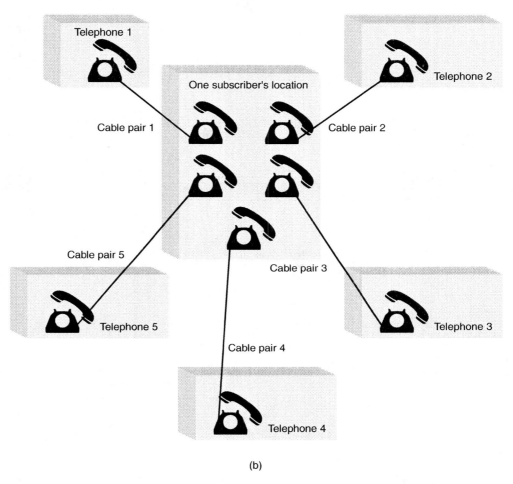

(b)

FIGURE 10-1 Dedicated telephone interconnections: (a) Interconnecting two subscribers;
(b) Interconnecting one subscriber to five other telephone sets; (*Continued*)

The number of lines required to interconnect any number of stations is determined by the following equation:

$$N = \frac{n(n-1)}{2}$$ (10-1)

where n = number of stations (parties)
       N = number of interconnecting lines

The number of dedicated lines necessary to interconnect 100 parties is

$$N = \frac{100(100-1)}{2} = 4950$$

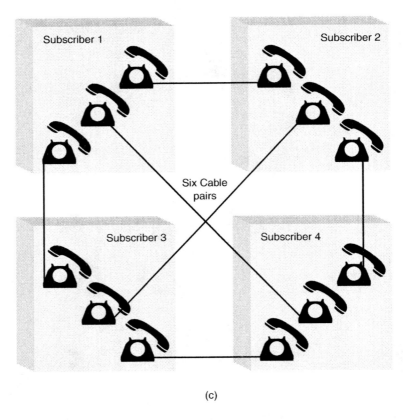

(c)

FIGURE 10-1 (*Continued*) (c) Interconnecting four subscribers

In addition, each station would require either 100 separate telephones or the capability of switching one telephone to any of 99 lines.

These limitations rapidly led to the development of the *central telephone exchange*. A telephone exchange allows any telephone connected to it to be interconnected to any of the other telephones connected to the exchange without requiring separate cable pairs and telephones for each connection. Generally, a community is served by only one telephone company. The community is divided into zones, and each zone is served by a different central telephone exchange. The number of stations served and the density determine the number of zones established in a given community. If a subscriber in one zone wishes to call a station in another zone, a minimum of two local exchanges is required.

10-6 OPERATOR-ASSISTED LOCAL EXCHANGES

The first commercial telephone switchboard began operation in New Haven, Connecticut, on January 28, 1878, marking the birth of the public switched telephone network. The switchboard served 21 telephones attached to only eight lines (obviously, some were party lines). On February 17 of the same year, Western Union opened the first large-city exchange in San Francisco, California, and on February 21, the New Haven District Telephone Company published the world's first telephone directory comprised of a single page listing only 50 names. The directory was immediately followed by a more comprehensive listing by the Boston Telephone Dispatch Company.

The first local telephone exchanges were *switchboards* (sometimes called *patch panels* or *patch boards*) where manual interconnects were accomplished using *patchcords* and

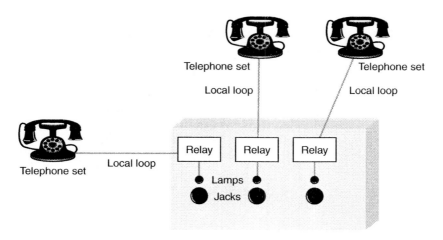

FIGURE 10-2   Patch panel configuration

jacks. All subscriber stations were connected through local loops to jacks on the switchboard. Whenever someone wished to initiate a call, they sent a ringing signal to the switchboard by manually turning a crank on their telephone. The ringing signal operated a relay at the switchboard, which in turn illuminated a supervisory lamp located above the jack for that line, as shown in Figure 10-2. Manual switchboards remained in operation until 1978, when the Bell System replaced their last cord switchboard on Santa Catalina Island off the coast of California near Los Angeles.

In the early days of telephone exchanges, each telephone line could have 10 or more subscribers (residents) connected to the central office exchange using the same local loop. This is called a *party line,* although only one subscriber could use their telephone at a time. Party lines are less expensive than private lines, but they are also less convenient. A private telephone line is more expensive because only telephones from one residence or business are connected to a local loop.

Connecting 100 private telephone lines to a single exchange required 100 local loops and a switchboard equipped with 100 relays, jacks, and lamps. When someone wished to initiate a telephone call, they rang the switchboard. An operator answered the call by saying, "Central." The calling party told the operator whom they wished to be connected to. The operator would then ring the destination, and when someone answered the telephone, the operator would remove her plug from the jack and connect the calling and called parties together with a special patchcord equipped with plugs on both ends. This type of system was called a *ringdown* system. If only a few subscribers were connected to a switchboard, the operator had little trouble keeping track of which jacks were for which subscriber (usually by name). However, as the popularity of the telephone grew, it soon became necessary to assign each subscriber line a unique telephone number. A switchboard using four digits could accommodate 10,000 telephone numbers (0000 to 9999).

Figure 10-3a shows a central office patch panel connected to four idle subscriber lines. Note that none of the telephone lines is connected to any of the other telephone lines. Figure 10-3b shows how subscriber 1 can be connected to subscriber 2 using a temporary connection provided by placing a patchcord between the jack for line 1 and the jack for line 2. Any subscriber can be connected to any other subscriber using patchcords.

(a)

(b)

FIGURE 10-3 Central office exchange: (a) without interconnects; (b) with an interconnect

10-7 AUTOMATED CENTRAL OFFICE SWITCHES AND EXCHANGES

As the number of telephones in the United States grew, it quickly became obvious that operator-assisted calls and manual patch panels could not meet the high demand for service. Thus, automated switching machines and exchange systems were developed.

An *automated switching system* is a system of sensors, switches, and other electrical and electronic devices that allows subscribers to give instructions directly to the switch without having to go through an operator. In addition, automated switches performed interconnections between subscribers without the assistance of a human and without using patchcords.

In 1890 an undertaker in Kansas City, Kansas, named Alman Brown Strowger was concerned that telephone company operators were diverting his business to his competitors. Consequently, he invented the first automated switching system using electromechanical relays. It is said that Strowger worked out his original design using a cardboard box, straight pins, and a pencil.

With the advent of the Strowger switch, mechanical dialing mechanisms were added to the basic telephone set. The mechanical dialer allowed subscribers to manually dial the telephone number of the party they wished to call. After a digit was entered (dialed), a relay in the switching machine connected the caller to another relay. The relays were called *stepping relays* because the system stepped through a series of relays as the digits were entered. The stepping process continued until all the digits of the telephone number were entered. This type of switching machine was called a *step-by-step* (SXS) switch, *stepper*, or, perhaps more commonly, a *Strowger* switch. A step-by-step switch is an example of a progressive switching machine, meaning that the connection between the calling and called parties was accomplished through a series of steps.

Between the early 1900s and the mid-1960s, the Strowger switch gradually replaced manual switchboards. The Bell System began using steppers in 1919 and continued using them until the early 1960s. In 1938, the Bell System began replacing the steppers with another electromechanical switching machine called the *crossbar* (XBAR) *switch*. The first No. 1 crossbar was cut into service at the Troy Avenue central office in Brooklyn, New York, on February 14, 1938. The crossbar switch used sets of contact points (called *crosspoints*) mounted on horizontal and vertical bars. Electromagnets were used to cause a vertical bar to cross a horizontal bar and make contact at a coordinate determined by the called number. The most versatile and popular crossbar switch was the #5XB. Although crossbar switches were an improvement over step-by-step switches, they were short lived, and most of them have been replaced with *electronic switching systems* (ESS).

In 1965, AT&T introduced the No. 1 ESS, which was the first computer-controlled central office switching system used on the PSTN. ESS switches differed from their predecessors in that they incorporate *stored program control* (SPC), which uses software to control practically all the switching functions. SPC increases the flexibility of the switch, dramatically increases its reliability, and allows for automatic monitoring of maintenance capabilities from a remote location. Virtually all the switching machines in use today are electronic stored program control switching machines. SPC systems require little maintenance and require considerably less space than their electromechanical predecessors. SPC systems make it possible for telephone companies to offer the myriad of services available today, such as three-way calling, call waiting, caller identification, call forwarding, call within, speed dialing, return call, automatic redial, and call tracing. Electronic switching systems evolved from the No. 1 ESS to the No. 5 ESS, which is the most advanced digital switching machine developed by the Bell System.

Automated central office switches paved the way for totally *automated central office exchanges*, which allow a caller located virtually anywhere in the world to direct dial virtually anyone else in the world. Automated central office exchanges interpret telephone numbers as an address on the PSTN. The network automatically locates the called number, tests its availability, and then completes the call.

10-7-1 Circuits, Circuit Switches, and Circuit Switching

A *circuit* is simply the path over which voice, data, or video signals propagate. In telecommunications terminology, a circuit is the path between a source and a destination (i.e., between a calling and a called party). Circuits are sometimes called *lines* (as in telephone lines). A *circuit switch* is a programmable matrix that allows circuits to be connected to one another. Telephone company circuit switches interconnect input loop or trunk circuits to output loop or trunk circuits. The switches are capable of interconnecting any circuit connected to it to any other circuit connected to it. For this reason, the switching process is called *circuit switching* and, therefore, the public telephone network is considered a *circuit-switched network*. Circuit switches are *transparent*. That is, they interconnect circuits without altering the information on them. Once a circuit switching operation has been performed, a transparent switch simply provides continuity between two circuits.

Telephone exchanges are strategically placed around a city to minimize the distance between a subscriber's location and the exchange and also to optimize the number of stations connected to any one exchange. The size of the service area covered by an exchange depends on subscriber density and subscriber calling patterns. Today, there are over 20,000 local exchanges in the United States.

Exchanges connected directly to local loops are appropriately called *local exchanges*. Because local exchanges are centrally located within the area they serve, they are often called *central offices* (CO). Local exchanges can directly interconnect any two subscribers whose local loops are connected to the same local exchange. Figure 10-4a shows a local exchange with six telephones connected to it. Note that all six telephone numbers begin with 87. One subscriber of the local exchange can call another subscriber by simply dialing their seven-digit telephone number. The switching machine performs all tests and switching operations necessary to complete the call. A telephone call completed within a single local exchange is called an *intraoffice call* (sometimes called an *intraswitch* call). Figure 10-4b shows how two stations serviced by the same exchange (874-3333 to 874-4444) are interconnected through a common local switch.

In the days of manual patch panels, to differentiate telephone numbers in one local exchange from telephone numbers in another local exchange and to make it easier for people to

(a)

(b)

FIGURE 10-4 Local exchange: (a) no interconnections;
(b) 874-3333 connected to 874-4444

remember telephone numbers, each exchange was given a name, such as Bronx, Redwood, Swift, Downtown, Main, and so on. The first two digits of a telephone number were derived from the first two letters of the exchange name. To accommodate the names with dial telephones, the digits 2 through 9 were each assigned three letters. Originally, only 24 of the 26 letters were assigned (Q and Z were omitted); however, modern telephones assign all 26 letters to oblige personalizing telephone numbers (the digits 7 and 9 are now assigned four letters each). As an example, telephone numbers in the Bronx exchange begin with 27 (B on a telephone dial equates to the digit 2, and R on a telephone dial equates to the digit 7). Using this system, a seven-digit telephone number can accommodate 100,000 telephone numbers. For example, the Bronx exchange was assigned telephone numbers between 270-0000 and 279-9999 inclusive. The same 100,000 numbers could also be assigned to the Redwood exchange (730-0000 to 739-9999).

10-7-3 Interoffice Trunks, Tandem Trunks, and Tandem Switches

Interoffice calls are calls placed between two stations that are connected to different local exchanges. Interoffice calls are sometimes called *interswitch* calls. Interoffice calls were originally accomplished by placing special plugs on the switchboards that were connected to cable pairs going to local exchange offices in other locations around the city or in nearby towns. Today telephone-switching machines in local exchanges are interconnected to other local exchange offices on special facilities called *trunks* or, more specifically, *interoffice trunks*. A subscriber in one local exchange can call a subscriber connected to another local exchange over an interoffice trunk circuit in much the same manner that they would call a subscriber connected to the same exchange. When a subscriber on one local exchange dials the telephone number of a subscriber on another local exchange, the two local exchanges are interconnected with an interoffice trunk for the duration of the call. After either party terminates the call, the interoffice trunk is disconnected from the two local loops and made available for another interoffice call. Figure 10-5 shows three exchange offices with

FIGURE 10-5 Interoffice exchange system

FIGURE 10-6 Interoffice call between subscribers serviced by two different exchanges

two subscribers connected to each. The telephone numbers for subscribers connected to the Bronx, Swift, and Uptown exchanges begin with the digits 27, 79, and 87, respectively. Figure 10-6 shows how two subscribers connected to different local exchanges can be interconnected using an interoffice trunk.

In larger metropolitan areas, it is virtually impossible to provide interoffice trunk circuits between all the local exchange offices. To interconnect local offices that do not have interoffice trunks directly between them, tandem offices are used. A *tandem office* is an exchange without any local loops connected to it (tandem meaning "in conjunction with" or "associated with"). The only facilities connected to the switching machine in a tandem office are trunks. Therefore, tandem switches interconnect local offices only. A *tandem switch* is called a *switcher's switch,* and trunk circuits that terminate in tandem switches are appropriately called *tandem trunks* or sometimes *intermediate trunks.*

Figure 10-7 shows two exchange areas that can be interconnected either with a tandem switch or through an interoffice trunk circuit. Note that tandem trunks are used to connect the Bronx and Uptown exchanges to the tandem switch. There is no name given to the tandem switch because there are no subscribers connected directly to it (i.e., no one receives dial tone from the tandem switch). Figure 10-8 shows how a subscriber in the Uptown exchange area is connected to a subscriber in the Bronx exchange area through a tandem switch. As the figure shows, tandem offices do not eliminate interoffice trunks. Very often, local offices have the capabilities to be interconnected with direct interoffice trunks as well as through a tandem office. When a telephone call is made from one local office to another, an interoffice trunk is selected if one is available. If not, a route through a tandem office is the second choice.

FIGURE 10-7 Interoffice switching between two local exchanges using tandem trunks and a tandem switch

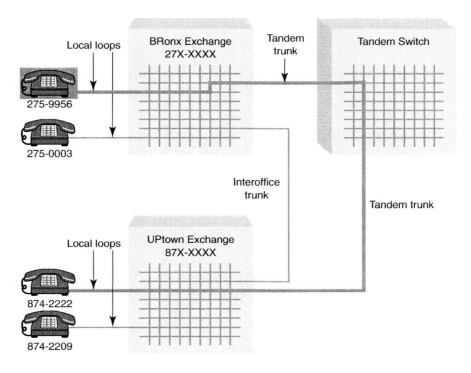

FIGURE 10-8 Interoffice call between two local exchanges through a tandem switch

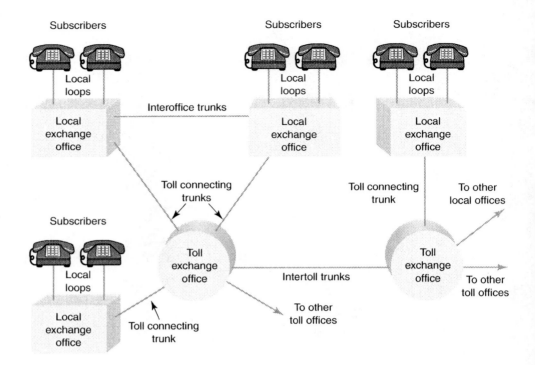

FIGURE 10-9 Relationship between local exchange offices and toll offices

10-7-4 Toll-Connecting Trunks, Intertoll Trunks, and Toll Offices

Interstate long-distance telephone calls require a special telephone office called a *toll office*. There are approximately 1200 toll offices in the United States. When a subscriber initiates a long-distance call, the local exchange connects the caller to a toll office through a facility called a *toll-connecting trunk* (sometimes called an *interoffice toll trunk*). Toll offices are connected to other toll offices with *intertoll trunks*. Figure 10-9 shows how local exchanges are connected to toll offices and how toll offices are connected to other toll offices. Figure 10-10 shows the network relationship between local exchange offices, tandem offices, toll offices, and their respective trunk circuits.

10-8 NORTH AMERICAN TELEPHONE NUMBERING PLAN AREAS

The *North American Telephone Numbering Plan* (NANP) was established to provide a telephone numbering system for the United States, Mexico, and Canada that would allow any subscriber in North America to direct dial virtually any other subscriber without the assistance of an operator. The network is often referred to as the DDD (*direct distance dialing*) network. Prior to the establishment of the NANP, placing a long-distance telephone call began by calling the long-distance operator and having her manually connect you to a trunk circuit to the city you wished to call. Any telephone number outside the caller's immediate area was considered a long-distance call.

North America is now divided into *numbering plan areas* (NPAs) with each NPA assigned a unique three-digit number called an *area code*. Each NPA is further subdivided into smaller service areas each with its own three-digit number called an *exchange code* (or

FIGURE 10-10   Relationship between local exchanges, tandem offices, and toll offices

prefix). Initially, each service area had only one central telephone switching office and one prefix. However, today a switching office can be assigned several exchange codes, depending on user density and the size of the area the office services. Each subscriber to a central office prefix is assigned a four-digit *extension number.* The three-digit area code represents the first three digits of a 10-digit telephone number, the three-digit prefix represents the next three digits, and the four-digit extension represents the last four digits of the telephone number.

Initially, within the North American Telephone Numbering Plan Area, if a digit could be any value from 0 through 9, the variable X designated it. If a digit could be any value from 2 through 9, the variable N designated it. If a digit could be only a 1 or a 0, it was designated by the variable 1/0 (one or zero). Area codes were expressed as N(1/0)N and exchange codes as NNX. Therefore, area codes could not begin or end with the digit 0 or 1, and the middle digit had to be either a 0 or a 1. Because of limitations imposed by electromechanical switching machines, the first two digits of exchange codes could not be 0 or 1, although the third digit could be any digit from 0 to 9. The four digits in the extension could be any digit value from 0 through 9. In addition, each NPA or area code could not have more than one local exchange with the same exchange code, and no two extension numbers within any exchanges codes could have the same four-digit number. The 18-digit telephone number was expressed as

$$N(1/0)N \text{ - } NNX \text{ - } XXXX$$

area code   prefix   extension

With the limitations listed for area codes, there were

$$N(1/0)N$$
$$(8)(2)(8) = 128 \text{ possibilities}$$

Each area code was assigned a cluster of exchange codes. In each cluster, there were

$$(N)(N)(X)$$
$$(8)(8)(10) = 640 \text{ possibilities}$$

Each exchange code served a cluster of extensions, in which there were

$$(X)(X)(X)(X)$$
$$(10)(10)(10)(10) = 10,000 \text{ possibilities}$$

With this numbering scheme, there were a total of $(128)(640)(10,000) = 819,200,000$ telephone numbers possible in North America.

When the NANP was initially placed into service, local exchange offices dropped their names and converted to their exchange number. Each exchange had 10 possible exchange codes. For example, the Bronx exchange was changed to 27 ($B = 2$ and $r = 7$). Therefore, it could accommodate the prefixes 270 through 279. Although most people do not realize it, telephone company employees still refer to local exchanges by their name. In January 1958, Wichita Falls, Texas, became the first American city to incorporate a true all-number calling system using a seven-digit number without attaching letters or names.

The popularity of cellular telephone has dramatically increased the demand for telephone numbers. By 1995, North America ran out of NPA area codes, so the requirement that the second digit be a 1 or a 0 was dropped. This was made possible because by 1995 there were very few electromagnetic switching machines in use in North America, and with the advent of SS7 signaling networks, telephone numbers no longer had to be transported over voice switching paths. This changed the numbering scheme to NXN-NNX-XXXX, which increased the number of area codes to 640 and the total number of telephones to 4,096,000,000. Figure 10-11 shows the North American Telephone Numbering Plan Areas as of January 2002.

The International Telecommunications Union has adopted an international numbering plan that adds a prefix in front of the area code, which outside North America is called a *city code*. The city code is one, two, or three digits long. For example, to call London, England, from the United States, one must dial 011-44-491-222-111. The 011 indicates an international call, 44 is the country code for England, 491 is the city code for London, 222 is the prefix for Piccadilly, and 111 is the three-digit extension number of the party you wish to call.

10-9 TELEPHONE SERVICE

A telephone connection may be as simple as two telephones and a single local switching office, or it may involve a multiplicity of communications links including several switching offices, transmission facilities, and telephone companies.

Telephone sets convert acoustic energy to electrical signals and vice versa. In addition, they also generate supervisory signals and address information. The subscriber loop provides a two-way path for conveying speech and data information and for exchanging ringing, switching, and supervisory signals. Since the telephone set and the subscriber loop are permanently associated with a particular subscriber, their combined transmission properties can be adjusted to meet their share of the total message channel objectives. For example, the higher efficiencies of new telephone sets and modems compensate for increased loop loss, permitting longer loop lengths or using smaller-gauge wire.

The small percentage of time (approximately 10% during busy hours) that a subscriber loop is utilized led to the development of line concentrators between subscribers and central offices. A concentrator allows many subscribers to share a limited number of lines

FIGURE 10-11 North American Telephone Numbering Plan Areas

to a central office switch. For example, there may be 100 subscriber loops connected to one side of a concentrator and only 10 lines connected between the concentrator and the central office switch. Therefore, only 10 of 100 (10%) of the subscribers could actually access the local office at any one time. The line from a concentrator to the central office is essentially a trunk circuit because it is shared (common usage) among many subscribers on an "as needed" basis. As previously described, trunk circuits of various types are used to interconnect local offices to other local offices, local offices to toll offices, and toll offices to other toll offices.

When subscribers are connected to a toll office through toll-connecting trunks, the message signal is generally handled on a two-wire basis (both directions of transmission on the same pair of wires). After appropriate switching and routing functions are performed at toll offices, messages are generally connected to intertoll trunks by means of a two-wire-to-four-wire *terminating set* (*term set* or *hybrid*), which splits the two directions of signal propagation so that the actual long-distance segment of the route can be accomplished on a four-wire basis (separate cable pairs for each direction). Signals are connected through intertoll trunks to remote toll-switching centers, which may in turn be connected by intertoll trunks to other toll-switching centers and ultimately reach the recipient of the call through a toll-connecting trunk, a local office, another four-wire-to-two-wire term set, a local switching office, and a final subscriber loop as shown in Figure 10-12. A normal two-point

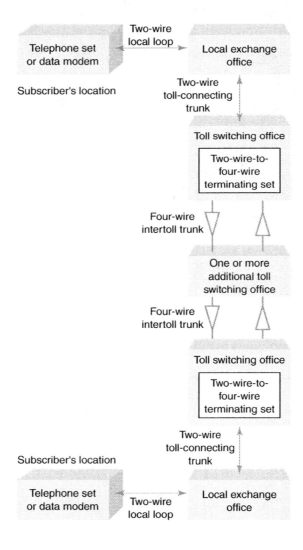

FIGURE 10-12 Long-distance telephone connection

telephone connection never requires more than two local exchange offices; however, there may be several toll-switching offices required, depending on the location of the originating and destination stations.

10-10 NORTH AMERICAN TELEPHONE SWITCHING HIERARCHY

With the advent of automated switching centers, a hierarchy of switching exchanges evolved in North America to accommodate the rapid increase in demand for long-distance calling. Thus, telephone company switching plans include a *switching hierarchy* that allows a certain degree of route selection when establishing a telephone call. A *route* is simply a path between two subscribers and is comprised of one or more switches, two local loops, and possibly one or more trunk circuits. The choice of routes is not offered to subscribers.

Telephone company switches, using software translation, select the best route available at the time a call is placed. The best route is not necessarily the shortest route. The best route is most likely the route requiring the fewest number of switches and trunk circuits. If a call cannot be completed because the necessary trunk circuits or switching paths are not available, the calling party receives an equipment (fast) busy signal. This is called *blocking*. Based on telephone company statistics, the likelihood that a call be blocked is approximately 1 in 100,000. Because software translations in automatic switching machines permit the use of alternate routes and each route may include several trunk circuits, the probability of using the same facilities on identical calls is unlikely. This is an obvious disadvantage of using the PSTN for data transmission because inconsistencies in transmission parameters occur from call to call.

10-10-1 Classes of Switching Offices

Before the divestiture of AT&T in 1984, the Bell System North American Switching Hierarchy consisted of five ranks or classes of switching centers as shown in Figure 10-13. The

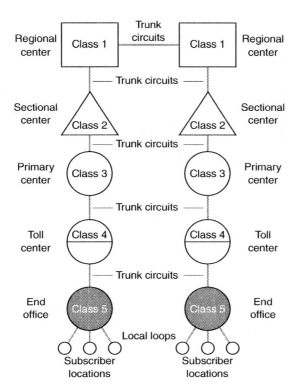

FIGURE 10-13 AT&T switching hierarchy prior to the 1984 divestiture

highest-ranking office was the regional center, and the lowest-ranking office was the end office. The five classifications of switching offices were as follows.

10-10-1-1 Class 5 end office. A class 5 office is a local exchange where subscriber loops terminated and received dial tone. End offices interconnected subscriber loops to other subscriber loops and subscriber loops to tandem trunks, interoffice trunks, and toll-connecting trunks. Subscribers received unlimited local call service in return for payment of a fixed charge each month, usually referred to as a *flat rate.* Some class 5 offices were classified as class 4/5. This type of office was called an *access tandem office,* as it was located in rural, low-volume areas and served as a dedicated class 5 office for local subscribers and also performed some of the functions of a class 4 toll office for long-distance calls.

10-10-1-2 Class 4 toll center. There were two types of class 4 offices. The class 4C toll centers provided human operators for both outward and inward calling service. Class 4P offices usually had only outward operator service or perhaps no operator service at all. Examples of operator-assisted services are person-to-person calls, collect calls, and credit card calls. Class 4 offices concentrated traffic in one switching center to direct outward traffic to the proper end office. Class 4 offices also provided centralized billing, provided toll customers with operator assistance, processed toll and intertoll traffic through its switching system, and converted signals from one trunk to another.

Class 3, 2, and 1 offices were responsible for switching intertoll-type calls efficiently and economically; to concentrate, collect, and distribute intertoll traffic; and to interconnect intertoll calls to all points of the direct distance dialing (DDD) network.

10-10-1-3 Class 3 primary center. This office provided service to small groups of class 4 offices within a small area of a state. Class 3 offices provided no operator assistance; however, they could serve the same switching functions as class 4 offices. A class 3 office generally had direct trunks to either a sectional or regional center.

10-10-1-4 Class 2 sectional center. Sectional centers could provide service to geographical regions varying in size from part of a state to all of several states, depending on population density. No operator services were provided; however, a class 2 office could serve the same switching functions as class 3 and class 4 offices.

10-10-1-5 Class 1 regional center. Regional centers were the highest-ranking office in the DDD network in terms of the size of the geographical area served and the trunking options available. Ten regional centers were located in the United States and two in Canada. Class 1 offices provided no operator services; however, they could serve the same switching functions as class 2, 3, or 4 offices. Class 1 offices had direct trunks to all the other regional centers.

10-10-2 Switching Routes

Regional centers served a large area called a *region.* Each region was subdivided into smaller areas called *sections,* which were served by primary centers. All remaining switching centers that did not fall into these categories were toll centers or end offices. The switching hierarchy provided a systematic and efficient method of handling long-distance telephone calls using hierarchical routing principles and various methods of automatic *alternate routing.* Alternate routing is a simple concept: If one route (path) is not available, select an alternate route that is available. Therefore, alternate routing often caused many toll offices to be interconnected in tandem to complete a call. When alternate routing is used, the actual path a telephone call takes may not resemble what the subscriber actually dialed. For example, a call placed between Phoenix, Arizona, and San Diego, California, may be routed from Phoenix to Albuquerque to Las Vegas to Los Angeles to San Diego. Common switching control equipment may have to add to, subtract from, or change the dialed information when

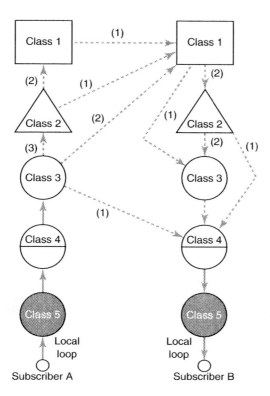

FIGURE 10-14   Choices of switching routes

routing a call to its destination. For example, an exchange office may have to add a prefix to a call with one, two, or three routing digits just to advance the call through an alternate route.

The five-class switching hierarchy is a *progressive switching scheme* that establishes an end-to-end route mainly through trial and error. Progressive switching is slow and unreliable by today's standards, as signaling messages are transported over the same facilities as subscriber's conversations using analog signals, such as multifrequency (MF) tones. Figure 10-14 shows examples of several choices for routes between subscriber A and subscriber B. For this example, there are 10 routes to choose from, of which only one requires the maximum of seven *intermediate links*. Intermediate links are toll trunks in tandem, excluding the two terminating links at the ends of the connection. In Figure 10-14, the first-choice route requires two intermediate links. Intermediate links are not always required, as in many cases a single *direct link,* which would be the first choice, exists between the originating and destination toll centers.

For the telephone office layout shown in Figure 10-15, the simplest connection would be a call between subscribers 1 and 2 in city A who are connected to the same end office. In this case, no trunk circuits are required. An interoffice call between stations 1 and 3 in city A would require using two tandem trunk circuits with an interconnection made in a tandem office. Consider a call originating from subscriber 1 in city A intended for subscriber 4 in city B. The route begins with subscriber 1 connected to end office 1 through a local loop. From the end office, the route uses a toll-connecting trunk to the toll center in city A. Between city A and city B, there are several route choices available. Because there is a high community of interest between the two cities, there is a direct intertoll trunk between City A and City B, which would be the first choice. However, there is an alternate route between city A and city B through the primary center in city C, which would probably be the second choice. From the primary center, there is a direct, high-usage intertoll trunk to both city A

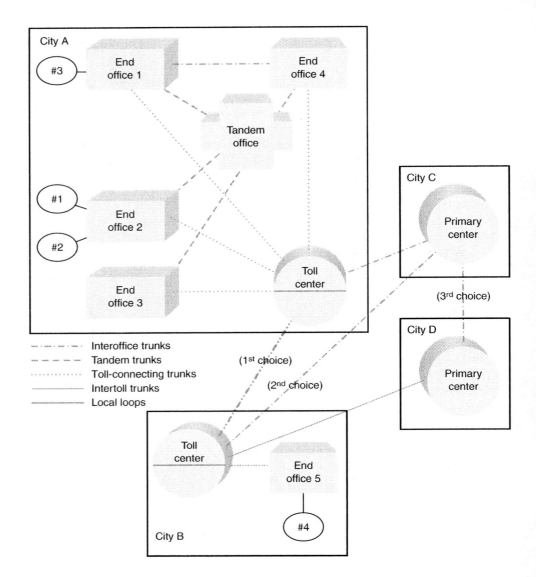

Interoffice trunks
Tandem trunks
Toll-connecting trunks
Intertoll trunks
Local loops

FIGURE 10-15 Typical switching routes

and city B (possibly the third choice), or, as a last resort, the toll centers in city A and city B could be interconnected using the primary centers in city C and city D (fourth choice).

The probability that a telephone call would require more than n links in tandem to reach the final destination decreases rapidly as n increases from 2 to 7. This is primarily because a large majority of long-distance toll calls are made between end offices associated with the same regional switching center, which of course would require fewer than seven toll trunks. Although the maximum number of trunks is seven, the average number for a typical toll call is only three. In addition, even when a telephone call was between telephones associated with different regional centers, the call was routed over the maximum of seven intermediate trunks only when all the normally available high-usage trunks are busy. The probability of this happening is only ρ^5, where ρ is the probability that all trunks in any one high-usage group are busy. Finally, many calls do not originate all the way down the hierarchy since each higher class of office will usually have class 5 offices homing on it that will act as class 4 offices for them.

Common Channel Signaling System No. 7 (i.e., SS7 or C7) is a global standard for telecommunications defined by the International Telecommunications Union (ITU) Telecommunications Sector (ITU-T). SS7 was developed as an alternate and much improved means of transporting signaling information through the public telephone network. The SS7 standard defines the procedures and protocol necessary to exchange information over the PSTN using a separate digital signaling network to provide wireless (cellular) and wireline telephone call setup, routing, and control. SS7 determines the switching path before any switches are actually enabled, which is a much faster and more reliable switching method than the old five-class progressive switching scheme. The SS7 signaling network performs its functions by exchanging telephone control messages between the SS7 components that support completing the subscribers' connection.

The functions of the SS7 network and protocol are as follows:

1. Basic call setup, management, and tear-down procedures
2. Wireless services, such as personal communications services (PCS), wireless roaming, and mobile subscriber authentication
3. Local number portability (LNP)
4. Toll-free (800/888) and toll (900) wire-line services
5. Enhanced call features, such as call forwarding, calling party name/number display, and three-way calling
6. Efficient and secure worldwide telecommunications service

10-11-1 Evolution of SS7

When telephone networks and network switching hierarchies were first engineered, their creators gave little thought about future technological advancements. Early telephone systems were based on transferring analog voice signals using analog equipment over analog transmission media. As a result, early telephone systems were not well suited for modern-day digital services, such as data, digitized voice, or digitized video transmission. Therefore, when digital services were first offered in the early 1960s, the telephone networks were ill prepared to handle them, and the need for an intelligent all-digital network rapidly became evident.

The ITU commissioned the Comiteé Consultatif International Téléphonique et Télégraphique (CCITT) to study the possibility of developing an intelligent all-digital telecommunications network. In the mid-1960s, the ITU-TS (International Telecommunications Union Telecommunications—Standardization Sector) developed a digital signaling standard known as *Signaling System No. 6* (SS6) that modernized the telephone industry. *Signaling* refers to the exchange of information between call components required to provide and maintain service. SS6, based on a proprietary, high-speed data communications network, evolved into *Signaling System No. 7* (SS7), which is now the telephone industry standard for most of the civilized world ("civilized world" because it was estimated that in 2002, more than half the people in the world had never used a telephone). High-speed packet data and out-of-band signaling characterize SS7. Out-of-band signaling is signaling that does not take place over the same path as the conversation. Out-of-band signaling establishes a separate digital channel for exchanging signaling information. This channel is called a *signaling link*.

The protocol used with SS7 uses a message structure, similar to X.25 and other message-based protocols, to request services from other networks. The messages propagate from one network to another in small bundles of data called *packets* that are independent of the subscriber voice or data signals they pertain to. In the early 1960s, the ITU-TS developed a *common channel signaling* (CCS) known as *Common Channel Interoffice Signaling System No. 6* (SS6). The basic concept of the common channel signaling is to use a facility (separate from the voice facilities) for transferring control and signaling information between telephone offices.

When first deployed in the United States, SS6 used a packet switching network with 2.4-kbps data links, which were later upgraded to 4.8 kbps. Signaling messages were sent as part of a data packet and used to request connections on voice trunks between switching offices. SS6 was the first system to use packet switching in the PSTN. Packets consisted of a block of data comprised of 12 signal units of 28 bits each, which is similar to the method used today with SS7.

SS7 is an architecture for performing out-of-band signaling in support of common telephone system functions, such as call establishment, billing, call routing, and information exchange functions of the PSTN. SS7 identifies functions and enables protocols performed by a telephone signaling network. The major advantages of SS7 include better monitoring, maintenance, and network administration. The major disadvantage is its complex coding.

Because SS7 evolved from SS6, there are many similarities between the two systems. SS7 uses variable-length signal units with a maximum length, therefore making it more versatile and flexible than SS6. In addition, SS7 uses 56-kbps data links (64 kbps for international links), which provide a much faster and efficient signaling network. In the future, data rates of 1.544 Mbps nationally and 2.048 Mbps internationally are expected.

In 1983 (just prior to the AT&T divestiture), SS6 was still widely used in the United States. When SS7 came into use in the mid-1980s, SS6 began to be phased out of the system, although SS6 was still used in local switching offices for several more years. SS7 was originally used for accessing remote databases rather than for call setup and termination. In the 1980s, AT&T began offering Wide Area Telephone Service (WATS), which uses a common 800 area code regardless of the location of the destination. Because of the common area code, telephone switching systems had a problem dealing with WATS numbers. This is because telephone switches used the area code to route a call through the public switched network. The solution involved adding a second number to every 800 number that is used by the switching equipment to actually route a call through the voice network. The second number is placed in a common, centralized database accessible to all central offices. When an 800 number is called, switching equipment uses a data link to access the database and retrieve the actual routing number. This process is, of course, transparent to the user. Once the routing number is known, the switching equipment can route the call using standard signaling methods.

Shortly after implementing the WATS network, the SS7 network was expanded to provide other services, such as call setup and termination. However, the database concept has proven to be the biggest advantage of SS7, as it can also be used to provide routing and billing information for all telephone services, including 800 and 900 numbers, 911 services, custom calling features, caller identifications, and a host of other services not yet invented.

In 1996, the FCC mandated *local number portability* (LNP), which requires all telephone companies to support the *porting* of a telephone number. Porting allows customers to change to a different service and still keep the same telephone number. For example, a subscriber may wish to change from *plain old telephone service* (POTS) to ISDN, which would have required changing telephone numbers. With LNP, the telephone number would remain the same because the SS7 database can be used to determine which network switch is assigned to a particular telephone number.

Today, SS7 is being used throughout the Bell Operating Companies telephone network and most of the independent telephone companies. This in itself makes SS7 the world's largest data communications network, as it links wireline telephone companies, cellular telephone companies, and long-distance telephone companies together with a common signaling system. Because SS7 has the ability to transfer all types of digital information, it supports most of the new telephone features and applications and is used with ATM, ISDN, and cellular telephone.

Today, the North American telephone system is divided into two distinct functional areas: signaling and switching. The signaling network for the telephone system is SS7, which is used to determine how subscriber's voice and data signals are routed through the network. The switching network is the portion of the telephone network that actually transports the voice and data from one subscriber to another. The signaling part of the network establishes and disconnects the circuits that actually carry the subscriber's information.

After the divestiture of AT&T, technological advances allowed many of the functions distributed among the five classes of telephone offices to be combined. In addition, switching equipment was improved, giving them the capability to act as local switches, tandem switches, or toll switches. The new North American Switching Hierarchy consolidated many of the functions of the old hierarchy into two layers, with many of the functions once performed by the higher layers being located in the end office. Therefore, the postdivestiture telephone network can no longer be described as a hierarchy of five classes of offices. It is now seen as a system involving two decision points. The postdivestiture North American Switching Hierarchy is shown in Figure 10-16. Long-distance access is now accomplished through an access point called the *point-of-presence* (POP). The term *point-of-presence* is a telecommunications term that describes the legal boundaries for the responsibility of maintaining equipment and transmission lines. In essence, it is a demarcation point separating two companies.

After the divestiture of AT&T, calling areas were redefined and changed to *Local Access and Transport Areas* (LATAs) with each LATA having its own three-level hierarchy. Although the United States was originally divided into only 160 local access and transport areas, there are presently over 300 LATA dispersed throughout the United States. Within these areas, local telephone companies provide the facilities and equipment to interconnect

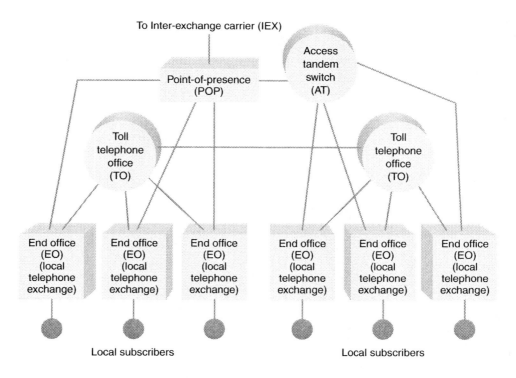

FIGURE 10-16 Postdivestiture North American Switching Hierarchy

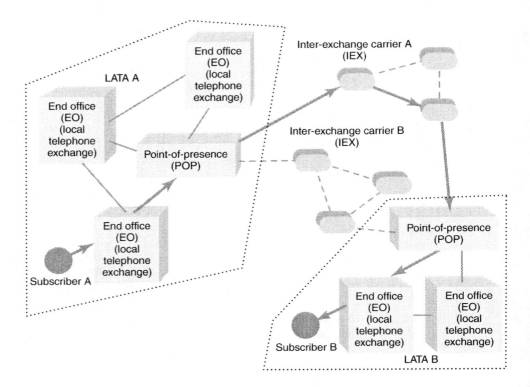

FIGURE 10-17 Example of an interexchange call between subscriber A in LATA A to subscriber B in LATA B

subscribers within the LATA. The telephone companies are called *local exchange carriers* (LECs), *exchange carriers* (ECs), *operating telephone companies* (OTCs), and *telephone operating companies* (TOCs). The areas serviced by local exchanges were redistributed by the Justice Department to provide telephone companies a more evenly divided area with equal revenue potential. Telephone calls made within a LATA are considered a function of the *intra-LATA network*.

Telephone companies further divided each LATA into a *local market* and a *toll market*. The toll market for a company is within its LATA but is still considered a long-distance call because it involves a substantial distance between the two local offices handling the call. These are essentially the only long-distance telephone calls local operating companies are allowed to provide, and they are very expensive. If the destination telephone number is in a different LATA than the originating telephone number, the operating company must switch to an *interexchange carrier* (IC, IEC, or IXC) selected by the calling party. In many cases, a direct connection is not possible, and an interexchange call must be switched first to an access tandem (AT) switch and then to the interexchange carrier point-of-presence. Figure 10-17 shows an example of an interexchange call between subscriber A in LATA A through interexchange carrier A to subscriber B in LATA B.

10-11-3 SS7 Signaling Points

Signaling points provide access to the SS7 network, access to databases used by switches inside and outside the network, and the transfer of SS7 messages to other signaling points within the network.

Every network has an addressing scheme to enable a node within the network to exchange signaling information with nodes it is not connected to by a physical link. Each node

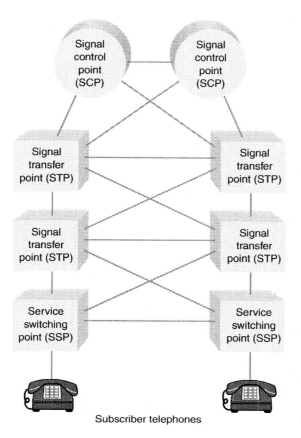

FIGURE 10-18 SS7 signaling point topology

Subscriber telephones

is uniquely identified by a numeric *point code*. Point codes are carried in signaling messages exchanged between signaling points to identify the source and destination of each message (i.e., an *originating point code* and a *destination point code*). Each signaling point is identified as a *member* part of a cluster of signaling points. Similarly, a cluster is defined as being part of a complete network. Therefore, every node in the American SS7 network can be addressed with a three-level code that is defined by its network, cluster, and member numbers. Each number is an eight-bit binary number between 0 and 255. This three-level address is called the *point code*. A point code uniquely identifies a signaling point within the SS7 network and is used whenever it is addressed. A neutral party assigns network codes on a nationwide basis. Because there are a limited number of network numbers, networks must meet a certain size requirement to receive one. Smaller networks may be assigned one or more cluster numbers within network numbers 1, 2, 3, and 4. The smallest networks are assigned point codes within network number 5. The cluster they are assigned to is determined by the state where they are located. Network number 0 is not available for assignment, and network number 255 is reserved for future use.

The three types of signaling points are listed here, and a typical SS7 topology is shown in Figure 10-18.

10-11-3-1 Service switching points (SSPs). Service switching points (sometimes called *signal switching points*) are local telephone switches (in either end or tandem offices) equipped with SS7-compatible software and terminating signal links. The SSP provides the functionality of communicating with the voice switch by creating the packets or signal units necessary for transmission over the SS7 network. An SSP must convert signaling information from voice switches into SS7 signaling format. SSPs are basically local access points that send signaling messages to other SSPs to originate, terminate, or switch calls. SSPs may also send query messages to centralized databases to determine how to route a call.

10-11-3-2 Signal transfer points (STPs). Signal transfer points are the packet switches of the SS7 network. STPs serve as routers in the SS7 network, as they receive and route incoming signaling messages to the proper destination. STPs seldom originate a message. STPs route each incoming message to an outgoing signaling link based on routing information contained in the SS7 message. Because an STP acts like a network router, it provides improved utilization of the SS7 network by eliminating the need for direct links between all signaling points.

10-11-3-3 Service control points (SCPs). Service control points (sometimes called *signal control points*) serve as an interface to telephone company databases. The databases store information about subscriber's services, routing of special service numbers (such as 800 and 900 numbers), and calling card validation for fraud protection and provide information necessary for advanced call-processing capabilities. SCPs also perform protocol conversion from SS7 to X.25, or they can provide the capability of communicating with the database directly using an interface called a *primitive,* which provides access from one level of the protocol to another level. SCPs also send responses to SSPs containing a routing number(s) associated with the called number.

SSPs, STPs, and SCPs are interconnected with digital carriers, such as T1 or DS-0 links, which carry the signaling messages between the SS7 network devices.

10-11-4   SS7 Call Setup Example

A typical call setup procedure using the SS7 signaling network is as follows:

1. Subscriber A goes off hook and touch tones out the destination telephone number of subscriber B.
2. The local telephone translates the tones to binary digits.
3. The local telephone exchange compares the digits to numbers stored in a routing table to determine whether subscriber B resides in the same local switch as subscriber A. If not, the call must be transferred onto an outgoing trunk circuit to another local exchange.
4. After the switch determines that subscriber B is served by a different local exchange, an SS7 message is sent onto the SS7 network. The purposes of the message are as follows:
   i. To find out if the destination number is idle.
   ii. If the destination number is idle, the SS7 network makes sure a connection between the two telephone numbers is also available.
   iii. The SS7 network instructs the destination switch to ring subscriber B.
5. When subscriber B answers the telephone, the switching path is completed.
6. When either subscriber A or subscriber B terminates the call by hanging up, the SS7 network releases the switching path, making the trunk circuits and switching paths available to other subscribers of the network.

10-1. What are the purposes of telephone network *signaling functions?*

10-2. What are the two types of subscribers to the public telephone network? Briefly describe them.

10-3. What is the difference between *dedicated* and *switched* facilities?

10-4. Describe the term *service provider.*

10-5. Briefly describe the following terms: *instruments, local loops, trunk circuits,* and *exchanges.*

10-6. What is a *local office telephone exchange?*

10-7. What is an *automated central office switch?*

10-8. Briefly describe the following terms: *circuits, circuit switches,* and *circuit switching.*

10-9. What is the difference between a *local telephone exchange* and an *exchange area?*

10-10. Briefly describe *interoffice trunks, tandem trunks,* and *tandem switches.*

10-11. Briefly describe *toll-connecting trunks, intertoll trunks,* and *toll offices.*

10-12. Briefly describe the *North American Telephone Numbering Plan.*

10-13. What is the difference between an *area code,* a *prefix,* and an *extension?*

10-14. What is meant by the term *common usage?*

10-15. What does *blocking* mean? When does it occur?

10-16. Briefly describe the *predivestiture North American Telephone Switching Hierarchy.*

10-17. Briefly describe the five *classes* of the predivestiture North American Switching Hierarchy.

10-18. What is meant by the term *switching route?*

10-19. What is meant by the term *progressive switching scheme?*

10-20. What is *SS7?*

10-21. What is *common channel signaling?*

10-22. What is meant by the term *local number portability?*

10-23. What is meant by the term *plain old telephone service?*

10-24. Briefly describe the *postdivestiture North American Switching Hierarchy.*

10-25. What is a LATA?

10-26. What is meant by the term *point-of-presence?*

10-27. Describe what is meant by the term *local exchange carrier.*

10-28. Briefly describe what is meant by SS7 *signaling points.*

10-29. List and describe the three SS7 signaling points.

10-30. What is meant by the term *point code?*

C H A P T E R   11

Cellular Telephone Concepts

OBJECTIVES

- Give a brief history of mobile telephone service
- Define *cellular telephone*
- Define *cell* and explain why it has a honeycomb shape
- Describe the following types of cells: macrocell, microcell, and minicell
- Describe edge-excited, center-excited, and corner-excited cells
- Define *service areas, clusters,* and *cells*
- Define *frequency reuse*
- Explain frequency reuse factor
- Define *interference*
- Describe co-channel and adjacent channel interference
- Describe the processes of cell splitting, sectoring, segmentation, and dualization
- Explain the differences between cell-site controllers and mobile telephone switching offices
- Define *base stations*
- Define and explain roaming and handoffs
- Briefly describe the purpose of the IS-41 protocol standard
- Define and describe the following cellular telephone network components: electronic switching center, cell-site controller, system interconnects, mobile and portable telephone units, and communications protocols
- Describe the cellular call procedures involved in making the following types of calls: mobile to wireline, mobile to mobile, and wireline to mobile

The basic concepts of *two-way mobile telephone* are quite simple; however, mobile telephone systems involve intricate and rather complex communications networks comprised of analog and digital communications methodologies, sophisticated computer-controlled switching centers, and involved protocols and procedures. Cellular telephone evolved from two-way mobile FM radio. The purpose of this chapter is to present the fundamental concepts of cellular telephone service. Cellular services include standard *cellular telephone service* (CTS), *personal communications systems* (PCS), and *personal communications satellite systems* (PCSS).

11-2 MOBILE TELEPHONE SERVICE

Mobile telephone services began in the 1940s and were called MTSs (*mobile telephone systems* or sometimes *manual telephone systems,* as all calls were handled by an operator). MTS systems utilized frequency modulation and were generally assigned a single carrier frequency in the 35-MHz to 45-MHz range that was used by both the mobile unit and the base station. The mobile unit used a push-to-talk (PTT) switch to activate the transceiver. Depressing the PTT button turned the transmitter on and the receiver off, whereas releasing the PTT turned the receiver on and the transmitter off. Placing a call from a MTS mobile telephone was similar to making a call through a manual switchboard in the public telephone network. When the PTT switch was depressed, the transmitter turned on and sent a carrier frequency to the base station, illuminating a lamp on a switchboard. An operator answered the call by plugging a headset into a jack on the switchboard. After the calling party verbally told the operator the telephone number they wished to call, the operator connected the mobile unit with a patchcord to a trunk circuit connected to the appropriate public telephone network destination office. Because there was only one carrier frequency, the conversation was limited to half-duplex operation, and only one conversation could take place at a time. The MTS system was comparable to a party line, as all subscribers with their mobile telephones turned on could hear any conversation. Mobile units called other mobile units by signaling the operator who rang the destination mobile unit. Once the destination mobile unit answered, the operator disconnected from the conversation, and the two mobile units communicated directly with one another through the airways using a single carrier frequency.

MTS mobile identification numbers had no relationship to the telephone numbering system used by the public telephone network. Local telephone companies in each state, which were generally Bell System Operating Companies, kept a record of the numbers assigned to MTS subscribers in that state. MTS numbers were generally five digits long and could not be accessed directly through the public switched telephone network (PSTN).

In 1964, the Improved Mobile Telephone System (IMTS) was introduced, which used several carrier frequencies and could, therefore, handle several simultaneous mobile conversations at the same time. IMTS subscribers were assigned a regular PSTN telephone number; therefore, callers could reach an IMTS mobile phone by dialing the PSTN directly, eliminating the need for an operator. IMTS and MTS base station transmitters outputted powers in the 100-W to 200-W range, and mobile units transmitted between 5 W and 25 W. Therefore, IMTS and MTS mobile telephone systems typically covered a wide area using only one base station transmitter.

Because of their high cost, limited availability, and narrow frequency allocation, early mobile telephone systems were not widely used. However, in recent years, factors such as technological advancements, wider frequency spectrum, increased availability, and improved reliability have stimulated a phenomenal increase in people's desire to talk on the telephone from virtually anywhere, at any time, regardless of whether it is necessary, safe, or productive.

Today, mobile telephone stations are small handsets, easily carried by a person in their pocket or purse. In early radio terminology, the term *mobile* suggested any radio transmitter, receiver, or transceiver that could be moved while in operation. The term *portable* described a relatively small radio unit that was handheld, battery powered, and easily carried by a person moving at walking speed. The contemporary definition of mobile has come to mean moving at high speed, such as in a boat, airplane, or automobile, or at low speed, such as in the pocket of a pedestrian. Hence, the modern, all-inclusive definition of mobile telephone is any wireless telephone capable of operating while moving at any speed, battery powered, and small enough to be easily carried by a person.

Cellular telephone is similar to two-way mobile radio in that most communications occurs between base stations and mobile units. Base stations are fixed-position transceivers with relatively high-power transmitters and sensitive receivers. Cellular telephones communicate directly with base stations. Cellular telephone is best described by pointing out the primary difference between it and two-way mobile radio. Two-way mobile radio systems operate half-duplex and use PTT transceivers. With PTT transceivers, depressing the PTT button turns on the transmitter and turns off the receiver, whereas releasing the PTT button turns on the receiver and turns off the transmitter. With two-way mobile telephone, all transmissions (unless scrambled) can be heard by any listener with a receiver tuned to that channel. Hence, two-way mobile radio is a *one-to-many* radio communications system. Examples of two-way mobile radio are *citizens band* (CB), which is an AM system, and *public land mobile radio,* which is a two-way FM system such as those used by police and fire departments. Most two-way mobile radio systems can access the public telephone network only through a special arrangement called an *autopatch,* and then they are limited to half-duplex operation where neither party can interrupt the other. Another limitation of two-way mobile radio is that transmissions are limited to relatively small geographic areas unless they utilize complicated and expensive repeater networks.

On the other hand, cellular telephone offers full-duplex transmissions and operates much the same way as the standard wireline telephone service provided to homes and businesses by local telephone companies. Mobile telephone is a *one-to-one* system that permits two-way simultaneous transmissions and, for privacy, each cellular telephone is assigned a unique telephone number. Coded transmissions from base stations activate only the intended receiver. With mobile telephone, a person can virtually call anyone with a telephone number, whether it be through a cellular or a wireline service.

Cellular telephone systems offer a relatively high user capacity within a limited frequency spectrum providing a significant innovation in solving inherent mobile telephone communications problems, such as spectral congestion and user capacity. Cellular telephone systems replaced mobile systems serving large areas (cells) operating with a single base station and a single high-power transmitter with many smaller areas (cells), each with its own base station and low-power transmitter. Each base station is allocated a fraction of the total channels available to the system, and adjacent cells are assigned different groups of channels to minimize interference between cells. When demand for service increases in a given area, the number of base stations can be increased, providing an increase in mobile-unit capacity without increasing the radio-frequency spectrum.

11-3 EVOLUTION OF CELLULAR TELEPHONE

In the July 28, 1945, *Saturday Evening Post,* E. K. Jett, then the commissioner of the FCC, hinted of a cellular telephone scheme that he referred to as simply a *small-zone* radio-telephone system. On June 17, 1946, in St. Louis, Missouri, AT&T and Southwestern Bell introduced the first American commercial mobile radio-telephone service to private customers. In the same year, similar services were offered to 25 major cities throughout the United States. Each city utilized one base station consisting of a high-powered transmitter and a sensitive receiver that were centrally located on a hilltop or tower that covered an area within a 30- to 50-mile radius of the base station. In 1947, AT&T introduced a radio-telephone service they called *highway service* between New York and Boston. The system operated in the 35-MHz to 45-MHz band.

The first half-duplex, PTT FM mobile telephone systems introduced in the 1940s operated in the 35-MHz to 45-MHz band and required 120-kHz bandwidth per channel. In the early 1950s, the FCC doubled the number of mobile telephone channels by reducing the bandwidth to 60 kHz per channel. In 1960, AT&T introduced direct-dialing, full-duplex mobile telephone service with other performance enhancements, and in 1968, AT&T proposed the concept of a cellular mobile system to the FCC with the intent of alleviating the problem of spectrum congestion in the existing mobile telephone systems. Cellular mobile telephone systems, such as the *Improved Mobile Telephone System* (IMTS), were developed, and recently developed miniature integrated circuits enabled management of the necessarily complex algorithms needed to control network switching and control operations. Channel bandwidth was again halved to 30 kHz, increasing the number of mobile telephone channels by twofold.

In 1966, Don Adams, in a television show called *Get Smart,* unveiled the most famous mobile telephone to date: the fully mobile shoe phone. Some argue that the 1966 *Batphone supra* was even more remarkable, but it remained firmly anchored to the Batmobile, limiting Batman and Robin to vehicle-based telephone communications.

In 1974, the FCC allocated an additional 40-MHz bandwidth for cellular telephone service (825 MHz to 845 MHz and 870 MHz to 890 MHz). These frequency bands were previously allocated to UHF television channels 70 to 83. In 1975, the FCC granted AT&T the first license to operate a developmental cellular telephone service in Chicago. By 1976, the Bell Mobile Phone service for metropolitan New York City (approximately 10 million people) offered only 12 channels that could serve a maximum of 543 subscribers. In 1976, the FCC granted authorization to the American Radio Telephone Service (ARTS) to install a second developmental system in the Baltimore–Washington, D.C., area. In 1983, the FCC allocated 666 30-kHz half-duplex mobile telephone channels to AT&T to form the first U.S. cellular telephone system called Advanced Mobile Phone System (AMPS).

In 1991, the first digital cellular services were introduced in several major U.S. cities, enabling a more efficient utilization of the available bandwidth using voice compression. The calling capacity specified in the U.S. Digital Cellular (USDC) standard (EIA IS-54) accommodates three times the user capacity of AMPS, which used conventional frequency modulation (FM) and frequency-division multiple accessing (FDMA). The USDC standard specifies digital modulation, speech coding, and time-division multiple accessing (TDMA). Qualcomm developed the first cellular telephone system based on code-division multiple accessing (CDMA). The Telecommunications Industry Association (TIA) standardized Qualcomm's system as Interim Standard 95 (IS-95). On November 17, 1998, a subsidiary of Motorola Corporation implemented Iridium, a satellite-based wireless personal communications satellite system (PCSS).

11-4 CELLULAR TELEPHONE

The key principles of *cellular telephone* (sometimes called *cellular radio*) were uncovered in 1947 by researchers at Bell Telephone Laboratories and other telecommunications companies throughout the world when they developed the basic concepts and theory of cellular telephone. It was determined that by subdividing a relatively large geographic market area, called a *coverage zone,* into small sections, called *cells,* the concept of *frequency reuse* could be employed to dramatically increase the capacity of a mobile telephone channel. Frequency reuse is described in a later section of this chapter. In essence, cellular telephone systems allow a large number of users to share the limited number of *common-usage* radio

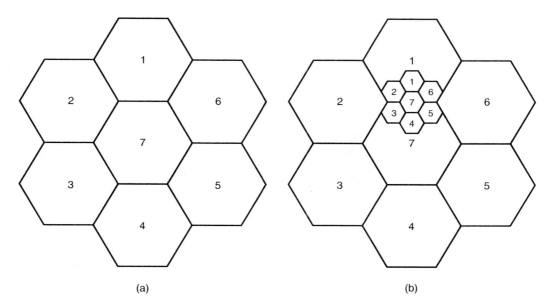

FIGURE 11-1 (a) Honeycomb cell pattern; (b) honeycomb pattern with two sizes of cells

channels available in a region. In addition, integrated-circuit technology, microprocessors and microcontroller chips, and the implementation of Signaling System No. 7 (SS7) have recently enabled complex radio and logic circuits to be used in electronic switching machines to store programs that provide faster and more efficient call processing.

11-4-1 Fundamental Concepts of Cellular Telephone

The fundamental concepts of cellular telephone are quite simple. The FCC originally defined geographic cellular radio coverage areas on the basis of modified 1980 census figures. With the cellular concept, each area is further divided into hexagonal-shaped cells that fit together to form a *honeycomb* pattern as shown in Figure 11-1a. The hexagon shape was chosen because it provides the most effective transmission by approximating a circular pattern while eliminating gaps inherently present between adjacent circles. A cell is defined by its physical size and, more importantly, by the size of its population and traffic patterns. The number of cells per system and the size of the cells are not specifically defined by the FCC and has been left to the providers to establish in accordance with anticipated traffic patterns. Each geographical area is allocated a fixed number of cellular voice channels. The physical size of a cell varies, depending on user density and calling patterns. For example, large cells (called *macrocells*) typically have a radius between 1 mile and 15 miles with base station transmit powers between 1 W and 6 W. The smallest cells (called *microcells*) typically have a radius of 1500 feet or less with base station transmit powers between 0.1 W and 1 W. Figure 11-1b shows a cellular configuration with two sizes of cell.

Microcells are used most often in high-density areas such as found in large cities and inside buildings. By virtue of their low effective working radius, microcells exhibit milder propagation impairments, such as reflections and signal delays. Macrocells may overlay clusters of microcells with slow-moving mobile units using the microcells and faster-moving units using the macrocells. The mobile unit is able to identify itself as either fast or slow moving, thus allowing it to do fewer cell transfers and location updates. Cell transfer algorithms can be modified to allow for the small distances between a mobile unit and the

FIGURE 11-2 Hexagonal cell grid superimposed over a metropolitan area

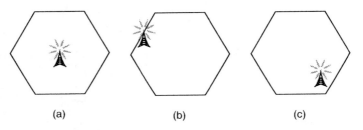

(a)   (b)   (c)

FIGURE 11-3 (a) Center excited cell; (b) edge excited cell; (c) corner excited cell

microcellular base station it is communicating with. Figure 11-2 shows what a hexagonal cell grid might look like when superimposed over a metropolitan area.

Occasionally, cellular radio signals are too weak to provide reliable communications indoors. This is especially true in well-shielded areas or areas with high levels of interference. In these circumstances, very small cells, called *picocells,* are used. Indoor picocells can use the same frequencies as regular cells in the same areas if the surrounding infrastructure is conducive, such as in underground malls.

When designing a system using hexagonal-shaped cells, base station transmitters can be located in the center of a cell (*center-excited cell* shown in Figure 11-3a), or on three of the cells' six vertices (*edge-* or *corner-excited cells* shown in Figures 11-3b and c). *Omnidirectional* antennas are normally used in center-excited cells, and sectored directional antennas are used in edge- and corner-excited cells (omnidirectional antennas radiate and receive signals equally well in all directions).

Cellular telephone is an intriguing mobile radio concept that calls for replacing a single, high-powered fixed base station located high above the center of a city with multiple, low-powered duplicates of the fixed infrastructure distributed over the coverage area on sites placed closer to the ground. The cellular concept adds a spatial dimension to the simple cable-trunking model found in typical wireline telephone systems.

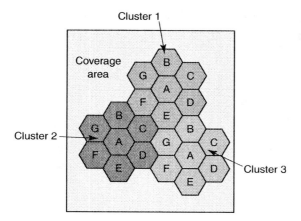

FIGURE 11-4   Cellular frequency
reuse concept

11-5   FREQUENCY REUSE

Frequency reuse is the process in which the same set of frequencies (channels) can be allocated to more than one cell, provided the cells are separated by sufficient distance. Reducing each cell's coverage area invites frequency reuse. Cells using the same set of radio channels can avoid mutual interference, provided they are properly separated. Each cell base station is allocated a group of channel frequencies that are different from those of neighboring cells, and base station antennas are chosen to achieve a desired coverage pattern within its cell. However, as long as a coverage area is limited to within a cell's boundaries, the same group of channel frequencies may be used in different cells without interfering with each other, provided the two cells are sufficient distance from one another.

Figure 11-4 illustrates the concept of frequency reuse in a cellular telephone system. The figure shows a geographic cellular radio coverage area containing three groups of cells called *clusters.* Each cluster has seven cells in it, and all cells are assigned the same number of full-duplex cellular telephone channels. Cells with the same letter use the same set of channel frequencies. As the figure shows, the same sets of frequencies are used in all three clusters, which essentially increases the number of usable cellular channels available threefold. The letters A, B, C, D, E, F, and G denote the seven sets of frequencies.

The frequency reuse concept can be illustrated mathematically by considering a system with a fixed number of full-duplex channels available in a given area. Each service area is divided into clusters and allocated a group of channels, which is divided among N cells in a unique and disjoint channel grouping where all cells have the same number of channels but do not necessarily cover the same size area. Thus, the total number of cellular channels available in a cluster can be expressed mathematically as

$$F = GN \qquad (11\text{-}1)$$

where F = number of full-duplex cellular channels available in a cluster
   G = number of channels in a cell
   N = number of cells in a cluster

The cells that collectively use the complete set of available channel frequencies make up the cluster. When a cluster is duplicated m times within a given service area, the total number of full-duplex channels can be expressed mathematically as

$$C = mGN$$

or $$= mF \qquad (11\text{-}2)$$

where C = total channel capacity in a given area
      m = number of clusters in a given area
      G = number of channels in a cell
      N = number of cells in a cluster

Example 11-1

Determine the number of channels per cluster and the total channel capacity for a cellular telephone area comprised of 10 clusters with seven cells in each cluster and 10 channels in each cell.

Solution Substituting into Equation 11-1, the total number of full-duplex channels is

$$F = (10)(7)$$
$$= 70 \text{ channels per cluster}$$

Substituting into Equation 11-3, the total channel capacity is

$$C = (10)(7)(10)$$
$$= 700 \text{ channels total}$$

From Example 11-1, it can be seen that through frequency reuse, 70 channels (frequencies), reused in 10 clusters, produce 700 usable channels within a single cellular telephone area.

From Equations 11-1 and 11-2, it can be seen that the channel capacity of a cellular telephone system is directly proportional to the number of times a cluster is duplicated in a given service area. The factor N is called the *cluster size* and is typically equal to 3, 7, or 12. When the cluster size is reduced and the cell size held constant, more clusters are required to cover a given area, and the total channel capacity increases. The frequency reuse factor of a cellular telephone system is inversely proportional to the number of cells in a cluster (i.e., $1/N$). Therefore, each cell within a cluster is assigned $1/N$th of the total available channels in the cluster.

The number of subscribers who can use the same set of frequencies (channels) in non-adjacent cells at the same time in a small area, such as a city, is dependent on the total number of cells in the area. The number of simultaneous users is generally four, but in densely populated areas, that number may be significantly higher. The number of users is called the frequency reuse factor (FRF). The frequency reuse factor is defined mathematically as

$$FRF = \frac{N}{C} \tag{11-3}$$

where FRF = frequency reuse factor (unitless)
      N = total number of full-duplex channels in an area
      C = total number of full-duplex channels in a cell

Meeting the needs of projected growth in cellular traffic is accomplished by reducing the size of a cell by splitting it into several cells, each with its own base station. Splitting cells effectively allows more calls to be handled by the system, provided the cells do not become too small. If a cell becomes smaller than 1500 feet in diameter, the base stations in adjacent cells would most likely interfere with one another. The relationship between frequency reuse and cluster size determines how cellular telephone systems can be rescaled when subscriber density increases. As the number of cells per cluster decreases, the possibility that one channel will interfere with another channel increases.

Cells use a hexagonal shape, which provides exactly six equidistant neighboring cells, and the lines joining the centers of any cell with its neighboring cell are separated by multiples of 60. Therefore, a limited number of cluster sizes and cell layouts is possible. To connect cells without gaps in between (*tessellate*), the geometry of a hexagon is such that the number of cells per cluster can have only values that satisfy the equation

$$N = i^2 + ij + j^2 \tag{11-4}$$

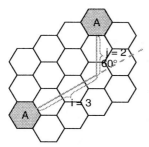

FIGURE 11-5 Locating first tier co-channel cells

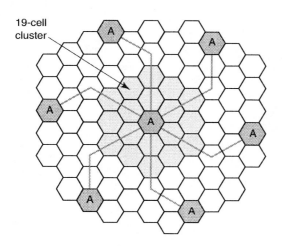

19-cell cluster

FIGURE 11-6 Determining first tier co-channel cells for Example 11-2

where N = number of cells per cluster
             i and j = nonnegative integer values

The process of finding the tier with the nearest co-channel cells (called the *first tier*) is as follows and shown in Figure 11-5:

1. Move i cells through the center of successive cells.
2. Turn 60° in a counterclockwise direction.
3. Move j cells forward through the center of successive cells.

Example 11-2

Determine the number of cells in a cluster and locate the first-tier co-channel cells for the following values: $j = 2$ and $i = 3$.

Solution The number of cells in the cluster is determined from Equation 11-4:

$$N = 3^2 + (3)(2) + 2^2$$
$$N = 19$$

Figure 11-6 shows the six nearest first-tier 1 co-channel cells for cell A.

11-6 INTERFERENCE

The two major kinds of interferences produced within a cellular telephone system are *co-channel interference* and *adjacent-channel interference.*

When frequency reuse is implemented, several cells within a given coverage area use the same set of frequencies. Two cells using the same set of frequencies are called *co-channel cells,* and the interference between them is called *co-channel interference.* Unlike thermal noise, co-channel interference cannot be reduced by simply increasing transmit powers because increasing the transmit power in one cell increases the likelihood of that cell's transmissions interfering with another cell's transmission. To reduce co-channel interference, a certain minimum distance must separate co-channels.

Figure 11-7 shows co-channel interference. The base station in cell A of cluster 1 is transmitting on frequency f_1, and at the same time, the base station in cell A of cluster 2 is transmitting on the same frequency. Although the two cells are in different clusters, they both use the A-group of frequencies. The mobile unit in cluster 2 is receiving the same frequency from two different base stations. Although the mobile unit is under the control of the base station in cluster 2, the signal from cluster 1 is received at a lower power level as co-channel interference.

Interference between cells is proportional not to the distance between the two cells but rather to the ratio of the distance to the cell's radius. Since a cell's radius is proportional to transmit power, more radio channels can be added to a system by either (1) decreasing the transmit power per cell, (2) making cells smaller, or (3) filling vacated coverage areas with new cells. In a cellular system where all cells are approximately the same size, co-channel interference is dependent on the radius (R) of the cells and the distance to the center of the nearest co-channel cell (D) as shown in Figure 11-8. Increasing the D/R ratio (sometimes called *co-channel reuse ratio*) increases the spatial separation between co-channel cells

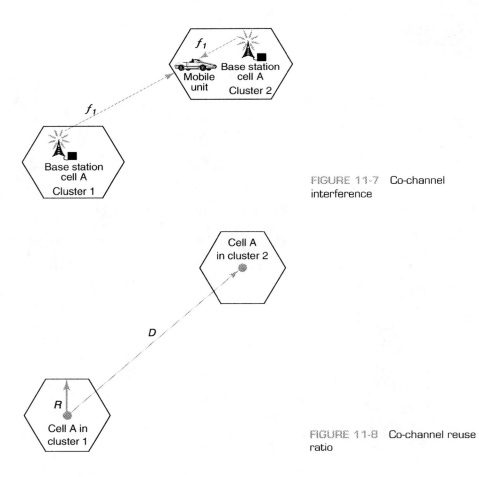

FIGURE 11-7   Co-channel interference

FIGURE 11-8   Co-channel reuse ratio

relative to the coverage distance. Therefore, increasing the co-channel reuse ratio (Q) can reduce co-channel interference. For a hexagonal geometry,

$$Q = \frac{D}{R}$$

(11-5)

where $\quad Q$ = co-channel reuse ratio (unitless)
$\qquad D$ = distance to center of the nearest co-channel cell (kilometers)
$\qquad R$ = cell radius (kilometers)

The smaller the value of Q, the larger the channel capacity since the cluster size is also smaller. However, a large value of Q improves the co-channel interference and, thus, the overall transmission quality. Obviously, in actual cellular system design, a trade-off must be made between the two conflicting objectives.

11-6-2 Adjacent-Channel Interference

Adjacent-channel interference occurs when transmissions from *adjacent channels* (channels next to one another in the frequency domain) interfere with each other. Adjacent-channel interference results from imperfect filters in receivers that allow nearby frequencies to enter the receiver. Adjacent-channel interference is most prevalent when an adjacent channel is transmitting very close to a mobile unit's receiver at the same time the mobile unit is trying to receive transmissions from the base station on an adjacent frequency. This is called the *near-far effect* and is most prevalent when a mobile unit is receiving a weak signal from the base station.

Adjacent-channel interference is depicted in Figure 11-9. Mobile unit 1 is receiving frequency f_1 from base station A. At the same time, base station A is transmitting frequency f_2 to mobile unit 2. Because mobile unit 2 is much farther from the base station than mobile unit 1, f_2 is transmitted at a much higher power level than f_1. Mobile unit 1 is located very close to the base station, and f_2 is located next to f_1 in the frequency spectrum (i.e., the adjacent channel); therefore, mobile unit 1 is receiving f_2 at a much higher power level than f_1. Because of the high power level, the filters in mobile unit 1 cannot block all the energy from f_2, and the signal intended for mobile unit 2 interferes with mobile unit 1's reception

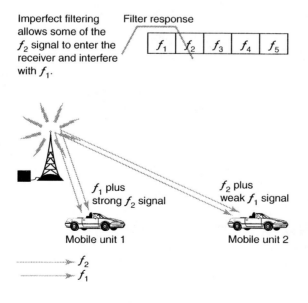

FIGURE 11-9   Adjacent-channel interference

of f_1. f_1 does not interfere with mobile unit 2's reception because f_1 is received at a much lower power level than f_2.

Using precise filtering and making careful channel assignments can minimize adjacent-channel interference in receivers. Maintaining a reasonable frequency separation between channels in a given cell can also reduce adjacent-channel interference. However, if the reuse factor is small, the separation between adjacent channels may not be sufficient to maintain an adequate adjacent-channel interference level.

11-7 CELL SPLITTING, SECTORING, SEGMENTATION, AND DUALIZATION

The Bell System proposed cellular telephone systems in the early 1960s as a means of alleviating congested frequency spectrums indigenous to wide-area mobile telephone systems using line-of-sight, high-powered transmitters. These early systems offered reasonable coverage over large areas, but the available channels were rapidly used up. For example, in the early 1970s, the Bell System could handle only 12 simultaneous mobile telephone calls at a time in New York City. Modern-day cellular telephone systems use relatively low-power transmitters and generally serve a much smaller geographical area.

Increases in demand for cellular service in a given area rapidly consume the cellular channels assigned the area. Two methods of increasing the capacity of a cellular telephone system are cell splitting and sectoring. Cell splitting provides for an orderly growth of a cellular system, whereas sectoring utilizes directional antennas to reduce co-channel and adjacent-channel interference and allow channel frequencies to be reassigned (reused).

11-7-1 Cell Splitting

Cell splitting is when the area of a cell, or independent component coverage areas of a cellular system, is further divided, thus creating more cell areas. The purpose of cell splitting is to increase the channel capacity and improve the availability and reliability of a cellular telephone network. The point when a cell reaches maximum capacity occurs when the number of subscribers wishing to place a call at any given time equals the number of channels in the cell. This is called the *maximum traffic load* of the cell. Splitting cell areas creates new cells, providing an increase in the degree of frequency reuse, thus increasing the channel capacity of a cellular network. Cell splitting provides for orderly growth in a cellular system. The major drawback of cell splitting is that it results in more *base station transfers* (handoffs) per call and a higher processing load per subscriber. It has been proven that a reduction of a cell radius by a factor of 4 produces a 10-fold increase in the handoff rate per subscriber.

Cell splitting is the resizing or redistribution of cell areas. In essence, cell splitting is the process of subdividing highly congested cells into smaller cells each with their own base station and set of channel frequencies. With cell splitting, a large number of low-power transmitters take over an area previously served by a single, higher-powered transmitter. Cell splitting occurs when traffic levels in a cell reach the point where channel availability is jeopardized. If a new call is initiated in an area where all the channels are in use, a condition called *blocking* occurs. A high occurrence of blocking indicates that a system is overloaded.

Providing wide-area coverage with small cells is indeed a costly operation. Therefore, cells are initially set up to cover relatively large areas, and then the cells are divided into smaller areas when the need arises. The area of a circle is proportional to its radius squared. Therefore, if the radius of a cell is divided in half, four times as many smaller cells could be created to provide service to the same coverage area. If each new cell has the same number of channels as the original cell, the capacity is also increased by a factor of 4. Cell splitting allows a system's capacity to increase by replacing large cells with several smaller cells while not disturbing the channel allocation scheme required to prevent interference between cells.

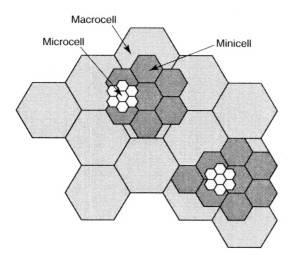

Macrocell

Microcell

Minicell

FIGURE 11-10 Cell splitting

Figure 11-10 illustrates the concept of cell splitting. Macrocells are divided into mini-cells, which are then further divided into microcells as traffic density increases. Each time a cell is split, its transmit power is reduced. As Figure 11-10 shows, cell splitting increases the channel capacity of a cellular telephone system by rescaling the system and increasing the number of channels per unit area (channel density). Hence, cell splitting decreases the cell radius while maintaining the same co-channel reuse ratio (D/R).

Example 11-3

Determine

a. The channel capacity for a cellular telephone area comprised of seven macrocells with 10 channels per cell.
b. Channel capacity if each macrocell is split into four minicells.
c. Channel capacity if each minicell is further split into four microcells.

Solution   a.
$$\frac{10 \text{ channels}}{\text{cell}} \times \frac{7 \text{ cells}}{\text{area}} = 70 \text{ channels/area}$$

b. Splitting each macrocell into four minicells increases the total number of cells in the area to $4 \times 7 = 28$. Therefore,
$$\frac{10 \text{ channels}}{\text{cell}} \times \frac{28 \text{ cells}}{\text{area}} = 280 \text{ channels/area}$$

c. Further splitting each minicell into four microcells increases the total number of cells in the area to $4 \times 28 = 112$. Therefore,
$$\frac{10 \text{ channels}}{\text{cell}} \times \frac{112 \text{ cells}}{\text{area}} = 1120 \text{ channels/area}$$

From Example 11-3, it can be seen that each time the cells were split, the coverage area appreciated a fourfold increase in channel capacity. For the situation described in Example 11-3, splitting the cells twice increased the total capacity by a factor of 16 from 70 channels to 1120 channels.

11-7-2   Sectoring

Another means of increasing the channel capacity of a cellular telephone system is to decrease the D/R ratio while maintaining the same cell radius. Capacity improvement can be achieved by reducing the number of cells in a cluster, thus increasing the frequency reuse. To accomplish this, the relative interference must be reduced without decreasing transmit power.

In a cellular telephone system, co-channel interference can be decreased by replacing a single omnidirectional antenna with several directional antennas, each radiating within a

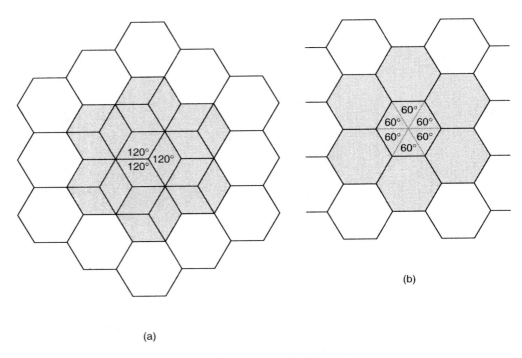

(b)

(a)

FIGURE 11-11   Sectoring: (a) 120-degree sectors; (b) 60-degree sectors

smaller area. These smaller areas are called *sectors,* and decreasing co-channel interference while increasing capacity by using directional antennas is called *sectoring.* The degree in which co-channel interference is reduced is dependent on the amount of sectoring used. A cell is normally partitioned either into three 60° or six 120° sectors as shown in Figure 11-11. In the three-sector configuration shown in Figure 11-11b, three antennas would be placed in each 120° sector—one transmit antenna and two receive antennas. Placing two receive antennas (one above the other) is called *space diversity.* Space diversity improves reception by effectively providing a larger target for signals radiated from mobile units. The separation between the two receive antennas depends on the height of the antennas above the ground. This height is generally taken to be the height of the tower holding the antenna. As a rule, antennas located 30 meters above the ground require a separation of eight wavelengths, and antennas located 50 meters above the ground require a separation of 11 wavelengths.

When sectoring is used, the channels utilized in a particular sector are broken down into sectored groups that are used only within a particular sector. With seven-cell reuse and 120° sectors, the number of interfering cells in the closest tier is reduced from six to two. Sectoring improves the signal-to-interference ratio, thus increasing the system's capacity.

11-7-3 Segmentation and Dualization

Segmentation and *dualization* are techniques incorporated when additional cells are required within the reuse distance. Segmentation divides a group of channels into smaller groupings or segments of mutually exclusive frequencies; cell sites, which are within the reuse distance, are assigned their own segment of the channel group. Segmentation is a means of avoiding co-channel interference, although it lowers the capacity of a cell by enabling reuse inside the reuse distance, which is normally prohibited.

Dualization is a means of avoiding full-cell splitting where the entire area would otherwise need to be segmented into smaller cells. When a new cell is set up requiring the same channel group as an existing cell (cell 1) and a second cell (cell 2) is not sufficiently far from cell 1 for normal reuse, the busy part of cell 1 (the center) is converted to a primary cell, and the same channel frequencies can be assigned to the new competing cell (cell 2). If all available channels need to be used in cell 2, a problem would arise because the larger secondary cell in cell 1 uses some of these, and there would be interference. In practice, however, cells are assigned different channels, so this is generally not a problem. A drawback of dualization is that it requires an extra base station in the middle of cell 1. There are now two base stations in cell 1: one a high-power station that covers the entire secondary cell and one a low-power station that covers the smaller primary cell.

11-8 CELLULAR SYSTEM TOPOLOGY

Figure 11-12 shows a simplified cellular telephone system that includes all the basic components necessary for cellular telephone communications. The figure shows a wireless radio network covering a set of geographical areas (cells) inside of which mobile two-way radio units, such as cellular or PCS telephones, can communicate. The radio network is defined by a set of radio-frequency transceivers located within each of the cells. The locations of these radio-frequency transceivers are called *base stations*. A base station serves as central control for all users within that cell. Mobile units (such as automobiles and pedestrians) communicate directly with the base stations, and the base stations communicate

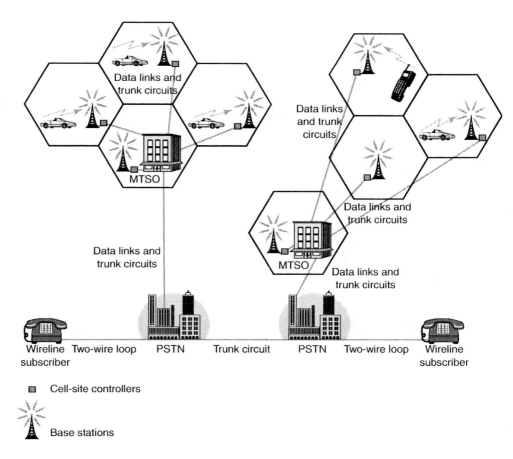

FIGURE 11-12 Simplified cellular telephone system

directly with a *Mobile Telephone Switching Office* (MTSO). An MTSO controls channel assignment, call processing, call setup, and call termination, which includes signaling, switching, supervision, and allocating radio-frequency channels. The MTSO provides a centralized administration and maintenance point for the entire network and interfaces with the public telephone network over wireline voice trunks and data links. MTSOs are equivalent to class 4 toll offices, except smaller. Local loops (or the cellular equivalent) do not terminate in MTSOs. The only facilities that connect to an MTSO are trunk circuits. Most MTSOs are connected to the SS7 signaling network, which allows cellular telephones to operate outside their service area.

Base stations can improve the transmission quality, but they cannot increase the channel capacity within the fixed bandwidth of the network. Base stations are distributed over the area of system coverage and are managed and controlled by an on-site computerized *cell-site controller* that handles all cell-site control and switching functions. Base stations communicate not only directly with mobile units through the airways using control channels but also directly with the MTSO over dedicated data control links (usually four wire, full duplex). Figure 11-12 shows how trunk circuits interconnect cell-site controllers to MTSOs and MTSOs with exchange offices within the PSTN.

The base station consists of a low-power radio transceiver, power amplifiers, a control unit (computer), and other hardware, depending on the system configuration. Cellular and PCS telephones use several moderately powered transceivers over a relatively wide service area. The function of the base station is to provide an interface between mobile telephone sets and the MTSO. Base stations communicate with the MTSO over dedicated data links, both metallic and nonmetallic facilities, and with mobile units over the airwaves using control channels. The MTSO provides a centralized administration and maintenance point for the entire network, and it interfaces with the PSTN over wireline voice trunks to honor services from conventional wireline telephone subscribers.

To complicate the issue, an MTSO is known by several different names, depending on the manufacturer and the system configuration. *Mobile Telephone Switching Office* (MTSO) is the name given by Bell Telephone Laboratories, *Electronic Mobile Xchange* (EMX) by Motorola, *AEX* by Ericcson, *NEAX* by NEC, and *Switching Mobile Center* (SMC) and *Master Mobile Center* (MMC) by Novatel. In PCS networks, the mobile switching center is called the MCS.

Each geographic area or cell can generally accommodate many different user channels simultaneously. The number of user channels depends on the accessing technique used. Within a cell, each radio-frequency channel can support up to 20 mobile telephone users at one time. Channels may be statically or dynamically assigned. Statically assigned channels are assigned a mobile unit for the duration of a call, whereas dynamically assigned channels are assigned a mobile unit only when it is being used. With both static and dynamic assignments, mobile units can be assigned any available radio channel.

11-9 ROAMING AND HANDOFFS

Roaming is when a mobile unit moves from one cell to another—possibly from one company's service area into another company's service area (requiring *roaming agreements*). As a mobile unit (car or pedestrian) moves away from the base station transceiver it is communicating with, the signal strength begins to decrease. The output power of the mobile unit is controlled by the base station through the transmission of up/down commands, which depends on the signal strength the base station is currently receiving from the mobile unit. When the signal strength drops below a predetermined threshold level, the electronic switching center locates the cell in the honeycomb pattern that is receiving the strongest signal from the particular mobile unit and then transfers the mobile unit to the base station in the new cell.

One of the most important features of a cellular system is its ability to transfer calls that are already in progress from one cell-site controller to another as the mobile unit moves

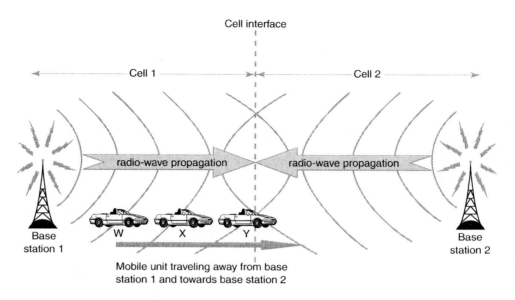

Cell interface

Cell 1   Cell 2

radio-wave propagation   radio-wave propagation

Base station 1

W   X   Y

Base station 2

Mobile unit traveling away from base
station 1 and towards base station 2

FIGURE 11-13   Handoff

from cell to cell within the cellular network. The base station transfer includes converting the call to an available channel within the new cell's allocated frequency subset. The transfer of a mobile unit from one base station's control to another base station's control is called a *handoff* (or *handover*). Handoffs should be performed as infrequently as possible and be completely *transparent* (*seamless*) to the subscriber (i.e., the subscribers cannot perceive that their facility has been switched). A handoff consists of four stages: (1) initiation, (2) resource reservation, (3) execution, and (4) completion. A connection that is momentarily broken during the cell-to-cell transfer is called a *hard handoff.* A hard handoff is a *break-before-make process.* With a hard handoff, the mobile unit breaks its connection with one base station before establishing voice communications with a new base station. Hard handoffs generally occur when a mobile unit is passed between disjointed systems with different frequency assignments, air interface characteristics, or technologies. A flawless handoff (i.e., no perceivable interruption of service) is called a *soft handoff* and normally takes approximately 200 ms, which is imperceptible to voice telephone users, although the delay may be disruptive when transmitting data. With a soft handoff, a mobile unit establishes contact with a new base station before giving up its current radio channel by transmitting coded speech signals to two base stations simultaneously. Both base stations send their received signals to the MTSO, which estimates the quality of the two signals and determines when the transfer should occur. A complementary process occurs in the opposite direction. A soft handoff requires that the two base stations operate synchronously with one another.

Figure 11-13 shows how a base station transfer is accomplished when a mobile unit moves from one cell into another (the figure shows a soft handoff). The mobile unit is moving away from base station 1 (i.e., toward base station 2). When the mobile unit is at positions W and X, it is well within the range of base station 1 and very distant from base station 2. However, when the mobile unit reaches position Y, it receives signals from base station 1 and base station 2 at approximately the same power level, and the two base stations should be setting up for a handoff (i.e., initiation and resource reservation). When the mobile unit crosses from cell 1 into cell 2, the handoff should be executed and completed.

Computers at cell-site controllers should transfer calls from cell to cell with minimal disruption and no degradation in the quality of transmission. The computers use *handoff decision algorithms* based on variations in signal strength and signal quality. When a call is in progress, the switching center monitors the received signal strength of each user channel. Handoffs can be initiated when the signal strength (or signal-to-interference ratio), measured by either the base station or the mobile unit's receiver, falls below a predetermined threshold level (typically between -90 dBm and -100 dBm) or when a network resource management needs to force a handoff to free resources to place an emergency call. During a handoff, information about the user stored in the first base station is transferred to the new base station. A condition called *blocking* occurs when the signal level drops below a usable level and there are no usable channels available in the target cell to switch to. To help avoid blocking or loss of a call during a handoff, the system employs a load-balancing scheme that frees channels for handoffs and sets handoff priorities. Programmers at the central switching site continually update the switching algorithm to amend the system to accommodate changing traffic loads.

The handoff process involves four basic steps:

1. *Initiation.* Either the mobile unit or the network determines the need for a handoff and initiates the necessary network procedures.
2. *Resource reservation.* Appropriate network procedures reserve the resources needed to support the handoff (i.e., a voice and a control channel).
3. *Execution.* The actual transfer of control from one base station to another base station takes place.
4. *Completion.* Unnecessary network resources are relinquished and made available to other mobile units.

11-9-1 IS-41 Standard

In the United States, roaming from one company's calling area into another company's calling area is called *interoperator roaming* and requires prior agreements between the two service providers. To provide seamless roaming between calling areas served by different companies, the Electronics Industries Association/Telecommunications Industry Association (EIA/TIA) developed the IS-41 protocol, which was endorsed by the Cellular Telecommunication Industry Association (CITA). IS-41 aligns with a subprotocol of the SS7 protocol stack that facilitates communications among databases and other network entities. The IS-41 standard is separated into a series of recommendations.

The principal purposes of IS-41 are to allow mobile units to roam and to perform handoffs of calls already in progress when a mobile unit moves from one cellular system into another without subscriber intervention. Before deployment of SS7, X.25 provided the carrier services for data messages traveling from one cell (the *home location register* [HLR]) to another cell (the *visitor location register* [VLR]). IS-41 provides the information and exchanges necessary to establish and cancel registration in various databases. IS-41 aligns with the ANSI version of SS7 to communicate with databases and other network functional entities.

IS-41 relies on a feature called *autonomous registration,* the process where a mobile unit notifies a serving MTSO of its presence and location through a base station controller. The mobile unit accomplishes autonomous registration by periodically transmitting its identity information, thus allowing the serving MTSO to continuously update its customer list. IS-41 allows MTSOs in neighboring systems to automatically register and validate locations of roaming mobile units so that users no longer need to manually register as they travel.

11-10 CELLULAR TELEPHONE NETWORK COMPONENTS

There are six essential components of a cellular telephone system: (1) an electronic switching center, (2) a cell-site controller, (3) radio transceivers, (4) system interconnections, (5) mobile telephone units, and (6) a common communications protocol.

11-10-1 Electronic Switching Centers

The *electronic switching center* is a digital telephone exchange located in the MTSO that is the heart of a cellular telephone system. The electronic switch performs two essential functions: (1) It controls switching between the public wireline telephone network and the cell-site base stations for wireline-to-mobile, mobile-to-wireline, and mobile-to-mobile calls, and (2) it processes data received from the cell-site controllers concerning mobile unit status, diagnostic data, and bill-compiling information. Electronic switches communicate with cell-site controllers using a data link protocol, such as X.25, at a transmission rate of 9.6 kbps or higher.

11-10-2 Cell-Site Controllers

Each cell contains one *cell-site controller* (sometimes called *base station controller*) that operates under the direction of the switching center (MTSO). Cell-site controllers manage each of the radio channels at each site, supervises calls, turns the radio transmitter and receiver on and off, injects data onto the control and voice channels, and performs diagnostic tests on the cell-site equipment. Base station controllers make up one part of the *base station subsystem.* The second part is the *base transceiver station* (BTS).

11-10-3 Radio Transceivers

Radio transceivers are also part of the base station subsystem. The radio transceivers (combination transmitter/receiver) used with cellular telephone system voice channels can be either narrowband FM for analog systems or either PSK or QAM for digital systems with an effective audio-frequency band comparable to a standard telephone circuit (approximately 300 Hz to 3000 Hz). The control channels use either FSK or PSK. The maximum output power of a cellular transmitter depends on the type of cellular system. Each cell base station typically contains one radio transmitter and two radio receivers tuned to the same channel (frequency). The radio receiver that detects the strongest signal is selected. This arrangement is called *receiver diversity.* The radio transceivers in base stations include the antennas (both transmit and receive). Modern cellular base station antennas are more aesthetically appealing than most antennas and can resemble anything from a window shutter to a palm tree to an architectural feature on a building.

11-10-4 System Interconnects

Four-wire leased lines are generally used to connect switching centers to cell sites and to the public telephone network. There is one dedicated four-wire trunk circuit for each of the cell's voice channels. There must also be at least one four-wire trunk circuit to connect switching centers to each cell-site controller for transferring control signals.

11-10-5 Mobile and Portable Telephone Units

Mobile and *portable telephone units* are essentially identical. The only differences are that portable units have a lower output power, have a less efficient antenna, and operate exclusively on batteries. Each mobile telephone unit consists of a control unit, a multiple-frequency radio transceiver (i.e., multiple channel), a logic unit, and a mobile antenna. The control unit houses all the user interfaces, including a built-in handset. The transceiver uses a frequency synthesizer to tune into any designated cellular system channel. The logic unit interrupts subscriber actions and system commands while managing the operation of the transceiver (including transmit power) and control units.

11-10-6 Communications Protocol

The last constituent of a cellular telephone system is the *communications protocol,* which governs the way telephone calls are established and disconnected. There are several layers of protocols used with cellular telephone systems, and these protocols differ between cellular networks. The protocol implemented depends on whether the voice and control channels are analog or digital and what method subscribers use to access the network. Examples of cellular communications protocols are IS-54, IS-136.2, and IS-95.

Telephone calls over cellular networks require using two full-duplex radio-frequency channels simultaneously, one called the *user channel* and one called the *control channel*. The user channel is the actual voice channel where mobile users communicate directly with other mobile and wireline subscribers through a base station. The control channel is used for transferring control and diagnostic information between mobile users and a central cellular telephone switch through a base station. Base stations transmit on the *forward control channel* and *forward voice channel* and receive on the *reverse control channel* and *reverse voice channel*. Mobile units transmit on the reverse control channel and reverse voice channel and receive on the forward control channel and forward voice channel.

Completing a call within a cellular telephone system is similar to completing a call using the wireline PSTN. When a mobile unit is first turned on, it performs a series of start-up procedures and then samples the receive signal strength on all user channels. The mobile unit automatically tunes to the control channel with the strongest receive signal strength and synchronizes to the control data transmitted by the cell-site controller. The mobile unit interprets the data and continues monitoring the control channel(s). The mobile unit automatically rescans periodically to ensure that it is using the best control channel.

11-11-1 Call Procedures

Within a cellular telephone system, three types of calls can take place involving mobile cellular telephones: (1) mobile (cellular)-to-wireline (PSTN), (2) mobile (cellular)-to-mobile (cellular), and (3) wireline (PSTN)-to-mobile (cellular). A general description is given for the procedures involved in completing each of the three types of calls involving mobile cellular telephones.

11-11-1-1 Mobile (cellular)-to-wireline (PSTN) call procedures.

1. Calls from mobile telephones to wireline telephones can be initiated in one of two ways:
   a. The mobile unit is equivalently taken off hook (usually by depressing a talk button). After the mobile unit receives a dial tone, the subscriber enters the wireline telephone number using either a standard Touch-Tone keypad or with speed dialing. After the last digit is depressed, the number is transmitted through a reverse control channel to the base station controller along with the mobile unit's unique identification number (which is not the mobile unit's telephone number).
   b. The mobile subscriber enters the wireline telephone number into the unit's memory using a standard Touch-Tone keypad. The subscriber then depresses a send key, which transmits the called number as well as the mobile unit's identification number over a reverse control channel to the base station switch.
2. If the mobile unit's ID number is valid, the cell-site controller routes the called number over a wireline trunk circuit to the MTSO.
3. The MTSO uses either standard call progress signals or the SS7 signaling network to locate a switching path through the PSTN to the destination party.
4. Using the cell-site controller, the MTSO assigns the mobile unit a nonbusy user channel and instructs the mobile unit to tune to that channel.
5. After the cell-site controller receives verification that the mobile unit has tuned to the selected channel and it has been determined that the called number is on hook, the mobile unit receives an audible call progress tone (ring-back) while the wireline caller receives a standard ringing signal.
6. If a suitable switching path is available to the wireline telephone number, the call is completed when the wireline party goes off hook (answers the telephone).

11-11-1-2 Mobile (cellular)-to-mobile (cellular) call procedures.

1. The originating mobile unit initiates the call in the same manner as it would for a mobile-to-wireline call.
2. The cell-site controller receives the caller's identification number and the destination telephone number through a reverse control channel, which are then forwarded to the MTSO.
3. The MTSO sends a page command to all cell-site controllers to locate the destination party (which may be anywhere in or out of the service area).
4. Once the destination mobile unit is located, the destination cell-site controller sends a page request through a control channel to the destination party to determine if the unit is on or off hook.
5. After receiving a positive response to the page, idle user channels are assigned to both mobile units.
6. Call progress tones are applied in both directions (ring and ring-back).
7. When the system receives notice that the called party has answered the telephone, the switches terminate the call progress tones, and the conversation begins.
8. If a mobile subscriber wishes to initiate a call and all user channels are busy, the switch sends a directed retry command, instructing the subscriber's unit to reattempt the call through a neighboring cell.
9. If the system cannot allocate user channels through a neighboring cell, the switch transmits an intercept message to the calling mobile unit over the control channel.
10. If the called party is off hook, the calling party receives a busy signal.
11. If the called number is invalid, the calling party receives a recorded message announcing that the call cannot be processed.

11-11-1-3 Wireline (PSTN)-to-mobile (cellular) call procedures.

1. The wireline telephone goes off hook to complete the loop, receives a dial tone, and then inputs the mobile unit's telephone number.
2. The telephone number is transferred from the PSTN switch to the cellular network switch (MTSO) that services the destination mobile number.
3. The cellular network MTSO receives the incoming call from the PSTN, translates the received digits, and locates the base station nearest the mobile unit, which determines if the mobile unit is on or off hook (i.e., available).
4. If the mobile unit is available, a positive page response is sent over a reverse control channel to the cell-site controller, which is forwarded to the network switch (MTSO).
5. The cell-site controller assigns an idle user channel to the mobile unit and then instructs the mobile unit to tune to the selected channel.
6. The mobile unit sends verification of channel tuning through the cell-site controller.
7. The cell-site controller sends an audible call progress tone to the subscriber's mobile telephone, causing it to ring. At the same time, a ring-back signal is sent back to the wireline calling party.
8. The mobile answers (goes off hook), the switch terminates the call progress tones, and the conversation begins.

QUESTIONS

11-1. What is the contemporary mobile telephone meaning for the term *mobile?*

11-2. Contrast the similarities and differences between *two-way mobile radio* and *cellular telephone.*

11-3. Describe the differences between a cellular telephone *service area,* a *cluster,* and a *cell.*

11-4. Why was a *honeycomb pattern* selected for a cell area?

11-5. What are the differences between *macrocells, minicells,* and *microcells?*

11-6. What is meant by a *center-excited* cell? *Edge-excited* cell? *Corner-excited* cell?

11-7. Describe *frequency reuse.* Why is it useful in cellular telephone systems?

11-8. What is meant by *frequency reuse factor?*

11-8. Name and describe the two most prevalent types of interference in cellular telephone systems.

11-9. What significance does the *co-channel reuse factor* have on cellular telephone systems?

11-10. What is meant by the *near-far effect?*

11-11. Describe the concept of *cell splitting.* Why is it used?

11-12. Describe the term *blocking.*

11-13. Describe what is meant by *channel density.*

11-14. Describe *sectoring* and state why it is used.

11-15. What is the difference between a *MTSO* and a *cell-site controller?*

11-16. Explain what the term *roaming* means.

11-17. Explain the term *handoff.*

11-18. What is the difference between a *soft* and a *hard* handoff?

11-19. Explain the term *break before make* and state when it applies.

11-20. Briefly describe the purpose of the IS-41 standard.

11-21. Describe the following terms: *home location register, visitor location register,* and *autonomous registration.*

11-22. List and describe the six essential components of a *cellular telephone network.*

11-23. Describe what is meant by the term *forward channel; reverse channel.*

PROBLEMS

11-1. Determine the number of channels per cluster and the total channel capacity for a cellular telephone area comprised of 12 clusters with seven cells in each cluster and 16 channels in each cell.

11-2. Determine the number of cells in clusters for the following values: $j = 4$ and $i = 2$ and $j = 3$ and $i = 3$.

11-3. Determine the co-channel reuse ratio for a cell radius of 0.5 miles separated from the nearest co-channel cell by a distance of 4 miles.

11-4. Determine the distance from the nearest co-channel cell for a cell radius of 0.4 miles and a co-channel reuse factor of 12.

11-5. Determine

    a. The channel capacity for a cellular telephone area comprised of seven macrocells with 16 channels per cell.

    b. Channel capacity if each macrocell is split into four minicells.

    c. Channel capacity if each minicell is further split into four microcells.

11-6. A cellular telephone company has acquired 150 full-duplex channels for a given service area. The company decided to divide the service area into 15 clusters and use a seven-cell reuse pattern and use the same number of channels in each cell. Determine the total number of channels the company has available for its subscribers at any one time.

C H A P T E R 12

Cellular Telephone Systems

OBJECTIVES

- Define *first-generation analog cellular telephone systems*
- Describe and outline the frequency allocation for the Advanced Mobile Telephone System (AMPS)
- Explain frequency-division multiple accessing (FDMA)
- Describe the operation of AMPS control channels
- Explain the AMPS classification of cellular telephones
- Describe the concepts of personal communications systems (PCS)
- Outline the advantages and disadvantages of PCS compared to standard cellular telephone
- Describe second-generation cellular telephone systems
- Explain the operation of N-AMPS cellular telephone systems
- Define *digital cellular telephone*
- Describe the advantages and disadvantages of digital cellular telephone compared to analog cellular telephone
- Describe time-division multiple accessing (TDMA)
- Describe the purpose of IS-54 and what is meant by dual-mode operation
- Describe IS-136 and explain its relationship to IS-54
- Describe the format for a USDC digital voice channel
- Explain the classifications of USDC radiated power
- Describe the basic concepts and outline the specifications of IS-95
- Describe code-division multiple accessing (CDMA)

- Outline the CDMA frequency and channel allocation for cellular telephone
- Explain the classifications of CDMA radiated power
- Summarize North American cellular and PCS systems
- Describe global system for mobile communications (GSM)
- Describe the services provided by GSM
- Explain GSM system architecture
- Describe the GSM radio subsystem
- Describe the basic concepts of a Personal Communications Satellite System (PCSS)
- Outline the advantages and disadvantages of PCSS over terrestrial cellular telephone systems

12-1 INTRODUCTION

Like nearly everything in the modern world of electronic communications, cellular telephone began as a relatively simple concept. However, the increased demand for cellular services has caused cellular telephone systems to evolve into complicated networks and internetworks comprised of several types of cellular communications systems. New systems have evoked new terms, such as *standard cellular telephone service* (CTS), *personal communications systems* (PCS), and *Personal Communications Satellite System* (PCSS), all of which are full-duplex mobile telephone systems that utilize the cellular concept.

Cellular telephone began as a relatively simple two-way analog communications system using frequency modulation (FM) for voice and frequency-shift keying (FSK) for transporting control and signaling information. The most recent cellular telephone systems use higher-level digital modulation schemes for conveying both voice and control information. In addition, the Federal Communications Commission has recently assigned new frequency bands for cellular telephone. The following sections are intended to give the reader a basic understanding of the fundamental meaning of the common cellular telephone systems and the terminology used to describe them.

12-2 FIRST-GENERATION ANALOG CELLULAR TELEPHONE

In 1971, Bell Telephone Laboratories in Murry Hill, New Jersey, proposed the cellular telephone concept as the *Advanced Mobile Telephone System* (AMPS). The cellular telephone concept was an intriguing idea that added a depth or spatial dimension to the conventional wireline trunking model used by the public telephone company at the time. The cellular plan called for using many low-profile, low-power cell-site transceivers linked through a central computer-controlled switching and control center. AMPS is a standard cellular telephone service (CTS) initially placed into operation on October 13, 1983, by Illinois Bell that incorporated several large cell areas to cover approximately 2100 square miles in the Chicago area. The original system used omnidirectional antennas to minimize initial equipment costs and employed low-power (7-watt) transmitters in both base stations and mobile units. Voice-channel radio transceivers with AMPS cellular telephones use narrowband frequency modulation (NBFM) with a usable audio-frequency band from 300 Hz to 3 kHz and a maximum frequency deviation of ±12 kHz for 100% modulation. Using Carson's rule, this corresponds to an approximate bandwidth of 30 kHz. Empirical information determined that an AMPS 30-kHz telephone channel requires a minimum signal-to-interference ratio (SIR) of 18 dB for satisfactory performance. The smallest reuse factor that satisfied this requirement utilizing 120° directional antennas was 7. Consequently, the AMPS system uses a seven-cell reuse pattern with provisions for cell splitting and sectoring to increase channel capacity when needed.

12-2-1 AMPS Frequency Allocation

In 1980, the Federal Communications Commission decided to license two common carriers per cellular service area. The idea was to eliminate the possibility of a monopoly and

Reverse channels – mobile unit transmit and base station receive frequencies

Forward channels – mobile unit transmit and base station receive frequencies

*Shaded areas denote control channels (A-system: 313 to 333 and B-system: 334 to 354)

FIGURE 12-1 Original Advanced Mobile Phone Service (AMPS) frequency spectrum

provide the advantages that generally accompany a competitive environment. Subsequently, two frequency allocation plans emerged—system A and system B—each with its own group of channels that shared the allocated frequency spectrum. System A is defined for the non-wireline companies (i.e., cellular telephone companies) and system B for existing wireline companies (i.e., local telephone companies). The Federal Communications Commission initially assigned the AMPS system a 40-MHz frequency band consisting of 666 two-way channels per service area with 30-kHz spacing between adjacent channels.

Figure 12-1 shows the original frequency management system for the AMPS cellular telephone system. The A channels are designated 1 to 333, and the B channels are designated 334 to 666. For mobile units, channel 1 has a transmit frequency of 825.03 MHz, and channel 666 has a transmit frequency of 844.98 MHz. For base stations, channel 1 has a transmit frequency of 870.03 MHz, and channel 666 has a transmit frequency of 889.98 MHz. The receive frequencies are, of course, just the opposite.

Simultaneous transmission in both directions is a transmission mode called *full duplex* (FDX) or simply *duplexing*. Duplexing can be accomplished using frequency- or time-domain methods. *Frequency-division duplexing* (FDD) is used with AMPS and occurs when two distinct frequency bands are provided to each user. In FDD, each duplex channel actually consists of two simplex (one-way) channels (base station to mobile and mobile to base station). A special device called a duplexer is used in each mobile unit and base station to allow simultaneous transmission and reception on duplex channels.

Transmissions from base stations to mobile units are called *forward links,* whereas transmission from mobile units to base stations are called *reverse links.* (Forward links are

Reverse channels – mobile unit transmit and base station receive frequencies

Forward channels – mobile unit transmit and base station receive frequencies

*Shaded areas denote control channels (A-system: 313 to 333 and B-system: 334 to 354)

FIGURE 12-2   Complete Advanced Mobile Phone Service (AMPS) frequency spectrum

sometimes called *downlinks* and reverse links are sometimes called *uplinks*.) The receiver for each channel operates 45 MHz above the transmit frequency. Consequently, every two-way AMPS radio channel consists of a pair of simplex channels separated by 45 MHz. The 45-MHz separation between transmit and receive frequencies was chosen to make use of inexpensive but highly selective duplexers in the mobile units.

In 1989, the Federal Communications Commission added an additional 10-MHz frequency spectrum to the original 40-MHz band, which increased the number of simplex channels by 166 for a total of 832 (416 full duplex). The additional frequencies are called the *expanded spectrum* and include channels 667 to 799 and 991 to 1023. The complete AMPS frequency assignment is shown in Figure 12-2. Note that 33 of the new channels were added below the original frequency spectrum and that the remaining 133 were added above the original frequency spectrum. With AMPS, a maximum of 128 channels could be used in each cell.

The mobile unit's transmit carrier frequency in MHz for any channel is calculated as follows:

$$f_t = 0.03\,N + 825 \qquad \text{for } 1 \leq N \leq 866 \qquad (12\text{-}1)$$

$$f_t = 0.03(N - 1023) + 825 \qquad \text{for } 990 \leq N \leq 1023 \qquad (12\text{-}2)$$

where f_t = transmit carrier frequency (MHz)
N = channel number

The mobile unit's receive carrier frequency is obtained by simply adding 45 MHz to the transmit frequency:

$$f_r = f_t + 45 \text{ MHz} \qquad (12\text{-}3)$$

The base station's transmit frequency for any channel is simply the mobile unit's receive frequency, and the base station's receive frequency is simply the mobile unit's transmit frequency.

Example 12-1

Determine the transmit and receive carrier frequencies for

a. AMPS channel 3.

b. AMPS channel 991.

Solution

a. The transmit and receive carrier frequencies for channel 3 can be determined from Equations 12-1 and 12-3:

transmit

$$f_t = 0.03N + 825$$
$$= 0.03(3) + 825$$
$$= 825.09 \text{ MHz}$$

receive

$$f_r = 825.09 \text{ MHz} + 45 \text{ MHz}$$
$$= 870.09 \text{ MHz}$$

b. The transmit and receive carrier frequencies for channel 991 can be determined from Equations 12-2 and 12-3:

transmit

$$f_t = 0.03(991 - 1023) + 825$$
$$= 824.04 \text{ MHz}$$

receive

$$f_r = 824.04 \text{ MHz} + 45 \text{ MHz}$$
$$= 869.04 \text{ MHz}$$

Table 12-1 summarizes the frequency assignments for AMPS. The set of control channels may be split by the system operator into subsets of dedicated control channels, paging channels, or access channels.

The Federal Communications Commission controls the allocation of cellular telephone frequencies (channels) and also issues licenses to cellular telephone companies to operate specified frequencies in geographic areas called *cellular geographic serving areas* (CGSA). CGSAs are generally designed to lie within the borders of a standard metropolitan statistical area (SMSA), which defines geographic areas used by marketing agencies that generally correspond to the area covered by a specific wireline LATA (local access and transport area).

12-2-2 Frequency-Division Multiple Accessing

Standard cellular telephone subscribers access the AMPS system using a technique called *frequency-division multiple accessing* (FDMA). With FDMA, transmissions are separated in the frequency domain—each channel is allocated a carrier frequency and channel bandwidth within the total system frequency spectrum. Subscribers are assigned a pair of voice channels (forward and reverse) for the duration of their call. Once assigned a voice channel, a subscriber is the only mobile unit using that channel within a given cell. Simultaneous transmissions from multiple subscribers can occur at the same time without interfering with one another because their transmissions are on different channels and occupy different frequency bands.

12-2-3 AMPS Identification Codes

The AMPS system specifies several identification codes for each mobile unit (see Table 12-2). The *mobile identification number* (MIN) is a 34-bit binary code, which in the United States represents the standard 10-digit telephone number. The MIN is comprised of a three-digit area code, a three-digit prefix (exchange number), and a four-digit subscriber (extension) number. The exchange number is assigned to the cellular operating company. If a subscriber changes service from one cellular company to another, the subscriber must be assigned a new cellular telephone number.

Table 12-1   AMPS Frequency Allocation

	AMPS
Channel spacing	30 kHz
Spectrum allocation	40 MHz
Additional spectrum	10 MHz
Total number of channels	832

System A Frequency Allocation

AMPS

Channel Number	Mobile TX, MHz	Mobile RX, MHz
1	825.030	870.030
313[a]	834.390	879.390
333[b]	843.990	879.990
667	845.010	890.010
716	846.480	891.480
991	824.040	869.040
1023	825.000	870.000

System B Frequency Allocation

Channel Number	Mobile TX, MHz	Mobile RX, MHz
334[c]	835.020	880.020
354[d]	835.620	880.620
666	844.980	890.000
717	846.510	891.000
799	848.970	894.000

[a]First dedicated control channel for system A.
[b]Last dedicated control channel for system A.
[c]First dedicated control channel for system B.
[d]Last dedicated control channel for system B.

Table 12-2   AMPS Identification Codes

Notation	Name	Length (Bits)	Description
MIN	Mobile identifier	34	Directory number assigned by operating company to a subscriber (telephone number)
ESN	Electronic serial number	32	Assigned by manufacturer to a mobile station (telephone)
SID	System identifier	15	Assigned by regulators to a geographical service area
SCM	Station class mark	4	Indicates capabilities of a mobile station
SAT	Supervisory audio tone	*	Assigned by operating company to each base station
DCC	Digital color code	2	Assigned by operating company to each base station

Another identification code used with AMPS is the *electronic serial number* (ESN), which is a 32-bit binary code permanently assigned to each mobile unit. The ESN are similar to the VIN (vehicle identification number) assigned to an automobile or the MAC address on a network interface card (NIC) in that the number is unique and positively identifies a specific unit.

Table 12-3   AMPS Mobile Phone Power Levels

Power Level	Class I		Class II		Class III	
	dBm	mW	dBm	mW	dBm	mW
0	36	4000	32	1600	28	640
1	32	1600	32	1600	28	640
2	28	640	28	640	28	640
3	24	256	24	256	24	256
4	20	102	20	102	20	102
5	16	41	16	41	16	41
6	12	16	12	16	12	16
7	8	6.6	8	6.6	8	6.6

The third identification code used with AMPS is the four-bit *station class mark* (SCM), which indicates whether the terminal has access to all 832 AMPS channels or only 666. The SCM also specifies the maximum radiated power for the unit (Table 12-3).

The *system identifier* (SID) is a 15-bit binary code issued by the FCC to an operating company when it issues it a license to provide AMPS cellular service to an area. The SID is stored in all base stations and all mobile units to identify the operating company and MTSO and any additional shared MTSO. Every mobile unit knows the SID of the system it is subscribed to, which is the mobile unit's *home system*. Whenever a mobile unit initializes, it compares its SID to the SID broadcast by the local base station. If the SIDs are the same, the mobile unit is communicating with its home system. If the SIDs are different, the mobile unit is roaming.

Local operating companies assign a two-bit *digital color code* (DCC) and a *supervisory audio tone* (SAT) to each of their base stations. The DCC and SAT help the mobile units distinguish one base station from a neighboring base station. The SAT is one of three analog frequencies (5970 Hz, 6000 Hz, or 6030 Hz), and the DCC is one of four binary codes (00, 01, 10, or 11). Neighboring base stations transmit different SAT frequencies and DCCs.

12-2-4   AMPS Control Channels

The AMPS channel spectrums are divided into two basic sets or groups. One set of channels is dedicated for exchanging control information between mobile units and base stations and is appropriately termed *control channels* (shaded areas in Figures 12-1 and 12-2). Control channels cannot carry voice information; they are used exclusively to carry service information. There are 21 control channels in the A system and 21 control channels in the B system. The remaining 790 channels make up the second group, termed *voice* or *user channels*. User channels are used for propagating actual voice conversations or subscriber data.

Control channels are used in cellular telephone systems to enable mobile units to communicate with the cellular network through base stations without interfering with normal voice traffic occurring on the normal voice or user channels. Control channels are used for call origination, for call termination, and to obtain system information. With the AMPS system, voice channels are analog FM, while control channels are digital and employ FSK. Therefore, voice channels cannot carry control signals, and control channels cannot carry voice information. Control channels are used exclusively to carry service information. With AMPS, base stations broadcast on the *forward control channel* (FCC) and listen on the *reverse control channel* (RCC). The control channels are sometimes called *setup* or *paging channels*. All AMPS base stations continuously transmit FSK data on the FCC so that idle cellular telephones can maintain lock on the strongest FCC regardless of their location. A subscriber's unit must be *locked* (sometimes called *camped*) on an FCC before it can originate or receive calls.

Each base station uses a control channel to simultaneously page mobile units to alert them of the presence of incoming calls and to move established calls to a vacant voice channel. The forward control channel transmits a 10-kbps data signal using FSK. Forward

FIGURE 12-3 Control channel format: (a) forward control channel; (b) reverse control channel

control channels from base stations may contain overhead data, mobile station control information, or control file information.

Figure 12-3a shows the format for an AMPS forward control channel. As the figure shows, the control channel message is preceded by a 10-bit *dotting scheme,* which is a sequence of alternating 1s and 0s. The dotting scheme is followed by an 11-bit *synchronization word* with a unique sequence of 1s and 0s that enables a receiver to instantly acquire synchronization. The sync word is immediately followed by the message repeated five times. The redundancy helps compensate for the ill effects of fading. If three of the five words are identical, the receiver assumes that as the message.

Forward control channel data formats consist of three discrete information streams: stream A, stream B, and the busy-idle stream. The three data streams are multiplexed together. Messages to the mobile unit with the least-significant bit of their 32-bit *mobile identification number* (MIN) equal to 0 are transmitted on stream A, and MINs with the least-significant bit equal to 1 are transmitted on stream B. The busy-idle data stream contains *busy-idle bits,* which are used to indicate the current status of the reverse control channel (0 = busy and 1 = idle). There is a busy-idle bit at the beginning of each dotting sequence, at the beginning of each synchronization word, at the beginning of the first repeat of word A, and after every 10 message bits thereafter. Each message word contains 40 bits, and forward control channels can contain one or more words.

The types of messages transmitted over the FCC are the *mobile station control message* and the *overhead message train.* Mobile station control messages control or command mobile units to do a particular task when the mobile unit has not been assigned a voice channel. Overhead message trains contain *system parameter overhead messages, global action overhead messages,* and *control filler messages.* Typical mobile-unit control messages are *initial voice channel designation messages, directed retry messages, alert messages,* and *change power messages.*

Figure 12-3b shows the format for the reverse control channel that is transmitted from the mobile unit to the base station. The control data are transmitted at a 10-kbps rate and include *page responses, access requests,* and *registration requests.* All RCC messages begin with the RCC seizure precursor, which consists of a 30-bit *dotting sequence,* an 11-bit *synchronization word,* and the coded *digital color code* (DCC), which is added so that the control channel is not confused with a control channel from a nonadjacent cell that is reusing the same frequency. The mobile telephone reads the base station's DCC and then returns a coded version of it, verifying that the unit is locked onto the correct signal. When the call is finished, a 1.8-second *signaling time-out signal* is transmitted. Each message word contains 40 bits and is repeated five times for a total of 200 bits.

12-2-5 Voice-Channel Signaling

Analog cellular channels carry both voice using FM and digital signaling information using binary FSK. When transmitting digital signaling information, voice transmissions are inhibited. This is called *blank and burst:* The voice is blanked, and the data are transmitted in a short burst. The bit rate of the digital information is 10 kbps. Figure 12-4a shows the voice-channel signaling format for a forward voice channel, and Figure 12-4b shows the format for the reverse channel. The digital signaling sequence begins with a 101-bit dotting sequence that readies the receiver to receive digital information. After the dotting sequence, a synchronization word is sent to indicate the start of the message. On the forward voice channel, digital signaling messages are repeated 11 times to ensure the integrity of the message, and on the receive channel they are repeated 5 times. The forward channel uses 40-bit words, and the reverse channel uses 48-bit words.

12-3 PERSONAL COMMUNICATIONS SYSTEM

The Personal Communications System (PCS) is a relatively new class of cellular telephony based on the same basic philosophies as standard cellular telephone systems (CTSs), such as AMPS. However, PCS systems are a combination of cellular telephone networks and the *Intelligent Network,* which is the entity of the SS7 interoffice protocol that distinguishes the physical components of the switching network, such as the signal service point (SSP), signal control point (SCP), and signal transfer point (STP), from the services provided by the SS7 network. The services provided are distinctly different from the switching systems and protocols that promote and support them. PCS was initially considered a new service, although different companies have different visions of exactly what PCS is and what services it should provide. The Federal Communications Commission defines PCS mobile telephone as "a family of mobile or portable radio communications services, which provides services to individuals and business and is integrated with a variety of competing networks." In essence, PCS is the North American implementation of the European GSM standard.

Existing cellular telephone companies want PCS to provide broad coverage areas and fill in service gaps between their current service areas. In other words, they want PCS to be an extension of the current first- and second-generation cellular system to the 1850-MHz to 2200-MHz band using identical standards for both frequency bands. Other companies would like PCS to compete with standard cellular telephone systems but offer enhanced services and better quality using extensions of existing standards or entirely new standards. Therefore, some cellular system engineers describe PCS as a third-generation cellular telephone system, although the U.S. implementation of PCS uses modifications of existing cellular protocols, such as IS-54 and IS-95. Most cellular telephone companies reserve the designation third-generation PCS to those systems designed for transporting data as well as voice.

Although PCS systems share many similarities with first-generation cellular telephone systems, PCS has several significant differences that, most agree, warrant the use of a different name. Many of the differences are transparent (or at least not obvious) to the users of the networks. Probably the primary reason for establishing a new PCS cellular telephone system was because first-generation cellular systems were already overcrowded, and it was obvious that they would not be able to handle the projected demand

DOT1 = 101 bit dotting sequence
DOT2 = 37 bit dotting sequence
SYNC = Synchronization word
WN = Message word (N)
N = Number of repeated message words

(a)

DOT1 = 101 bit dotting sequence
DOT2 = 37 bit dotting sequence
SYNC = Synchronization word
WN = Message word
N = Number of repeated message words

(b)

FIGURE 12-4   Voice channel format: (a) forward channel; (b) reverse channel

for future cellular telephone services. In essence, PCS services were conceived to provide subscribers with a low-cost, feature-rich wireless telephone service.

Differences between PCS systems and standard cellular telephone systems generally include but are certainly not limited to the following: (1) smaller cell size, (2) all digital, and (3) additional features. Cellular systems generally classified as PCS include IS-136 TDMA, GSM, and IS-95 CDMA.

The concept of *personal communications services* (also PCS) originated in the United Kingdom when three companies were allocated a band of frequencies in the 1.8-GHz band to develop a *personal communications network* (PCN) throughout Great Britain. The terms *PCS* and *PCN* are often used interchangeably. However, PCN refers to a wireless networking concept where any user can initiate or receive calls regardless of where they are using a portable, personalized transceiver. PCS refers to a new wireless system that incorporates enhanced network features and is more personalized than existing standard cellular telephone systems but does not offer all the features of an ideal PCN.

In 1990, the Federal Communications Commission adopted the term PCS to mean *personal communications services,* which is the North American implementation of the *global system for mobile communications.* However, to some people, PCS means *personal communications system,* which specifies a category or type of cellular telephone system. The exact nature of the services provided by PCS is not completely defined by the cellular telephone industry. However, the intention of PCS systems is to provide enhanced features to first- and second-generation cellular telephone systems, such as messaging, paging, and data services.

PCS is more of a concept than a technology. The concept being to assign everyone a *personal telephone number* (PTN) that is stored in a database on the SS7 network. This database keeps track of where each mobile unit can be reached. When a call is placed from a mobile unit, an *artificial intelligence network* (AIN) in SS7 determines where and how the call should be directed. The PCS network is similar to the D-AMPS system in that the MTSO stores three essential databases: *home location register, visitor location register,* and *equipment identification registry.*

> *Home location register* (HLR). The HLR is a database that stores information about the user, including home subscription information and what supplementary services the user is subscribed to, such as call waiting, call hold, call forwarding, and call conferencing (three-way calling). There is generally only one HLR per mobile network. Data stored on the HLR are semipermanent, as they do not usually change from call to call.
>
> *Visitor location register* (VLR). The VLR is a database that stores information about subscribers in a particular MTSO serving area, such as whether the unit is on or off and whether any of the supplementary services are activated or deactivated. There is generally only one VLR per mobile switch. The VLR stores permanent data, such as that found in the HLR, plus temporary data, such as the subscriber's current location.
>
> *Equipment identification registry* (EIR). The EIR is a database that stores information pertaining to the identification and type of equipment that exists in the mobile unit. The EIR also helps the network identify stolen or fraudulent mobile units.

Many of the services offered by PCS systems are not currently available with standard cellular telephone systems, such as available mode, screen, private, and unavailable.

> *Available mode.* The available mode allows all calls to pass through the network to the subscriber except for a minimal number of telephone numbers that can be blocked. The available mode relies on the delivery of the calling party number, which is checked against a database to ensure that it is not a blocked number. Subscribers can update or make changes in the database through the dial pad on their PCS handset.
>
> *Screen mode.* The screen mode is the PCS equivalent to caller ID. With the screen mode, the name of the calling party appears on the mobile unit's display, which allows PCS users to screen calls. Unanswered calls are automatically forwarded to a *forwarding destination* specified by the subscriber, such as voice mail or another telephone number.
>
> *Private mode.* With the private mode, all calls except those specified by the subscriber are automatically forwarded to a forwarding destination without ringing the subscriber's handset. Subscribers can make changes in the list of allowed calling numbers through the dial pad on their handset.

Unavailable mode. With the unavailable mode, no calls are allowed to pass through to the subscriber. Hence, all incoming calls are automatically forwarded to a forwarding destination.

PCS telephones are intended to be small enough to fit into a shirt pocket and use digital technology, which is quieter than analog. Their transmit power is relatively low; therefore, PCS systems utilize smaller cells and require more base stations than standard cellular systems for a given service area. PCS systems are sometimes called *microcellular* systems. The fundamental concept of PCS is to assign each mobile unit a PTN that is stored in a database on the SS7 common signaling network. The database keeps track of where mobile units are. When a call is placed for a mobile unit, the SS7 artificial intelligence network determines where the call should be directed.

The primary disadvantage of PCS is network cost. Employing small cells requires using more base stations, which equates to more transceivers, antennas, and trunk circuits. Antenna placement is critical with PCS. Large towers typically used with standard cellular systems are unacceptable in neighborhoods, which is where a large majority of PCS antennas must be placed.

PCS base stations communicate with other networks (cellular, PCS, and wireline) through a PCS switching center (PSC). The PSC is connected directly to the SS7 signaling network with a link to a signaling transfer point. PCS networks rely extensively on the SS7 signaling network for interconnecting to other telephone networks and databases.

PCS systems generally operate in a higher frequency band than standard cellular telephone systems. The FCC recently allocated an additional 160-MHz band in the 1850-MHz to 2200-MHz range. PCS systems operating in the 1900-MHz range are often referred to as *personal communications system 1900* (PCS 1900).

12-4 SECOND-GENERATION CELLULAR TELEPHONE SYSTEMS

First-generation cellular telephone systems were designed primarily for a limited customer base, such as business customers and a limited number of affluent residential customers. When the demand for cellular service increased, manufacturers searched for new technologies to improve the inherent problems with the existing cellular telephones, such as poor battery performance and channel unavailability. Improved batteries were also needed to reduce the size and cost of mobile units, especially those that were designed to be handheld. Weak signal strengths resulted in poor performance and a high rate of falsely initiated handoffs (*false handoffs*).

It was determined that improved battery performance and higher signal quality were possible only by employing digital technologies. In the United States, the shortcomings of the first-generation cellular systems led to the development of several second-generation cellular telephone systems, such as narrowband AMPS (N-AMPS) and systems employing the IS-54, IS-136, and IS-95 standards. A second-generation standard, known as *Global System for Mobile Communications* (GSM), emerged in Europe.

12-5 N-AMPS

Because of uncertainties about the practicality and cost effectiveness of implementing digital cellular telephone systems, Motorola developed a narrowband AMPS system called N-AMPS to increase the capacity of the AMPS system in large cellular markets. N-AMPS was originally intended to provide a short-term solution to the traffic congestion problem in the AMPS system. N-AMPS allows as many as three mobile units to use a single 30-kHz cellular channel at the same time. With N-AMPS, the maximum frequency deviation is reduced, reducing the required bandwidth to 10 kHz and thus providing a threefold increase in user capacity. One N-AMPS channel uses the carrier frequency for the existing AMPS channel and, with the other two channels, the carrier frequencies are offset by ±10 kHz. Each 10-kHz subchannel is capable of handling its own calls. Reducing the bandwidth degrades speech quality by lowering the signal-to-interference ratio. With narrower bandwidths, voice channels are more vulnerable to interference than standard AMPS channels and would generally require a higher frequency reuse factor. This is compensated for with the addition of an *interference avoidance scheme* called *Mobile Reported Interference* (MRI), which uses voice companding to provide synthetic voice channel quieting.

N-AMPS systems are *dual mode* in that mobile units are capable of operating with 30-kHz channels or with 10-kHz channels. N-AMPS systems use standard AMPS control channels for call setup and termination. N-AMPS mobile units are capable of utilizing four types of handoffs: *wide channel to wide channel* (30 kHz to 30 kHz), *wide channel to narrow channel* (30 kHz to 10 kHz), *narrow channel to narrow channel* (10 kHz to 10 kHz), and *narrow channel to wide channel* (10 kHz to 30 kHz).

12-6 DIGITAL CELLULAR TELEPHONE

Cellular telephone companies were faced with the problem of a rapidly expanding customer base while at the same time the allocated frequency spectrum remained unchanged. As is evident with N-AMPS, user capacity can be expanded by subdividing existing channels (band splitting), partitioning cells into smaller subcells (cell splitting), and modifying antenna radiation patterns (sectoring). However, the degree of subdivision and redirection is limited by the complexity and amount of overhead required to process handoffs between cells. Another serious restriction is the availability and cost of purchasing or leasing property for cell sites in the higher-density traffic areas.

Digital cellular telephone systems have several inherent advantages over analog cellular telephone systems, including better utilization of bandwidth, more privacy, and incorporation of error detection and correction.

AMPS is a first-generation analog cellular telephone system that was not designed to support the high-capacity demands of the modern world, especially in high-density metropolitan areas. In the late 1980s, several major manufacturers of cellular equipment determined that digital cellular telephone systems could provide substantial improvements in both capacity and performance. Consequently, the *United States Digital Cellular* (USDC) system was designed and developed with the intent of supporting a higher user density within a fixed-bandwidth frequency spectrum. Cellular telephone systems that use digital modulation, such as USDC, are called *digital cellular.*

The USDC cellular telephone system was originally designed to utilize the AMPS frequency allocation scheme. USDC systems comply with IS-54, which specifies dual-mode operation and backward compatibility with standard AMPS. USDC was originally designed to use the same carrier frequencies, frequency reuse plan, and base stations. Therefore, base stations and mobile units can be equipped with both AMPS and USDC channels within the same telephone equipment. In supporting both systems, cellular carriers are able to provide new customers with digital USDC telephones while still providing service to existing customers with analog AMPS telephones. Because the USDC system maintains compatibility with AMPS systems in several ways, it is also known as *Digital AMPS* (D-AMPS or sometimes DAMPS).

The USDC cellular telephone system has an additional frequency band in the 1.9-GHz range that is not compatible with the AMPS frequency allocation. Figure 12-5 shows the frequency spectrum and channel assignments for the 1.9-GHz band (sometimes called the PCS band). The total usable spectrum is subdivided into subbands (A through F); however, the individual channel bandwidth is limited to 30 kHz (the same as AMPS).

1.85	1.865	1.87	1.885	1.89	1.895	1.91

A-band (15 MHz) 449 30-kHz channels	D-band (15 MHz) 449 30-kHz channels	B-band (15 MHz) 449 30-kHz channels	E-band (15 MHz) 449 30-kHz channels	F-band (15 MHz) 449 30-kHz channels	C-band (15 MHz) 449 30-kHz channels

20 MHz separation between forward and reverse transmit frequency bands

Reverse channel transmit frequency (GHz)

1.93	1.945	1.95	1.965	1.97	1.975	1.99

A-band (15 MHz) 449 30-kHz channels	D-band (15 MHz) 449 30-kHz channels	B-band (15 MHz) 449 30-kHz channels	E-band (15 MHz) 449 30-kHz channels	F-band (15 MHz) 449 30-kHz channels	C-band (15 MHz) 449 30-kHz channels

FIGURE 12-5   1.9-GHz cellular frequency band

12-6-1   Time-Division Multiple Accessing

USDC uses *time-division multiple accessing* (TDMA) as well as frequency-division multiple accessing (FDMA). USDC, like AMPS, divides the total available radio-frequency spectrum into individual 30-kHz cellular channels (i.e., FDMA). However, TDMA allows more than one mobile unit to use a channel at the same time by further dividing transmissions within each cellular channel into time slots, one for each mobile unit using that channel. In addition, with AMPS FDMA systems, subscribers are assigned a channel for the duration of their call. However, with USDC TDMA systems, mobile-unit subscribers can only *hold* a channel while they are actually talking on it. During pauses or other normal breaks in a conversation, users must relinquish their channel so that other mobile units can use it. This technique of *time-sharing* channels significantly increases the capacity of a system, allowing more mobile-unit subscribers to use a system at virtually the same time within a given geographical area.

A USDC TDMA transmission frame consists of six equal-duration time slots enabling each 30-kHz AMPS channel to support three full-rate or six half-rate users. Hence, USDC offers as much as six times the channel capacity as AMPS. The original USDC standard also utilizes the same 50-MHz frequency spectrum and frequency-division duplexing scheme as AMPS.

The advantages of digital TDMA multiple-accessing systems over analog AMPS FDMA multiple-accessing systems are as follows:

1. Interleaving transmissions in the time domain allows for a threefold to sixfold increase in the number of mobile subscribers using a single cellular channel. Time-sharing is realized because of digital compression techniques that produce bit rates approximately one-tenth that of the initial digital sample rate and about one-fifth the initial rate when error detection/correction (EDC) bits are included.
2. Digital signals are much easier to process than analog signals. Many of the more advanced modulation schemes and information processing techniques were developed for use in a digital environment.
3. Digital signals (bits) can be easily encrypted and decrypted, safeguarding against eavesdropping.
4. The entire telephone system is compatible with other digital formats, such as those used in computers and computer networks.
5. Digital systems inherently provide a quieter (less noisy) environment than their analog counterparts.

In 1990, the Electronics Industries Association and Telecommunications Industry Association (EIA/TIA) standardized the dual-mode USDC/AMPS system as Interim Standard 54 (IS-54), *Cellular Dual Mode Subscriber Equipment*. *Dual mode* specifies that a mobile station complying with the IS-54 standard must be capable of operating in either the analog AMPS or the digital (USDC) mode for voice transmissions. Using IS-54, a cellular telephone carrier could convert any or all of its existing analog channels to digital. The key criterion for achieving dual-mode operation is that IS-54 digital channels cannot interfere with transmissions from existing analog AMPS base and mobile stations. This goal is achieved with IS-54 by providing digital control channels and both analog and digital voice channels. Dual-mode mobile units can operate in either the digital or the analog mode for voice and access the system with the standard AMPS digital control channel. Before a voice channel is assigned, IS-54 mobile units use AMPS forward and reverse control channels to carry out user authentications and call management operations. When a dual-mode mobile unit transmits an access request, it indicates that it is capable of operating in the digital mode; then the base station will allocate a digital voice channel, provided one is available. The allocation procedure indicates the channel number (frequency) and the specific time slot (or slots) within that particular channel's TDMA frame. IS-54 specifies a 48.6-kbps rate per 30-kHz voice channel divided among three simultaneous users. Each user is allocated 13 kbps, and the remaining 9.6 kbps is used for timing and control overhead.

In many rural areas of the United States, analog cellular telephone systems use only the original 666 AMPS channels (1 through 666). In these areas, USDC channels can be added in the extended frequency spectrum (channels 667 through 799 and 991 through 1023) to support USDC telephones that roam into the system from other areas. In high-density urban areas, selected frequency bands are gradually being converted one at a time to the USDC digital standard to help alleviate traffic congestion. Unfortunately, this gradual changeover from AMPS to USDC often results in an increase in the interference and number of dropped calls experienced by subscribers of the AMPS system.

The successful and graceful transition from analog cellular systems to digital cellular systems using the same frequency band was a primary consideration in the development of the USDC standard. The introduction of N-AMPS and a new digital spread-spectrum standard has delayed the widespread deployment of the USDC standard throughout the United States.

12-6-3   USDC Control Channels and IS-136.2

The IS-54 USDC standard specifies the same 42 *primary control channels* as AMPS and 42 additional control channels called *secondary control channels*. Thus, USDC offers twice as many control channels as AMPS and is, therefore, capable of providing twice the capacity of control traffic within a given market area. Carriers are allowed to dedicate the secondary control channels for USDC-only use since AMPS mobile users do not monitor and cannot decode the new secondary control channels. In addition, to maintain compatibility with existing AMPS cellular telephone systems, the primary forward and reverse control channels in USDC cellular systems use the same signaling techniques and modulation scheme (FSK) as AMPS. However, a new standard, IS-136.2 (formerly IS-54, Rev.C), replaces FSK with $\pi/4$ DQPSK modulation for the 42 dedicated USDC secondary control channels, allowing digital mobile units to operate entirely in the digital domain. The IS-136.2 standard is often called North American-Time Division Multiple Accessing (NA-TDMA). IS-54 Rev.C was introduced to provide PSK (phase-shift keying) rather than FSK on dedicated USDC control channels to increase the control data rates and provide additional specialized services, such as paging and short messaging between private mobile user groups. *Short message service* allows for brief paging-type messages and short e-mail messages (up to 239 characters) that can be read on the mobile phone's display and entered using the keypad.

IS-136 was developed to provide a host of new features and services, positioning itself in a competitive market with the newer PCS systems. Because IS-136 specifies short messaging capabilities and private user-group features, it is well suited as a wireless paging system. IS-136 also provides an additional *sleep mode,* which conserves power in the mobile units. IS-136 mobile units are not compatible with IS-54 units, as FSK control channels are not supported.

The digital control channel is necessarily complex, and a complete description is beyond the scope of this book. Therefore, the following discussion is meant to present a general overview of the operation of a USDC digital control channel.

The IS-54 standard specifies three types of channels: analog control channels, analog voice channels, and a 10-kbps binary FSK digital control channel (DCCH). The IS-54 Rev.C standard (IS-136) provides for the same three types of channels plus a fourth—a digital control channel with a signaling rate of 48.6 kbps on USDC-only control channels. The new digital control channel is meant to eventually replace the analog control channel. With the addition of a digital control channel, a mobile unit is able to operate entirely in the digital domain, using the digital control channel for system and cell selection and channel accessing and the digital voice channel for digitized voice transmissions.

IS-136 details the exact functionality of the USDC digital control channel. The initial version of IS-136 was version 0, which has since been updated by revision A. Version 0 added numerous new services and features to the USDC digital cellular telephone system, including enhanced user services, such as short messaging and displaying the telephone number of the incoming call; sleep mode, which gives the telephone set a longer battery life when in the standby mode; private or residential system service; and enhanced security and validation against fraud. The newest version of IS-136, revision A, was developed to provide numerous new features and services by introducing an enhanced vocoder, over-the-air activation where the network operators are allowed to program information into telephones directly over the air, calling name and number ID, and enhanced hands-off and priority access to control channels.

IS-136 specifies several private user-group features, making it well adapted for wireless PBX and paging applications. However, IS-136 user terminals operate at 48.6 kbps and are, therefore, not compatible with IS-54 FSK terminals. Thus, IS-136 modems are more cost effective, as it is necessary to include only the 48.6-kbps modem in the terminal equipment.

12-6-3-1 Logical channels. The new digital control channel includes several *logical channels* with different functions, including the *random access channel* (RACH); the *SMS point-to-point, paging, and access response channel* (SPACH); the *broadcast control channel* (BCCH); and the *shared channel feedback* (SCF) channel. Figure 12-6 shows the logical control channels for the IS-136 standard.

12-6-3-2 Random access channel (RACH). RACH is used by mobile units to request access to the cellular telephone system. RACH is a unidirectional channel specified for transmissions from mobile-to-base units only. Access messages, such as origination, registration, page responses, audit confirmation, serial number, and message confirmation, are transmitted on the RACH. It also transmits messages that provide information on authentication, security parameter updates, and *short message service* (SMS) point-to-point messages. RACH is capable of operating in two modes using contention resolution similar to voice channels. RACH can also operate in a *reservation mode* for replying to a base-station command.

12-6-3-3 SMS point-to-point, paging, and access response channel (SPACH). SPACH is used to transmit information from base stations to specific mobile stations. RACH is a unidirectional channel specified for transmission from base stations to mobile units only and is shared by all mobile units. Information transmitted on the SPACH channel includes three separate logical subchannels: *SMS point-to-point messages, paging messages,* and *access response messages.* SPACH can carry messages related to a single mo-

FIGURE 12-6 USDC IS-136 digital control channel—logical channel and logical subchannels

bile unit or to a small group of mobile units and allows larger messages to be broken down into smaller blocks for transmission.

The paging channel (PCH) is a subchannel of the logical channel of SPACH. PCH is dedicated to delivering pages and orders. The PCH transmits *paging messages, message-waiting messages,* and *user-alerting messages.* Each PCH message can carry up to five mobile identifiers. Page messages are always transmitted and then repeated a second time. Messages such as *call history count updates* and *shared secret data updates* used for the authentication and encryption process also are sent on the PCH.

The access response channel (ARCH) is also a logical subchannel of SPACH. A mobile unit automatically moves to an ARCH immediately after successful completion of contention- or reservation-based access on a RACH. ARCH can be used to carry assignments to another resource or other responses to the mobile station's access attempt. Messages assigning a mobile unit to an analog voice channel or a digital voice channel or redirecting the mobile to a different cell are also sent on the ARCH along with registration access (accept, reject, or release) messages.

The SMS channel (SMSCH) is used to deliver short point-to-point messages to a specific mobile station. Each message is limited to a maximum of 200 characters of text. Mobile-originated SMS is also supported; however, SMS where a base station can broadcast a short message designated for several mobile units is not supported in IS-136.

12-6-3-4 Broadcast control channel (BCCH). BCCH is an acronym referring to the F-BCCH, E-BCCH, and S-BCCH logical subchannels. These channels are used to carry generic, system-related information. BCCH is a unidirectional base station-to-mobile unit transmission shared by all mobile units.

The *fast broadcast control channel* (F-BCCH) broadcasts digital control channel (DCCH) structure parameters, including information about the number of F-BCCH, E-BCCH, and S-BCCH time slots in the DCCH frame. Mobile units use F-BCCH information when initially accessing the system to determine the beginning and ending of each logical channel in the DCCH frame. F-BCCH also includes information pertaining to access parameters, including information necessary for authentication and encryptions and information for mobile access attempts, such as the number of access retries, access burst size, initial access power level, and indication of whether the cell is barred. Information addressing the different types of registration, registration periods, and system identification information, including network type, mobile country code, and protocol revision, is also provided by the F-BCCH channel.

The *extended broadcast control channel* (E-BCCH) carries less critical broadcast information than F-BCCH intended for the mobile units. E-BCCH carries information about neighboring analog and TDMA cells and optional messages, such as emergency information, time and date messaging, and the types of services supported by neighboring cells.

The *SMS broadcast control channel* (S-BCCH) is a logical channel used for sending short messages to individual mobile units.

12-6-3-5 Shared channel feedback (SCF) channel.

SCF is used to support random access channel operation by providing information about which time slots the mobile unit can use for access attempts and also if a mobile unit's previous RACH transmission was successfully received.

12-6-4 USDC Digital Voice Channel

Like AMPS, each USDC voice channel is assigned a 30-kHz bandwidth on both the forward and the reverse link. With USDC, however, each voice channel can support as many as three full-rate mobile users simultaneously by using digital modulation and a TDMA format called *North American Digital Cellular* (NADC). Each radio-frequency voice channel in the total AMPS FDMA frequency band consists of one 40-ms TDMA frame comprised of six time slots containing 324 bits each, as shown in Figure 12-7. For full-speech rate, three users

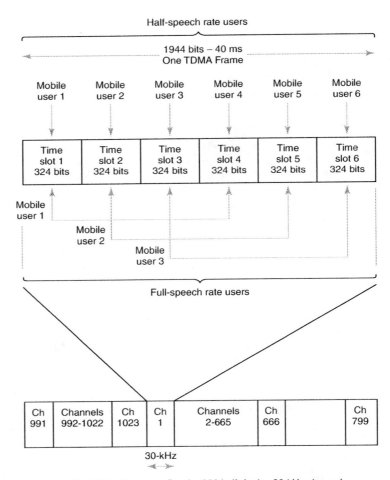

FIGURE 12-7   North American Digital Cellular TDMA frame format

share the six time slots in an equally spaced manner. For example, mobile user 1 occupies time slots 1 and 4, mobile user 2 occupies time slots 2 and 5, and mobile user 3 occupies time slots 3 and 6. For half-rate speech, each user occupies one time slot per frame. During their respective time slots, mobile units transmit short bursts (6.67 ms) of a digital-modulated carrier to the base station (i.e., *uplink transmissions*). Hence, full-rate users transmit two bursts during each TDMA frame. In the *downlink* path (i.e., from base stations to mobile units), base stations generally transmit continuously. However, mobile units only listen during their assigned time slot. The average cost per subscriber per base station equipment is lower with TDMA since each base station transceiver can be shared by up to six users at a time.

General Motors Corporation implemented a TDMA scheme called E-TDMA, which incorporates six half-rate users transmitting at half the bit rate of standard USDC TDMA systems. E-TDMA systems also incorporate *digital speech interpolation* (DSI) to dynamically assign more than one user to a time slot, deleting silence on calls. Consequently, E-TDMA can handle approximately 12 times the user traffic as standard AMPS systems and four times that of systems complying with IS-54.

Each time slot in every USDC voice-channel frame contains four data channels— three for control and one for digitized voice and user data. The full-duplex *digital traffic channel* (DTC) carries digitized voice information and consists of a *reverse digital traffic channel* (RDTC) and a *forward digital traffic channel* (FDTC) that carry digitized speech information or user data. The RDTC carries speech data from the mobile unit to the base station, and the FDTC carries user speech data from the base station to the mobile unit. The three supervisory channels are the *coded digital verification color code* (CDVCC), the *slow associated control channel* (SACCH), and the *fast associated control channel* (FACCH).

12-6-4-1 Coded digital verification color code. The purpose of the CDVCC color code is to provide co-channel identification similar to the SAT signal transmitted in the AMPS system. The CDVCC is a 12-bit message transmitted in every time slot. The CDVCC consists of an eight-bit digital voice color code number between 1 and 255 appended with four additional coding bits derived from a shortened Hamming code. The base station transmits a CDVCC number on the forward voice channel, and each mobile unit using the TDMA channel must receive, decode, and retransmit the same CDVCC code (handshake) back to the base station on the reverse voice channel. If the two CDVCC values are not the same, the time slot is relinquished for other users, and the mobile unit's transmitter will be automatically turned off.

12-6-4-2 Slow associated control channel. The SACCH is a signaling channel for transmission of control and supervision messages between the digital mobile unit and the base station while the mobile unit is involved with a call. The SACCH uses 12 coded bits per TDMA burst and is transmitted in every time slot, thus providing a signaling channel in parallel with the digitized speech information. Therefore, SACCH messages can be transmitted without interfering with the processing of digitized speech signals. Because the SACCH consists of only 12 bits per frame, it can take up to 22 frames for a single SACCH message to be transmitted. The SACCH carries various control and supervisory information between the mobile unit and the base station, such as communicating power-level changes and hand-off requests. The SACCH is also used by the mobile unit to report signal-strength measurements of neighboring base stations so, when necessary, the base station can initiate a *mobile-assisted handoff* (MAHO).

12-6-4-3 Fast associated control channel. The FACCH is a second signaling channel for transmission of control and specialized supervision and traffic messages between the base station and the mobile units. Unlike the CDVCC and SACCH, the FACCH does not have a dedicated time slot. The FACCH is a *blank-and-burst* type of transmission that, when transmitted, replaces digitized speech information with control and supervision messages within a subscriber's time slot. There is no limit on the number of speech frames that can be replaced with FACCH data. However, the digitized voice information is somewhat

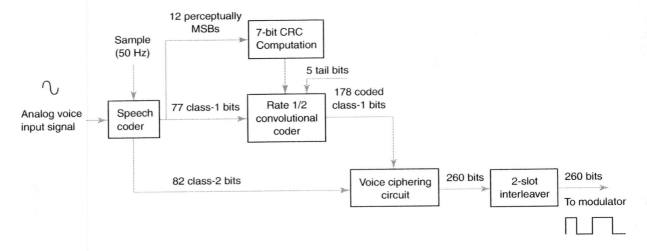

FIGURE 12-8   USDC digital voice-channel speech coder

protected by preventing an entire digitized voice transmission from being replaced by FACCH data. The 13-kbps net digitized voice transmission rate cannot be reduced below 3250 bps in any given time slot. There are no fields within a standard time slot to identify it as digitized speech or an FACCH message. To determine if an FACCH message is being received, the mobile unit must attempt to decode the data as speech. If it decodes in error, it then decodes the data as an FACCH message. If the cyclic redundancy character (CRC) calculates correctly, the message is assumed to be an FACCH message. The FACCH supports transmission of dual-tone multiple-frequency (DTMF) Touch-Tones, call release instruction, flash hook instructions, and mobile-assisted handoff or mobile-unit status requests. The FACCH data are packaged and interleaved to fit in a time slot similar to the way digitized speech is handled.

12-6-5   Speech Coding

Figure 12-8 shows the block diagram for a USDC digital voice-channel speech encoder. Channel error control for the digitized speech data uses three mechanisms for minimizing channel errors: (1) A rate one-half convolutional code is used to protect the more vulnerable bits of the speech coder data stream; (2) transmitted data are interleaved for each speech coder frame over two time slots to reduce the effects of Rayleigh fading; and (3) a cyclic redundancy check is performed on the most perceptually significant bits of the digitized speech data.

With USDC, incoming analog voice signals are sampled first and then converted to a binary PCM in a special *speech coder* (*vocoder*) called a *vector sum exciter linear predictive* (VSELP) *coder* or a *stochastically excited linear predictive* (SELP) *coder.* Linear predictive coders are time-domain types of vocoders that attempt to extract the most significant characteristics from the time-varying speech waveform. With linear predictive coders, it is possible to transmit good-quality voice at 4.8 kbps and acceptable, although poorer-quality, voice at lower bit rates.

Because there are many predictable orders in spoken word patterns, it is possible, using advanced algorithms, to compress the binary samples and transmit the resulting bit stream at a 13-kbps rate. A consortium of companies, including Motorola, developed the VSELP algorithm, which was subsequently adopted for the IS-54 standard. Error-detection and -correction (EDC) bits are added to the digitally compressed voice signals to reduce the effects of interference, bringing the final voice data rate to 48.6 kbps. Compression/ expansion and error-detection/correction functions are implemented in the telephone handset by a special microprocessor called a digital signal processor (DSP).

FIGURE 12-9   USDC digital voice channel slot and frame format

The VSELP coders output 7950 bps and produce a speech frame every 20 ms, or

$$\frac{7950 \text{ bits}}{\text{second}} \times \frac{20 \text{ ms}}{\text{frame}} = 159 \text{ bits-per-frame}$$

Fifty speech frames are outputted each second containing 159 bits each, or

$$\frac{50 \text{ frames}}{\text{second}} \times \frac{159 \text{ bits}}{\text{frame}} = 7950 \text{ bps}$$

The 159 bits included in each speech coder frame are divided into two classes according to the significance in which they are perceived. There are 77 class 1 bits and 82 class 2 bits. The class 1 bits are the most significant and are, therefore, error protected. The 12 most significant class 1 bits are block coded using a seven-bit CRC error-detection code to ensure that the most significant speech coder bits are decoded with a low probability of error. The less significant class 2 bits have no means of error protection.

After coding the 159 bits, each speech code frame is converted in a 1/2 convolution coder to 260 channel-coded bits per frame, and 50 frames are transmitted each second. Hence, the transmission bit rate is increased from 7950 bps for each digital voice channel to 13 kbps:

$$\frac{260 \text{ bits}}{\text{frame}} \times \frac{50 \text{ frames}}{\text{second}} = 13 \text{ kbps}$$

Figure 12-9 shows the time slot and frame format for the forward (base station to mobile unit) and reverse (mobile unit to base station) links of a USDC digital voice channel. USDC voice channels use frequency-division duplexing; thus, forward and reverse channel time slots operate on different frequencies at the same time. Each time slot carries interleaved digital voice data from the two adjacent frames outputted from the speech coder.

G1	RSDSDVSDWSDXSDYS	G2

Where   G1 = 6-bit guard time

R = 6-bit length ramp time

S = 28-bit synchronization word

D = 12-bit CDVCC code

G2 = 44-bit guard time

V = 0000

W = 00000000

X = 000000000000

Y = 0000000000000000

FIGURE 12-10   USDC shortened burst digital voice channel format

In the reverse channel, each time slot contains two bursts of 122 digitized voice bits and one burst of 16 bits for a total of 260 digitized voice bits per frame. In addition, each time slot contains 28 synchronization bits, 12 bits of SACCH data, 12 bits of CDVCC bits, and six guard bits to compensate for differences in the distances between mobile units and base stations. The guard time is present in only the reverse channel time slots to prevent overlapping of received bursts due to radio signal transit time. The ramp-up time consists of six bits that allow gradual rising and falling of the RF signal energy within the time slot. Thus, a reverse channel time slot consists of 324 bits. If an FACCH is sent instead of speech data, one time slot of speech coding data is replaced with a 260-bit block of FACCH data.

In the forward channel, each time slot contains two 130-bit bursts of digitized voice data (or FACCH data if digitized speech is not being sent) for a total of 260 bits per frame. In addition, each forward channel frame contains 28 synchronization bits, 12 bits of SACCH data, 12 CDVCC bits, and 12 reserved bits for a total of 324 bits per time slot. Therefore, both forward and reverse voice channels have a data transmission rate of

$$\frac{324 \text{ bits}}{\text{time slot}} \times \frac{6 \text{ time slots}}{40 \text{ ms}} = 48.6 \text{ kbps}$$

A third frame format, called a *shortened burst,* is shown in Figure 12-10. Shortened bursts are transmitted when a mobile unit begins operating in a larger-diameter cell because the propagation time between the mobile and base is unknown. A mobile unit transmits shortened burst slots until the base station determines the required time offset. The default delay between the receive and transmit slots in the mobile is 44 symbols, which results in a maximum distance at which a mobile station can operate in a cell to 72 miles for an IS-54 cell.

12-6-6   USDC Digital Modulation Scheme

To achieve a transmission bit rate of 48.6 kbps in a 30-kHz AMPS voice channel, a *bandwidth (spectral) efficiency* of 1.62 bps/Hz is required, which is well beyond the capabilities of binary FSK. The spectral efficiency requirements can be met by using conventional pulse-shaped, four-phase modulation schemes, such as QPSK and OQPSK. However, USDC voice and control channels use a *symmetrical differential, phase-shift keying* technique known as $\pi/4$ DQPSK, or $\pi/4$ *differential quadriphase shift keying* (DQPSK), which offers several advantages in a mobile radio environment, such as improved co-channel rejection and bandwidth efficiency.

A 48.6-kbps data rate requires a symbol (baud) rate of 24.3 kbps (24.3 kilobaud per second) with a symbol duration of 41.1523 µs. The use of pulse shaping and $\pi/4$ DQPSK supports the transmission of three different 48.6-kbps digitized speech signals in a 30-kHz

Table 12-4   NA-TDMA Mobile Phone Power Levels

Power Level	Class I		Class II		Class III		Class IV
	dBm	mW	dBm	mW	dBm	mW	dBm
0	36	4000	32	1600	28	640	28
1	32	1600	32	1600	28	640	28
2	28	640	28	640	28	640	28
3	24	256	24	256	24	256	24
4	20	102	20	102	20	102	20
5	16	41	16	41	16	41	16
6	12	16	12	16	12	16	12
7	8	6.6	8	6.6	8	6.6	8
8	—	—	Dual mode only		—	— 4 dBm ± 3 dB	
9	—	—	Dual mode only		—	— 0 dBm ± 6 dB	
10	—	—	Dual mode only		—	— − 4 dBm ± 9 dB	

bandwidth with as much as 50 dB of adjacent-channel isolation. Thus, the bandwidth efficiency using $\pi/4$ DQPSK is

$$\eta = \frac{3 \times 48.6 \text{ kbps}}{30 \text{ kHz}}$$

$$= 4.86 \text{ bps/Hz}$$

where η is the bandwidth efficiency.

In a $\pi/4$ DQPSK modulator, data bits are split into two parallel channels that produce a specific phase shift in the analog carrier and, since there are four possible bit pairs, there are four possible phase shifts using a quadrature I/Q modulator. The four possible differential phase changes, $\pi/4$, $-\pi/4$, $3\pi/4$, and $-3\pi/4$, define eight possible carrier phases. Pulse shaping is used to minimize the bandwidth while limiting the intersymbol interference. In the transmitter, the PSK signal is filtered using a square-root raised cosine filter with a roll-off factor of 0.35. PSK signals, after pulse shaping, become a linear modulation technique, requiring linear amplification to preserve the pulse shape. Using pulse shaping with $\pi/4$ DQPSK allows for the simultaneous transmission of three separate 48.6-kbps speech signals in a 30-kHz bandwidth.

12-6-7   USDC Radiated Power

NA-TDMA specifies 11 radiated power levels for four classifications of mobile units, including the eight power levels used by standard AMPS transmitters. The fourth classification is for dual-mode TDMA/analog cellular telephones. The NA-TDMA power classifications are listed in Table 12-4. The highest power level is 4 W (36 dBm), and successive levels differ by 4 dB, with the lowest level for classes I through III being 8 dBm (6.6 mW). The lowest transmit power level for dual-mode mobile units is −4 dBm (0.4 mW) ± 9 dB. In a dual-mode system, the three lowest power levels can be assigned only to digital voice channels and digital control channels. Analog voice channels and FSK control channels transmitting in the standard AMPS format are confined to the eight power levels in the AMPS specification. Transmitters in the TDMA mode are active only one-third of the time; therefore, the average transmitted power is 4.8 dB below specifications.

12-7   INTERIM STANDARD 95 (IS-95)

FDMA is an access method used with standard analog AMPS, and both FDMA and TDMA are used with USDC. Both FDMA and TDMA use a frequency channelization approach to frequency spectrum management; however, TDMA also utilizes a time-division accessing approach. With FDMA and TDMA cellular telephones, the entire available cellular radio-frequency spectrum is subdivided into narrowband radio channels to be used for one-way communications links between cellular mobile units and base stations.

In 1984, Qualcomm Inc. proposed a cellular telephone system and standard based on spread-spectrum technology with the primary goal of increasing capacity. Qualcomm's new system enabled a totally digital mobile telephone system to be made available in the United States based on *code-division multiple accessing* (CDMA). The U.S. Telecommunications Industry Association recently standardized the CDMA system as Interim Standard 95 (IS-95), which is a mobile-to-base station compatibility standard for dual-mode wideband spread-spectrum communications. CDMA allows users to differentiate from one another by a unique code rather than a frequency or time assignment and, therefore, offers several advantages over cellular telephone systems using TDMA and FDMA, such as increased capacity and improved performance and reliability. IS-95, like IS-54, was designed to be compatible with existing analog cellular telephone system (AMPS) frequency band; therefore, mobile units and base stations can easily be designed for dual-mode operation. Pilot CDMA systems developed by Qualcomm were first made available in 1994.

NA-TDMA channels occupy exactly the same bandwidth as standard analog AMPS signals. Therefore, individual AMPS channel units can be directly replaced with TDMA channels, which are capable of carrying three times the user capacity as AMPS channels. Because of the wide bandwidths associated with CDMA transmissions, IS-95 specifies an entirely different channel frequency allocation plan than AMPS.

The IS-95 standard specifies the following:

1. Modulation—digital OQPSK (uplink) and digital QPSK (downlink)
2. 800-MHz band (IS-95A)
   45-MHz forward and reverse separation
   50-MHz spectral allocation
3. 1900-MHz band (IS-95B)
   90-MHz forward and reverse separation
   120-MHz spectral allocation
4. 2.46-MHz total bandwidth
   1.23-MHz reverse CDMA channel bandwidth
   1.23-MHz forward CDMA channel bandwidth
5. Direct-sequence CDMA accessing
6. 8-kHz voice bandwidth
7. 64 total channels per CDMA channel bandwidth
8. 55 voice channels per CDMA channel bandwidth

12-7-1 CDMA

With IS-95, each mobile user within a given cell, and mobile subscribers in adjacent cells use the same radio-frequency channels. In essence, frequency reuse is available in all cells. This is made possible because IS-95 specifies a direct-sequence, spread-spectrum CDMA system and does not follow the channelization principles of traditional cellular radio communications systems. Rather than dividing the allocated frequency spectrum into narrow-bandwidth channels, one for each user, information is transmitted (spread) over a very wide frequency spectrum with as many as 20 mobile subscriber units simultaneously using the same carrier frequency within the same frequency band. Interference is incorporated into the system so that there is no limit to the number of subscribers that CDMA can support. As more mobile subscribers are added to the system, there is a *graceful degradation* of communications quality.

With CDMA, unlike other cellular telephone standards, subscriber data change in real time, depending on the voice activity and requirements of the network and other users of the network. IS-95 also specifies a different modulation and spreading technique for the forward and reverse channels. On the forward channel, the base station simultaneously transmits user data from all current mobile units in that cell by using different spreading sequences (codes) for each user's transmissions. A pilot code is transmitted with the user data at a higher power level, thus allowing all mobile units to use coherent detection. On the reverse link, all mobile units respond in an asynchronous manner (i.e., no time or duration limitations) with a constant signal level controlled by the base station.

The speech coder used with IS-95 is the Qualcomm 9600-bps *Code-Excited Linear Predictive* (QCELP) coder. The vocoder converts an 8-kbps compressed data stream to a 9.6-kbps data stream. The vocoder's original design detects voice activity and automatically reduces the data rate to 1200 bps during silent periods. Intermediate mobile user data rates of 2400 bps and 4800 bps are also used for special purposes. In 1995, Qualcomm introduced a 14,400-bps vocoder that transmits 13.4 kbps of compressed digital voice information.

12-7-1-1 CDMA frequency and channel allocations. CDMA reduces the importance of frequency planning within a given cellular market. The AMPS U.S. cellular telephone system is allocated a 50-MHz frequency spectrum (25 MHz for each direction of propagation), and each service provider (system A and system B) is assigned half the available spectrum (12.5 MHz). AMPS common carriers must provide a 270-kHz guard band (approximately nine AMPS channels) on either side of the CDMA frequency spectrum. To facilitate a graceful transition from AMPS to CDMA, each IS-95 channel is allocated a 1.25-MHz frequency spectrum for each one-way CDMA communications channel. This equates to 10% of the total available frequency spectrum of each U.S. cellular telephone provider. CDMA channels can coexist within the AMPS frequency spectrum by having a wireless operator clear a 1.25-MHz band of frequencies to accommodate transmissions on the CDMA channel. A single CDMA radio channel takes up the same bandwidth as approximately 42 30-kHz AMPS voice channels. However, because of the frequency reuse advantage of CDMA, CDMA offers approximately a 10-to-1 channel advantage over standard analog AMPS and a 3-to-1 advantage over USDC digital AMPS.

For reverse (downlink) operation, IS-95 specifies the 824-MHz to 849-MHz band and forward (uplink) channels the 869-MHz to 894-MHz band. CDMA cellular systems also use a modified frequency allocation plan in the 1900-MHz band. As with AMPS, the transmit and receive carrier frequencies used by CDMA are separated by 45 MHz. Figure 12-11a shows the frequency spacing for two adjacent CDMA channels in the AMPS frequency band. As the figure shows, each CDMA channel is 1.23 MHz wide with a 1.25-MHz frequency separation between adjacent carriers, producing a 200-kHz guard band between CDMA channels. Guard bands are necessary to ensure that the CDMA carriers do not interfere with one another. Figure 12-11b shows the CDMA channel location within the AMPS frequency spectrum. The lowest CDMA carrier frequency in the A band is at AMPS channel 283, and the lowest CDMA carrier frequency in the B band is at AMPS channel 384. Because the band available between 667 and 716 is only 1.5 MHz in the A band, A band operators have to acquire permission from B band carriers to use a CDMA carrier in that portion of the frequency spectrum. When a CDMA carrier is being used next to a non-CDMA carrier, the carrier spacing must be 1.77 MHz. There are as many as nine CDMA carriers available for the A and B band operator in the AMPS frequency spectrum. However, the A and B band operators have 30-MHz bandwidth in the 1900-MHz frequency band, where they can facilitate up to 11 CDMA channels.

With CDMA, many users can share common transmit and receive channels with a transmission data rate of 9.6 kbps. Using several techniques, however, subscriber information is spread by a factor of 128 to a channel chip rate of 1.2288 Mchips/s, and transmit and receive channels use different spreading processes.

(a)

AMPS channel number

(b)

FIGURE 12-11 (a) CDMA channel bandwidth, guard band, and frequency separation;
(b) CDMA channel location within the AMPS frequency spectrum

   In the uplink channel, subscriber data are encoded using a rate 1/2 convolutional
code, interleaved, and spread by one of 64 orthogonal spreading sequences using Walsh
functions. Orthogonality among all uplink cellular channel subscribers within a given cell
is maintained because all the cell signals are scrambled synchronously.

   Downlink channels use a different spreading strategy since each mobile unit's received signal takes a different transmission path and, therefore, arrives at the base station at
a different time. Downlink channel data streams are first convolutional encoded with a rate

1/3 convolution code. After interleaving, each block of six encoded symbols is mapped to one of the available orthogonal Walsh functions, ensuring 64-ary orthogonal signaling. An additional fourfold spreading is performed by subscriber-specified and base station-specific codes having periods of 2^{14} chips and 2^{15} chips, respectively, increasing the transmission rate to 1.2288 Mchips/s. Stringent requirements are enforced in the downlink channel's transmit power to avoid the near-far problem caused by varied receive power levels.

Each mobile unit in a given cell is assigned a unique spreading sequence, which ensures near perfect separation among the signals from different subscriber units and allows transmission differentiation between users. All signals in a particular cell are scrambled using a pseudorandom sequence of length 2^{15} chips. This reduces radio-frequency interference between mobiles in neighboring cells that may be using the same spreading sequence and provides the desired wideband spectral characteristics even though all Walsh codes do not yield a wideband power spectrum.

Two commonly used techniques for spreading the spectrum are *frequency hopping* and *direct sequencing.* Both of these techniques are characteristic of transmissions over a bandwidth much wider than that normally used in narrowband FDMA/TDMA cellular telephone systems, such as AMPS and USDC. For a more detailed description of frequency hopping and direct sequencing, refer to Chapter 25.

12-7-1-2 Frequency-hopping spread spectrum. Frequency-hopping spread spectrum was first used by the military to ensure reliable antijam and to secure communications in a battlefield environment. The fundamental concept of frequency hopping is to break a message into fixed-size blocks of data with each block transmitted in sequence except on a different carrier frequency. With frequency hopping, a pseudorandom code is used to generate a unique frequency-hopping sequence. The sequence in which the frequencies are selected must be known by both the transmitter and the receiver prior to the beginning of the transmission. The transmitter sends one block on a radio-frequency carrier and then switches (hops) to the next frequency in the sequence and so on. After reception of a block of data on one frequency, the receiver switches to the next frequency in the sequence. Each transmitter in the system has a different hopping sequence to prevent one subscriber from interfering with transmissions from other subscribers using the same radio channel frequency.

12-7-1-3 Direct-sequence spread spectrum. In direct-sequence systems, a high-bit-rate pseudorandom code is added to a low-bit-rate information signal to generate a high-bit-rate pseudorandom signal closely resembling noise that contains both the original data signal and the pseudorandom code. Again, before successful transmission, the pseudorandom code must be known to both the transmitter and the intended receiver. When a receiver detects a direct-sequence transmission, it simply subtracts the pseudorandom signal from the composite receive signal to extract the information data. In CDMA cellular telephone systems, the total radio-frequency bandwidth is divided into a few broadband radio channels that have a much higher bandwidth than the digitized voice signal. The digitized voice signal is added to the generated high-bit-rate signal and transmitted in such a way that it occupies the entire broadband radio channel. Adding a high-bit-rate pseudorandom signal to the voice information makes the signal more dominant and less susceptible to interference, allowing lower-power transmission and, hence, a lower number of transmitters and less expensive receivers.

12-7-2 CDMA Traffic Channels

CDMA traffic channels consist of a downlink (base station to mobile unit) channel and an uplink (mobile station to base station) channel. A CDMA downlink traffic channel is shown in Figure 12-12a. As the figure shows, the downlink traffic channel consists of up to 64 channels, including a broadcast channel used for control and traffic channels used to carry subscriber information. The broadcast channel consists of a pilot channel, a synchronization channel, up to seven paging channels, and up to 63 traffic channels. All these channels share the same 1.25-MHz CDMA frequency assignment. The traffic channel is identified

Pilot Channel	Synchronization Channel	Paging ———— Paging Channel 1 Channel 7	Traffic ———— Traffic Channel 1 Channel 62

Optional and Variable (0–7) Variable (55–62)

(a)

Access Channel 1	Access ———— Access Channel 2 Channel 32	Traffic ———— Traffic Channel 1 Channel 62

Variable (1–32) Variable (31–62)

(b)

FIGURE 12-12 IS-95 traffic channels: (a) down-link; (b) up-link

by a distinct user-specific long-code sequence, and each access channel is identified by a distinct access channel long-code sequence.

The pilot channel is included in every cell with the purpose of providing a signal for the receiver to use to acquire timing and provide a phase reference for coherent demodulation. The pilot channel is also used by mobile units to compare signal strengths between base stations to determine when a handoff should be initiated. The synchronization channel uses a Walsh W32 code and the same pseudorandom sequence and phase offset as the pilot channel, allowing it to be demodulated by any receiver that can acquire the pilot signal. The synchronization channel broadcasts synchronization messages to mobile units and operates at 1200 bps. Paging channels convey information from the base station to the mobile station, such as system parameter messages, access parameter messages, CDMA channel list messages, and channel assignment messages. Paging channels are optional and can range in number between zero and seven. The paging channel is used to transmit control information and paging messages from the base station to the mobile units and operates at either 9600 bps, 4800 bps, or 2400 bps. A single 9600-bps pilot channel can typically support about 180 pages per second for a total capacity of 1260 pages per second.

Data on the downlink traffic channel are grouped into 20-ms frames. The data are first convolutionally coded and then formatted and interleaved to compensate for differences in the actual user data rates, which vary. The resulting signal is spread with a Walsh code and a long pseudorandom sequence at a rate of 1.2288 Mchips/s.

The uplink radio channel transmitter is shown in Figure 12-12b and consists of access channels and up to 62 uplink traffic channels. The access and uplink traffic channels use the same frequency assignment using direct-sequence CDMA techniques. The access channels are uplink only, shared, point-to-point channels that provide communications from mobile units to base stations when the mobile unit is not using a traffic channel. Access channels are used by the mobile unit to initiate communications with a base station and to respond to paging channel messages. Typical access channel messages include acknowledgements and sequence number, mobile identification parameter messages, and authentication parameters. The access channel is a random access channel with each channel subscriber uniquely identified by their pseudorandom codes. The uplink CDMA channel can contain up to a maximum of 32 access channels per supported paging channel. The uplink traffic channel operates at a variable data rate mode, and the access channels operate at a fixed 4800-bps rate. Access channel messages consist of registration, order, data burst, origination, page response, authentication challenge response, status response, and assignment completion messages.

Table 12-5 CDMA Power Levels

Class	Minimum EIRP	Maximum EIRP
I	−2 dBW (630 mW)	3 dBW (2.0 W)
II	−7 dBW (200 mW)	0 dBW (1.0 W)
III	−12 dBW (63 mW)	−3 dBW (500 mW)
IV	−17 dBW (20 mW)	−6 dBW (250 mW)
V	−22 dBW (6.3 mW)	−9 dBW (130 mW)

Subscriber data on the uplink radio channel transmitter are also grouped into 20-ms frames, convolutionally encoded, block interleaved, modulated by a 64-ary orthogonal modulation, and spread prior to transmission.

12-7-2-1 CDMA radiated power.   IS-95 specifies complex procedures for regulating the power transmitted by each mobile unit. The goal is to make all reverse-direction signals within a single CDMA channel arrive at the base station with approximately the same signal strength (± 1 dB), which is essential for CDMA operation. Because signal paths change continuously with moving units, mobile units perform power adjustments as many as 800 times per second (once every 1.25 ms) under control of the base station. Base stations instruct mobile units to increase or decrease their transmitted power in 1-dB increments (± 0.5 dB).

When a mobile unit is first turned on, it measures the power of the signal received from the base station. The mobile unit assumes that the signal loss is the same in each direction (forward and reverse) and adjusts its transmit power on the basis of the power level of the signal it receives from the base station. This process is called *open-loop power setting*. A typical formula used by mobile units for determining their transmit power is

$$P_t \text{ dBm} = -76 \text{ dB} - P_r \qquad (12\text{-}4)$$

where P_t = transmit power (dBm)
P_r = received power (dBm)

Example 12-2

Determine the transmit power for a CDMA mobile unit that is receiving a signal from the base station at −100 dBm.

Solution   Substituting into Equation 12-4 gives

$$P_t = -76 - (-100)$$
$$P_t = 24 \text{ dBm, or } 250 \text{ mW}$$

With CDMA, rather than limit the maximum transmit power, the minimum and maximum effective isotropic radiated power (EIRP) is specified (EIRP is the power radiated by an antenna times the gain of the antenna). Table 12-5 lists the maximum EIRPs for five classes of CDMA mobile units. The maximum radiated power of base stations is limited to 100 W per 1.23-MHz CDMA channel.

12-8 NORTH AMERICAN CELLULAR AND PCS SUMMARY

Table 12-6 summarizes several of the parameters common to North American cellular and PCS telephone systems (AMPS, USDC, and PCS).

Table 12-6 Cellular and PCS Telephone Summary

Parameter	Cellular System		
	AMPS	USDC (IS-54)	IS-95
Access method	FDMA	FDMA/TDMA	CDMA/FDMA
Modulation	FM	$\pi/4$ DQPSK	BPSK/QPSK
Frequency band			
Base station	869–894 MHz	869–894 MHz	869–894 MHz
Mobile unit	824–849 MHz	824–849 MHz	824–849 MHz
Base station	—	1.85–1.91 GHz	1.85–1.91 GHz
Mobile unit	—	1.93–1.99 GHz	1.93–1.99 GHz
RF channel bandwidth	30 kHz	30 kHz	1.25 MHz
Maximum radiated power	4 W	4 W	2 W
Control channel	FSK	PSK	PSK
Voice channels per carrier	1	3 or 6	Up to 20
Frequency assignment	Fixed	Fixed	Dynamic

12-9 GLOBAL SYSTEM FOR MOBILE COMMUNICATIONS

In the early 1980s, analog cellular telephone systems were experiencing a period of rapid growth in western Europe, particularly in Scandinavia and the United Kingdom and to a lesser extent in France and Germany. Each country subsequently developed its own cellular telephone system, which was incompatible with everyone else's system from both an equipment and an operational standpoint. Most of the existing systems operated at different frequencies, and all were analog. In 1982, the *Conference of European Posts and Telegraphs* (CEPT) formed a study group called *Groupe Spécial Mobile* (GSM) to study the development of a pan-European (*pan* meaning "all") public land mobile telephone system using ISDN. In 1989, the responsibility of GSM was transferred to the *European Telecommunications Standards Institute* (ETSI), and phase I of the GSM specifications was published in 1990. GSM had the advantage of being designed from scratch with little or no concern for being backward compatible with any existing analog cellular telephone system. GSM provides its subscribers with good quality, privacy, and security. GSM is sometimes referred to as the *Pan-European cellular system*.

Commercial GSM service began in Germany in 1991, and by 1993 there were 36 GSM networks in 22 countries. GSM networks are now either operational or planned in over 80 countries around the world. North America made a late entry into the GSM market with a derivative of GSM called *PCS-1900*. GSM systems now exist on every continent, and the acronym GSM now stands for *Global System for Mobile Communications*. The first GSM system developed was GSM-900 (phase I), which operates in the 900-MHz band for voice only. Phase 2 was introduced in 1995, which included facsimile, video, and data communications services. After implementing PCS frequencies (1800 MHz in Europe and 1900 MHz in North America) in 1997, GSM-1800 and GSM-1900 were created.

GSM is a second-generation cellular telephone system initially developed to solve the fragmentation problems inherent in first-generation cellular telephone systems in Europe. Before implementing GSM, all European countries used different cellular telephone standards; thus, it was impossible for a subscriber to use a single telephone set throughout Europe. GSM was the world's first totally digital cellular telephone system designed to use the services of SS7 signaling and an all-digital data network called *integrated services digital network* (ISDN) to provide a wide range of network services. With between 20 and 50 million subscribers, GSM is now the world's most popular standard for new cellular telephone and personal communications equipment.

12-9-1 GSM Services

The original intention was to make GSM compatible with ISDN in terms of services offered and control signaling. Unfortunately, radio-channel bandwidth limitations and cost prohibited GSM from operating at the 64-kbps ISDN basic data rate.

GSM telephone services can be broadly classified into three categories: *bearer services, teleservices,* and *supplementary services.* Probably the most basic bearer service provided by GSM is telephony. With GSM, analog speech signals are digitally encoded and then transmitted through the network as a digital data stream. There is also an emergency service where the closest emergency service provider is notified by dialing three digits similar to 911 services in the United States. A wide variety of data services is offered through GSM, where users can send and receive data at rates up to 9600 bps to subscribers in POTS (plain old telephone service), ISDN networks, Packet Switched Public Data Networks (PSPDN), and Circuit Switched Public Data Networks (CSPDN) using a wide variety of access methods and protocols, such as X.25. In addition, since GSM is a digital network, a modem is not required between the user and the GSM network.

Other GSM data services include Group 3 facsimile per ITU-T recommendation T.30. One unique feature of GSM that is not found in older analog systems is the *Short Message Service* (SMS), which is a bidirectional service for sending alphanumeric messages up to 160 bytes in length. SMS can be transported through the system in a store-and-forward fashion. SMS can also be used in a *cell-broadcast mode* for sending messages simultaneously to multiple receivers. Several supplemental services, such as *call forwarding* and *call barring,* are also offered with GSM.

12-9-2 GSM System Architecture

The system architecture for GSM as shown in Figure 12-13 consists of three major interconnected subsystems that interact among one another and with subscribers through

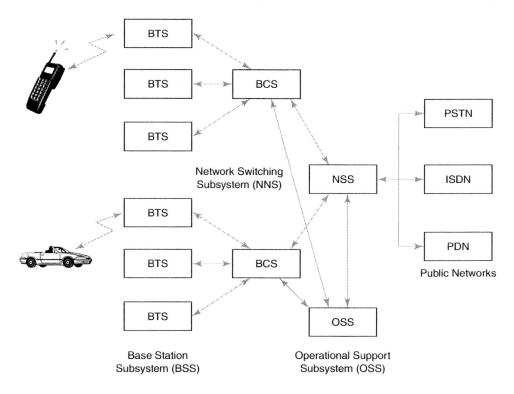

FIGURE 12-13 GSM system architecture

specified network interfaces. The three primary subsystems of GSM are *Base Station Subsystem* (BSS), *Network Switching Subsystem* (NSS), and *Operational Support Subsystem* (OSS). Although the mobile station is technically another subsystem, it is generally considered part of the base station subsystem.

The BSS is sometimes known as the radio *subsystem* because it provides and manages radio-frequency transmission paths between mobile units and the mobile switching center (MSC). The BSS also manages the radio interface between mobile units and all other GSM subsystems. Each BSS consists of many base station controllers (BSCs), which are used to connect the MCS to the NSS through one or more MSCs. The NSS manages switching functions for the system and allows the MSCs to communicate with other telephone networks, such as the public switched telephone network and ISDN. The OSS supports operation and maintenance of the system and allows engineers to monitor, diagnose, and troubleshoot every aspect of the GSM network.

12-9-3 GSM Radio Subsystem

GSM was originally designed for 200 full-duplex channels per cell with transmission frequencies in the 900-MHz band; however, frequencies were later allocated at 1800 MHz. A second system, called DSC-1800, was established that closely resembles GSM. GSM uses two 25-MHz frequency bands that have been set aside for system use in all member companies. The 890-MHz to 915-MHz band is used for mobile unit-to-base station transmissions (reverse-link transmissions), and the 935-MHz to 960-MHz frequency band is used for base station–to–mobile unit transmission (forward-link transmissions). GSM uses frequency-division duplexing and a combination of TDMA and FDMA techniques to provide base stations simultaneous access to multiple mobile units. The available forward and reverse frequency bands are subdivided into 200-kHz wide voice channels called *absolute radio-frequency channel numbers* (ARFCN). The ARFCN number designates a forward/reverse channel pair with 45-MHz separation between them. Each voice channel is shared among as many as eight mobile units using TDMA.

Each of the ARFCN channel subscribers occupies a unique time slot within the TDMA frame. Radio transmission in both directions is at a 270.833-kbps rate using binary Gaussian minimum shift keying (GMSK) modulation with an effective channel transmission rate of 33.833 kbps per user.

The basic parameters of GSM are the following:

1. GMSK modulation (Gaussian MSK)
2. 50-MHz bandwidth:
   890-MHz to 915-MHz mobile transmit band (reverse channel)
   935-MHz to 960-MHz base station transmit band (forward channel)
3. FDMA/TDMA accessing
4. Eight 25-kHz channels within each 200-kHz traffic channel
5. 200-kHz traffic channel
6. 992 full-duplex channels
7. Supplementary ISDN services, such as call diversion, closed user groups, caller identification, and *short messaging service* (SMS), which restricts GSM users and base stations to transmitting alphanumeric pages limited to a maximum of 160 seven-bit ASCII characters while simultaneously carrying normal voice messages.

12-10 PERSONAL SATELLITE COMMUNICATIONS SYSTEM

Mobile Satellite Systems (MSS) provide the vehicle for a new generation of wireless telephone services called *personal communications satellite systems* (PCSS). Universal wireless telephone coverage is a developing MSS service that promises to deliver mobile subscribers both traditional and enhanced telephone features while providing wide-area global coverage.

MSS satellites are, in essence, radio repeaters in the sky, and their usefulness for mobile communications depends on several factors, such as the space-vehicle altitude, orbital pattern, transmit power, receiver sensitivity, modulation technique, antenna radiation pattern (footprint), and number of satellites in its constellation. Satellite communications systems have traditionally provided both narrowband and wideband voice, data, video, facsimile, and networking services using large and very expensive, high-powered earth station transmitters communicating via high-altitude, geosynchronous earth-orbit (GEO) satellites. Personal communications satellite services, however, use low earth-orbit (LEO) and medium earth-orbit (MEO) satellites that communicate directly with small, low-power mobile telephone units. The intention of PCSS mobile telephone is to provide the same features and services offered by traditional, terrestrial cellular telephone providers. However, PCSS telephones will be able to make or receive calls anytime, anywhere in the world. A simplified diagram of a PCSS system is shown in Figure 12-14.

The key providers in the PCSS market include American Mobile Satellite Corporation (AMSC), Celsat, Comsat, Constellation Communications (Aries), Ellipsat (Ellipso), INMARSAT, LEOSAT, Loral/Qualcomm (Globalstar), TMI communications, TWR (Odysse), and Iridium LLC.

12-10-1 PCSS Advantages and Disadvantages

The primary and probably most obvious advantage of PCSS mobile telephone is that it provides mobile telephone coverage and a host of other integrated services virtually anywhere in the world to a truly global customer base. PCSS can fill the vacancies between land-based cellular and PCS telephone systems and provide wide-area coverage on a regional or global basis.

FIGURE 12-14 Overview of Iridium PCSS mobile telephone system

PCSS is ideally suited to fixed cellular telephone applications, as it can provide a full complement of telephone services to places where cables can never go because of economical, technical, or physical constraints. PCSS can also provide complementary and backup telephone services to large companies and organizations with multiple operations in diverse locations, such as retail, manufacturing, finance, transportation, government, military, and insurance.

Most of the disadvantages of PCSS are closely related to economics, with the primary disadvantage being the high risk associated with the high costs of designing, building, and launching satellites. There is also a high cost for the terrestrial-based networking and interface infrastructure necessary to maintain, coordinate, and manage the network once it is in operation. In addition, the intricate low-power, dual-mode transceivers are more cumbersome and expensive than most mobile telephone units used with terrestrial cellular and PCS systems.

12-10-2   PCSS Industry Requirements

PCSS mobile telephone systems require transparent interfaces and feature sets among the multitude of terrestrial networks currently providing mobile and wireline telephone services. In addition, the interfaces must be capable of operating with both ANSI and CCITT network constraints and be able to provide interpretability with AMPS, USDC, GMS, and PCS cellular telephone systems. PCSS must also be capable of operating dual-mode with *air-access protocols,* such as FDMA, TDMA, or CDMA. PCSS should also provide unique MSS feature sets and characteristics, such as inter-/intrasatellite handoffs, land based-to-satellite handoffs, and land-based/PCSS dual registration.

12-10-3   Iridium Satellite System

Iridium LLC is an international consortium owned by a host of prominent companies, agencies, and governments, including the following: Motorola, General Electric, Lockheed, Raytheon, McDonnell Douglas, Scientific Atlanta, Sony, Kyocera, Mitsubishi, DDI, Kruchinew Enterprises, Mawarid Group of Saudi Arabia, STET of Italy, Nippon Iridium Corporation of Japan, the government of Brazil, Muidiri Investments BVI, LTD of Venezuela, Great Wall Industry of China, United Communications of Thailand, the U.S. Department of Defense, Sprint, and BCE Siemens.

The *Iridium project,* which even sounds like something out of *Star Wars,* is undoubtedly the largest commercial venture undertaken in the history of the world. It is the system with the most satellites, the highest price tag, the largest public relations team, and the most peculiar design. The $5 billion, gold-plated *Iridium* mobile telephone system is undoubtedly (or at least intended to be) the Cadillac of mobile telephone systems. Unfortunately (and somewhat ironically), in August 1999, on Friday the 13th, Iridium LLC, the beleaguered satellite-telephone system spawned by Motorola's Satellite Communications Group in Chandler, Arizona, filed for bankruptcy under protection of Chapter 11. However, Motorola Inc., the largest stockholder in Iridium, says it will continue to support the company and its customers and does not expect any interruption in service while reorganization is under way.

Iridium is a satellite-based wireless personal communications network designed to permit a wide range of mobile telephone services, including voice, data, networking, facsimile, and paging. The system is called Iridium after the element on the periodic table with the atomic number 77 because Iridium's original design called for 77 satellites. The final design, however, requires only 66 satellites. Apparently, someone decided that element 66, dysprosium, did not have the same charismatic appeal as Iridium, and the root meaning of the word is "bad approach." The 66-vehicle LEO interlinked satellite constellation can track the location of a subscriber's telephone handset, determine the best routing through a network of ground-based gateways and intersatellite links, establish the best path for the telephone call, initiate all the necessary connections, and terminate the call on completion. The system also provides applicable revenue tracking.

With Iridium, two-way global communications is possible even when the destination subscriber's location is unknown to the caller. In essence, the intent of the Iridium system is to provide the best service in the telephone world, allowing telecommunication anywhere, anytime, and any place. The FCC granted the Iridium program a full license in January 1995 for construction and operation in the United States.

Iridium uses a GSM-based telephony architecture to provide a digitally switched telephone network and global dial tone to call and receive calls from any place in the world. This global roaming feature is designed into the system. Each subscriber is assigned a personal phone number and will receive only one bill, no matter in what country or area they use the telephone.

The Iridium project has a satellite network control facility in Landsdowne, Virginia, with a backup facility in Italy. A third engineering control complex is located at Motorola's SATCOM location in Chandler, Arizona.

12-10-3-1 System layout. Figure 12-14 shows an overview of the Iridium system. Subscriber telephone sets used in the Iridium system transmit and receive L-band frequencies and utilize both frequency- and time-division multiplexing to make the most efficient use of a limited frequency spectrum. Other communications links used in Iridium include EHF and SHF bands between satellites for telemetry, command, and control as well as routing digital voice packets to and from gateways. An Iridium telephone enables the subscriber to connect either to the local cellular telephone infrastructure or to the space constellation using its *dual-mode* feature.

Iridium gateways are prime examples of the advances in satellite infrastructures that are responsible for the delivery of a host of new satellite services. The purpose of the gateways is to support and manage roaming subscribers as well as to interconnect Iridium subscribers to the public switched telephone network. Gateway functions include the following:

1. Set up and maintain basic and supplementary telephony services
2. Provide an interface for two-way telephone communications between two Iridium subscribers and Iridium subscribers to subscribers of the public switched telephone network
3. Provide Iridium subscribers with messaging, facsimile, and data services
4. Facilitate the business activities of the Iridium system through a set of cooperative mutual agreements

12-10-3-2 Satellite constellation. Providing full-earth coverage is the underlying basis of the Iridium satellite system. Iridium uses 66 operational satellites (there are also some spares) configured at a mean elevation of 420 miles above Earth in six nearly-polar orbital planes (86.4° tilt), in which 11 satellites revolve around Earth in each orbit with an orbital time of 100 minutes, 28 seconds. This allows Iridium to cover the entire surface area of Earth and, whenever one satellite goes out of view of a subscriber, a different one replaces it. The satellites are phased appropriately in north–south necklaces forming *corotating planes* up one side of Earth, across the poles, and down the other side. The first and last planes rotate in opposite directions, creating a virtual *seam*. The corotating planes are separated by 31.6°, and the seam planes are 22° apart.

Each satellite is equipped with three L-band antennas forming a honeycomb pattern that consists of 48 individual spot beams with a total of 1628 cells aimed directly below the satellite, as shown in Figure 12-15. As the satellite moves in its orbit, the footprints move across Earth's surface, and subscriber signals are switched from one beam to the next or from one satellite to the next in a handoff process. When satellites approach the North or South Pole, their footprints converge, and the beams overlap. Outer beams are then turned off to eliminate this overlap and conserve power on the spacecraft. Each cell has 174 full-duplex voice channels for a total of 283,272 channels worldwide.

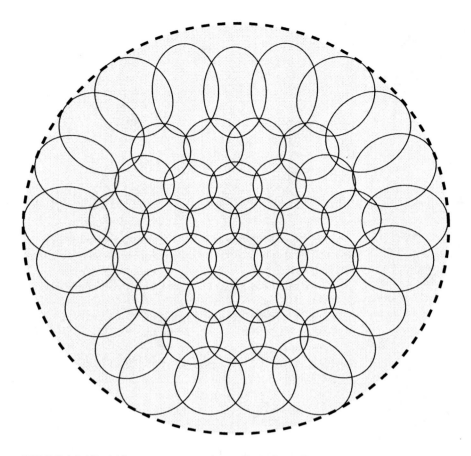

FIGURE 12-15   Iridium system spot beam footprint pattern

Using satellite *cross-links* is the unique key to the Iridium system and the primary differentiation between Iridium and the traditional satellite *bent-pipe system* where all transmissions follow a path from Earth to satellite to Earth. Iridium is the first mobile satellite to incorporate sophisticated, onboard digital processing on each satellite and cross-link capability between satellites.

Each satellite is equipped with four satellite-to-satellite cross-links to relay digital information around the globe. The cross-link antennas point toward the closest spacecraft orbiting in the same plane and the two adjacent corotating planes. *Feeder link* antennas relay information to the terrestrial gateways and the system control segment located at the earth stations.

12-10-3-3 Frequency plan and modulation.   On October 14, 1994, the Federal Communication Commission issued a report and order Dockett #92-166 defining L-band frequency sharing for subscriber units in the 1616-MHz to 1626.5-MHz band. Mobile satellite system cellular communications are assigned 5.15 MHz at the upper end of this spectrum for TDMA/FDMA service. CDMA access is assigned the remaining 11.35 MHz for their service uplinks and a proportionate amount of the S-band frequency spectrum at 2483.5 MHz to 2500 MHz for their downlinks. When a CDMA system is placed into operation, the CDMA L-band frequency spectrum will be reduced to 8.25 MHz. The remaining 3.1 MHz of the frequency spectrum will then be assigned to either the Iridium system or another TDMA/FDMA system.

All Ka-band uplinks, downlinks, and cross-links are packetized TDM/FDMA using quadrature phase-shift keying (QPSK) and FEC 1/2 rate convolutional coding with Viterbi decoding. Coded data rates are 6.25 Mbps for gateways and satellite control facility links and 25 Mbps for satellite cross-links. Both uplink and downlink transmissions occupy 100 MHz of bandwidth, and intersatellite links use 200 MHz of bandwidth. The frequency bands are as follows:

L-band subscriber-to-satellite voice links = 1.616 GHz to 1.6265 GHz
Ka-band gateway downlinks = 19.4 GHz to 19.6 GHz
Ka-band gateway uplinks = 29.1 GHz to 29.3 GHz
Ka-intersatellite cross-links = 23.18 GHz to 23.38 GHz

QUESTIONS

12-1. What is meant by a *first-generation* cellular telephone system?

12-2. Briefly describe the AMPS system.

12-3. Outline the AMPS *frequency allocation.*

12-4. What is meant by the term *frequency-division duplexing*?

12-5. What is the difference between a *wireline* and *nonwireline* company?

12-6. Describe a *cellular geographic serving area.*

12-7. List and describe the three *classifications* of AMPS cellular telephones.

12-8. What is meant by the *discontinuous transmission mode*?

12-9. List the features of a *personal communications system* that differentiate it from a *standard cellular telephone network.*

12-10. What is the difference between a *personal communications network* and *personal communications services*?

12-11. Briefly describe the functions of a *home location register.*

12-12. Briefly describe the functions of a *visitor location register.*

12-13. Briefly describe the functions of an *equipment identification registry.*

12-14. Describe the following services: *available mode, screen mode, private mode,* and *unavailable mode.*

12-15. What is meant by a *microcellular system*?

12-16. List the advantages of a *PCS cellular system* compared to a *standard cellular system.*

12-17. List the disadvantage of a PCS cellular system.

12-18. What is meant by the term *false handoff*?

12-19. Briefly describe the N-AMPS cellular telephone system.

12-20. What is an *interference avoidance scheme*?

12-21. What are the four types of *handoffs* possible with N-AMPS?

12-22. List the advantages of a *digital cellular system.*

12-23. Describe the *United States Digital Cellular* system.

12-24. Describe the *TDMA scheme* used with USDC.

12-25. List the advantages of *digital* TDMA over *analog* AMPS FDMA.

12-26. Briefly describe the EIA/TIA *Interim Standard IS-54.*

12-27. What is meant by the term *dual mode*?

12-28. Briefly describe the EIA/TIA *Interim Standard IS-136.*

12-29. What is meant by the term *sleep mode*?

12-30. Briefly describe the *North American Digital Cellular* format.

12-31. Briefly describe the E-TDMA scheme.

12-32. Describe the differences between the radiated power classifications for USDC and AMPS.

12-33. List the IS-95 specifications.

12-34. Describe the *CDMA format* used with IS-95.

12-35. Describe the differences between the *CDMA radiated power procedures* and AMPS.

12-36. Briefly describe the GSM cellular telephone system.

12-37. Outline and describe the *services* offered by GSM.

12-38. Briefly describe the GSM *system architecture.*

What are the three *primary subsystems* of GSM?

Briefly describe the GSM *radio subsystem.*

List the *basic parameters* of GSM.

Briefly describe the *architecture* of a PCSS.

List the *advantages* and *disadvantages* of PCSS.

Outline the *industry requirements* of PCSS.

CHAPTER 13

Microwave Radio Communications and System Gain

OBJECTIVES

- Define *microwave*
- Describe microwave frequencies and microwave frequency bands
- Contrast the advantages and disadvantages of microwave
- Contrast analog versus digital microwave
- Contrast frequency modulation with amplitude modulation microwave
- Describe the block diagram for a microwave radio system
- Describe the different types of microwave repeaters
- Define *diversity* and describe several diversity systems
- Define *protection switching arrangements* and describe several switching system configurations
- Describe the operation of the various components that make up microwave radio terminal and repeater stations
- Identify the free-space path characteristics and describe how they affect microwave system performance
- Define *system gain* and describe how it is calculated for FM microwave radio systems

Microwaves are generally described as electromagnetic waves with frequencies that range from approximately 500 MHz to 300 GHz or more. Therefore, microwave signals, because of their inherently high frequencies, have relatively short wavelengths, hence the name "micro" waves. For example, a 100-GHz microwave signal has a wavelength of 0.3 cm, whereas a 100-MHz commercial broadcast-band FM signal has a wavelength of 3 m. The wavelengths for microwave frequencies fall between 1 cm and 60 cm, slightly longer than infrared energy. Table 13-1 lists some of the microwave radio-frequency bands available in the United States. For full-duplex (two-way) operation as is generally required of microwave communications systems, each frequency band is divided in half with the lower half identified as the *low band* and the upper half as the *high band*. At any given radio station, transmitters are normally operating on either the low or the high band, while receivers are operating on the other band.

On August 17, 1951, the first transcontinental microwave radio system began operation. The system was comprised of 107 relay stations spaced an average of 30 miles apart to form a continuous radio link between New York and San Francisco that cost the Bell System approximately $40 million. By 1954, there were over 400 microwave stations scattered across the United States, and by 1958, microwave carriers were the dominate means of long-distance communications as they transported the equivalent of 13 million miles of telephone circuits.

The vast majority of electronic communications systems established since the mid-1980s have been digital in nature and, thus, carry voice, video, and data information in digital form.

However, terrestrial (earth-based) *microwave radio relay* systems using frequency (FM) or digitally modulated carriers (PSK or QAM) still provide approximately 35% of

Table 13-1   Microwave Radio-Frequency Assignments

Service	Frequency (MHz)	Band
Military	1710–1850	L
Operational fixed	1850–1990	L
Studio transmitter link	1990–2110	L
Common carrier	2110–2130	S
Operational fixed	2130–2150	S
Operational carrier	2160–2180	S
Operational fixed	2180–2200	S
Operational fixed television	2500–2690	S
Common carrier and satellite downlink	3700–4200	S
Military	4400–4990	C
Military	5250–5350	C
Common carrier and satellite uplink	5925–6425	C
Operational fixed	6575–6875	C
Studio transmitter link	6875–7125	C
Common carrier and satellite downlink	7250–7750	C
Common carrier and satellite uplink	7900–8400	X
Common carrier	10,700–11,700	X
Operational fixed	12,200–12,700	X
Cable television (CATV) studio link	12,700–12,950	Ku
Studio transmitter link	12,950–13,200	Ku
Military	14,400–15,250	Ka
Common carrier	17,700–19,300	Ka
Satellite uplink	26,000–32,000	K
Satellite downlink	39,000–42,000	Q
Satellite crosslink	50,000–51,000	V
Satellite crosslink	54,000–62,000	V

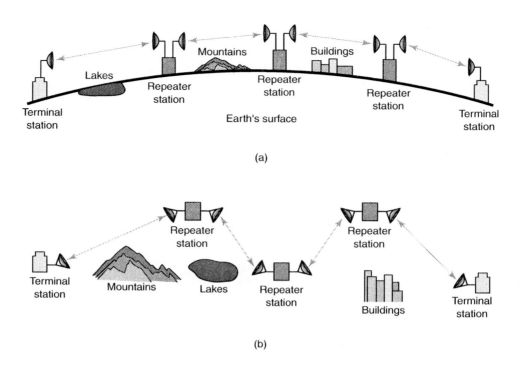

FIGURE 13-1 Microwave radio communications link: (a) side view; (b) top view

the total information-carrying circuit mileage in the United States. There are many different types of microwave systems operating over distances that vary from 15 miles to 4000 miles in length. *Intrastate* or *feeder service* microwave systems are generally categorized as *short haul* because they are used to carry information for relatively short distances, such as between cities within the same state. *Long-haul* microwave systems are those used to carry information for relatively long distances, such as *interstate* and *backbone* route applications. Microwave radio system capacities range from less than 12 voice-band channels to more than 22,000 channels. Early microwave systems carried frequency-division-multiplexed voice-band circuits and used conventional, noncoherent frequency-modulation techniques. More recently developed microwave systems carry pulse-code-modulated time-division-multiplexed voice-band circuits and use more modern digital modulation techniques, such as phase-shift keying (PSK) or quadrature amplitude modulation (QAM).

Figure 13-1 shows a typical layout for a microwave radio link. Information originates and terminates at the terminal stations, whereas the repeaters simply relay the information to the next downlink microwave station. Figure 13-1a shows a microwave radio link comprised of two terminal stations (one at each end) that are interconnected by three repeater stations. As the figure shows, the microwave stations must be geographically placed in such a way that the terrain (lakes, mountains, buildings, and so on) do not interfere with transmissions between stations. This sometimes necessitates placing the stations on top of hills, mountains, or tall buildings. Figure 13-1b shows how a microwave radio link appears from above. Again, the geographic location of the stations must be carefully selected such that natural and man-made barriers do not interfere with propagation between stations. Again, sometimes it is necessary to construct a microwave link around obstacles, such as large bodies of water, mountains, and tall buildings.

Microwave radios propagate signals through Earth's atmosphere between transmitters and receivers often located on top of towers spaced about 15 miles to 30 miles apart. Therefore, microwave radio systems have the obvious advantage of having the capacity to carry thousands of individual information channels between two points without the need for physical facilities such as coaxial cables or optical fibers. This, of course, avoids the need for acquiring rights-of-way through private property. In addition, radio waves are better suited for spanning large bodies of water, going over high mountains, or going through heavily wooded terrain that impose formidable barriers to cable systems. The advantages of microwave radio include the following:

13-2-1 Advantages of Microwave Radio

1. Radio systems do not require a right-of-way acquisition between stations.
2. Each station requires the purchase or lease of only a small area of land.
3. Because of their high operating frequencies, microwave radio systems can carry large quantities of information.
4. High frequencies mean short wavelengths, which require relatively small antennas.
5. Radio signals are more easily propagated around physical obstacles such as water and high mountains.
6. Fewer repeaters are necessary for amplification.
7. Distances between switching centers are less.
8. Underground facilities are minimized.
9. Minimum delay times are introduced.
10. Minimal crosstalk exists between voice channels.
11. Increased reliability and less maintenance are important factors.

13-2-2 Disadvantages of Microwave Radio

1. It is more difficult to analyze and design circuits at microwave frequencies.
2. Measuring techniques are more difficult to perfect and implement at microwave frequencies.
3. It is difficult to implement conventional circuit components (resistors, capacitors, inductors, and so on) at microwave frequencies.
4. Transient time is more critical at microwave frequencies.
5. It is often necessary to use specialized components for microwave frequencies.
6. Microwave frequencies propagate in a straight line, which limits their use to line-of-sight applications.

13-3 ANALOG VERSUS DIGITAL MICROWAVE

A vast majority of the existing microwave radio systems are frequency modulation, which of course is analog. Recently, however, systems have been developed that use either phase-shift keying or quadrature amplitude modulation, which are forms of digital modulation. This chapter deals primarily with conventional FDM/FM microwave radio systems. Although many of the system concepts are the same, the performance of digital signals are evaluated quite differently. Chapter 25 deals with satellite systems that utilize PCM/PSK. Satellite radio systems are similar to terrestrial microwave radio systems; in fact, the two systems share many of the same frequencies. The primary difference between satellite and terrestrial radio systems is that satellite systems propagate signals outside Earth's atmosphere and, thus, are capable of carrying signals much farther while utilizing fewer transmitters and receivers.

Frequency modulation (FM) is used in microwave radio systems rather than amplitude modulation (AM) because AM signals are more sensitive to amplitude nonlinearities inherent in *wideband microwave amplifiers*. FM signals are relatively insensitive to this type of nonlinear distortion and can be transmitted through amplifiers that have compression or amplitude nonlinearity with little penalty. In addition, FM signals are less sensitive to random noise and can be propagated with lower transmit powers.

Intermodulation noise is a major factor when designing FM radio systems. In AM systems, intermodulation noise is caused by repeater amplitude nonlinearity. In FM systems, intermodulation noise is caused primarily by transmission gain and delay distortion. Consequently, in AM systems, intermodulation noise is a function of signal amplitude, but in FM systems, it is a function of signal amplitude and the magnitude of the frequency deviation. Thus, the characteristics of FM signals are more suitable than AM signals for microwave transmission.

13-5 FREQUENCY-MODULATED MICROWAVE RADIO SYSTEM

Microwave radio systems using FM are widely recognized as providing flexible, reliable, and economical point-to-point communications using Earth's atmosphere for the transmission medium. FM microwave systems used with the appropriate multiplexing equipment are capable of simultaneously carrying from a few narrowband voice circuits up to thousands of voice and data circuits. Microwave radios can also be configured to carry high-speed data, facsimile, broadcast-quality audio, and commercial television signals. Comparative cost studies have proven that FM microwave radio is very often the most economical means for providing communications circuits where there are no existing metallic cables or optical fibers or where severe terrain or weather conditions exist. FM microwave systems are also easily expandable.

A simplified block diagram of an FM microwave radio is shown in Figure 13-2. The *baseband* is the composite signal that modulates the FM carrier and may comprise one or more of the following:

1. Frequency-division-multiplexed voice-band channels
2. Time-division-multiplexed voice-band channels
3. Broadcast-quality composite video or picturephone
4. Wideband data

13-5-1 FM Microwave Radio Transmitter

In the FM *microwave transmitter* shown in Figure 13-2a, a *preemphasis* network precedes the FM deviator. The preemphasis network provides an artificial boost in amplitude to the higher baseband frequencies. This allows the lower baseband frequencies to frequency modulate the IF carrier and the higher baseband frequencies to phase modulate it. This scheme ensures a more uniform signal-to-noise ratio throughout the entire baseband spectrum. An FM deviator provides the modulation of the IF carrier that eventually becomes the main microwave carrier. Typically, IF carrier frequencies are between 60 MHz and 80 MHz, with 70 MHz the most common. *Low-index* frequency modulation is used in the FM deviator. Typically, modulation indices are kept between 0.5 and 1. This produces a *narrowband* FM signal at the output of the deviator. Consequently, the IF bandwidth resembles conventional AM and is approximately equal to twice the highest baseband frequency.

The IF and its associated sidebands are up-converted to the microwave region by the mixer, microwave oscillator, and bandpass filter. Mixing, rather than multiplying, is used to translate the IF frequencies to RF frequencies because the modulation index is unchanged

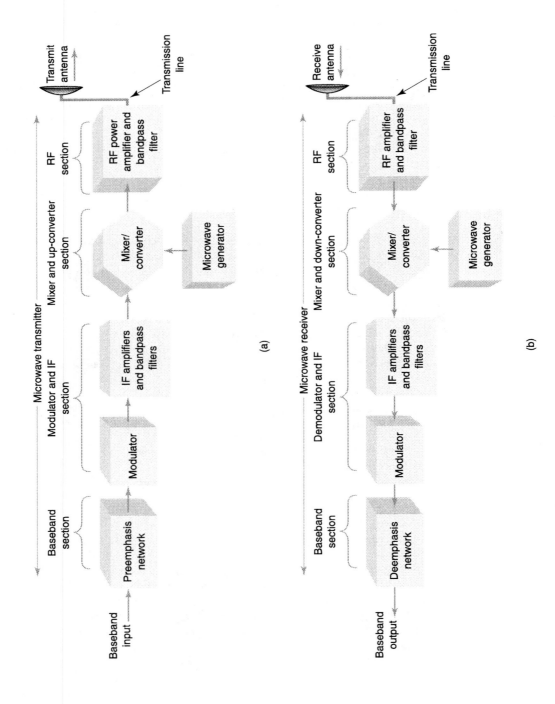

FIGURE 13-2 Simplified block diagram of a microwave radio: (a) transmitter; (b) receiver

by the heterodyning process. Multiplying the IF carrier would also multiply the frequency deviation and the modulation index, thus increasing the bandwidth.

Microwave generators consist of a crystal oscillator followed by a series of frequency multipliers. For example, a 125-MHz crystal oscillator followed by a series of multipliers with a combined multiplication factor of 48 could be used to a 6-GHz microwave carrier frequency. The channel-combining network provides a means of connecting more than one microwave transmitter to a single transmission line feeding the antenna.

13-5-2 FM Microwave Radio Receiver

In the FM microwave receiver shown in Figure 13-2b, the channel separation network provides the isolation and filtering necessary to separate individual microwave channels and direct them to their respective receivers. The bandpass filter, AM mixer, and microwave oscillator down-convert the RF microwave frequencies to IF frequencies and pass them on to the FM demodulator. The FM demodulator is a conventional, *noncoherent* FM detector (i.e., a discriminator or a PLL demodulator). At the output of the FM detector, a deemphasis network restores the baseband signal to its original amplitude-versus-frequency characteristics.

13-6 FM MICROWAVE RADIO REPEATERS

The permissible distance between an FM microwave transmitter and its associated microwave receiver depends on several system variables, such as transmitter output power, receiver noise threshold, terrain, atmospheric conditions, system capacity, reliability objectives, and performance expectations. Typically, this distance is between 15 miles and 40 miles. Long-haul microwave systems span distances considerably longer than this. Consequently, a single-hop microwave system, such as the one shown in Figure 13-2, is inadequate for most practical system applications. With systems that are longer than 40 miles or when geographical obstructions, such as a mountain, block the transmission path, *repeaters* are needed. A microwave repeater is a receiver and a transmitter placed back to back or in tandem with the system. A simplified block diagram of a microwave repeater is shown in Figure 13-3. The repeater station receives a signal, amplifies and reshapes it, and then retransmits the signal to the next repeater or terminal station down line from it.

The location of intermediate repeater sites is greatly influenced by the nature of the terrain between and surrounding the sites. Preliminary route planning generally assumes relatively flat areas, and path (hop) lengths will average between 25 miles and 35 miles between stations. In relatively flat terrain, increasing path length will dictate increasing the antenna tower heights. Transmitter output power and antenna gain will similarly enter into the selection process. The exact distance is determined primarily by line-of-site path clearance and received signal strength. For frequencies above 10 GHz, local rainfall patterns could also have a large bearing on path length. In all cases, however, paths should be as level as possible. In addition, the possibility of interference, either internal or external, must be considered.

FIGURE 13-3   Microwave repeater

Basically, there are three types of microwave repeaters: IF, baseband, and RF (see Figure 13-4). IF repeaters are also called *heterodyne* repeaters. With an IF repeater (Figure 13-4a), the received RF carrier is down-converted to an IF frequency, amplified, reshaped, up-converted to an RF frequency, and then retransmitted. The signal is never demodulated below IF. Consequently, the baseband intelligence is unmodified by the repeater. With a baseband repeater (Figure 13-4b), the received RF carrier is down-converted to an IF frequency, amplified, filtered, and then further demodulated to baseband. The baseband signal, which is typically frequency-division-multiplexed voice-band channels, is further demodulated to a mastergroup, supergroup, group, or even channel level. This allows the baseband signal to be reconfigured to meet the routing needs of the overall communications network. Once the baseband signal has been reconfigured, it FM modulates an IF carrier, which is up-converted to an RF carrier and then retransmitted.

Figure 13-4c shows another baseband repeater configuration. The repeater demodulates the RF to baseband, amplifies and reshapes it, and then modulates the FM carrier. With this technique, the baseband is not reconfigured. Essentially, this configuration accomplishes the same thing that an IF repeater accomplishes. The difference is that in a baseband configuration, the amplifier and equalizer act on baseband frequencies rather than IF frequencies. The baseband frequencies are generally less than 9 MHz, whereas the IF frequencies are in the range 60 MHz to 80 MHz. Consequently, the filters and amplifiers necessary for baseband repeaters are simpler to design and less expensive than the ones required for IF repeaters. The disadvantage of a baseband configuration is the addition of the FM terminal equipment.

Figure 13-4d shows an RF-to-RF repeater. With RF-to-RF repeaters, the received microwave signal is not down-converted to IF or baseband; it is simply mixed (heterodyned) with a local oscillator frequency in a nonlinear mixer. The output of the mixer is tuned to either the sum or the difference between the incoming RF and the local oscillator frequency, depending on whether frequency up- or down-conversion is desired. The local oscillator is sometimes called a *shift oscillator* and is considerably lower in frequency than either the received or the transmitted radio frequencies. For example, an incoming RF of 6.2 GHz is mixed with a 0.2-GHz local oscillator frequency producing sum and difference frequencies of 6.4 GHz and 6.0 GHz. For frequency up-conversion, the output of the mixer would be tuned to 6.4 GHz, and for frequency down-conversion, the output of the mixer would be tuned to 6.0 GHz. With RF-to-RF repeaters, the radio signal is simply converted in frequency and then reamplified and transmitted to the next down-line repeater or terminal station. Reconfiguring and reshaping are not possible with RF-to-RF repeaters.

13-7 DIVERSITY

Microwave systems use *line-of-site* transmission; therefore a direct signal path must exist between the transmit and the receive antennas. Consequently, if that signal path undergoes a severe degradation, a service interruption will occur. Over time, radio path losses vary with atmospheric conditions that can vary significantly, causing a corresponding reduction in the received signal strength of 20, 30, or 40 or more dB. This reduction in signal strength is temporary and referred to as *radio fade*. Radio fade can last for a few milliseconds (short term) or for several hours or even days (long term). Automatic gain control circuits, built into radio receivers, can compensate for fades of 25 dB to 40 dB, depending on system design; however, fades in excess of 40 dB can cause a total loss of the received signal. When this happens, service continuity is lost.

Diversity suggests that there is more than one transmission path or method of transmission available between a transmitter and a receiver. In a microwave system, the purpose of using diversity is to increase the reliability of the system by increasing its availability.

(a)

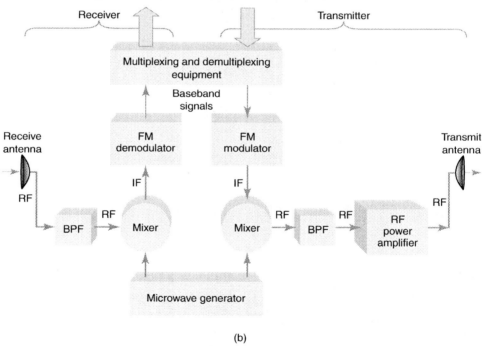

Baseband signals to and from other multiplexers and demultiplexers

(b)

FIGURE 13-4   Microwave repeaters: (a) IF; (b) baseband; (*Continued*)

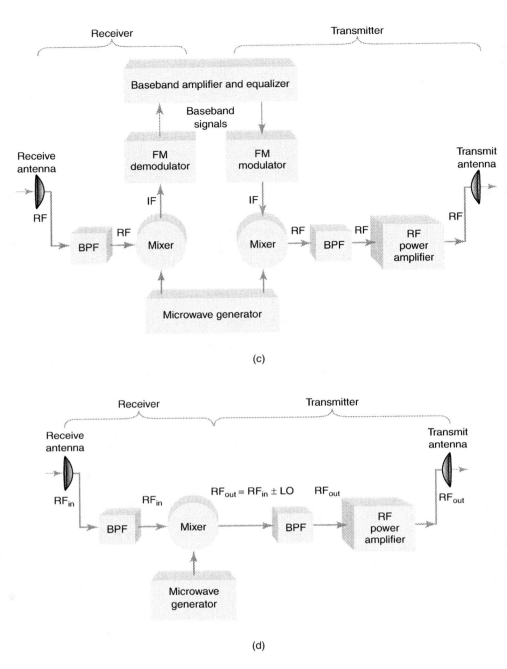

(c)

(d)

FIGURE 13-4 (*Continued*) Microwave repeaters: (c) baseband; (d) RF

Table 13-2 shows a relatively simple means of translating a given system reliability percentage into terms that are more easily related to experience. For example, a reliability percentage of 99.99% corresponds to about 53 minutes of outage time per year, while a reliability percentage of 99.9999% amounts to only about 32 seconds of outage time per year.

When there is more than one transmission path or method of transmission available, the system can select the path or method that produces the highest-quality received signal. Generally, the highest quality is determined by evaluating the carrier-to-noise (C/N) ratio at the receiver input or by simply measuring the received carrier power. Although there are

Table 13-2   Reliability and Outage Time

Reliability (%)	Outage Time (%)	Year (Hours)	Outage Time per Month (Hours)	Day (Hours)
0	100	8760	720	24
50	50	4380	360	12
80	20	1752	144	4.8
90	10	876	72	2.4
95	5	438	36	1.2
98	2	175	14	29 minutes
99	1	88	7	14.4 minutes
99.9	0.1	8.8	43 minutes	1.44 minutes
99.99	0.01	53 minutes	4.3 minutes	8.6 seconds
99.999	0.001	5.3 minutes	26 seconds	0.86 seconds
99.9999	0.0001	32 seconds	2.6 seconds	0.086 seconds

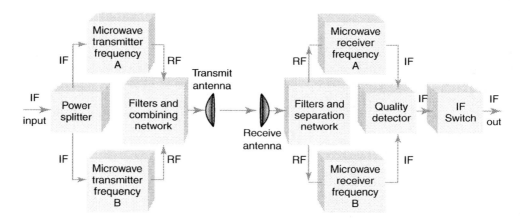

FIGURE 13-5   Frequency diversity microwave system

many ways of achieving diversity, the most common methods used are frequency, space, polarization, hybrid, or quad.

13-7-1   Frequency Diversity

Frequency diversity is simply modulating two different RF carrier frequencies with the same IF intelligence, then transmitting both RF signals to a given destination. At the destination, both carriers are demodulated, and the one that yields the better-quality IF signal is selected. Figure 13-5 shows a single-channel frequency-diversity microwave system.

In Figure 13-5a, the IF input signal is fed to a power splitter, which directs it to microwave transmitters A and B. The RF outputs from the two transmitters are combined in the channel-combining network and fed to the transmit antenna. At the receive end (Figure 13-5b), the channel separator directs the A and B RF carriers to their respective microwave receivers, where they are down-converted to IF. The quality detector circuit determines which channel, A or B, is the higher quality and directs that channel through the IF switch to be further demodulated to baseband. Many of the temporary, adverse atmospheric conditions that degrade an RF signal are frequency selective; they may degrade one frequency more than another. Therefore, over a given period of time, the IF switch may switch back and forth from receiver A to receiver B and vice versa many times.

Frequency-diversity arrangements provide complete and simple equipment redundance and have the additional advantage of providing two complete transmitter-to-receiver electrical paths. Its obvious disadvantage is that it doubles the amount of frequency spectrum and equipment necessary.

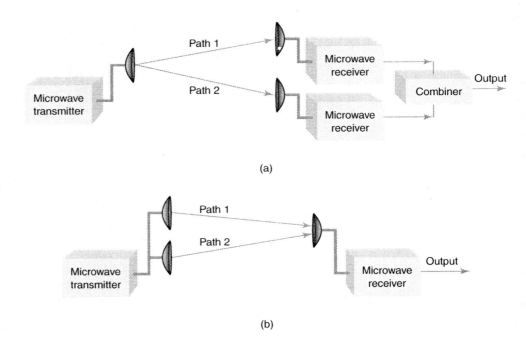

(a)

(b)

FIGURE 13-6　Space diversity: (a) two receive antennas; (b) two transmit antennas

13-7-2　Space Diversity

With space diversity, the output of a transmitter is fed to two or more antennas that are physically separated by an appreciable number of wavelengths. Similarly, at the receiving end, there may be more than one antenna providing the input signal to the receiver. If multiple receiving antennas are used, they must also be separated by an appreciable number of wavelengths. Figure 13-6 shows two ways to implement space diversity. Figure 13-6a shows a space diversity system using two transmit antennas, whereas Figure 13-6b shows a space diversity system using two receive antennas. The rule is to use two transmit antennas or two receive antennas but never two of each.

　　When space diversity is used, it is important that the electrical distance from a transmitter to each of its antennas and to a receiver from each of its antennas is an equal multiple of wavelengths long. This is to ensure that when two or more signals of the same frequency arrive at the input to a receiver, they are in phase and additive. If received out of phase, they will cancel and, consequently, result in less received signal power than if simply one antenna system were used. Adverse atmospheric conditions are often isolated to a very small geographical area. With space diversity, there is more than one transmission path between a transmitter and a receiver. When adverse atmospheric conditions exist in one of the paths, it is unlikely that the alternate path is experiencing the same degradation. Consequently, the probability of receiving an acceptable signal is higher when space diversity is used than when no diversity is used. An alternate method of space diversity uses a single transmitting antenna and two receiving antennas separated vertically. Depending on the atmospheric conditions at a particular time, one of the receiving antennas should be receiving an adequate signal. Again, there are two transmission paths that are unlikely to be affected simultaneously by fading.

　　Space-diversity arrangements provide for path redundancy but not equipment redundancy. Space diversity is more expensive than frequency diversity because of the additional antennas and waveguide. Space diversity, however, provides efficient frequency spectrum usage and a substantially greater protection than frequency diversity.

13-7-3 Polarization Diversity

With *polarization diversity,* a single RF carrier is propagated with two different electromagnetic polarizations (vertical and horizontal). Electromagnetic waves of different polarizations do not necessarily experience the same transmission impairments. Polarization diversity is generally used in conjunction with space diversity. One transmit/receive antenna pair is vertically polarized, and the other is horizontally polarized. It is also possible to use frequency, space, and polarization diversity simultaneously.

13-7-4 Receiver Diversity

Receiver diversity is using more than one receiver for a single radio-frequency channel. With frequency diversity, it is necessary to also use receiver diversity because each transmitted frequency requires its own receiver. However, sometimes two receivers are used for a single transmitted frequency.

13-7-5 Quad Diversity

Quad diversity is another form of hybrid diversity and undoubtedly provides the most reliable transmission; however, it is also the most expensive. The basic concept of quad diversity is quite simple: It combines frequency, space, polarization, and receiver diversity into one system. Its obvious disadvantage is providing redundant electronic equipment, frequencies, antennas, and waveguide, which are economical burdens.

13-7-6 Hybrid Diversity

Hybrid diversity is a somewhat specialized form of diversity that consists of a standard frequency-diversity path where the two transmitter/receiver pairs at one end of the path are separated from each other and connected to different antennas that are vertically separated as in space diversity. This arrangement provides a space-diversity effect in both directions—in one direction because the receivers are vertically spaced and in the other direction because the transmitters are vertically spaced. This arrangement combines the operational advantages of frequency diversity with the improved diversity protection of space diversity. Hybrid diversity has the disadvantage, however, of requiring two radio frequencies to obtain one working channel.

13-8 PROTECTION SWITCHING ARRANGEMENTS

To avoid a service interruption during periods of deep fades or equipment failures, alternate facilities are temporarily made available in a *protection switching* arrangement. The general concepts of protection switching and diversity are quite similar: Both provide protection against equipment failures and atmospheric fades. The primary difference between them is, simply, that diversity systems provide an alternate transmission path for only a single microwave link (i.e., between one transmitter and one receiver) within the overall communications system. Protection switching arrangements, on the other hand, provide protection for a much larger section of the communications system that generally includes several repeaters spanning a distance of 100 miles or more. Diversity systems also generally provide 100% protection to a single radio channel, whereas protection switching arrangements are usually shared between several radio channels.

Essentially, there are two types of protection switching arrangements: *hot standby* and *diversity.* With hot standby protection, each working radio channel has a dedicated backup or spare channel. With diversity protection, a single backup channel is made available to as many as 11 working channels. Hot standby systems offer 100% protection for each working radio channel. A diversity system offers 100% protection only to the first working channel to fail. If two radio channels fail at the same time, a service interruption will occur.

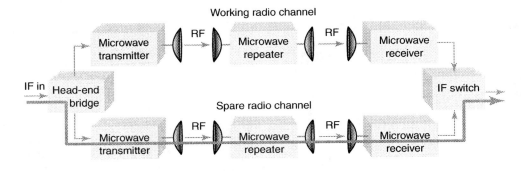

Working radio channel

Switching path for failed working channel

(a)

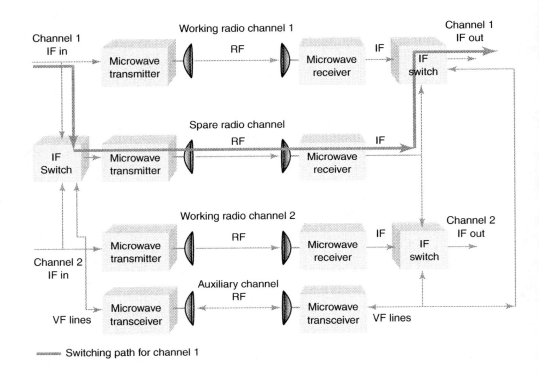

Switching path for channel 1

(b)

FIGURE 13-7   Microwave protection switching arrangements: (a) hot standby; (b) diversity

13-8-1   Hot Standby

Figure 13-7a shows a single-channel hot standby protection switching arrangement. At the transmitting end, the IF goes into a *head-end bridge,* which splits the signal power and directs it to the working and the spare (standby) microwave channels simultaneously. Consequently, both the working and the standby channels are carrying the same baseband information. At the receiving end, the IF switch passes the IF signal from the working channel to the FM terminal equipment. The IF switch continuously monitors the received signal power on the working channel and, if it fails, switches to the standby channel. When the IF signal on the working channel is restored, the IF switch resumes its normal position.

13-8-2 Diversity

Figure 13-7b shows a diversity protection switching arrangement. This system has two working channels (channel 1 and channel 2), one spare channel, and an *auxiliary* channel. The IF switch at the receive end continuously monitors the receive signal strength of both working channels. If either one should fail, the IF switch detects a loss of carrier and sends back to the transmitting station IF switch a VF (*voice frequency*) tone-encoded signal that directs it to switch the IF signal from the failed channel onto the spare microwave channel. When the failed channel is restored, the IF switches resume their normal positions. The auxiliary channel simply provides a transmission path between the two IF switches. Typically, the auxiliary channel is a low-capacity low-power microwave radio that is designed to be used for a maintenance channel only.

13-8-3 Reliability

The number of repeater stations between protection switches depends on the *reliability objectives* of the system. Typically, there are between two and six repeaters between switching stations.

As you can see, diversity systems and protection switching arrangements are quite similar. The primary difference between the two is that diversity systems are permanent arrangements and are intended only to compensate for temporary, abnormal atmospheric conditions between only two selected stations in a system. Protection switching arrangements, on the other hand, compensate for both radio fades and equipment failures and may include from six to eight repeater stations between switches. Protection channels also may be used as temporary communication facilities while routine maintenance is performed on a regular working channel. With a protection switching arrangement, all signal paths and radio equipment are protected. Diversity is used selectively—that is, only between stations that historically experience severe fading a high percentage of the time.

A statistical study of outage time (i.e., service interruptions) caused by radio fades, equipment failures, and maintenance is important in the design of a microwave radio system. From such a study, engineering decisions can be made on which type of diversity system and protection switching arrangement is best suited for a particular application.

Figure 13-8 shows a comparison between diversity and protection switching. As shown in the figure, protection switching arrangements protect against equipment failures

FIGURE 13-8 Comparison between diversity and protection switching in any of the electronic equipment (transmitters, receivers, and so on) in any of the microwave stations between the two switching stations. Diversity, however, protects only against adverse atmospheric conditions between a transmit antenna and a receive antenna.

13-9 FM MICROWAVE RADIO STATIONS

Basically, there are two types of FM microwave stations: terminals and repeaters. *Terminal stations* are points in the system where baseband signals either originate or terminate. *Repeater stations* are points in a system where baseband signals may be reconfigured or where RF carriers are simply "repeated" or amplified.

13-9-1 Terminal Station

Essentially, a terminal station consists of four major sections: the baseband, wireline entrance link (WLEL), FM-IF, and RF sections. Figure 13-9 shows a block diagram of the baseband, WLEL, and FM-IF sections. As mentioned, the baseband may be one of several different types of signals. For our example, frequency-division-multiplexed voice-band channels are used.

13-9-1-1 Wireline entrance link.
Often in large communications networks, such as the American Telephone and Telegraph Company (AT&T), the building that houses the radio station is quite large. Consequently, it is desirable that similar equipment be physically placed at a common location (i.e., all frequency-division-multiplexed [FDM] equipment in the same room). This simplifies alarm systems, providing dc power to the equipment, maintenance, and other general cabling requirements. Dissimilar equipment may be separated by a considerable distance. For example, the distance between the FDM equipment and the FM-IF section is typically several hundred feet and in some cases several miles. For this reason, a wireline entrance link (WLEL) is required. A WLEL serves as the interface between the multiplex terminal equipment and the FM-IF equipment. A WLEL generally consists of an amplifier and an equalizer (which together compensate for cable transmission losses) and level-shaping devices commonly called pre- and deemphasis networks.

FIGURE 13-9   Microwave terminal station: (a) transmitter; (b) receiver

13-9-1-2 IF section. The FM terminal equipment shown in Figure 13-9 generates a frequency-modulated IF carrier. This is accomplished by mixing the outputs of two deviated oscillators that differ in frequency by the desired IF carrier. The oscillators are deviated in phase opposition, which reduces the magnitude of phase deviation required of a single deviator by a factor of 2. This technique also reduces the deviation linearity requirements for the oscillators and provides for the partial cancellation of unwanted modulation products. Again, the receiver is a conventional noncoherent FM detector.

13-9-1-3 RF section. A block diagram of the RF section of a microwave terminal station is shown in Figure 13-10. The IF signal enters the transmitter (Figure 13-10a) through a protection switch. The IF and compression amplifiers help keep the IF signal power constant and at approximately the required input level to the transmit modulator (*transmod*). A transmod is a balanced modulator that, when used in conjunction with a microwave generator, power amplifier, and bandpass filter, up-converts the IF carrier to an RF carrier and amplifies the RF to the desired output power. Power amplifiers for microwave radios must be capable of amplifying very high frequencies and passing very wide bandwidth signals. *Klystron tubes, traveling-wave tubes* (TWTs), and *IMPATT* (impact/avalanche and transit time) diodes are several of the devices currently being used in microwave power amplifiers. Because high-gain antennas are used and the distance between microwave stations is relatively short, it is not necessary to develop a high output power from the transmitter output amplifiers. Typical gains for microwave antennas range from 10 dB to 40 dB, and typical transmitter output powers are between 0.5 W and 10 W.

A *microwave generator* provides the RF carrier input to the up-converter. It is called a microwave generator rather than an oscillator because it is difficult to construct a stable circuit that will oscillate in the gigahertz range. Instead, a crystal-controlled oscillator operating in the range 5 MHz to 25 MHz is used to provide a base frequency that is multiplied up to the desired RF carrier frequency.

An *isolator* is a unidirectional device often made from a ferrite material. The isolator is used in conjunction with a channel-combining network to prevent the output of one transmitter from interfering with the output of another transmitter.

The RF receiver (Figure 13-10b) is essentially the same as the transmitter except that it works in the opposite direction. However, one difference is the presence of an IF amplifier in the receiver. This IF amplifier has an *automatic gain control* (AGC) circuit. Also, very often, there are no RF amplifiers in the receiver. Typically, a highly sensitive, low-noise balanced demodulator is used for the receive demodulator (receive mod). This eliminates the need for an RF amplifier and improves the overall signal-to-noise ratio. When RF amplifiers are required, high-quality, *low-noise amplifiers* (LNAs) are used. Examples of commonly used LNAs are tunnel diodes and parametric amplifiers.

13-10 MICROWAVE REPEATER STATION

Figure 13-11 shows the block diagram of a microwave IF repeater station. The received RF signal enters the receiver through the channel separation network and bandpass filter. The receive mod down-converts the RF carrier to IF. The IF AMP/AGC and equalizer circuits amplify and reshape the IF. The equalizer compensates for *gain-versus-frequency nonlinearities* and *envelope delay distortion* introduced in the system. Again, the transmod up-converts the IF to RF for retransmission. However, in a repeater station, the method used to generate the RF microwave carrier frequencies is slightly different from the method used in a terminal station. In the IF repeater, only one microwave generator is required to supply both the transmod and the receive mod with an RF carrier signal. The microwave generator, shift oscillator, and shift modulator allow the repeater to receive one RF carrier frequency, down-convert it to IF, and then up-convert the IF to a different RF carrier

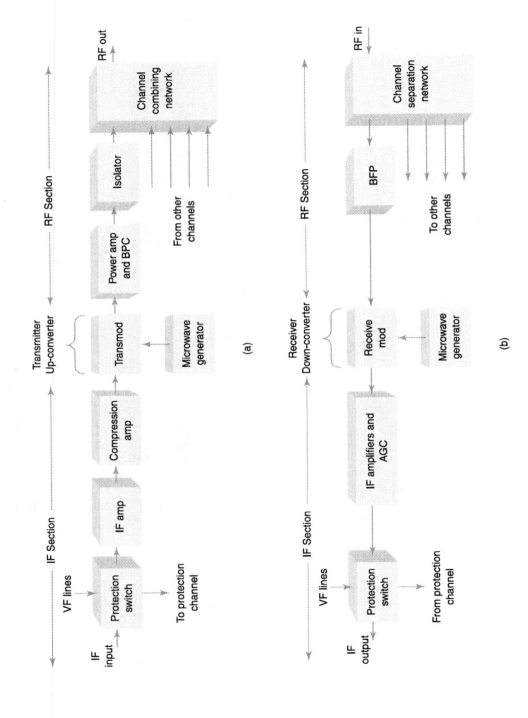

FIGURE 13-10 Microwave terminal station: (a) transmitter; (b) receiver

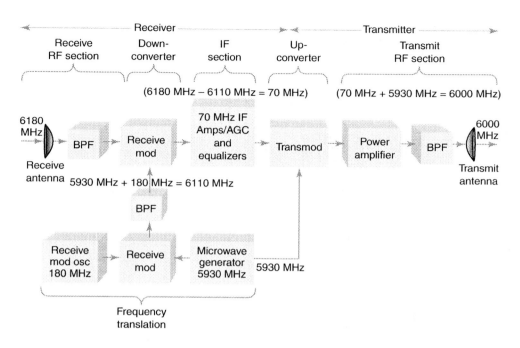

FIGURE 13-11 Microwave radio IF repeater block diagram

frequency. It is possible for station D to receive the transmissions from both station B and station C simultaneously (this is called *multihop interference* and is shown in Figure 13-12a). This can occur only when three stations are placed in a geographical straight line in the system. To prevent this from occurring, the allocated bandwidth for the system is divided in half, creating a low-frequency and a high-frequency band. Each station, in turn, alternates from a low-band to a high-band transmit carrier frequency (Figure 13-12b). If a transmission from station B is received by station D, it will be rejected in the channel separation network and cause no interference. This arrangement is called a high/low microwave repeater system. The rules are simple: If a repeater station receives a low-band RF carrier, then it retransmits a high-band RF carrier and vice versa. The only time that multiple carriers of the same frequency can be received is when a transmission from one station is received from another station that is three hops away. This is unlikely to happen.

Another reason for using a high/low-frequency scheme is to prevent the power that "leaks" out the back and sides of a transmit antenna from interfering with the signal entering the input of a nearby receive antenna. This is called *ringaround.* All antennas, no matter how high their gain or how directive their radiation pattern, radiate a small percentage of their power out the back and sides, giving a finite *front-to-back* ratio for the antenna. Although the front-to-back ratio of a typical microwave antenna is quite high, the relatively small amount of power that is radiated out the back of the antenna may be quite substantial compared with the normal received carrier power in the system. If the transmit and receive carrier frequencies are different, filters in the receiver separation network will prevent ringaround from occurring.

A high/low microwave repeater station (Figure 13-12b) needs two microwave carrier supplies for the down- and up-converting process. Rather than use two microwave generators, a single generator with a shift oscillator, a shift modulator, and a bandpass filter can generate the two required signals. One output from the microwave generator is fed directly into the transmod, and another output (from the same microwave generator) is mixed with the shift oscillator signal in the shift modulator to produce a second microwave carrier

(a)

(b)

FIGURE 13-12   (a) Multihop interference and (b) high/low microwave system

frequency. The second microwave carrier frequency is offset from the first by the shift oscillator frequency. The second microwave carrier frequency is fed into the receive modulator.

Example 13-1

In Figure 13-11, the received RF carrier frequency is 6180 MHz, and the transmitted RF carrier frequency is 6000 MHz. With a 70-MHz IF frequency, a 5930-MHz microwave generator frequency, and a 180-MHz shift oscillator frequency, the output filter of the shift mod must be tuned to 6110 MHz. This is the sum of the microwave generator and the shift oscillator frequencies (5930 MHz + 180 MHz = 6110 MHz).

This process does not reduce the number of oscillators required, but it is simpler and cheaper to build one microwave generator and one relatively low-frequency shift oscillator than to build two microwave generators. This arrangement also provides a certain degree of synchronization between repeaters. The obvious disadvantage of the high/low scheme is that the number of channels available in a given bandwidth is cut in half.

Figure 13-13 shows a high/low-frequency plan with eight channels (four high band and four low band). Each channel occupies a 29.7-MHz bandwidth. The west terminal transmits the low-band frequencies and receives the high-band frequencies. Channels 1 and 3 (Figure 13-13a) are designated as *V channels*. This means that they are propagated with vertical polarization. Channels 2 and 4 are designated as H, or horizontally polarized, channels. This is not a polarization diversity system. Channels 1 through 4 are totally independent of each other; they carry different baseband information. The transmission of *orthogonally* polarized carriers (90° out of phase) further enhances the isolation between the transmit and receive signals. In the west-to-east direction, the repeater receives the low-band frequencies and transmits the high-band frequencies. After channel 1 is received and down-converted to IF, it is up-converted to a different RF frequency and a different polarization for retransmission. The low-band channel 1 corresponds to the high-band channel 11, channel 2 to channel 12, and so on. The east-to-west direction (Figure 13-13b) propagates the high- and low-band carriers in the sequence opposite to the west-to-east system. The polarizations are also reversed. If some of the power from channel 1 of the west terminal were to propagate directly to the east terminal receiver, it would have a different frequency and polarization than channel 11's transmissions. Consequently, it would not interfere with

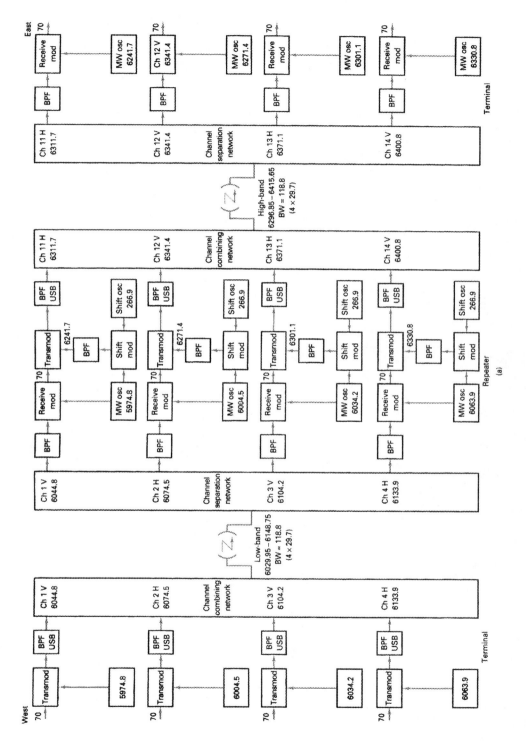

FIGURE 13-13 Eight-channel high/low frequency plan: (a) west to east; (*Continued*).

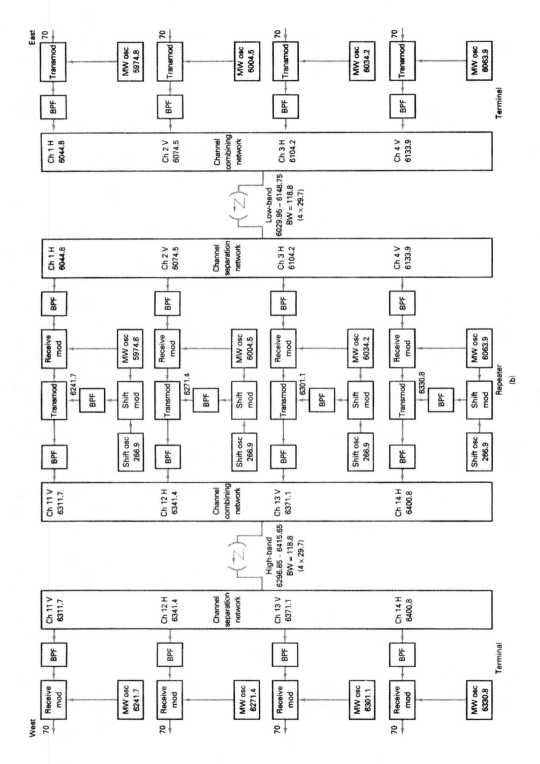

FIGURE 13-13 (*Continued*) Eight-channel high/low frequency plan: (b) east to west.

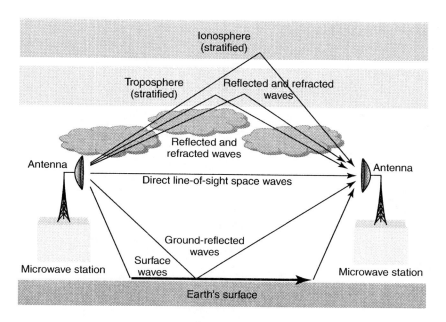

FIGURE 13-14   Microwave propagation paths

the reception of channel 11 (no multihop interference). Also, note that none of the transmit or receive channels at the repeater station has both the same frequency and polarization. Consequently, the interference from the transmitters to the receivers due to ringaround is insignificant.

13-11   LINE-OF-SIGHT PATH CHARACTERISTICS

The normal *propagation paths* between two radio antennas in a microwave radio system are shown in Figure 13-14. The *free-space path* is the *line-of-sight path* directly between the transmit and receive antennas (this is also called the *direct wave*). The *ground-reflected wave* is the portion of the transmit signal that is reflected off Earth's surface and captured by the receive antenna. The *surface wave* consists of the electric and magnetic fields associated with the currents induced in Earth's surface. The magnitude of the surface wave depends on the characteristics of Earth's surface and the electromagnetic polarization of the wave. The sum of these three paths (taking into account their amplitude and phase) is called the *ground wave*. The *sky wave* is the portion of the transmit signal that is returned (reflected) back to Earth's surface by the ionized layers of Earth's atmosphere.

All paths shown in Figure 13-14 exist in any microwave radio system, but some are negligible in certain frequency ranges. At frequencies below 1.5 MHz, the surface wave provides the primary coverage, and the sky wave helps extend this coverage at night when the absorption of the ionosphere is at a minimum. For frequencies above about 30 MHz to 50 MHz, the free-space and ground-reflected paths are generally the only paths of importance. The surface wave can also be neglected at these frequencies, provided that the antenna heights are not too low. The sky wave is only a source of occasional long-distance interference and not a reliable signal for microwave communications purposes. In this chapter, the surface and sky wave propagations are neglected, and attention is focused on those phenomena that affect the direct and reflected waves.

13-11-1 Free-Space Path Loss

Free-space path loss is often defined as the loss incurred by an electromagnetic wave as it propagates in a straight line through a vacuum with no absorption or reflection of energy from nearby objects. Free-space path loss is a misstated and often misleading definition because no energy is actually dissipated. Free-space path loss is a fabricated engineering quantity that evolved from manipulating communications system link budget equations, which include transmit antenna gain, free-space path loss, and the effective area of the receiving antenna (i.e., the receiving antenna gain) into a particular format. The manipulation of antenna gain terms results is a distance and frequency-dependent term called *free-space path loss.*

Free-space path loss assumes ideal atmospheric conditions, so no electromagnetic energy is actually lost or dissipated—it merely spreads out as it propagates away from the source, resulting in lower relative power densities. A more appropriate term for the phenomena is *spreading loss.* Spreading loss occurs simply because of the inverse square law. The mathematical expression for free-space path loss is

$$L_p = \left(\frac{4\pi D}{\lambda}\right)^2 \tag{13-1}$$

and because $\lambda = \frac{c}{f}$, Equation 14-26 can be written as

$$L_p = \left(\frac{4\pi f D}{c}\right)^2 \tag{13-2}$$

where L_p = free-space path loss (unitless)
        D = distance (kilometers)
        f = frequency (hertz)
        λ = wavelength (meters)
        c = velocity of light in free space (3 × 108 meters per second)

Converting to dB yields

$$L_p(\text{dB}) = 10 \log \left(\frac{4\pi f D}{c}\right)^2 \tag{13-3}$$

or

$$L_p(\text{dB}) = 20 \log \left(\frac{4\pi f D}{c}\right) \tag{13-4}$$

Separating the constants from the variables gives

$$L_p = 20 \log \left(\frac{4\pi}{c}\right) + 20 \log f + 20 \log D \tag{13-5}$$

For frequencies in MHz and distances in kilometers,

$$L_p = \left[\frac{4\pi (10^6)(10^3)}{3 \times 10^8}\right] + 20 \log f_{(\text{MHz})} + 20 \log D_{(\text{km})} \tag{13-6}$$

or

$$L_p = 32.4 + 20 \log f_{(\text{MHz})} + 20 \log D_{(\text{km})} \tag{13-7}$$

When the frequency is given in GHz and the distance in km,

$$L_p = 92.4 + 20 \log f_{(\text{GHz})} + 20 \log D_{(\text{km})} \tag{13-8}$$

When the frequency is given in GHz and the distance in miles,

$$L_p = 96.6 + 20 \log f_{(\text{GHz})} + 20 \log D_{(\text{miles})} \tag{13-9}$$

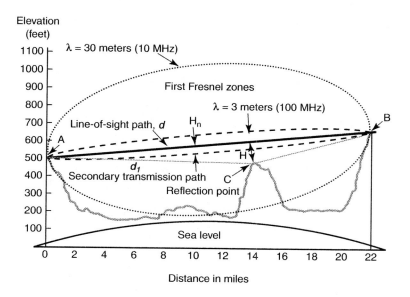

FIGURE 13-15 Microwave line-of-sight path showing first Fresnel zones

13-11-2 Path Clearance and Antenna Heights

The presence and topography of Earth's surface and the nonuniformity of the atmosphere above it can markedly affect the operating conditions of a microwave radio communications link. A majority of the time, the path loss of a typical microwave link can be approximated by the calculated free-space path loss. This is accomplished by engineering the path between transmit and receive antennas to provide an optical line-of-sight transmission path that should have adequate clearance with respect to surrounding objects. This clearance is necessary to ensure that the path loss under normal atmospheric conditions does not deviate from its nominal free-space value and to reduce the effects of severe fading that could occur during abnormal conditions.

The importance of providing an adequate path clearance is shown in Figure 13-15, which shows the profile of the path between the antennas of two microwave stations. For the antenna heights shown, the distance H represents the clearance of the line-of-sight path, AB, and the intervening terrain. Path ACB represents a secondary transmission path via reflection from the projection at location C. With no phase reversal at the point of reflection, the signal from the two paths would partially cancel whenever AB and ACB differed by an odd multiple of a half wavelength. When the grazing angle of the secondary wave is small, which is typically the case, a phase reversal will normally occur at the point of reflection (C). Therefore, whenever the distances AB and ACB differ by an odd multiple of a half wavelength, the energies of the received signals add rather than cancel. Conversely, if the lengths of the two paths differ by a whole number of half wavelengths, the signals from the two paths will tend to cancel.

The amount of clearance is generally described in terms of Fresnel (pronounced "franell") zones. All points from which a wave could be reflected with an additional path length of one-half wavelength form an ellipse that defines the first Fresnel zone. Similarly, the boundary of the nth Fresnel zone consists of all points in which the propagation delay is $n/2$ wavelengths. For any distance, d_1, from antenna A, the distance H_n from the line-of-sight path to the boundary of the nth Fresnel zone is approximated by a parabola described as

$$H_n = \sqrt{\frac{n\lambda d_1(d - d_1)}{d}}$$

(13-10)

where H_n = distance between direct path and parabola surrounding it

λ = wavelength (linear unit)

d = direct path length (linear unit)

d_1 = reflected path length (linear unit)

and   all linear units must be the same (feet, meters, cm, and so on).

The boundaries of the first Fresnel zones for $\lambda = 3$ meters (100 MHz) in the vertical plane through AB are shown in Figure 13-15. In any plane normal to AB, the Fresnel zones are concentric circles.

Measurements have shown that to achieve a normal transmission loss approximately equal to the free-space path loss, the transmission path should pass over all obstacles with a clearance of at least 0.6 times the distance of the first Fresnel zone and preferably by a distance equal to or greater than the first Fresnel zone distance. However, because of the effects of refraction, greater clearance is generally provided to reduce deep fading under adverse atmospheric conditions.

When determining the height of a microwave tower, a profile plot is made of the terrain between the proposed antenna sites, and the worst obstacle in the path, such as a mountain peak or ridge, is identified. The obstacle is used for a leverage point to determine the minimum path clearance between two locations from which the most suitable antenna heights are determined. Portable antennas, transmitters, and receivers are used to test the location to determine the optimum antenna heights.

13-11-3 Fading

The previous sections illustrated how free-space path loss is calculated. Path loss is a fixed loss, which remains constant over time. With very short path lengths at below 10 GHz, the signal level at the distant antenna can be calculated to within ±1 dB. Provided that the transmit power remains constant, receive signal level (RSL) should remain uniform and constant over long periods of time. As the path length is extended, however, the measured receive signal level can vary around a nominal median value and remain in that range for minutes or hours and then suddenly drop below the median range and then return to the median level again. At other times and/or on other radio paths, the variation in signal level can be continuous for varying periods. Drops in receive signal level can be as much as 30 dB or more. This reduction in receive signal level is called *fading*.

Fading is a general term applied to the reduction in signal strength at the input to a receiver. It applies to propagation variables in the physical radio path that affect changes in the path loss between transmit and receive antennas. The changes in the characteristics of a radio path are associated with both atmospheric conditions and the geometry of the path itself (i.e., the relative position of the antenna with respect to the ground and surrounding terrain and obstacles). Substantial atmospheric conditions can transform an otherwise adequate line-of-sight path into an obstructed path because the effective path clearance approaches zero or becomes negative. Fading can occur under conditions of heavy ground fog or when extremely cold air moves over warm ground. The result in either case is a substantial increase in path loss over a wide frequency band. The magnitude and rapidity of occurrence of slow, flat fading of this type can generally be reduced only by using greater antenna heights.

A more common form of fading is a relatively rapid, frequency selective type of fading caused by interference between two or more rays in the atmosphere. The separate paths between transmit and receive antennas are caused by irregularities in the dielectric permittivity of the air, which varies with height. The transmission margins that must be provided against both types of fading are important considerations in determining overall system parameters and reliability objectives.

An interference type of fade may occur to any depth, but, fortunately, the deeper the fade, the less frequently it occurs and the shorter its duration. Both the number of fades and the percentage of time a received signal is below a given level tend to increase as either the

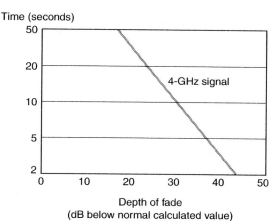

Time (seconds)

Depth of fade
(dB below normal calculated value)

FIGURE 13-16 Median duration of fast fading

repeater spacing or the frequency of operation increases. Multiple paths are usually overhead, although ground reflections can occasionally be a factor. Using frequency or space diversity can generally minimize the effects of multipath fading.

Figure 13-16 shows the median duration of radio fades on a 4-GHz signal for various depths with an average repeater spacing of 30 miles. As shown in the figure, a median duration of a 20-dB fade is about 30 seconds, and the median duration of a 40-dB fade is about 3 seconds. At any given depth of fade, the duration of 1% of the fades may be as much as 10 times or as little as one-tenth of the median duration.

Multipath fading occurs primarily during nighttime hours on typical microwave links operating between 2 GHz and 6 GHz. During daytime hours or whenever the lower atmosphere is thoroughly mixed by rising convection currents and winds, the signals on a line-of-sight path are normally steady and at or near the calculated free-space values. On clear nights with little or no wind, however, sizable irregularities or layers can form at random elevations, and these irregularities in refraction result in multiple transmission path lengths on the order of a million wavelengths or longer. Multipath fading has a tendency to build up during nighttime hours with a peak in the early morning and then disappear as convection currents caused by heat produced during the early daylight hours break up the layers. Both the occurrence of fades and the percentage of time below a given receive signal level tend to increase with increases in repeater spacing or frequency.

13-12   MICROWAVE RADIO SYSTEM GAIN

In its simplest form, *system gain* (G_s) is the difference between the nominal output power of a transmitter (P_t) and the minimum input power to a receiver (C_{min}) necessary to achieve satisfactory performance. System gain must be greater than or equal to the sum of all gains and losses incurred by a signal as it propagates from a transmitter to a receiver. In essence, system gain represents the net loss of a radio system, which is used to predict the reliability of a system for a given set of system parameters.

Ironically, system gain is actually a loss, as the losses a signal experiences as it propagates from a transmitter to a receiver are much higher than the gains. Therefore, the net system gain always equates to a negative dB value (i.e., a loss). Because system gain is defined as a net loss, individual losses are represented with positive dB values, while individual gains are represented with negative dB values. Figure 13-17 shows the diagram for a microwave system indicating where losses and gains typically occur.

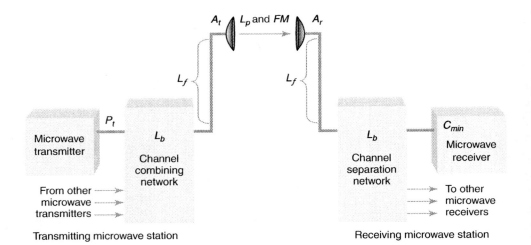

FIGURE 13-17   System gains and losses

Mathematically, system gain in its simplest form is

$$G_s = P_t - C_{min} \qquad (13\text{-}11)$$

where G_s = system gain (dB)
P_t = transmitter output power (dBm or dBW)
C_{min} = minimum receiver input power necessary to achieve a given reliability
and quality objective

and where

$$P_t - C_{min} \geq losses - gains \qquad (13\text{-}12)$$

Gains A_t = transmit antenna gain relative to an isotropic radiator (dB)
A_r = receive antenna gain relative to an isotropic radiator (dB)
Losses L_p = free-space path loss incurred as a signal propagates from the transmit antenna to the receive antenna through Earth's atmosphere (dB)
L_f = transmission line loss between the distribution network (channel-combining
network at the transmit station or channel separation network at the receive
station) and its respective antenna (dB)
L_b = total coupling or branching loss in the channel-combining network between
the output of a transmitter and the transmission line or from the output of a
channel separation network and the receiver (dB)
FM = fade margin for a given reliability objective (dB)

A more useful expression for system gain is

$$G_{s(dB)} = P_t - C_{min} \geq FM_{(dB)} + L_{p(dB)} + L_{f(dB)} + L_{b(dB)} - A_{(dB)t} - A_{r(dB)} \qquad (13\text{-}13)$$

Path loss can be determined from either Equation 13-8 or Equation 13-9, while feeder and
branching losses depend on individual component specifications and diversity arrangements. Table 13-3 lists component specifications for several types of transmission lines for
both space- and frequency-diversity systems. Antenna gain depends on the antenna's physical dimensions and the frequency of operation. Table 13-3 lists approximate antenna gains
for parabolic antennas with several different diameters. The magnitude of the fade margin
depends on several factors relating to the distance between transmit and receive antennas
and the type of terrain the signal propagates over. Fade margin calculations are described
in the next section of this chapter.

Table 13-3 System Gain Parameters

| Frequency (GHz) | Feeder Loss (L_f) | | Branching Loss (L_b) (dB) | | Antenna Gain (A_t or A_r) | |
| | Type | Loss (dB/100 Meters) | Diversity | | Diameter (Meters) | Gain (dB) |
			Frequency	Space		
1.8	Air-filled coaxial cable	5.4	4	2	1.2	25.2
					2.4	31.2
					3.0	33.2
					3.7	34.7
					4.8	37.2
7.4	EWP 64 elliptical waveguide	4.7	3	2	1.2	37.1
					1.5	38.8
					2.4	43.1
					3.0	44.8
					3.7	46.5
8.0	EWP 69 elliptical waveguide	6.5	3	2	1.2	37.8
					2.4	43.8
					3.0	45.6
					3.7	47.3
					4.8	49.8

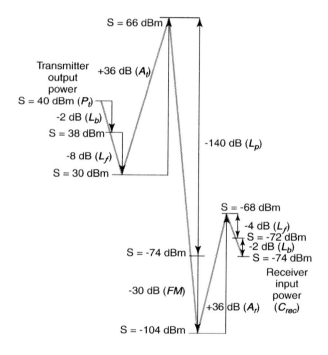

FIGURE 13-18 Microwave radio link signal levels relative to system gains and losses

Figure 13-18 shows a simplified diagram illustrating how the level of a signal changes as it propagates from a microwave transmitter to a microwave receiver for the following system parameters:

Transmit station $P_t = 40$ dBm

$L_b = 2$ dB

$L_f = 8$ dB

$A_t = 36$ dB

$$\text{Atmosphere} \qquad L_p = 140 \text{ dB}$$
$$FM = 30 \text{ dB}$$
$$\text{Receive station} \qquad A_r = 36 \text{ dB}$$
$$L_f = 4 \text{ dB}$$
$$L_b = 2 \text{ dB}$$

System gain is determined from Equation 13-13:

$$G_{s(\text{dB})} = FM_{(\text{dB})} + L_{p(\text{dB})} + L_{f(\text{dB})} + L_{b(\text{dB})} - A_{(\text{dB})t} - A_{r(\text{dB})}$$
$$= 30 \text{ dB} + 140 \text{ dB} + 12 \text{ dB} + 4 \text{ dB} - 36 \text{ dB} - 36 \text{ dB}$$
$$= 114 \text{ dB}$$

and the receive signal level (C_{rec}) is simply the transmit power (P_t) minus system gain (G_s) or

$$C_{\text{rec}} = 40 \text{ dBm} - 114 \text{ dB}$$
$$= -74 \text{ dBm}$$

13-12-1 Fade Margin

Fade margin (sometimes called *link margin*) is essentially a "fudge factor" included in system gain equations that considers the nonideal and less predictable characteristics of radio-wave propagation, such as multipath propagation (multipath loss) and terrain sensitivity. These characteristics cause temporary, abnormal atmospheric conditions that alter the free-space loss and are usually detrimental to the overall system performance. Fade margin also considers system reliability objectives. Thus, fade margin is included in system gain equations as a loss.

In April 1969, W. T. Barnett of Bell Telephone Laboratories described ways of calculating outage time due to fading on a nondiversity path as a function of terrain, climate, path length, and fade margin. In June 1970, Arvids Vignant (also of Bell Laboratories) derived formulas for calculating the effective improvement achievable by vertical space diversity as a function of the spacing distance, path length, and frequency. Solving the Barnett-Vignant reliability equations for a specified annual system availability for an unprotected, nondiversity system yields the following expression:

$$F_m = \underbrace{30 \log D}_{\substack{\text{multipath} \\ \text{effect}}} + \underbrace{10 \log (6ABf)}_{\substack{\text{terrain} \\ \text{sensitivity}}} - \underbrace{10 \log (1 - R)}_{\substack{\text{reliability} \\ \text{objectives}}} - \underbrace{70}_{\text{constant}} \qquad (13\text{-}14)$$

where F_m = fade margin (dB)
$\quad D$ = distance (kilometers)
$\quad f$ = frequency (gigahertz)
$\quad R$ = reliability expressed as a decimal (i.e., 99.99% = 0.9999 reliability)
$1 - R$ = reliability objective for a one-way 400-km route
$\quad A$ = roughness factor
$\qquad$ = 4 over water or a very smooth terrain
$\qquad$ = 1 over an average terrain
$\qquad$ = 0.25 over a very rough, mountainous terrain
$\quad B$ = factor to convert a worst-month probability to an annual probability
$\qquad$ = 1 to convert an annual availability to a worst-month basis
$\qquad$ = 0.5 for hot humid areas
$\qquad$ = 0.25 for average inland areas
$\qquad$ = 0.125 for very dry or mountainous areas

Example 13-2

Consider a space-diversity microwave radio system operating at an RF carrier frequency of 1.8 GHz. Each station has a 2.4-m-diameter parabolic antenna that is fed by 100 m of air-filled coaxial cable. The terrain is smooth, and the area has a humid climate. The distance between stations is 40 km. A reliability objective of 99.99% is desired. Determine the system gain.

Solution Substituting into Equation 13-14, we find that the fade margin is

$$F_m = 30 \log 40 + 10 \log [(6)(4)(0.5)(1.8)] - 10 \log (1 - 0.9999) - 70$$
$$= 48.06 + 13.34 - (-40) - 70$$
$$= 48.06 + 13.34 + 40 - 70 = 31.4 \text{ dB}$$

Substituting into Equation 13-8, we obtain path loss:

$$L_p = 92.4 + 20 \log 1.8 + 20 \log 40$$
$$= 92.4 + 5.11 + 32.04 = 129.55 \text{ dB}$$

From Table 13-3,

$$L_b = 4 \text{ dB } (2 + 2 = 4)$$
$$L_f = 10.8 \text{ dB } (100 \text{ m} + 100 \text{ m} = 200 \text{ m})$$
$$A_t = A_r = 31.2 \text{ dB}$$

Substituting into Equation 13-13 gives us system gain:

$$G_s = 31.4 + 129.55 + 10.8 + 4 - 31.2 - 31.2 = 113.35 \text{ dB}$$

The results indicate that for this system to perform at 99.99% reliability with the given terrain, distribution networks, transmission lines, and antennas, the transmitter output power must be at least 113.35 dB more than the minimum receive signal level.

13-12-2 Receiver Threshold

Carrier-to-noise (C/N) ratio is probably the most important parameter considered when evaluating the performance of a microwave communications system. The minimum wideband carrier power (C_{min}) at the input to a receiver that will provide a usable baseband output is called the receiver *threshold* or, sometimes, receiver *sensitivity*. The receiver threshold is dependent on the wideband noise power present at the input of a receiver, the noise introduced within the receiver, and the noise sensitivity of the baseband detector. Before C_{min} can be calculated, the input noise power must be determined. The input noise power is expressed mathematically as

$$N = KTB \qquad (13\text{-}15)$$

where N = noise power (watts)
  K = Boltzmann's constant (1.38×10^{-23} J/K)
  T = equivalent noise temperature of the receiver (kelvin) (room temperature = 290 kelvin)
  B = noise bandwidth (hertz)

Expressed in dBm,

$$N_{(dBm)} = 10 \log \frac{KTB}{0.001} = 10 \log \frac{KT}{0.001} + 10 \log B$$

For a 1-Hz bandwidth at room temperature,

$$N = 10 \log \frac{(1.38 \times 10^{-23})(290)}{0.001} + 10 \log 1$$
$$= -174 \text{ dBm}$$

Thus,
$$N_{(dBm)} = -174 \text{ dBm} + 10 \log B \qquad (13\text{-}16)$$

Example 13-3

For an equivalent noise bandwidth of 10 MHz, determine the noise power.

Solution   Substituting into Equation 13-16 yields

$$N = -174 \text{ dBm} + 10 \log (10 \times 10^6)$$
$$= -174 \text{ dBm} + 70 \text{ dB} = -104 \text{ dBm}$$

If the minimum C/N requirement for a receiver with a 10-MHz noise bandwidth is 24 dB, the minimum receive carrier power is

$$C_{\min} = \frac{C}{N} + N = 24 \text{ dB} + (-104 \text{ dBm}) = -80 \text{ dBm}$$

For a system gain of 113.35 dB, it would require a minimum transmit carrier power (P_t) of

$$P_t = G_s + C_{\min} = 113.35 \text{ dB} + (-80 \text{ dBm}) = 33.35 \text{ dBm}$$

This indicates that a minimum transmit power of 33.35 dBm (2.16 W) is required to achieve a carrier-to-noise ratio of 24 dB with a system gain of 113.35 dB and a bandwidth of 10 MHz.

13-12-3   Carrier-to-Noise versus Signal-to-Noise Ratio

Carrier-to-noise (C/N) is the ratio of the wideband "carrier" (actually, not just the carrier but rather the carrier and its associated sidebands) to the wideband noise power (the noise bandwidth of the receiver). C/N can be determined at an RF or an IF point in the receiver. Essentially, C/N is a *predetection* (before the FM demodulator) signal-to-noise ratio. Signal-to-noise (S/N) is a *postdetection* (after the FM demodulator) ratio. At a baseband point in the receiver, a single voice-band channel can be separated from the rest of the baseband and measured independently. At an RF or IF point in the receiver, it is impossible to separate a single voice-band channel from the composite FM signal. For example, a typical bandwidth for a single microwave channel is 30 MHz. The bandwidth of a voice-band channel is 4 kHz. C/N is the ratio of the power of the composite RF signal to the total noise power in the 30-MHz bandwidth. S/N is the ratio of the signal power of a single voice-band channel to the noise power in a 4-kHz bandwidth.

13-12-4   Noise Factor and Noise Figure

Noise factor (F) and *noise figure* (NF) are figures of merit used to indicate how much the signal-to-noise ratio deteriorates as a signal passes through a circuit or series of circuits. Noise factor is simply a ratio of input signal-to-noise ratio to output signal-to-noise ratio. In other words, a ratio of ratios. Mathematically, noise factor is

$$F = \frac{\text{input signal-to-noise ratio}}{\text{output signal-to-noise ratio}} \text{ (unitless ratio)} \qquad (13\text{-}17)$$

Noise figure is simply the noise factor stated in dB and is a parameter commonly used to indicate the quality of a receiver. Mathematically, noise figure is

$$NF = 10 \log \frac{\text{input signal-to-noise ratio}}{\text{output signal-to-noise ratio}} \text{ (dB)} \qquad (13\text{-}18)$$

or
$$NF = 10 \log F \qquad (13\text{-}19)$$

In essence, noise figure indicates how much the signal-to-noise ratio deteriorates as a waveform propagates from the input to the output of a circuit. For example, an amplifier with a noise figure of 6 dB means that the signal-to-noise ratio at the output is 6 dB less than it was at the input. If a circuit is perfectly noiseless and adds no additional noise to the signal, the signal-to-noise ratio at the output will equal the signal-to-noise ratio at the input. For a perfect, noiseless circuit, the noise factor is 1, and the noise figure is 0 dB.

An electronic circuit amplifies signals and noise within its passband equally well. Therefore, if the amplifier is ideal and noiseless, the input signal and noise are amplified the same, and the signal-to-noise ratio at the output will equal the signal-to-noise ratio at

FIGURE 13-19   System gain diagram for Example 13-4

the input. In reality, however, amplifiers are not ideal. Therefore, the amplifier adds internally generated noise to the waveform, reducing the overall signal-to-noise ratio. The most predominant noise is thermal noise, which is generated in all electrical components. Therefore, all networks, amplifiers, and systems add noise to the signal and, thus, reduce the overall signal-to-noise ratio as the signal passes through them.

Example 13-4

Refer to Figure 13-19. For a system gain of 112 dB, a total noise figure of 6.5 dB, an input noise power of -104 dBm, and a minimum $(S/N)_{out}$ of the FM demodulator of 32 dB, determine the minimum receive carrier power and the minimum transmit power.

Solution   To achieve a S/N ratio of 32 dB out of the FM demodulator, an input C/N of 15 dB is required (17 dB of improvement due to FM quieting). Solving for the receiver input carrier-to-noise ratio gives

$$\frac{C_{min}}{N} = \frac{C}{N} + NF_T = 15 \text{ dB} + 6.5 \text{ dB} = 21.5 \text{ dB}$$

Thus,

$$C_{min} = \frac{C_{min}}{N} + N = 21.5 \text{ dB} + (-104 \text{ dBm}) = -82.5 \text{ dBm}$$

$$P_t = G_s + C_{min} = 112 \text{ dB} + (-82.5 \text{ dBm}) = 29.5 \text{ dBm}$$

Example 13-5

For the system shown in Figure 13-20, determine the following: G_s, C_{min}/N, C_{min}, N, G_s, and P_r.

Solution   The minimum C/N at the input to the FM receiver is 23 dB:

$$\frac{C_{min}}{N} = \frac{C}{N} + NF_T = 23 \text{ dB} + 4.24 \text{ dB} = 27.24 \text{ dB}$$

Substituting into Equation 13-16 yields

$$N = -174 \text{ dBm} + 10 \log B = -174 \text{ dBm} + 68 \text{ dB} = -106 \text{ dBm}$$

$$C_{min} = \frac{C_{min}}{N} + N = 27.24 \text{ dB} + (-106 \text{ dBm}) = -78.76 \text{ dBm}$$

Substituting into Equation 13-14 gives us

$$F_m = 30 \log 50 + 10 \log [(6)(0.25)(0.125)(8)]$$
$$-10 \log (1 - 0.99999) - 70 = 32.76 \text{ dB}$$

Substituting into Equation 13-8, we have

$$L_p = 92.4 \text{ dB} + 20 \log 8 + 20 \log 50$$
$$= 92.4 \text{ dB} + 18.06 \text{ dB} + 33.98 \text{ dB} = 144.44 \text{ dB}$$

From Table 13-3,

$$L_b = 4 \text{ dB}$$
$$L_f = 0.75 (6.5 \text{ dB}) = 4.875 \text{ dB}$$
$$A_t = A_r = 37.8 \text{ dB}$$

FIGURE 13-20   System gain diagram for Example 13-5

Note: The gain of an antenna increases or decreases proportional to the square of its diameter (i.e., if its diameter changes by a factor of 2, its gain changes by a factor of 4, which is 6 dB).
Substituting into Equation 13-13 yields
$$G_s = 32.76 + 144.44 + 4.875 + 4 - 37.8 - 37.8 = 110.475 \text{ dB}$$
$$P_t = G_s + C_{min} = 110.475 \text{ dB} + (-78.76 \text{ dBm}) = 31.715 \text{ dBm}$$

QUESTIONS

13-1. What constitutes a short-haul microwave system? A long-haul microwave system?

13-2. Describe the baseband signal for a microwave system.

13-3. Why do FDM/FM microwave systems use low-index FM?

13-4. Describe a microwave repeater. Contrast baseband and IF repeaters.

13-5. Define *diversity*. Describe the three most commonly used diversity schemes.

13-6. Describe a protection switching arrangement. Contrast the two types of protection switching arrangements.

13-7. Briefly describe the four major sections of a microwave terminal station.

13-8. Define *ringaround*.

13-9. Briefly describe a high/low microwave system.

13-10. Define *system gain*.

13-11. Define the following terms: *free-space path loss, branching loss,* and *feeder loss.*

13-12. Define *fade margin*. Describe multipath losses, terrain sensitivity, and reliability objectives and how they affect fade margin.

13-13. Define *receiver threshold.*

13-14. Contrast carrier-to-noise ratio with signal-to-noise ratio.

13-15. Define *noise figure.*

PROBLEMS

13-1. Calculate the noise power at the input to a receiver that has a radio carrier frequency of 4 GHz and a bandwidth of 30 MHz (assume room temperature).

13-2. Determine the path loss for a 3.4-GHz signal propagating 20,000 m.

13-3. Determine the fade margin for a 60-km microwave hop. The RF carrier frequency is 6 GHz, the terrain is very smooth and dry, and the reliability objective is 99.95%.

13-4. Determine the noise power for a 20-MHz bandwidth at the input to a receiver with an input noise temperature of 290°C.

13-5. For a system gain of 120 dB, a minimum input C/N of 30 dB, and an input noise power of -115 dBm, determine the minimum transmit power (P_t).

13-6. Determine the amount of loss attributed to a reliability objective of 99.98%.

13-7. Determine the terrain sensitivity loss for a 4-GHz carrier that is propagating over a very dry, mountainous area.

13-8. A frequency-diversity microwave system operates at an RF carrier frequency of 7.4 GHz. The IF is a low-index frequency-modulated subcarrier. The baseband signal is the 1800-channel FDM system described in Chapter 11 (564 kHz to 8284 kHz). The antennas are 4.8-m-diameter parabolic dishes. The feeder lengths are 150 m at one station and 50 m at the other station. The reliability objective is 99.999%. The system propagates over an average terrain that has a very dry climate. The distance between stations is 50 km. The minimum carrier-to-noise ratio at the receiver input is 30 dB. Determine the following: fade margin, antenna gain, free-space path loss, total branching and feeder losses, receiver input noise power (C_{min}), minimum transmit power, and system gain.

13-9. Determine the overall noise figure for a receiver that has two RF amplifiers each with a noise figure of 6 dB and a gain of 10 dB, a mixer down-converter with a noise figure of 10 dB, and a conversion gain of -6 dB, and 40 dB of IF gain with a noise figure of 6 dB.

13-10. A microwave receiver has a total input noise power of -102 dBm and an overall noise figure of 4 dB. For a minimum C/N ratio of 20 dB at the input to the FM detector, determine the minimum receive carrier power.

13-11. Determine the path loss for the following frequencies and distances:

f (MHz)	D (km)
200	0.5
800	0.8
3000	5
5000	10
8000	25
18000	10

13-12. Determine the fade margin for a 30-km microwave hop. The RF frequency is 4 GHz, the terrain is water, and the reliability objective is 99.995%.

13-13. Determine the noise power for a 40-MHz bandwidth at the input to a receiver with an input temperature $T = 400°C$.

13-14. For a system gain of 114 dB, a minimum input C/N = 34 dB, and an input noise power of -111 dBm, determine the minimum transmit power (P_t).

13-15. Determine the amount of loss contributed to a reliability objective of 99.9995%.

13-16. Determine the terrain sensitivity loss for an 8-GHz carrier that is propagating over a very smooth and dry terrain.

13-17. A frequency-diversity microwave system operates at an RF = 7.4 GHz. The IF is a low-index frequency-modulated subcarrier. The baseband signal is a single mastergroup FDM system. The antennas are 2.4-m parabolic dishes. The feeder lengths are 120 m at one station and 80 m at the other station. The reliability objective is 99.995%. The system propagates over an average terrain that has a very dry climate. The distance between stations is 40 km. The minimum carrier-to-noise ratio at the receiver input is 28 dB. Determine the following: fade margin, antenna gain, free-space path loss, total branching and feeder losses, receiver input power (C_{min}), minimum transmit power, and system gain.

13-18. Determine the overall noise figure for a receiver that has two RF amplifiers each with a noise figure of 8 dB and a gain of 13 dB, a mixer down-converter with a noise figure of 6 dB, and a conversion gain of -6 dB, and 36 dB of IF gain with a noise figure of 10 dB.

13-19. A microwave receiver has a total input noise power of -108 dBm and an overall noise figure of 5 dB. For a minimum C/N ratio of 18 dB at the input to the FM detector, determine the minimum receive carrier power.

C H A P T E R 14

Satellite Communications

OBJECTIVES

- Define *satellite communications*
- Describe the history of satellite communications
- Explain Kepler's laws and how they relate to satellite communications
- Define and describe satellite orbital patterns and elevation categories
- Describe geosynchronous satellite systems and their advantages and disadvantages over other types of satellite systems
- Explain satellite look angles
- List and describe satellite classifications, spacing, and frequency allocation
- Describe the different types of satellite antenna radiation patterns
- Explain satellite system up- and downlink models
- Define and describe satellite system parameters
- Explain satellite system link equations
- Describe the significance of satellite link budgets and how they are calculated

In astronomical terms, a *satellite* is a celestial body that orbits around a planet (e.g., the moon is a satellite of Earth). In aerospace terms, however, a satellite is a space vehicle launched by humans and orbits Earth or another celestial body. Communications satellites are man-made satellites that orbit Earth, providing a multitude of communication functions to a wide variety of consumers, including military, governmental, private, and commercial subscribers.

In essence, a *communications satellite* is a microwave repeater in the sky that consists of a diverse combination of one or more of the following: receiver, transmitter, amplifier, regenerator, filter, onboard computer, multiplexer, demultiplexer, antenna, waveguide, and about any other electronic communications circuit ever developed. A satellite radio repeater is called a *transponder,* of which a satellite may have many. A *satellite system* consists of one or more satellite space vehicles, a ground-based station to control the operation of the system, and a user network of earth stations that provides the interface facilities for the transmission and reception of terrestrial communications traffic through the satellite system.

Transmissions to and from satellites are categorized as either *bus* or *payload.* The bus includes control mechanisms that support the payload operation. The payload is the actual user information conveyed through the system. Although in recent years new data services and television broadcasting are more and more in demand, the transmission of conventional speech telephone signals (in analog or digital form) is still the bulk of satellite payloads.

In the early 1960s, AT&T released studies indicating that a few powerful satellites of advanced design could handle more telephone traffic than the entire existing AT&T long-distance communications network. The cost of these satellites was estimated to be only a fraction of the cost of equivalent terrestrial microwave or underground cable facilities. Unfortunately, because AT&T was a utility and government regulations prevented them from developing the satellite systems, smaller and much less lucrative companies were left to develop the satellite systems, and AT&T continued for several more years investing billions of dollars each year in conventional terrestrial microwave and metallic cable systems. Because of this, early developments in satellite technology were slow in coming.

14-2   HISTORY OF SATELLITES

The simplest type of satellite is a *passive reflector,* which is a device that simply "bounces" signals from one place to another. A passive satellite reflects signals back to Earth, as there are no gain devices on board to amplify or modify the signals. The moon is a natural satellite of Earth, visible by reflection of sunlight and having a slightly elliptical orbit. Consequently, the moon became the first passive satellite in 1954, when the U.S. Navy successfully transmitted the first message over this Earth-to-moon-to-Earth communications system. In 1956, a relay service was established between Washington, D.C. and Hawaii and, until 1962, offered reliable long-distance radio communications service limited only by the availability of the moon. Over time, however, the moon proved to be an inconvenient and unreliable communications satellite, as it is above the horizon only half the time and its position relative to Earth is constantly changing.

An obvious advantage of passive satellites is that they do not require sophisticated electronic equipment on board, although they are not necessarily void of power. Some passive satellites require *radio beacon transmitters* for tracking and ranging purposes. A beacon is a continuously transmitted unmodulated carrier that an earth station can lock on to and use to determine the exact location of a satellite so the earth station can align its antennas. Another disadvantage of passive satellites is their inefficient use of transmitted power. For example, as little as 1 part in every 10^{18} of an earth station's transmitted power is actually returned to earth station receiving antennas.

In 1957, Russia launched *Sputnik I,* the first *active* earth satellite. An active satellite is capable of receiving, amplifying, reshaping, regenerating, and retransmitting information. *Sputnik I* transmitted telemetry information for 21 days. Later in the same year, the United States launched *Explorer I,* which transmitted telemetry information for nearly five months.

In 1958, NASA launched *Score,* a 150-pound conical-shaped satellite. With an on-board tape recording, *Score* rebroadcast President Eisenhower's 1958 Christmas message. *Score* was the first artificial satellite used for relaying terrestrial communications. *Score* was a *delayed repeater* satellite as it received transmissions from earth stations, stored them on magnetic tape, and then rebroadcast them later to ground stations farther along in its orbit.

In 1960, NASA in conjunction with Bell Telephone Laboratories and the Jet Propulsion Laboratory launched *Echo,* a 100-foot-diameter plastic balloon with an aluminum coating. *Echo* passively reflected radio signals it received from large earth station antennas. *Echo* was simple and reliable but required extremely high-power transmitters at the earth stations. The first transatlantic transmission using a satellite was accomplished using *Echo.* Also in 1960, the Department of Defense launched *Courier,* which was the first transponder-type satellite. *Courier* transmitted 3 W of power and lasted only 17 days.

In 1962, AT&T launched *Telstar I,* the first active satellite to simultaneously receive and transmit radio signals. The electronic equipment in *Telstar I* was damaged by radiation from the newly discovered Van Allen belts and, consequently, lasted for only a few weeks. *Telstar II* was successfully launched in 1963 and was electronically identical to *Telstar I* except more radiation resistant. *Telstar II* was used for telephone, television, facsimile, and data transmissions and accomplished the first successful transatlantic video transmission.

Syncom I, launched in February 1963, was the first attempt to place a geosynchronous satellite into orbit. Unfortunately, *Syncom I* was lost during orbit injection; however, *Syncom II* and *Syncom III* were successfully launched in February 1963 and August 1964, respectively. The *Syncom III* satellite was used to broadcast the 1964 Olympic Games from Tokyo. The *Syncom* satellites demonstrated the feasibility of using geosynchronous satellites.

Since the *Syncom* projects, a number of nations and private corporations have successfully launched satellites that are currently being used to provide national as well as regional and international global communications. Today, there are several hundred satellite communications systems operating in virtually every corner of the world. These companies provide worldwide, fixed common-carrier telephone and data circuits; point-to-point television broadcasting; network television distribution; music broadcasting; mobile telephone service; navigation service; and private communications networks for large corporations, government agencies, and military applications.

Intelsat I (called *Early Bird*) was the first commercial telecommunications satellite. It was launched from Cape Kennedy in 1965 and used two transponders and a 25-MHz bandwidth to simultaneously carry one television signal and 480 voice channels. Intelsat stands for *In*ternational *Tele*communications *Sat*ellite Organization. Intelsat is a commercial global satellite network that manifested in 1964 from within the United Nations. Intelsat is a consortium of over 120 nations with the commitment to provide worldwide, nondiscriminatory satellite communications using four basic service categories: international public switched telephony, broadcasting, private-line/business networks, and domestic/regional communications. Between 1966 and 1987, Intelsat launched a series of satellites designated *Intelsat II, III, IV, V,* and *VI. Intelsat VI* has a capacity of 80,000 voice channels. Intelsat's most recent satellite launches include the 500, 600, 700, and 800 series space vehicles.

The former Soviet Union launched the first set of *domestic satellites* (Domsats) in 1966 and called them *Molniya,* meaning "lightning." Domsats are satellites that are owned, operated, and used by a single country. In 1972, Canada launched its first commercial satellite designated *Anik,* which is an Inuit word meaning "little brother." Western Union launched their first Westar satellite in 1974, and Radio Corporation of America (RCA) launched its first Satcom (*Sat*ellite *Com*munications) satellites in 1975. In the United States today, a publicly owned company called *Com*munications *Sat*ellite Corporation (Comsat) regulates the use and operation of U.S. satellites and also sets their tariffs. Although a company or government may own a satellite, its utilities are generally made available to anyone willing to pay for them. The United States currently utilizes the largest share of available worldwide satellite time (24%); Great Britain is second with 13%, followed by France with 6%.

14-3 KEPLER'S LAWS

A satellite remains in orbit because the centrifugal force caused by its rotation around Earth is counterbalanced by Earth's gravitational pull. In the early seventeenth century while investigating the laws of planetary motion (i.e., motion of planets and their heavenly bodies called moons), German astronomer Johannes Kepler (1571–1630) discovered the laws that govern satellite motion. The laws of planetary motion describe the shape of the orbit, the velocities of the planet, and the distance a planet is with respect to the sun. *Kepler's laws* may be simply stated as (1) the planets move in ellipses with the sun at one focus, (2) the line joining the sun and a planet sweeps out equal areas in equal intervals of time, and (3) the square of the time of revolution of a planet divided by the cube of its mean distance from the sun gives a number that is the same for all planets. Kepler's laws can be applied to any two bodies in space that interact through gravitation. The larger of the two bodies is called the *primary*, and the smaller is called the *secondary* or *satellite*.

Kepler's first law states that a satellite will orbit a primary body (like Earth) following an elliptical path. An ellipse has two *focal points (foci)* as shown in Figure 14-1a (F_1 and F_2), and the center of mass (called the barycenter) of a two-body system is always centered on one of the foci. Because the mass of Earth is substantially greater than that of the satellite, the center of mass will always coincide with the center of Earth. The geometric properties of the ellipse are normally referenced to one of the foci which is logically selected to be the one at the center of Earth.

For the semimajor axis (α) and the semiminor axis (β) shown in Figure 14-1a, the *eccentricity* (abnormality) of the ellipse can be defined as

$$\epsilon = \frac{\sqrt{\alpha^2 - \beta^2}}{\alpha}$$
(14-1)

where ϵ is eccentricity.

Kepler's second law, enunciated with the first law in 1609, is known as the *law of areas*. Kepler's second law states that for equal intervals of time a satellite will sweep out equal areas in the orbital plane, focused at the barycenter. As shown in Figure 14-1b, for a satellite traveling distances D_1 and D_2 meters in 1 second, areas A_1 and A_2 will be equal. Because of the equal area law, distance D_1 must be greater than distance D_2, and, therefore, velocity V_1 must be greater than velocity V_2. The velocity will be greatest at the point of closest approach to Earth (known as the *perigee*), and the velocity will be least at the farthest point from Earth (known as the *apogee*). Kepler's second law is illustrated in Figure 14-1b.

Kepler's third law, announced in 1619, is sometimes known as the *harmonic law*. The third law states that the square of the periodic time of orbit is proportional to the cube of the mean distance between the primary and the satellite. This mean distance is equal to the semimajor axis; thus, Kepler's third law can be stated mathematically as

$$\alpha = AP^{2/3}$$
(14-2)

where A = constant (unitless)
α = semimajor axis (kilometers)
P = mean solar earth days

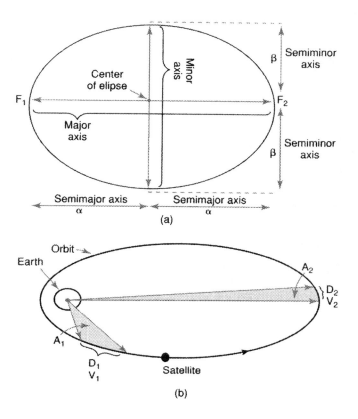

FIGURE 14-1 [a] Focal points F_1 and F_2, semimajor axis a, and semiminor axis b of an ellipse; [b] Kepler's second law

and P is the ratio of the time of one sidereal day (t_s = 23 hours and 56 minutes) to the time of one revolution of Earth on its own axis (t_e = 24 hours).

thus,

$$P = \frac{t_s}{t_e}$$

$$= \frac{1436 \text{ minutes}}{1440 \text{ minutes}}$$

$$= 0.9972$$

Rearranging Equation 14-2 and solving the constant A for earth yields

$$A = 42241.0979$$

Equations 14-1 and 14-2 apply for the ideal case when a satellite is orbiting around a perfectly spherical body with no outside forces. In actuality, Earth's equatorial bulge and external disturbing forces result in deviations in the satellite's ideal motion. Fortunately, however, the major deviations can be calculated and compensated for. Satellites orbiting close to Earth will be affected by atmospheric drag and by Earth's magnetic field. For more distant satellites, however, the primary disturbing forces are from the gravitational fields of the sun and moon.

Most of the satellites mentioned thus far are called *orbital* satellites, which are *nonsynchronous*. Nonsynchronous satellites rotate around Earth in an elliptical or circular pattern as shown in Figure 14-2a and b. In a circular orbit, the speed or rotation is constant; however, in elliptical orbits the speed depends on the height the satellite is above Earth. The speed of the satellite is greater when it is close to Earth than when it is farther away.

If the satellite is orbiting in the same direction as Earth's rotation (counterclockwise) and at an angular velocity greater than that of Earth ($\omega_s > \omega_e$), the orbit is called a *prograde* or *posigrade* orbit. If the satellite is orbiting in the opposite direction as Earth's rotation or in the same direction with an angular velocity less than that of Earth ($\omega_s < \omega_e$), the orbit is called a *retrograde* orbit. Most nonsynchronous satellites revolve around Earth in a prograde orbit. Therefore, the position of satellites in nonsynchronous orbits is continuously changing in respect to a fixed position on Earth. Consequently, nonsynchronous satellites have to be used when available, which may be as little as 15 minutes per orbit. Another disadvantage of orbital satellites is the need for complicated and expensive tracking equipment at the earth stations so they can locate the satellite as it comes into view on each orbit and then lock its antenna onto the satellite and track it as it passes overhead. A major advantage of orbital satellites, however, is that propulsion rockets are not required on board the satellites to keep them in their respective orbits.

14-4-1 Satellite Elevation Categories

Satellites are generally classified as having either a *low earth orbit* (LEO), *medium earth orbit* (MEO), or *geosynchronous earth orbit* (GEO). Most LEO satellites operate in the 1.0-GHz to 2.5-GHz frequency range. Motorola's satellite-based mobile-telephone system, *Iridium*,

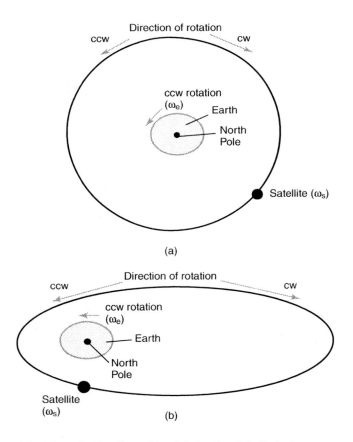

FIGURE 14-2 Satellite orbits: [a] circular; [b] elliptical

is a LEO system utilizing a 66-satellite constellation orbiting approximately 480 miles above Earth's surface. The main advantage of LEO satellites is that the path loss between earth stations and space vehicles is much lower than for satellites revolving in medium- or high-altitude orbits. Less path loss equates to lower transmit powers, smaller antennas, and less weight.

MEO satellites operate in the 1.2-GHz to 1.66-GHz frequency band and orbit between 6000 miles and 12,000 miles above Earth. The Department of Defense's satellite-based global positioning system, *NAVSTAR,* is a MEO system with a constellation of 21 working satellites and six spares orbiting approximately 9500 miles above Earth.

Geosynchronous satellites are high-altitude earth-orbit satellites operating primarily in the 2-GHz to 18-GHz frequency spectrum with orbits 22,300 miles above Earth's surface. Most commercial communications satellites are in geosynchronous orbit. Geosynchronous or *geostationary* satellites are those that orbit in a circular pattern with an angular velocity equal to that of Earth. Geostationary satellites have an orbital time of approximately 24 hours, the same as Earth; thus, geosynchronous satellites appear to be stationary, as they remain in a fixed position in respect to a given point on Earth.

Satellites in high-elevation, nonsynchronous circular orbits between 19,000 miles and 25,000 miles above Earth are said to be in *near-synchronous* orbit. When the near-synchronous orbit is slightly lower than 22,300 miles above Earth, the satellite's orbital time is lower than Earth's rotational period. Therefore, the satellite is moving slowly around Earth in a west-to-east direction. This type of near-synchronous orbit is called *sub-synchronous.* If the orbit is higher than 22,300 miles above Earth, the satellite's orbital time is longer than Earth's rotational period, and the satellite will appear to have a reverse (retrograde) motion from east to west.

14-4-2 Satellite Orbital Patterns

Before examining satellite orbital paths, a basic understanding of some terms used to describe orbits is necessary. For the following definitions, refer to Figure 14-3:

Apogee. The point in an orbit that is located farthest from Earth

Perigee. The point in an orbit that is located closest to Earth

Major axis. The line joining the perigee and apogee through the center of Earth; sometimes called *line of apsides*

Minor axis. The line perpendicular to the major axis and halfway between the perigee and apogee (Half the distance of the minor axis is called the semiminor axis.)

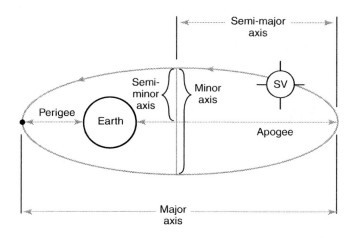

FIGURE 14-3 Satellite orbital terms

Although there is an infinite number of orbital paths, only three are useful for communications satellites. Figure 14-4 shows three paths that a satellite can follow as it rotates around Earth: inclined, equatorial, or polar. All satellites rotate around Earth in an orbit that forms a plane that passes through the center of gravity of Earth called the *geocenter*.

Inclined orbits are virtually all orbits except those that travel directly above the equator or directly over the North and South Poles. Figure 14-5a shows the *angle of inclination* of a satellite orbit. The angle of inclination is the angle between the Earth's equatorial plane and the

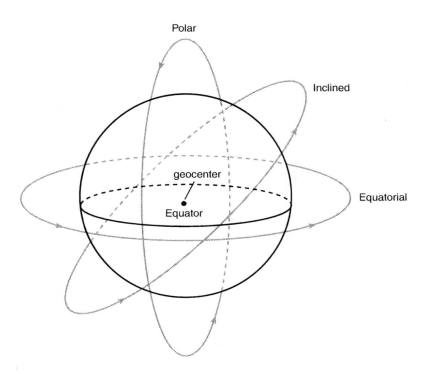

FIGURE 14-4   Satellite orbital patterns

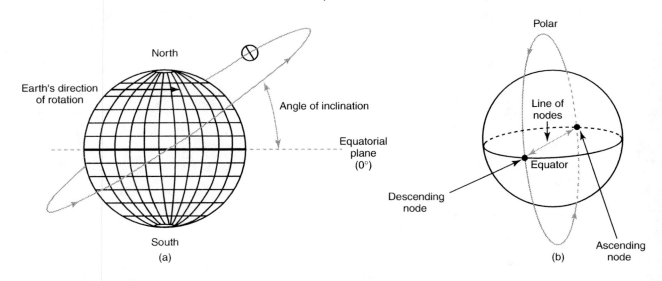

FIGURE 14-5   [a] Angle of inclination; [b] ascending node, descending node, and line of nodes

orbital plane of a satellite measured counterclockwise at the point in the orbit where it crosses the equatorial plane traveling from south to north. This point is called the *ascending node* and is shown in Figure 14-5b. The point where a polar or inclined orbit crosses the equatorial plane traveling from north to south is called the *descending node,* and the line joining the ascending and descending nodes through the center of Earth is called the *line of nodes.* Angles of inclination vary between 0° and 180°. To provide coverage to regions of high latitudes, inclined orbits are generally elliptical. Kepler's second law shows that the angular velocity of the satellite is slowest at its apogee. Therefore, the satellite remains visible for a longer period of time to the higher latitude regions if the apogee is placed above the high-latitude region.

An *equatorial orbit* is when the satellite rotates in an orbit directly above the equator, usually in a circular path. With an equatorial orbit, the angle of inclination is 0°, and there are no ascending or descending nodes and, hence, no line of nodes. All geosynchronous satellites are in equatorial orbits.

A *polar orbit* is when the satellite rotates in a path that takes it over the North and South Poles in an orbit perpendicular to the equatorial plane. Polar orbiting satellites follow a low-altitude path that is close to Earth and passes over and very close to both the North and South Poles. The angle of inclination of a satellite in a polar orbit is nearly 90°. It is interesting to note that 100% of Earth's surface can be covered with a single satellite in a polar orbit. Satellites in polar orbits rotate around Earth in a longitudinal orbit while Earth is rotating on its axis in a latitudinal rotation. Consequently, the satellite's radiation pattern is a diagonal line that forms a spiral around the surface of Earth that resembles a barber pole. As a result, every location on Earth lies within the radiation pattern of a satellite in a polar orbit twice each day.

Earth is not a perfect sphere, as it bulges at the equator. In fact, until the early 1800s, a 20,700-foot mountain in Ecuador called Volcan Chimborazo was erroneously thought to be the highest point on the planet. However, because of equatorial bulge, Volcan Chimborazo proved to be the farthest point from the center of the Earth. An important effect of the Earth's equatorial bulge is causing elliptical orbits to rotate in a manner that causes the apogee and perigee to move around the Earth. This phenomena is called *rotation of the line of apsides;* however, for an angle of inclination of 63.4°, the rotation of the line of apsides is zero. Thus, satellites required to have an apogee over a particular location are launched into orbit with an angle of inclination of 63.4°, which is referred to as the 63° slot.

One of the more interesting orbital satellite systems currently in use is the Commonwealth of Independent States (CIS) *Molniya* system of satellites, which is shown in Figure 14-6. The CIS is the former Soviet Union. Molniya can also be spelled *Molnya* and *Molnia,* which means "lightning" in Russian (in colloquial Russian, *Molniya* means "news flash"). *Molniya* satellites are used for government communications, telephone, television, and video.

The *Molniya* series of satellites use highly inclined elliptical orbits to provide service to the more northerly regions where antennas would have to be aimed too close to the horizon to detect signals from geostationary space vehicles rotating in an equatorial orbit. *Molniya* satellites have an apogee at about 40,000 km and a perigee at about 400 km. The apogee is reached while over the Northern Hemisphere and the perigee while over the Southern Hemisphere. The size of the ellipse was chosen to make its period exactly one-half a *sidereal day.* One sidereal day is the time it takes Earth to rotate back to the same constellation. The sidereal day for Earth is 23 hours and 56 minutes, slightly less than the time required for Earth to make one complete rotation around its own axis—24 hours. A sidereal day is sometimes called the *period* or *sidereal period.*

Because of its unique orbital pattern, the *Molniya* satellite is synchronous with the rotation of Earth. During a satellite's 12-hour orbit, it spends about 11 hours over the Northern Hemisphere. Three or more space vehicles follow each other in this orbit and *pass off* communications to each other so that continuous communications is possible while minimal earth station antenna tracking is necessary. Satellites with orbital patterns like *Molniya* are sometimes classified as having a highly elliptical orbit (HEO).

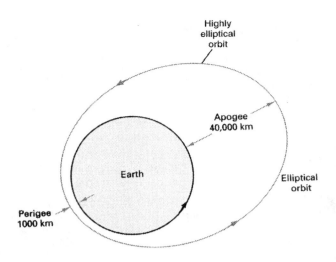

FIGURE 14-6   Soviet *Molniya* satellite orbit

14-5   GEOSYNCHRONOUS SATELLITES

As stated, geosynchronous satellites orbit Earth above the equator with the same angular velocity as Earth. Hence, geosynchronous (sometimes called *stationary* or *geostationary*) satellites appear to remain in a fixed location above one spot on Earth's surface. Since a geosynchronous satellite appears to remain in a fixed location, no special antenna tracking equipment is necessary—earth station antennas are simply pointed at the satellite. A single high-altitude geosynchronous satellite can provide reliable communications to approximately 40% of the earth's surface.

Satellites remain in orbit as a result of a balance between centrifugal and gravitational forces. If a satellite is traveling at too high a velocity, its centrifugal force will overcome Earth's gravitational pull, and the satellite will break out of orbit and escape into space. At lower velocities, the satellite's centrifugal force is insufficient, and gravity tends to pull the vehicle toward Earth. Obviously, there is a delicate balance between acceleration, speed, and distance that will exactly balance the effects of centrifugal and gravitational forces.

The closer to Earth a satellite rotates, the greater the gravitational pull and the greater the velocity required to keep it from being pulled to Earth. Low-altitude satellites orbiting 100 miles above Earth travel at approximately 17,500 mph. At this speed, it takes approximately 1.5 hours to rotate around Earth. Consequently, the time that a satellite is in line of sight of a particular earth station is 0.25 hour or less per orbit. Medium-altitude Earth-orbit satellites have a rotation period of between 5 and 12 hours and remain in line of sight of a particular earth station for between 2 and 4 hours per orbit. High-altitude earth-orbit satellites in geosynchronous orbits travel at approximately 6840 mph and complete one revolution of Earth in approximately 24 hours.

Geosynchronous orbits are circular; therefore, the speed of rotation is constant throughout the orbit. There is only one geosynchronous earth orbit; however, it is occupied by a large number of satellites. In fact, the geosynchronous orbit is the most widely used earth orbit for the obvious reason that satellites in a geosynchronous orbit remain in a fixed position relative to Earth and, therefore, do not have to be tracked by earth station antennas.

Ideally, geosynchronous satellites should remain stationary above a chosen location over the equator in an equatorial orbit; however, the sun and the moon exert gravitational forces, solar winds sweep past Earth, and Earth is not perfectly spherical. Therefore, these unbalanced forces cause geosynchronous satellites to drift slowly away from their assigned locations in a figure-eight excursion with a 24-hour period that follows a wandering path slightly above and below the equatorial plane. In essence, it occurs in a special type of inclined orbit sometimes called a *stationary inclined orbit*. Ground controllers must periodically adjust satellite positions to counteract these forces. If not, the excursion above and below the equator would build up at a rate of between 0.6° and 0.9° per year. In addition, geosynchronous satellites in an elliptical orbit also rift in an east or west direction as viewed from Earth. The process of maneuvering a satellite within a preassigned window is called *station keeping*.

There are several requirements for satellites in geostationary orbits. The first and most obvious is that geosynchronous satellites must have a 0° angle of inclination (i.e., the satellite vehicle must be orbiting directly above Earth's equatorial plane). The satellite must also be orbiting in the same direction as Earth's rotation (eastward—toward the morning sun) with the same angular (rotational) velocity—one revolution per day.

The semimajor axis of a geosynchronous earth orbit is the distance from a satellite revolving in the geosynchronous orbit to the center of Earth (i.e., the radius of the orbit measured from Earth's geocenter to the satellite vehicle). Using Kepler's third law as stated in Equation 14-2 with $A = 42241.0979$ and $P = 0.9972$, the semimajor axis α is

$$\alpha = AP^{2/3}$$

$$= (42241.0979)(0.9972)^{2/3}$$

$$= 42{,}164 \text{ km} \tag{14-3}$$

Hence, geosynchronous earth-orbit satellites revolve around Earth in a circular pattern directly above the equator 42,164 km from the center of Earth. Because Earth's equatorial radius is approximately 6378 km, the height above mean sea level (h) of a satellite in a geosynchronous orbit around Earth is

$$h = 42{,}164 \text{ km} - 6378 \text{ km}$$

$$= 35{,}786 \text{ km}$$

or approximately 22,300 miles above Earth's surface.

14-5-1 Geosynchronous Satellite Orbital Velocity
The circumference (C) of a geosynchronous orbit is

$$C = 2\pi(42{,}164 \text{ km})$$

$$= 264{,}790 \text{ km}$$

Therefore, the velocity (v) of a geosynchronous satellite is

$$v = \frac{264{,}790 \text{ km}}{24 \text{ hr}}$$

$$= 11{,}033 \text{ km/hr}$$

or $\qquad\qquad v \approx 6840 \text{ mph}$

14-5-2 Round-Trip Time Delay of Geosynchronous Satellites
The round-trip propagation delay between a satellite and an earth station located directly below it is

$$t = \frac{d}{c}$$

$$= \frac{2(35{,}768 \text{ km})}{3 \times 10^5 \text{ km/s}}$$

$$= 238 \text{ ms}$$

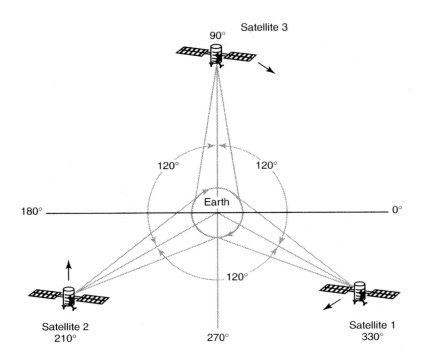

FIGURE 14-7   Three geosynchronous satellites in Clarke orbits

Including the time delay within the earth station and satellite equipment, it takes more than a quarter of a second for an electromagnetic wave to travel from an earth station to a satellite and back when the earth station is located at a point on Earth directly below the satellite. For earth stations located at more distant locations, the propagation delay is even more substantial and can be significant with two-way telephone conversations or data transmissions.

14-5-3   Clarke Orbit

A geosynchronous earth orbit is sometimes referred to as the *Clarke orbit* or *Clarke belt,* after Arthur C. Clarke, who first suggested its existence in 1945 and proposed its use for communications satellites. Clarke was an engineer, a scientist, and a science fiction author who wrote several books including *2001: A Space Odyssey.* The Clarke orbit meets the concise set of specifications for geosynchronous satellite orbits: (1) be located directly above the equator, (2) travel in the same direction as Earth's rotation at 6840 mph, (3) have an altitude of 22,300 miles above Earth, and (4) complete one revolution in 24 hours. As shown in Figure 14-7, three satellites in Clarke orbits separated by 120° in longitude can provide communications over the entire globe except the polar regions.

An international agreement initially mandated that all satellites placed in the Clarke orbit must be separated by at least 1833 miles. This stipulation equates to an angular separation of 4° or more, which limits the number of satellite vehicles in a geosynchronous earth orbit to less than 100. Today, however, international agreements allow satellites to be placed much closer together. Figure 14-8 shows the locations of several satellites in geosynchronous orbit around Earth.

14-5-4   Advantages and Disadvantages of Geosynchronous Satellites

The advantages of geosynchronous satellites are as follows:

1. Geosynchronous satellites remain almost stationary in respect to a given earth station. Consequently, expensive tracking equipment is not required at the earth stations.

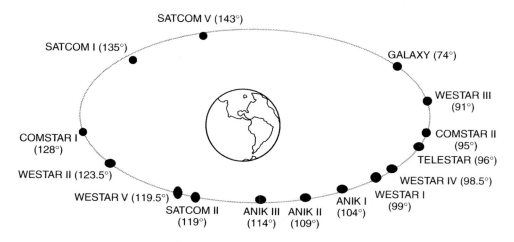

FIGURE 14-8 Satellites in geosynchronous earth orbits

2. Geosynchronous satellites are available to all earth stations within their *shadow* 100% of the time. The shadow of a satellite includes all the earth stations that have a line-of-sight path to it and lie within the radiation pattern of the satellite's antennas.

3. There is no need to switch from one geosynchronous satellite to another as they orbit overhead. Consequently, there are no transmission breaks due to switching times.

4. The effects of Doppler shift are negligible.

The disadvantages of geosynchronous satellites are as follows:

1. Geosynchronous satellites require sophisticated and heavy propulsion devices onboard to keep them in a fixed orbit.

2. High-altitude geosynchronous satellites introduce much longer propagation delays. The round-trip propagation delay between two earth stations through a geosynchronous satellite is between 500 ms and 600 ms.

3. Geosynchronous satellites require higher transmit powers and more sensitive receivers because of the longer distances and greater path losses.

4. High-precision spacemanship is required to place a geosynchronous satellite into orbit and to keep it there.

14-6 ANTENNA LOOK ANGLES

To optimize the performance of a satellite communications system, the direction of maximum gain of an earth station antenna (sometimes referred to as the *boresight*) must be pointed directly at the satellite. To ensure that the earth station antenna is aligned, two angles must be determined: the *azimuth* and the *elevation angle*. Azimuth angle and elevation angle are jointly referred to as the antenna *look angles*. With geosynchronous satellites, the look angles of earth station antennas need to be adjusted only once, as the satellite will remain in a given position permanently, except for occasional minor variations.

The location of a satellite is generally specified in terms of latitude and longitude similar to the way the location of a point on Earth is described; however, because a satellite is orbiting many miles above the Earth's surface, it has no latitude or longitude. Therefore, its location is identified by a point on the surface of earth directly below the satellite. This point is called the *subsatellite point* (SSP), and for geosynchronous satellites the SSP must fall on the equator. Subsatellite points and earth station locations are specified using standard

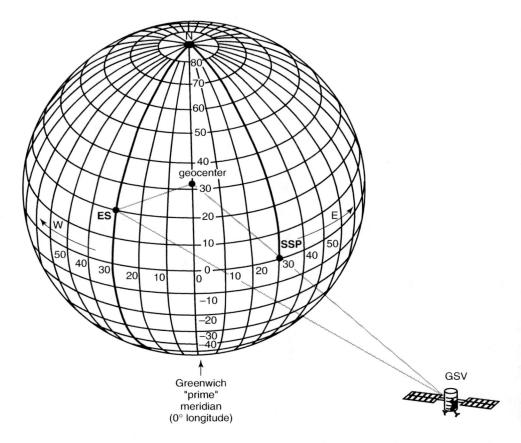

FIGURE 14-9 Geosynchronous satellite position, subsatellite point, and Earth longitude and latitude coordinate system

latitude and longitude coordinates. The standard convention specifies angles of longitude between 0° and 180° either east or west of the Greenwich prime meridian. Latitudes in the Northern Hemisphere are angles between 0° and 90°N and latitudes in the Southern Hemisphere are angles between 0° and 90°S. Since geosynchronous satellites are located directly above the equator, they all have a 0° latitude. Hence, geosynchronous satellite locations are normally given in degrees longitude east or west of the Greenwich meridian (for example, 122°W or 78°E). Figure 14-9 shows the position of a hypothetical geosynchronous satellite vehicle (GSV), its respective subsatellite point (SSP), and an arbitrarily selected earth station (ES) all relative to Earth's geocenter. The SSP for the satellite shown in the figure is 30°E longitude and 0° latitude. The earth station has a location of 30°W longitude and 20°N latitude.

14-6-1 Angle of Elevation

Angle of elevation (sometimes called *elevation angle*) is the vertical angle formed between the direction of travel of an electromagnetic wave radiated from an earth station antenna pointing directly toward a satellite and the horizontal plane. The smaller the angle of elevation, the greater the distance a propagated wave must pass through Earth's atmosphere. As with any wave propagated through Earth's atmosphere, it suffers absorption and may also be severely contaminated by noise. Consequently, if the angle of elevation is too small and the distance the wave travels through Earth's atmosphere is too long, the wave may

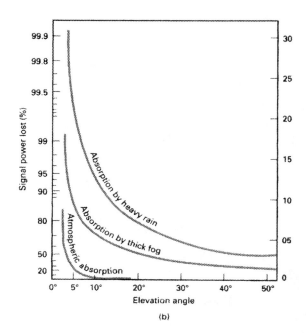

FIGURE 14-10   Attenuation due to atmospheric absorption: [a] 6/4-GHz band;
[b] 14/12-GHz band

deteriorate to the extent that it no longer provides acceptable transmission quality. Generally, 5° is considered as the minimum acceptable angle of elevation. Figure 14-10 shows how the angle of elevation affects the signal strength of a propagated electromagnetic wave due to normal atmospheric absorption, absorption due to thick fog, and absorption due to heavy rainfall. It can be seen that the 14/12-GHz band shown in Figure 14-10b is more severely affected than the 6/4-GHz band shown in Figure 14-10a because of the smaller wavelengths associated with the higher frequencies. The figure also shows that at elevation angles less than 5°, the amount of signal power lost increases significantly. Figure 14-10b illustrates angle of elevation of an earth station antenna with respect to a horizontal plane.

14-6-2   Azimuth Angle

Azimuth is the horizontal angular distance from a reference direction, either the southern or northern most point of the horizon. *Azimuth angle* is defined as the horizontal pointing angle of an earth station antenna. For navigation purposes, azimuth angle is usually measured in a clockwise direction in degrees from true north. However, for satellite earth stations in the Northern Hemisphere and satellite vehicles in geosynchronous orbits, azimuth angle is generally referenced to true south (i.e., 180°). Figure 14-11a illustrates the azimuth angle referenced to due north (0°) and due south (180°), and Figure 14-11c shows elevation angle and azimuth of an earth station antenna relative to a satellite.

Angle of elevation and azimuth angle both depend on the latitude of the earth station and the longitude of both the earth station and the orbiting satellite. For a geosynchronous satellite in an equatorial orbit, the procedure for determining angle of elevation and azimuth is as follows: From a good map, determine the longitude and latitude of the earth station.

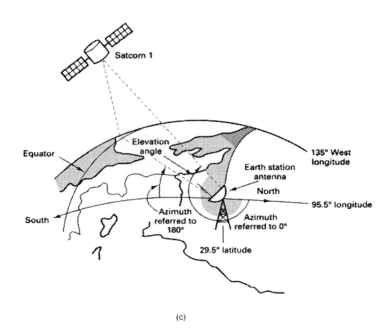

FIGURE 14-11   Azimuth and angle of elevation, "lookangles"

From Table 14-1, determine the longitude of the satellite of interest. Calculate the difference, in degrees (ΔL), between the longitude of the satellite and the longitude of the earth station. Then from Figure 14-12 determine the azimuth angle, and from Figure 14-13 determine the elevation angle. Figures 14-12 and 14-13 are for geosynchronous satellites in equatorial orbits.

Example 14-1

An earth station is located in Houston, Texas, which has a longitude of 95.5°W and a latitude of 29.5°N. The satellite of interest is RCA's *Satcom 1*, which has a longitude of 135°W. Determine the azimuth angle and elevation angle for the earth station.

Solution   First determine the difference between the longitude of the earth station and the satellite vehicle:

$$\Delta L = 135° - 95.5°$$
$$= 39.5°$$

Table 14-1 Longitudinal Position of Several Current Synchronous Satellites Parked in an Equatorial Arc[a]

Satellite	Longitude (°W)
Satcom I	135
Satcom II	119
Satcom V	143
Satcom C1	137
Satcom C3	131
Anik 1	104
Anik 2	109
Anik 3	114
Anik C1	109.25
Anik C2	109.15
Anik C3	114.9
Anik E1	111.1
Anik E2	107.3
Westar I	99
Westar II	123.5
Westar III	91
Westar IV	98.5
Westar V	119.5
Mexico	116.5
Galaxy III	93.5
Galaxy IV	99
Galaxy V	125
Galaxy VI	74
Telstar	96
Comstar I	128
Comstar II	95
Comstar D2	76.6
Comstar D4	75.4
Intelsat 501	268.5
Intelsat 601	27.5
Intelsat 701	186

[a]0° latitude.

Locate the intersection of ΔL and the earth station's latitude on Figure 14-12. From the figure, the azimuth angle is approximately 59° west of south (i.e., west of 180°). On Figure 14-13, locate the intersection of ΔL and the earth station's latitude. The angle of elevation is approximately 35°.

14-6-3 Limits of Visibility

For an earth station in any given location, the Earth's curvature establishes the *limits of visibility* (i.e., *line-of-sight limits*), which determine the farthest satellite away that can be seen looking east or west of the earth station's longitude. Theoretically, the maximum line-of-sight distance is achieved when the earth station's antenna is pointing along the horizontal (zero elevation angle) plane. In practice, however, the noise picked up from Earth and the signal attenuation from Earth's atmosphere at zero elevation angle is excessive. Therefore, an elevation angle of 5° is generally accepted as being the minimum usable elevation angle. The limits of visibility depend in part on the antenna's elevation and the earth station's longitude and latitude.

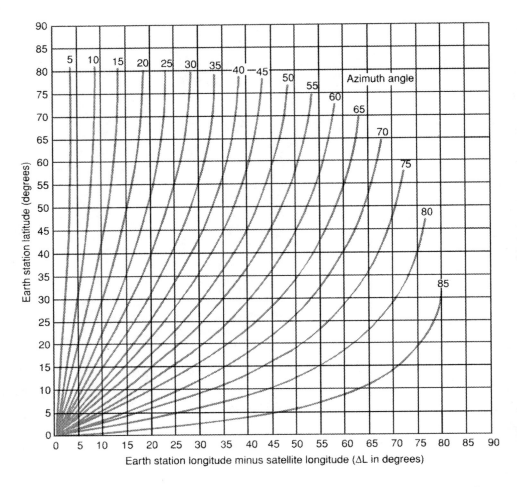

FIGURE 14-12 Azimuth angles for earth stations located in the northern hemisphere referenced to 180 degrees

14-7 SATELLITE CLASSIFICATIONS, SPACING, AND FREQUENCY ALLOCATION

The two primary classifications for communications satellites are *spinners* and *three-axis stabilizer satellites.* A spinner satellite uses the angular momentum of its spinning body to provide roll and yaw stabilization. With a three-axis stabilizer, the body remains fixed relative to Earth's surface, while an internal subsystem provides roll and yaw stabilization. Figure 14-14 shows the two main classifications of communications satellites.

Geosynchronous satellites must share a limited space and frequency spectrum within a given arc of a geostationary orbit. Each communications satellite is assigned a longitude in the geostationary arc approximately 22,300 miles above the equator. The position in the slot depends on the communications frequency band used. Satellites operating at or near the same frequency must be sufficiently separated in space to avoid interfering with each other (Figure 14-15). There is a realistic limit to the number of satellite structures that can be

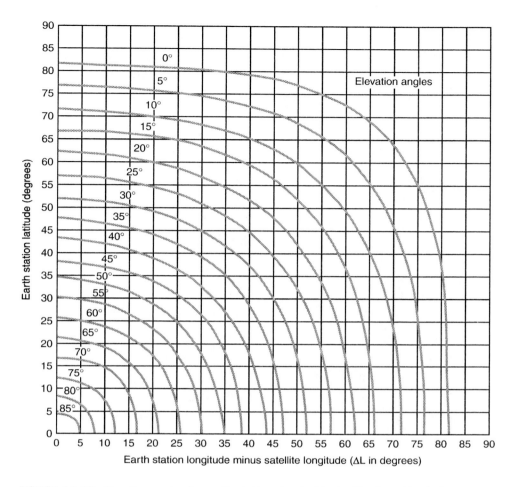

FIGURE 14-13　Elevation angles for earth stations located in the Northern Hemisphere

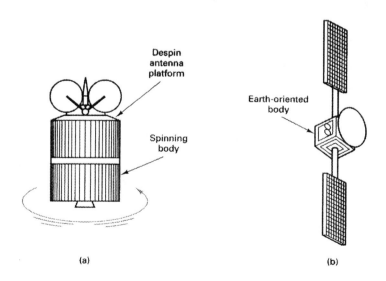

FIGURE 14-14　Satellite classes: [a] spinner; [b] three-axis stabilizer

FIGURE 14-15 Spatial separation of satellites in geosynchronous orbit

stationed (*parked*) within a given area in space. The required *spatial separation* is dependent on the following variables:

1. Beamwidths and side lobe radiation of both the earth station and satellite antennas
2. RF carrier frequency
3. Encoding or modulation technique used
4. Acceptable limits of interference
5. Transmit carrier power

Generally, 1° to 4° of spatial separation is required, depending on the variables stated previously.

The most common carrier frequencies used for satellite communications are the 6/4-GHz and 14/12-GHz bands. The first number is the uplink (earth station-to-transponder) frequency, and the second number is the downlink (transponder-to-earth station) frequency. Different uplink and downlink frequencies are used to prevent ringaround from occurring (Chapter 24). The higher the carrier frequency, the smaller the diameter required of an antenna for a given gain. Most domestic satellites use the 6/4-GHz band. Unfortunately, this band is also used extensively for terrestrial microwave systems. Care must be taken when designing a satellite network to avoid interference from or with established microwave links.

Certain positions in the geosynchronous orbit are in higher demand than the others. For example, the mid-Atlantic position, which is used to interconnect North America and Europe, is in exceptionally high demand; the mid-Pacific position is another.

The frequencies allocated by the World Administrative Radio Conference (WARC) are summarized in Figure 14-16. Table 14-2 shows the bandwidths available for various services in the United States. These services include *fixed point* (between earth stations located at fixed geographical points on Earth), *broadcast* (wide-area coverage), *mobile* (ground-to-aircraft, ships, or land vehicles), and *intersatellite* (satellite-to-satellite cross-links).

↑ Up-link   ↓ Down-link   → Cross-link

FIGURE 14-16   WARC satellite frequency assignments

Table 14-2   Satellite Bandwidths Available in the United States

	Frequency Band (GHz)			
Band	Uplink	Cross-Link	Downlink	Bandwidth (MHz)
C	5.9–6.4		3.7–4.2	500
X	7.9–8.4		7.25–7.75	500
Ku	14–14.5		11.7–12.2	500
Ka	27–30		17–20	—
	30–31		20–21	—
Q	—		40–41	1000
	—		41–43	2000
V	50–51		—	1000
(ISL)		54–58		3900
		59–64		5000

14-8   SATELLITE ANTENNA RADIATION PATTERNS: FOOTPRINTS

The area on Earth covered by a satellite depends on the location of the satellite in its orbit, its carrier frequency, and the gain of its antenna. Satellite engineers select the antenna and carrier frequency for a particular spacecraft to concentrate the limited transmitted power on a specific area of Earth's surface. The geographical representation of a satellite antenna's radiation pattern is called a *footprint* or sometimes a *footprint map*. In essence, a footprint of a satellite is the area on Earth's surface that the satellite can receive from or transmit to.

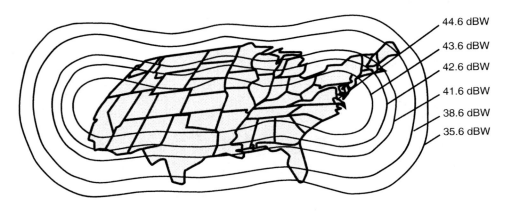

FIGURE 14-17   Satellite antenna radiation patterns (footprints)

The shape of a satellite's footprint depends on the satellite orbital path, height, and the type of antenna used. The higher the satellite, the more of the Earth's surface it can cover. A typical satellite footprint is shown in Figure 14-17. The contour lines represent limits of equal receive power density.

Downlink satellite antennas broadcast microwave-frequency signals to a selected geographic region within view (line of sight) of the spacecraft. The effective power transmitted is called *effective isotropic radiated power* (EIRP) and is generally expressed in dBm or dBW. A footprint map is constructed by drawing continuous lines between all points on a map with equal EIRPs. A distinctive footprint map is essentially a series of contour lines superimposed on a geographical map of the region served. A different footprint could exist for each beam from each communications satellite.

The pattern of the contour lines and power levels of a footprint are determined by precise details of the downlink antenna design as well as by the level of microwave power generated by each onboard channel. Although each transponder is a physically separate electronic circuit, signals from multiple transponders are typically downlinked through the same antenna. As might be expected, receive power levels are higher in areas targeted by the downlink antenna boresight and weaker in off-target areas. A receive antenna dish near the edge of a satellite coverage area must be larger than those located at or near the center of the footprint map. Extremely large-diameter earth station antennas are necessary for reception of satellite broadcasts in geographic areas located great distances from the downlink antenna boresight.

Characteristically, there are variations in footprint maps among satellites. For example, European Ku-band spacecraft generally have footprint radiation patterns that are circularly symmetric with power levels that decrease linearly in areas removed progressively further from the center of the satellite's boresight. American C-band satellites typically have relatively flat power levels over the region of coverage with fairly sharp drop-offs in power beyond the edges. Recently launched satellites such as the American DBS-1 (direct-broadcast satellites) have employed more sophisticated beam-shaping downlink antennas that permit designers to shape footprints to reach only specified targeted areas, hence not wasting power in nontargeted areas.

It is possible to design satellite downlink antennas that can broadcast microwave signals to cover areas on Earth ranging in size from extremely small cities to as much as 42% of the Earth's surface. The size, shape, and orientation of a satellite downlink antenna and the power generated by each transponder determine geographic coverage and EIRPs. Radiation patterns from a satellite antenna are generally categorized as either *spot, zonal, hemispherical,* or *earth* (global). The radiation patterns are shown in Figure 14-18.

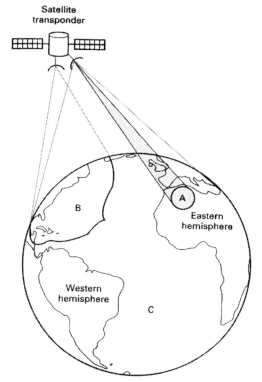

FIGURE 14-18   Beams: [a] spot;
[b] zonal; [c] earth

14-8-1   Spot and Zonal Beams

The smallest beams are *spot beams* followed by *zonal beams*. Spot beams concentrate their power to very small geographical areas and, therefore, typically have proportionately higher EIRPs than those targeting much larger areas because a given output power can be more concentrated. Spot and zonal beams blanket less than 10% of the Earth's surface. The higher the downlink frequency, the more easily a beam can be focused into a smaller spot pattern. For example, the new breed of high-power Ku-band satellites can have multiple spot beams that relay the same frequencies by transmitting different signals to areas within a given country. In general, most Ku-band footprints do not blanket entire continental areas and have a more limited geographic coverage than their C-band counterparts. Therefore, a more detailed knowledge of the local EIRP is important when attempting to receive broadcasts from Ku-band satellite transmissions.

14-8-2   Hemispherical Beams

Hemispherical downlink antennas typically target up to 20% of the Earth's surface and, therefore, have EIRPs that are 3 dB or 50% lower than those transmitted by spot beams that typically cover only 10% of the Earth's surface.

14-8-3   Earth [Global] Beams

The radiation patterns of *earth coverage* antennas have a beamwidth of approximately 17° and are capable of covering approximately 42% of Earth's surface, which is the maximum view of any one geosynchronous satellite. Power levels are considerably lower with earth beams than with spot, zonal, or hemispherical beams, and large receive dishes are necessary to adequately detect video, audio, and data broadcasts.

14-8-4 Reuse

When an allocated frequency band is filled, additional capacity can be achieved by *reuse* of the frequency spectrum. By increasing the size of an antenna (i.e., increasing the antenna gain), the beamwidth of the antenna is also reduced. Thus, different beams of the same frequency can be directed to different geographical areas of Earth. This is called *frequency reuse*. Another method of frequency reuse is to use *dual polarization*. Different information signals can be transmitted to different earth station receivers using the same band of frequencies simply by orienting their electromagnetic polarizations in an orthogonal manner (90° out of phase). Dual polarization is less effective because Earth's atmosphere has a tendency to reorient or repolarize an electromagnetic wave as it passes through. Reuse is simply another way to increase the capacity of a limited bandwidth.

14-9 SATELLITE SYSTEM LINK MODELS

Essentially, a satellite system consists of three basic sections: an uplink, a satellite transponder, and a downlink.

14-9-1 Uplink Model

The primary component within the *uplink* section of a satellite system is the earth station transmitter. A typical earth station transmitter consists of an IF modulator, an IF-to-RF microwave up-converter, a high-power amplifier (HPA), and some means of bandlimiting the final output spectrum (i.e., an output bandpass filter). Figure 14-19 shows the block diagram of a satellite earth station transmitter. The IF modulator converts the input baseband signals to either an FM-, a PSK-, or a QAM-modulated intermediate frequency. The up-converter (mixer and bandpass filter) converts the IF to an appropriate RF carrier frequency. The HPA provides adequate gain and output power to propagate the signal to the satellite transponder. HPAs commonly used are klystons and traveling-wave tubes.

14-9-2 Transponder

A typical *satellite transponder* consists of an input bandlimiting device (BPF), an input *low-noise amplifier* (LNA), a *frequency translator,* a low-level power amplifier, and an output bandpass filter. Figure 14-20 shows a simplified block diagram of a satellite transponder. This transponder is an RF-to-RF repeater. Other transponder configurations are IF and baseband repeaters similar to those used in microwave repeaters. In Figure 14-20,

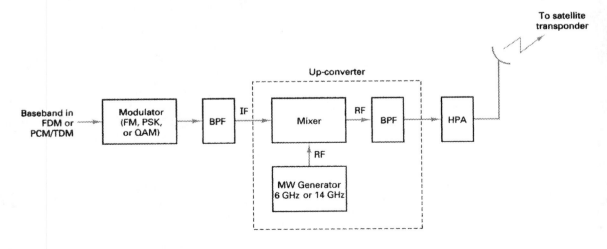

FIGURE 14-19 Satellite uplink model

FIGURE 14-20   Satellite transponder

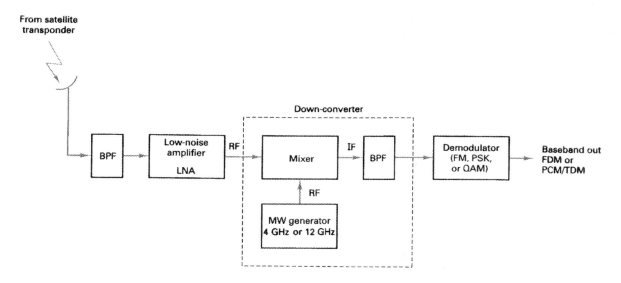

FIGURE 14-21   Satellite downlink model

the input BPF limits the total noise applied to the input of the LNA. (A common device used as an LNA is a tunnel diode.) The output of the LNA is fed to a frequency translator (a shift oscillator and a BPF), which converts the high-band uplink frequency to the low-band downlink frequency. The low-level power amplifier, which is commonly a traveling-wave tube, amplifies the RF signal for transmission through the downlink to earth station receivers. Each RF satellite channel requires a separate transponder.

14-9-3   Downlink Model

An earth station receiver includes an input BPF, an LNA, and an RF-to-IF down-converter. Figure 14-21 shows a block diagram of a typical earth station receiver. Again, the BPF limits the input noise power to the LNA. The LNA is a highly sensitive, low-noise device, such as a tunnel diode amplifier or a parametric amplifier. The RF-to-IF down-converter is a mixer/bandpass filter combination that converts the received RF signal to an IF frequency.

FIGURE 14-22   Intersatellite link

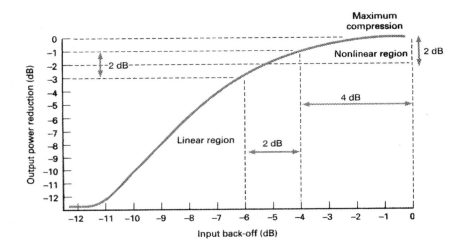

FIGURE 14-23   HPA input/output characteristic curve

14-9-4   Cross-Links

Occasionally, there is an application where it is necessary to communicate between satellites. This is done using *satellite cross-links* or *intersatellite links* (ISLs), shown in Figure 14-22. A disadvantage of using an ISL is that both the transmitter and the receiver are *space bound*. Consequently, both the transmitter's output power and the receiver's input sensitivity are limited.

14-10   SATELLITE SYSTEM PARAMETERS

14-10-1   Back-Off Loss

High-power amplifiers used in earth station transmitters and the traveling-wave tubes typically used in satellite transponders are *nonlinear devices;* their gain (output power versus input power) is dependent on input signal level. A typical input/output power characteristic curve is shown in Figure 14-23. It can be seen that as the input power is reduced by 4 dB, the output power is reduced by only 1 dB. There is an obvious *power compression.* To reduce the amount of intermodulation distortion caused by the nonlinear amplification of the HPA, the input power must be reduced (*backed off*) by several dB. This allows the HPA to operate in a more *linear* region. The amount the output level is backed off from rated levels is equivalent to a loss and is appropriately called *back-off loss* (L_{bo}).

14-10-2 Transmit Power and Bit Energy

To operate as efficiently as possible, a power amplifier should be operated as close as possible to saturation. The *saturated output power* is designated $P_{o(sat)}$ or simply P_t. The output power of a typical satellite earth station transmitter is much higher than the output power from a terrestrial microwave power amplifier. Consequently, when dealing with satellite systems, P_t is generally expressed in dBW (decibels in respect to 1 W) rather than in dBm (decibels in respect to 1 mW).

Most modern satellite systems use either phase-shift keying (PSK) or quadrature amplitude modulation (QAM) rather than conventional frequency modulation (FM). With PSK and QAM, the input baseband is generally a PCM-encoded, time-division-multiplexed signal that is digital in nature. Also, with PSK and QAM, several bits may be encoded in a single transmit signaling element. Consequently, a parameter more meaningful than carrier power is *energy per bit* (E_b). Mathematically, E_b is

$$E_b = P_t T_b \qquad (14\text{-}4)$$

where
E_b = energy of a single bit (joules per bit)
P_t = total saturated output power (watts or joules per second)
T_b = time of a single bit (seconds)

or, because $T_b = 1/f_b$, where f_b is the bit rate in bits per second,

$$E_b = \frac{P_t}{f_b} = \frac{\text{J/s}}{\text{b/s}} = \frac{\text{joules}}{\text{bit}} \qquad (14\text{-}5)$$

Example 14-2

For a total transmit power (P_t) of 1000 W, determine the energy per bit (E_b) for a transmission rate of 50 Mbps.

Solution

$$T_b = \frac{1}{f_b} = \frac{1}{50 \times 10^6 \text{ bps}} = 0.02 \times 10^{-6} \text{ s}$$

(It appears that the units for T_b should be s/bit, but the per bit is implied in the definition of T_b, time of bit.)
Substituting into Equation 14-4 yields
$$E_b = 1000 \text{ J/s } (0.02 \times 10^{-6} \text{ s/bit}) = 20 \text{ } \mu\text{J}$$
(Again the units appear to be J/bit, but the per bit is implied in the definition of E_b, energy per bit.)

$$E_b = \frac{1000 \text{ J/s}}{50 \times 10^6 \text{ bps}} = 20 \text{ } \mu\text{J}$$

Expressed as a log with 1 joule as the reference,
$$E_b = 10 \log(20 \times 10^{-6}) = -47 \text{ dBJ}$$
It is common to express P_t in dBW and E_b in dBW/bps. Thus,
$$P_t = 10 \log 1000 = 30 \text{ dBW}$$
$$E_b = P_t - 10 \log f_b = P_t - 10 \log (50 \times 10^6)$$
$$= 30 \text{ dBW} - 77 \text{ dB} = -47 \text{ dBW/bps}$$

or simply -47 dBJ.

14-10-3 Effective Isotropic Radiated Power

Effective isotropic radiated power (EIRP) is defined as an equivalent transmit power and is expressed mathematically as

$$\text{EIRP} = P_{in}A_t \qquad (14\text{-}6)$$

where   EIRP = effective isotropic radiated power (watts)
       P_{in} = antenna input power (watts)
       A_t = transmit antenna gain (unitless ratio)

Expressed as a log,

$$\text{EIRP}_{(dBW)} = P_{in(dBW)} + A_{t(dB)} \qquad (14\text{-}7)$$

In respect to the transmitter output,

$$P_{in} = P_t - L_{bo} - L_{bf}$$

Thus, $$\text{EIRP} = P_t - L_{bo} - L_{bf} + A_t \qquad (14\text{-}8)$$

where P_{in} = antenna input power (dBW per watt)
       L_{bo} = back-off losses of HPA (decibels)
       L_{bf} = total branching and feeder loss (decibels)
       A_t = transmit antenna gain (decibels)
       P_t = saturated amplifier output power (dBW per watt)

Example 14-3

For an earth station transmitter with an antenna output power of 40 dBW (10,000 W), a back-off loss of 3 dB, a total branching and feeder loss of 3 dB, and a transmit antenna gain of 40 dB, determine the EIRP.

Solution   Substituting into Equation 14-6 yields

$$\text{EIRP} = P_t - L_{bo} - L_{bf} + A_t$$
$$= 40 \text{ dBW} - 3 \text{ dB} - 3 \text{ dB} + 40 \text{ dB} = 74 \text{ dBW}$$

14-10-4 Equivalent Noise Temperature

With terrestrial microwave systems, the noise introduced in a receiver or a component within a receiver was commonly specified by the parameter noise figure. In satellite communications systems, it is often necessary to differentiate or measure noise in increments as small as a tenth or a hundredth of a decibel. Noise figure, in its standard form, is inadequate for such precise calculations. Consequently, it is common to use *environmental temperature* (T) and *equivalent noise temperature* (T_e) when evaluating the performance of a satellite system. In Chapter 24, total noise power was expressed mathematically as

$$N = KTB \qquad (14\text{-}9)$$

Rearranging and solving for T gives us

$$T = \frac{N}{KB} \qquad (14\text{-}10)$$

where N = total noise power (watts)
       K = Boltzmann's constant (joules per kelvin)
       B = bandwidth (hertz)
       T = temperature of the environment (kelvin)

Again from Chapter 24,

$$F = 1 + \frac{T_e}{T} \qquad (14\text{-}11)$$

Table 14-3 Noise Unit Comparison

Noise Factor (F) (unitless)	Noise Figure (NF) (dB)	Equivalent Temperature (T_e) (°K)	dBK
1.2	0.79	60	17.78
1.3	1.14	90	19.54
1.4	1.46	120	20.79
2.5	4	450	26.53
10	10	2700	34.31

where T_e = equivalent noise temperature (kelvin)
        F = noise factor (unitless)
        T = temperature of the environment (kelvin)

Rearranging Equation 14-9, we have

$$T_e = T(F - 1) \tag{14-12}$$

Typically, equivalent noise temperatures of the receivers used in satellite transponders are about 1000 K. For earth station receivers, T_e values are between 20 K and 1000 K. Equivalent noise temperature is generally more useful when expressed logarithmically referenced to 1 K with the unit of dBK, as follows:

$$T_{e(\mathbf{dBK})} = 10 \log T_e \tag{14-13}$$

For an equivalent noise temperature of 100 K, $T_{e(\mathbf{dBK})}$ is

$$T_e = 10 \log 100 \ \ \text{or} \ \ 20 \text{ dBK}$$

Equivalent noise temperature is a hypothetical value that can be calculated but cannot be measured. Equivalent noise temperature is often used rather than noise figure because it is a more accurate method of expressing the noise contributed by a device or a receiver when evaluating its performance. Essentially, equivalent noise temperature (T_e) represents the noise power present at the input to a device plus the noise added internally by that device. This allows us to analyze the noise characteristics of a device by simply evaluating an equivalent input noise temperature. As you will see in subsequent discussions, T_e is a very useful parameter when evaluating the performance of a satellite system.

Noise factor, noise figure, equivalent noise temperature, and dBK are summarized in Table 14-3.

Example 14-4

Convert noise figures of 4 dB and 4.1 dB to equivalent noise temperatures. Use 300 K for the environmental temperature.

Solution Converting the noise figures to noise factors yields

$$\text{NF} = 4 \text{ dB}, \text{F} = 2.512$$
$$\text{NF} = 4.1 \text{ dB}, \text{F} = 2.57$$

Substituting into Equation 14-10 yields

$$T_e = 300(2.512 - 1)$$
$$= 453.6 \text{ K}$$
$$T_e = 300(2.57 - 1)$$
$$= 471 \text{ K}$$

From Example 14-4, it can be seen that a 0.1-dB difference in the two noise figures equated to a 17.4° difference in the two equivalent noise temperatures. Hence, equivalent noise temperature is a more accurate method of comparing the noise performances of two receivers or devices.

14-10-5   Noise Density

Simply stated, *noise density* (N_0) is the noise power normalized to a 1-Hz bandwidth, or the noise power present in a 1-Hz bandwidth. Mathematically, noise density is

$$N_0 = \frac{N}{B} = \frac{KT_eB}{B} = KT_e \qquad (14\text{-}14)$$

where N_0 = noise density (watts/per hertz) (N_0 is generally expressed as simply watts; the per hertz is implied in the definition of N_0),

$$1 \text{ W/Hz} = \frac{1 \text{ joule/sec}}{1 \text{ cycle/sec}} = \frac{1 \text{ joule}}{\text{cycle}}$$

N = total noise power (watts)
B = bandwidth (hertz)
K = Boltzmann's constant (joules/per kelvin)
T_e = equivalent noise temperature (kelvin)

Expressed as a log with 1 W/Hz as the reference,

$$N_{0(\text{dBW/Hz})} = 10 \log N - 10 \log B \qquad (14\text{-}15)$$

$$= 10 \log K + 10 \log T_e \qquad (14\text{-}16)$$

Example 14-5

For an equivalent noise bandwidth of 10 MHz and a total noise power of 0.0276 pW, determine the noise density and equivalent noise temperature.

Solution   Substituting into Equation 14-12, we have

$$N_0 = \frac{N}{B} = \frac{276 \times 10^{-16} \text{ W}}{10 \times 10^6 \text{ Hz}} = 276 \times 10^{-23} \text{ W/Hz}$$

or simply 276×10^{-23} W.

$$N_0 = 10 \log(276 \times 10^{-23}) = -205.6 \text{ dBW/Hz}$$

or simply -205.6 dBW. Substituting into Equation 14-13 gives us

$$N_0 = 10 \log 276 \times 10^{-16} - 10 \log 10 \text{ MHz}$$

$$= -135.6 \text{ dBW} - 70 \text{ dB} = -205.6 \text{ dBW}$$

Rearranging Equation 14-12 and solving for equivalent noise temperature yields

$$T_e = \frac{N_0}{K}$$

$$= \frac{276 \times 10^{-23} \text{ J/cycle}}{1.38 \times 10^{-23} \text{ J/K}} = 200 \text{ K/cycle}$$

Expressed as a log, $T_e = 10 \log 200 = 23$ dBK

$$= N_0 - 10 \log K = N_0 - 10 \log 1.38 \times 10^{-23}$$

$$= -205.6 \text{ dBW} - (-228.6 \text{ dBWK}) = 23 \text{ dBK}$$

14-10-6   Carrier–to–Noise Density Ratio

C/N_0 is the average wideband carrier power-to-noise density ratio. The *wideband carrier power* is the combined power of the carrier and its associated sidebands. The noise density is the thermal noise present in a normalized 1-Hz bandwidth. The carrier-to-noise density ratio may also be written as a function of noise temperature. Mathematically, C/N_0 is

$$\frac{C}{N_0} = \frac{C}{KT_e} \qquad (14\text{-}17)$$

Expressed as a log,

$$\frac{C}{N_0}(\text{dB}) = C_{(\text{dBW})} - N_{0(\text{dBW})} \qquad (14\text{-}18)$$

14-10-7 Energy of Bit-to-Noise Density Ratio

E_b/N_0 is one of the most important and most often used parameters when evaluating a digital radio system. The E_b/N_0 ratio is a convenient way to compare digital systems that use different transmission rates, modulation schemes, or encoding techniques. Mathematically, E_b/N_0 is

$$\frac{E_b}{N_0} = \frac{C/f_b}{N/B} = \frac{CB}{Nf_b} \qquad (14\text{-}19)$$

E_b/N_0 is a convenient term used for digital system calculations and performance comparisons, but in the real world, it is more convenient to measure the wideband carrier power-to-noise density ratio and convert it to E_b/N_0. Rearranging Equation 14-18 yields the following expression:

$$\frac{E_b}{N_0} = \frac{C}{N} \times \frac{B}{f_b} \qquad (14\text{-}20)$$

The E_b/N_0 ratio is the product of the carrier-to-noise ratio (C/N) and the noise bandwidth–to–bit rate ratio (B/f_b). Expressed as a log,

$$\frac{E_b}{N_0}(\text{dB}) = \frac{C}{N}(\text{dB}) + \frac{B}{f_b}(\text{dB}) \qquad (14\text{-}21)$$

The energy per bit (E_b) will remain constant as long as the total wideband carrier power (C) and the transmission rate (bps) remain unchanged. Also, the noise density (N_0) will remain constant as long as the noise temperature remains constant. The following conclusion can be made: For a given carrier power, bit rate, and noise temperature, the E_b/N_0 ratio will remain constant regardless of the encoding technique, modulation scheme, or bandwidth.

Figure 14-24 graphically illustrates the relationship between an expected probability of error $P(e)$ and the minimum C/N ratio required to achieve the $P(e)$. The C/N specified is for the minimum double-sided Nyquist bandwidth. Figure 14-25 graphically illustrates the relationship between an expected $P(e)$ and the minimum E_b/N_0 ratio required to achieve that $P(e)$.

A $P(e)$ of $10^{-5}(1/10^5)$ indicates a probability that one bit will be in error for every 100,000 bits transmitted. $P(e)$ is analogous to the bit error rate (BER).

Example 14-6

A coherent binary phase-shift-keyed (BPSK) transmitter operates at a bit rate of 20 Mbps. For a probability of error $P(e)$ of 10^{-4},

a. Determine the minimum theoretical C/N and E_b/N_0 ratios for a receiver bandwidth equal to the minimum double-sided Nyquist bandwidth.

b. Determine the C/N if the noise is measured at a point prior to the bandpass filter where the bandwidth is equal to twice the Nyquist bandwidth.

c. Determine the C/N if the noise is measured at a point prior to the bandpass filter where the bandwidth is equal to three times the Nyquist bandwidth.

Solution a. With BPSK, the minimum bandwidth is equal to the bit rate, 20 MHz. From Figure 14-24, the minimum C/N is 8.8 dB. Substituting into Equation 14-20 gives us

$$\frac{E_b}{N_0} = \frac{C}{N} + \frac{B}{f_b}$$

$$= 8.8 \text{ dB} + 10 \log \frac{20 \times 10^6}{20 \times 10^6}$$

$$= 8.8 \text{ dB} + 0 \text{ dB} = 8.8 \text{ dB}$$

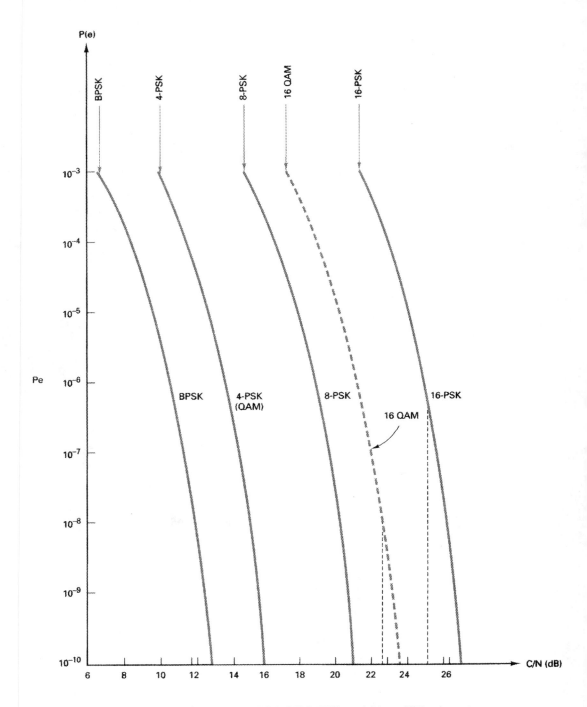

FIGURE 14-24 $P(e)$ performance of M-ary PSK, QAM, QPR, and M-ary APK coherent systems. The rms C/N is specified in the double-sided Nyquist bandwidth

Note: The minimum E_b/N_0 equals the minimum C/N when the receiver noise bandwidth equals the bit rate which for BPSK also equals the minimum Nyquist bandwidth. The minimum E_b/N_0 of 8.8 can be verified from Figure 14-25.

What effect does increasing the noise bandwidth have on the minimum C/N and E_b/N_0 ratios? The wideband carrier power is totally independent of the noise bandwidth. However, an increase in the bandwidth causes a corresponding increase in the noise power. Consequently, a decrease in C/N

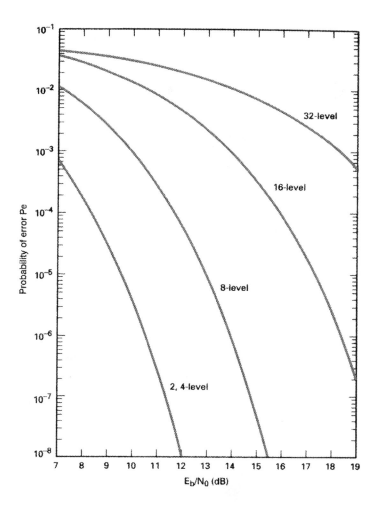

FIGURE 14-25   Probability of error $P(e)$ versus E_b/N_0 ratio for
various digital modulation schemes

is realized that is directly proportional to the increase in the noise bandwidth. E_b is dependent on the wideband carrier power and the bit rate only. Therefore, E_b is unaffected by an increase in the noise bandwidth. N_0 is the noise power normalized to a 1-Hz bandwidth and, consequently, is also unaffected by an increase in the noise bandwidth.

h. Because E_b/N_0 is independent of bandwidth, measuring the C/N at a point in the receiver where the bandwidth is equal to twice the minimum Nyquist bandwidth has absolutely no effect on E_b/N_0. Therefore, E_b/N_0 becomes the constant in Equation 14-20 and is used to solve for the new value of C/N. Rearranging Equation 14-20 and using the calculated E_b/N_0 ratio, we have

$$\frac{C}{N} = \frac{E_b}{N_0} - \frac{B}{f_b}$$

$$= 8.8 \text{ dB} - 10 \log \frac{40 \times 10^6}{20 \times 10^6}$$

$$= 8.8 \text{ dB} - 10 \log 2$$

$$= 8.8 \text{ dB} - 3 \text{ dB} = 5.8 \text{ dB}$$

c. Measuring the C/N ratio at a point in the receiver where the bandwidth equals three times the minimum bandwidth yields the following results for C/N:

$$\frac{C}{N} = \frac{E_b}{N_0} - 10 \log \frac{60 \times 10^6}{20 \times 10^6}$$

$$= 8.8 \text{ dB} - 10 \log 3 = 4.03 \text{ dB}$$

The C/N ratios of 8.8, 5.8, and 4.03 dB indicate the C/N ratios that could be measured at the three specified points in the receiver and still achieve the desired minimum E_b/N_0 and $P(e)$.

Because E_b/N_0 cannot be directly measured to determine the E_b/N_0 ratio, the wideband carrier-to-noise ratio is measured and, then, substituted into Equation 14-20. Consequently, to accurately determine the E_b/N_0 ratio, the noise bandwidth of the receiver must be known.

Example 14-7

A coherent 8-PSK transmitter operates at a bit rate of 90 Mbps. For a probability of error of 10^{-5},

a. Determine the minimum theoretical C/N and E_b/N_0 ratios for a receiver bandwidth equal to the minimum double-sided Nyquist bandwidth.
b. Determine the C/N if the noise is measured at a point prior to the bandpass filter where the bandwidth is equal to twice the Nyquist bandwidth.
c. Determine the C/N if the noise is measured at a point prior to the bandpass filter where the bandwidth is equal to three times the Nyquist bandwidth.

Solution a. 8-PSK has a bandwidth efficiency of 3 bps/Hz and, consequently, requires a minimum bandwidth of one-third the bit rate, or 30 MHz. From Figure 14-24, the minimum C/N is 18.5 dB. Substituting into Equation 14-20, we obtain

$$\frac{E_b}{N_0} = 18.5 \text{ dB} + 10 \log \frac{30 \text{ MHz}}{90 \text{ Mbps}}$$

$$= 18.5 \text{ dB} + (-4.8 \text{ dB}) = 13.7 \text{ dB}$$

b. Rearranging Equation 14-20 and substituting for E_b/N_0 yields

$$\frac{C}{N} = 13.7 \text{ dB} - 10 \log \frac{60 \text{ MHz}}{90 \text{ Mbps}}$$

$$= 13.7 \text{ dB} - (-1.77 \text{ dB}) = 15.47 \text{ dB}$$

c. Again, rearranging Equation 14-20 and substituting for E_b/N_0 gives us

$$\frac{C}{N} = 13.7 \text{ dB} - 10 \log \frac{90 \text{ MHz}}{90 \text{ Mbps}}$$

$$= 13.7 \text{ dB (dB)} = 13.7 \text{ dB}$$

It should be evident from Examples 14-6 and 14-7 that the E_b/N_0 and C/N ratios are equal only when the noise bandwidth is equal to the bit rate. Also, as the bandwidth at the point of measurement increases, the C/N decreases.

When the modulation scheme, bit rate, bandwidth, and C/N ratios of two digital radio systems are different, it is often difficult to determine which system has the lower probability of error. E_b/N_0 is independent of bandwidth and modulation scheme, so it is a convenient common denominator to use for comparing the probability of error performance of two digital radio systems.

14-10-8 Gain-To-Equivalent Noise Temperature Ratio

Gain-to-equivalent noise temperature ratio (G/T_e) is a figure of merit used to represent the quality of a satellite or earth station receiver. The G/T_e ratio is the ratio of the receive antenna gain (G) to the equivalent system noise temperature (T_e) of the receiver. G/T_e is expressed mathematically as

$$\frac{G}{T_e} = G - 10 \log(T_s) \tag{14-22}$$

where G = receive antenna gain (dB)
T_s = operating or system temperature (degrees Kelvin)

and $\quad T_s = T_a + T_r$

where $\quad T_a$ = antenna temperature (degrees Kelvin)

$\quad\quad T_r$ = receiver effective input noise temperature (degrees Kelvin)

It should be noted that the ratio of G to T_e involves two different quantities. Antenna gain is a unitless value, whereas temperature has the unit of degrees Kelvin. The reference temperature is 1 K; therefore, the decibel notation for G/T_e is dBK^{-1} or dB/K, which should not be interpreted as decibels per degree Kelvin.

14-11 SATELLITE SYSTEM LINK EQUATIONS

The error performance of a digital satellite system is quite predictable. Figure 14-26 shows a simplified block diagram of a digital satellite system and identifies the various gains and losses that may affect the system performance. When evaluating the performance of a digital satellite system, the uplink and downlink parameters are first considered separately, then the overall performance is determined by combining them in the appropriate manner. Keep in mind, a digital microwave or satellite radio simply means that the original and demodulated baseband signals are digital in nature. The RF portion of the radio is analog, that is, FSK, PSK, QAM, or some other higher-level modulation riding on an analog microwave carrier.

14-11-1 Link Equations

The following *link equations* are used to separately analyze the uplink and downlink sections of a single radio-frequency carrier satellite system. These equations consider only the ideal gains and losses and effects of thermal noise associated with the earth station transmitter, earth station receiver, and the satellite transponder.

Uplink Equation

$$\frac{C}{N_0} = \frac{A_t P_{\text{in}}(L_p L_u) A_r}{K T_e} = \frac{A_t P_{\text{in}}(L_p L_u)}{K} \times \frac{G}{T_e} \quad\quad (14\text{-}23)$$

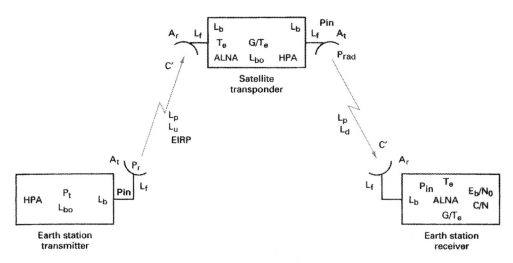

FIGURE 14-26 Overall satellite system showing the gains and losses incurred in both the uplink and downlink sections. HPA, high-power amplifier; P_t, HPA output power; L_{bo}, back-off loss; L_f, feeder loss; L_b, branching loss; A_t, transmit antenna gain; P_r, total radiated power = $P_t - L_{bo} - L_b - L_f$; EIRP, effective isotropic radiated power $P_{rad} A_t$; L_u, additional uplink losses due to atmosphere; L_p, path loss; A_r, receive antenna gain; G/T_e, gain-to-equivalent noise ratio; L_d, additional downlink losses due to atmosphere; LNA, low-noise amplifier; C/T_e, carrier-to-equivalent noise ratio; C/N_0, carrier-to-noise density ratio; E_b/N_0, energy of bit-to-noise density ratio; C/N, carrier-to-noise ratio

where L_d and L_u are the additional uplink and downlink atmospheric losses, respectively. The uplink and downlink signals must pass through Earth's atmosphere, where they are partially absorbed by the moisture, oxygen, and particulates in the air. Depending on the elevation angle, the distance the RF signal travels through the atmosphere varies from one earth station to another. Because L_p, L_u, and L_d represent losses, they are decimal values less than 1. G/T_e is the receive antenna gain plus the gain of the LNA divided by the equivalent input noise temperature.

Expressed as a log,

$$\frac{C}{N_0} = \underbrace{10 \log A_t P_{in}}_{\substack{\text{EIRP} \\ \text{earth} \\ \text{station}}} - \underbrace{20 \log\left(\frac{4\pi D}{\lambda}\right)}_{\substack{\text{free-space} \\ \text{path loss} \\ L_p}} + \underbrace{10 \log\left(\frac{G}{T_e}\right)}_{\substack{\text{satellite} \\ G/T_e}} - \underbrace{10 \log L_u}_{\substack{\text{additional} \\ \text{atmospheric} \\ \text{losses}}} - \underbrace{10 \log K}_{\substack{\text{Boltzmann's} \\ \text{constant}}} \quad (14\text{-}24)$$

$$= \text{EIRP (dBW)} - L_p(\text{dB}) + \frac{G}{T_e}(\text{dBK}^{-1}) - L_u(\text{dB}) - K(\text{dBWK}) \quad (14\text{-}25)$$

Downlink Equation

$$\frac{C}{N_0} = \frac{A_t P_{in}(L_p L_d) A_r}{K T_e} = \frac{A_t P_{in}(L_p L_d)}{K} \times \frac{G}{T_e} \quad (14\text{-}26)$$

Expressed as a log,

$$\frac{C}{N_0} = \underbrace{10 \log A_t P_{in}}_{\substack{\text{EIRP} \\ \text{satellite}}} - \underbrace{20 \log\left(\frac{4\pi D}{\lambda}\right)}_{\substack{\text{free-space} \\ \text{path loss} \\ L_p}} + \underbrace{10 \log\left(\frac{G}{T_e}\right)}_{\substack{\text{earth} \\ \text{station} \\ G/T_e}} - \underbrace{10 \log L_d}_{\substack{\text{additional} \\ \text{atmospheric} \\ \text{losses}}} - \underbrace{10 \log K}_{\substack{\text{Boltzmann's} \\ \text{constant}}} \quad (14\text{-}27)$$

$$= \text{EIRP(dBW)} - L_p(\text{dB}) + \frac{G}{T_e}(\text{dBK}^{-1}) - L_d(\text{dB}) - K(\text{dBWK})$$

14-12 LINK BUDGET

Table 14-4 lists the system parameters for three typical satellite communication systems. The systems and their parameters are not necessarily for an existing or future system; they are hypothetical examples only. The system parameters are used to construct a *link budget*. A link budget identifies the system parameters and is used to determine the projected C/N and E_b/N_0 ratios at both the satellite and earth station receivers for a given modulation scheme and desired $P(e)$.

Example 14-8

Complete the link budget for a satellite system with the following parameters.

Uplink

1. Earth station transmitter output power at saturation, 2000 W	33 dBW
2. Earth station back-off loss	3 dB
3. Earth station branching and feeder losses	4 dB
4. Earth station transmit antenna gain (from Figure 14-27, 15 m at 14 GHz)	64 dB
5. Additional uplink atmospheric losses	0.6 dB
6. Free-space path loss (from Figure 14-28, at 14 GHz)	206.5 dB
7. Satellite receiver G/T_e ratio	-5.3 dBK^{-1}
8. Satellite branching and feeder losses	0 dB
9. Bit rate	120 Mbps
10. Modulation scheme	8-PSK

Table 14-4   System Parameters for Three Hypothetical Satellite Systems

	System A: 6/4 GHz, earth coverage QPSK modulation, 60 Mbps	System B: 14/12 GHz, earth coverage 8-PSK modulation, 90 Mbps	System C: 14/12 GHz, earth coverage 8-PSK modulation, 120 Mbps
Uplink			
Transmitter output power (saturation, dBW)	35	25	33
Earth station back-off loss (dB)	2	2	3
Earth station branching and feeder loss (dB)	3	3	4
Additional atmospheric (dB)	0.6	0.4	0.6
Earth station antenna gain (dB)	55	45	64
Free-space path loss (dB)	200	208	206.5
Satellite receive antenna gain (dB)	20	45	23.7
Satellite branching and feeder loss (dB)	1	1	0
Satellite equivalent noise temperature (K)	1000	800	800
Satellite G/T_e (dBK^{-1})	-10	16	-5.3
Downlink			
Transmitter output power (saturation, dBW)	18	20	10
Satellite back-off loss (dB)	0.5	0.2	0.1
Satellite branching and feeder loss (dB)	1	1	0.5
Additional atmospheric loss (dB)	0.8	1.4	0.4
Satellite antenna gain (dB)	16	44	30.8
Free-space path loss (dB)	197	206	205.6
Earth station receive antenna gain (dB)	51	44	62
Earth station branching and feeder loss (dB)	3	3	0
Earth station equivalent noise temperature (K)	250	1000	270
Earth station G/T_e (dBK^{-1})	27	14	37.7

Downlink

1. Satellite transmitter output power at saturation, 10 W ..... 10 dBW
2. Satellite back-off loss ..... 0.1 dB
3. Satellite branching and feeder losses ..... 0.5 dB
4. Satellite transmit antenna gain (from Figure 14-27, 0.37 m at 12 GHz) ..... 30.8 dB
5. Additional downlink atmospheric losses ..... 0.4 dB
6. Free-space path loss (from Figure 14-28, at 12 GHz) ..... 205.6 dB
7. Earth station receive antenna gain (15 m, 12 GHz) ..... 62 dB
8. Earth station branching and feeder losses ..... 0 dB
9. Earth station equivalent noise temperature ..... 270 K
10. Earth station G/T_e ratio ..... 37.7 dBK^{-1}
11. Bit rate ..... 120 Mbps
12. Modulation scheme ..... 8 -PSK

Solution   *Uplink budget:* Expressed as a log,

$$\text{EIRP (earth station)} = P_t + A_t - L_{\text{bo}} - L_{bf}$$
$$= 33 \text{ dBW} + 64 \text{ dB} - 3 \text{ dB} - 4 \text{ dB} = 90 \text{ dBW}$$

Carrier power density at the satellite antenna:

$$C' = \text{EIRP (earth station)} - L_p - L_u$$
$$= 90 \text{ dBW} - 206.5 \text{ dB} - 0.6 \text{ dB} = -117.1 \text{ dBW}$$

C/N_0 at the satellite:

$$\frac{C}{N_0} = \frac{C}{KT_e} = \frac{C}{T_e} \times \frac{1}{K} \qquad \text{where } \frac{C}{T_e} = C' \times \frac{G}{T_e}$$

Thus,

$$\frac{C}{N_0} = C' \times \frac{G}{T_e} \times \frac{1}{K}$$

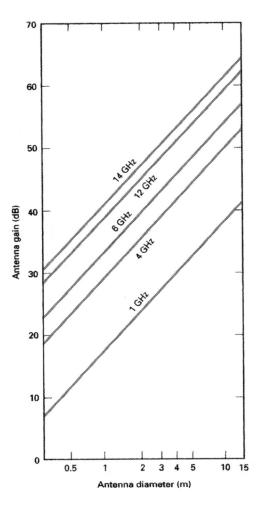

FIGURE 14-27 Antenna gain based on the gain equation for a parabolic antenna:

$$A \, [\text{db}] = 10 \log \eta \, [\pi \, D/\lambda]^2$$

where D is the antenna diameter, $\lambda =$ the wavelength, and $\eta =$ the antenna efficiency. Here $\eta = 0.55$. To correct for a 100% efficient antenna, add 2.66 dB to the value.

Expressed as a log,

$$\frac{C}{N_0} = C' + \frac{G}{T_e} - 10 \log(1.38 \times 10^{-23})$$

$$= -117.1 \text{ dBW} + (-5.3 \text{ dBK}^{-1}) - (-228.6 \text{ dBWK}) = 106.2 \text{ dB}$$

Thus,

$$\frac{E_b}{N_0} = \frac{C/f_b}{N_0} = \frac{C}{N_0} - 10 \log f_b$$

$$= 106.2 \text{ dB} - 10 \, (\log 120 \times 10^6) = 25.4 \text{ dB}$$

and for a minimum bandwidth system,

$$\frac{C}{N} = \frac{E_b}{N_0} - \frac{B}{f_b} = 25.4 - 10 \log \frac{40 \times 10^6}{120 \times 10^6} = 30.2 \text{ dB}$$

Downlink budget: Expressed as a log,

$$\text{EIRP (satellite transponder)} = P_t + A_t - L_{\text{bo}} - L_{bf}$$

$$= 10 \text{ dBW} + 30.8 \text{ dB} - 0.1 \text{ dB} - 0.5 \text{ dB}$$

$$= 40.2 \text{ dBW}$$

Carrier power density at earth station antenna:

$$C' = \text{EIRP} - L_p - L_d$$

$$= 40.2 \text{ dBW} - 205.6 \text{ dB} - 0.4 \text{ dB} = -165.8 \text{ dBW}$$

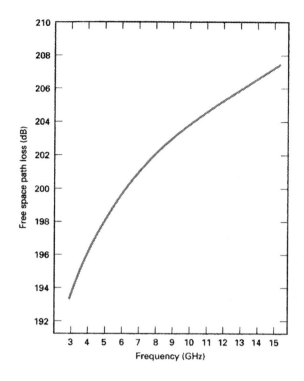

Elevation angle correction:	
Angle	+dB
90°	0
45°	0.44
0°	1.33

FIGURE 14-28　Free-space path loss [L_p] determined from L_p = 183.5 + 20 log f [GHz], elevation angle = 90°, and distance = 35,930 km

C/N_0 at the earth station receiver:

$$\frac{C}{N_0} = \frac{C}{KT_e} = \frac{C}{T_e} \times \frac{1}{K} \quad \text{where} \quad \frac{C}{T_e} = C' \times \frac{G}{T_e}$$

Thus,

$$\frac{C}{N_0} = C' \times \frac{G}{T_e} \times \frac{1}{K}$$

Expressed as a log,

$$\frac{C}{N_0} = C' + \frac{G}{T_e} - 10 \log(1.38 \times 10^{-23})$$

$$= -165.8 \text{ dBW} + (37.7 \text{ dBK}^{-1}) - (-228.6 \text{ dBWK}) = 100.5 \text{ dB}$$

An alternative method of solving for C/N_0 is

$$\frac{C}{N_0} = C' + A_r - T_e - K$$

$$= -165.8 \text{ dBW} + 62 \text{ dB} - 10 \log 270 - (-228.6 \text{ dBWK})$$

$$= -165.8 \text{ dBW} + 62 \text{ dB} - 24.3 \text{ dBK}^{-1} + 228.6 \text{ dBWK} = 100.5 \text{ dB}$$

$$\frac{E_b}{N_0} = \frac{C}{N_0} - 10 \log f_b$$

$$= 100.5 \text{ dB} - 10 \log(120 \times 10^6)$$

$$= 100.5 \text{ dB} - 80.8 \text{ dB} = 19.7 \text{ dB}$$

and for a minimum bandwidth system,

$$\frac{C}{N} = \frac{E_b}{N_0} - \frac{B}{f_b} = 19.7 - 10 \log \frac{40 \times 10^6}{120 \times 10^6} = 24.5 \text{ dB}$$

With careful analysis and a little algebra, it can be shown that the overall energy of bit-to-noise density ratio (E_b/N_0), which includes the combined effects of the uplink ratio (E_b/N_0)$_u$ and the downlink ratio $(E_b/N_0)_d$, is a standard product over the sum relationship and is expressed mathematically as

$$\frac{E_b}{N_0}(\text{overall}) = \frac{(E_b/N_0)_u(E_b/N_0)_d}{(E_b/N_0)_u + (E_b/N_0)_d}$$ (14-28)

where all E_b/N_0 ratios are in absolute values. For Example 14-25, the overall E_b/N_0 ratio is

$$\frac{E_b}{N_0}(\text{overall}) = \frac{(346.7)(93.3)}{346.7 + 93.3} = 73.5$$

$$= 10 \log 73.5 = 18.7 \text{ dB}$$

As with all product-over-sum relationships, the smaller of the two numbers dominates. If one number is substantially smaller than the other, the overall result is approximately equal to the smaller of the two numbers.

The system parameters used for Example 14-9 were taken from system C in Table 14-4. A complete link budget for the system is shown in Table 14-5.

Table 14-5   Link Budget for Example 14-10

Uplink	
1. Earth station transmitter output power at saturation, 2000 W	33 dBW
2. Earth station back-off loss	3 dB
3. Earth station branching and feeder losses	4 dB
4. Earth station transmit antenna gain	64 dB
5. Earth station EIRP	90 dBW
6. Additional uplink atmospheric losses	0.6 dB
7. Free-space path loss	206.5 dB
8. Carrier power density at satellite	-117.1 dBW
9. Satellite branching and feeder losses	0 dB
10. Satellite G/T_e ratio	-5.3 dBK^{-1}
11. Satellite C/T_e ratio	-122.4 dBWK^{-1}
12. Satellite C/N_0 ratio	106.2 dB
13. Satellite C/N ratio	30.2 dB
14. Satellite E_b/N_0 ratio	25.4 dB
15. Bit rate	120 Mbps
16. Modulation scheme	8-PSK
Downlink	
1. Satellite transmitter output power at saturation, 10 W	10 dBW
2. Satellite back-off loss	0.1 dB
3. Satellite branching and feeder losses	0.5 dB
4. Satellite transmit antenna gain	30.8 dB
5. Satellite EIRP	40.2 dBW
6. Additional downlink atmospheric losses	0.4 dB
7. Free-space path loss	205.6 dB
8. Earth station receive antenna gain	62 dB
9. Earth station equivalent noise temperature	270 K
10. Earth station branching and feeder losses	0 dB
11. Earth station G/T_e ratio	37.7 dBK^{-1}
12. Carrier power density at earth station	-165.8 dBW
13. Earth station C/T_e ratio	-128.1 dBWK^{-1}
14. Earth station C/N_0 ratio	100.5 dB
15. Earth station C/N ratio	24.5 dB
16. Earth station E_b/N_0 ratio	19.7 dB
17. Bit rate	120 Mbps
18. Modulation scheme	8-PSK

14-1. Briefly describe a satellite.

14-2. What is a passive satellite? An active satellite?

14-3. Contrast nonsynchronous and synchronous satellites.

14-4. Define *prograde* and *retrograde*.

14-5. Define *apogee* and *perigee*.

14-6. Briefly explain the characteristics of low-, medium-, and high-altitude satellite orbits.

14-7. Explain equatorial, polar, and inclined orbits.

14-8. Contrast the advantages and disadvantages of geosynchronous satellites.

14-9. Define *look angles, angle of elevation,* and *azimuth.*

14-10. Define *satellite spatial separation* and list its restrictions.

14-11. Describe a "footprint."

14-12. Describe spot, zonal, and earth coverage radiation patterns.

14-13. Explain *reuse.*

14-14. Briefly describe the functional characteristics of an uplink, a transponder, and a downlink model for a satellite system.

14-15. Define *back-off loss* and its relationship to saturated and transmit power.

14-16. Define *bit energy.*

14-17. Define *effective isotropic radiated power.*

14-18. Define *equivalent noise temperature.*

14-19. Define *noise density.*

14-20. Define *carrier-to-noise density ratio* and *energy of bit-to-noise density ratio.*

14-21. Define *gain-to-equivalent noise temperature ratio.*

14-22. Describe what a satellite link budget is and how it is used.

14-1. An earth station is located at Houston, Texas, that has a longitude of 99.5° and a latitude of 29.5° north. The satellite of interest is *Satcom V.* Determine the look angles for the earth station antenna.

14-2. A satellite system operates at 14-GHz uplink and 11-GHz downlink and has a projected $P(e)$ of 10^{-7}. The modulation scheme is 8-PSK, and the system will carry 120 Mbps. The equivalent noise temperature of the receiver is 400 K, and the receiver noise bandwidth is equal to the minimum Nyquist frequency. Determine the following parameters: minimum theoretical C/N ratio, minimum theoretical E_b/N_0 ratio, noise density, total receiver input noise, minimum receive carrier power, and the minimum energy per bit at the receiver input.

14-3. A satellite system operates at 6-GHz uplink and 4-GHz downlink and has a projected $P(e)$ of 10^{-6}. The modulation scheme is QPSK and the system will carry 100 Mbps. The equivalent receiver noise temperature is 290 K, and the receiver noise bandwidth is equal to the minimum Nyquist frequency. Determine the C/N ratio that would be measured at a point in the receiver prior to the BPF where the bandwidth is equal to (a) 1½ times the minimum Nyquist frequency and (b) 3 times the minimum Nyquist frequency.

14-4. Which system has the best projected BER?
   a. 8-QAM, C/N = 15 dB, $B = 2f_N$, f_b = 60 Mbps
   b. QPSK, C/N = 16 dB, $B = f_N$, f_b = 40 Mbps

14-5. An earth station satellite transmitter has an HPA with a rated saturated output power of 10,000 W. The back-off ratio is 6 dB, the branching loss is 2 dB, the feeder loss is 4 dB, and the antenna gain is 40 dB. Determine the actual radiated power and the EIRP.

14-6. Determine the total noise power for a receiver with an input bandwidth of 20 MHz and an equivalent noise temperature of 600 K.

14-7. Determine the noise density for Problem 14-6.

14-8. Determine the minimum C/N ratio required to achieve a $P(e)$ of 10^{-5} for an 8-PSK receiver with a bandwidth equal to f_N.

14-9. Determine the energy per bit-to-noise density ratio when the receiver input carrier power is -100 dBW, the receiver input noise temperature is 290 K, and a 60-Mbps transmission rate is used.

14-10. Determine the carrier-to-noise density ratio for a receiver with a -70-dBW input carrier power, an equivalent noise temperature of 180 K, and a bandwidth of 20 MHz.

14-11. Determine the minimum C/N ratio for an 8-PSK system when the transmission rate is 60 Mbps, the minimum energy of bit-to-noise density ratio is 15 dB, and the receiver bandwidth is equal to the minimum Nyquist frequency.

14-12. For an earth station receiver with an equivalent input temperature of 200 K, a noise bandwidth of 20 MHz, a receive antenna gain of 50 dB, and a carrier frequency of 12 GHz, determine the following: G/T_e, N_0, and N.

14-13. For a satellite with an uplink E_b/N_0 of 14 dB and a downlink E_b/N_0 of 18 dB, determine the overall E_b/N_0 ratio.

14-14. Complete the following link budget:

Uplink parameters
  1. Earth station transmitter output power at saturation, 1 kW
  2. Earth station back-off loss, 3 dB
  3. Earth station total branching and feeder losses, 3 dB
  4. Earth station transmit antenna gain for a 10-m parabolic dish at 14 GHz
  5. Free-space path loss for 14 GHz
  6. Additional uplink losses due to the Earth's atmosphere, 0.8 dB
  7. Satellite transponder G/T_e, -4.6 dBK^{-1}
  8. Transmission bit rate, 90 Mbps, 8-PSK

Downlink parameters
  1. Satellite transmitter output power at saturation, 10 W
  2. Satellite transmit antenna gain for a 0.5-m parabolic dish at 12 GHz
  3. Satellite modulation back-off loss, 0.8 dB
  4. Free-space path loss for 12 GHz
  5. Additional downlink losses due to Earth's atmosphere, 0.6 dB
  6. Earth station receive antenna gain for a 10-m parabolic dish at 12 GHz
  7. Earth station equivalent noise temperature, 200 K
  8. Earth station branching and feeder losses, 0 dB
  9. Transmission bit rate, 90 Mbps, 8-PSK

14-15. An earth station is located at Houston, Texas, that has a longitude of 99.5° and a latitude of 29.5° north. The satellite of interest is *Westar III*. Determine the look angles from the earth station antenna.

14-16. A satellite system operates at 14 GHz uplink and 11 GHz downlink and has a projected $P(e)$ of one bit error in every 1 million bits transmitted. The modulation scheme is 8-PSK, and the system will carry 90 Mbps. The equivalent noise temperature of the receiver is 350 K, and the receiver noise bandwidth is equal to the minimum Nyquist frequency. Determine the following parameters: minimum theoretical C/N ratio, minimum theoretical E_b/N_0 ratio, noise density, total receiver input noise, minimum receive carrier power, and the minimum energy per bit at the receiver input.

14-17. A satellite system operates a 6-GHz uplink and 4-GHz downlink and has a projected $P(e)$ of one bit error in every 100,000 bits transmitted. The modulation scheme is 4-PSK, and the system will carry 80 Mbps. The equivalent receiver noise temperature is 120 K, and the receiver noise bandwidth is equal to the minimum Nyquist frequency. Determine the following:
  a. The C/N ratio that would be measured at a point in the receiver prior to the BPF where the bandwidth is equal to two times the minimum Nyquist frequency.
  b. The C/N ratio that would be measured at a point in the receiver prior to the BPF where the bandwidth is equal to three times the minimum Nyquist frequency.

14-18. Which system has the best projected BER?

    a. QPSK, C/N = 16 dB, $B = 2f_N$, f_b = 40 Mbps

    b. 8-PSK, C/N = 18 dB, $B = f_N$, f_b = 60 Mbps

14-19. An earth station satellite transmitter has an HPA with a rated saturated output power of 12,000 W. The back-off ratio of 4 dB, the branching loss is 1.5 dB, the feeder loss is 5 dB, and the antenna gain is 38 dB. Determine the actual radiated power and the EIRP.

14-20. Determine the total noise power for a receiver with an input bandwidth of 40 MHz and an equivalent noise temperature of 800 K.

14-21. Determine the noise density for Problem 14-20.

14-22. Determine the minimum C/N ratio required to achieve a $P(e)$ of one bit error for every 1 million bits transmitted for a QPSK receiver with a bandwidth equal to the minimum Nyquist frequency.

14-23. Determine the energy of bit-to-noise density ratio when the receiver input carrier power is −85 dBW, the receiver input noise temperature is 400 K, and a 50-Mbps transmission rate.

14-24. Determine the carrier-to-noise density ratio for a receiver with a −80-dBW carrier input power, equivalent noise temperature of 240 K, and a bandwidth of 10 MHz.

14-25. Determine the minimum C/N ratio for a QPSK system when the transmission rate is 80 Mbps, the minimum energy of bit-to-noise density ratio is 16 dB, and the receiver bandwidth is equal to the Nyquist frequency.

14-26. For an earth station receiver with an equivalent input temperature of 400 K, a noise bandwidth of 30 MHz, a receive antenna gain of 44 dB, and a carrier frequency of 12 GHz, determine the following: G/T_e, N_0, and N.

14-27. For a satellite with an uplink E_b/N_0 of 16 dB and a downlink E_b/N_0 of 13 dB, determine the overall E_b/N_0.

14-28. Complete the following link budget:

Uplink parameters
1. Earth station output power at saturation, 12 kW
2. Earth station back-off loss, 4 dB
3. Earth station branching and feeder losses, 2 dB
4. Earth station antenna gain for a 10-m parabolic dish at 14 GHz
5. Free-space path loss for 14 GHz
6. Additional uplink losses due to Earth's atmosphere, 1 dB
7. Satellite transponder G/T_e, −3 dBk
8. Transmission bit rate, 80 Mbps
9. Modulation scheme, 4-PSK

Downlink parameters
1. Satellite transmitter output power at saturation, 5 W
2. Satellite station transmit antenna gain for a 0.5-m parabolic dish at 12 GHz
3. Satellite modulation back-off loss, 1 dB
4. Free-space path loss for 12 GHz
5. Additional downlink losses due to Earth's atmosphere, 1 dB
6. Earth station receive antenna gain for a 10-m parabolic dish at 12 GHz
7. Earth station equivalent noise temperature, 300 K
8. Transmission bit rate, 80 Mbps
9. Modulation scheme, 4-PSK

C H A P T E R 15

Satellite Multiple Accessing Arrangements

OBJECTIVES

- Define *multiple accessing*
- Describe the operation of FDM/FM satellite systems
- Describe frequency-division multiple accessing
- Describe time-division multiple accessing
- Describe code-division multiple accessing
- Define *channel capacity*
- Explain the basic concepts of satellite radio navigation
- Describe the operation of the NAVSTAR Global Positioning System

15-1 INTRODUCTION

In Chapter 25 we analyzed the link parameters of *single-channel satellite transponders.* In this chapter, we will extend the discussion of satellite communications to systems designed for *multiple carriers.* Whenever multiple carriers are utilized in satellite communications, it is necessary that a *multiple-accessing format* be established over the system. This format allows for a distinct separation between the uplink and downlink transmissions to and from a multitude of different earth stations. Each format has its own specific characteristics, advantages, and disadvantages.

Figure 15-1a shows a single-link (two earth stations) *fixed-frequency* FDM/FM system using a single satellite transponder. With earth coverage antennas and for full-duplex operation, each link requires two RF satellite channels (i.e., four RF carrier frequencies, two uplink and two downlink). In Figure 15-1a, earth station 1 transmits on a high-band carrier (f11, f12, f13, and so on) and receives on a low-band carrier (f1, f2, f3, and so on). To avoid interfering with earth station 1, earth station 2 must transmit and receive on different RF carrier frequencies. The RF carrier frequencies are fixed and the satellite transponder is simply an RF-to-RF repeater that provides the uplink/downlink frequency translation. This arrangement is economically impractical and also extremely inefficient. Additional earth stations can communicate through different transponders within the same satellite structure (Figure 15-1b), but each additional link requires four more RF carrier frequencies. It is unlikely that any two-point link would require the capacity available in an entire RF satellite channel. Consequently, most of the available bandwidth is wasted. Also, with this arrangement, each earth station can communicate with only one other earth station. The RF satellite channels are fixed between any two earth stations; thus, the voice-band channels from each earth station are committed to a single destination.

In a system where three or more earth stations wish to communicate with each other, fixed-frequency or *dedicated-channel* systems such as those shown in Figure 15-1, are inadequate; a method of *multiple accessing* is required. That is, each earth station using the satellite system has a means of communicating with each of the other earth stations in the

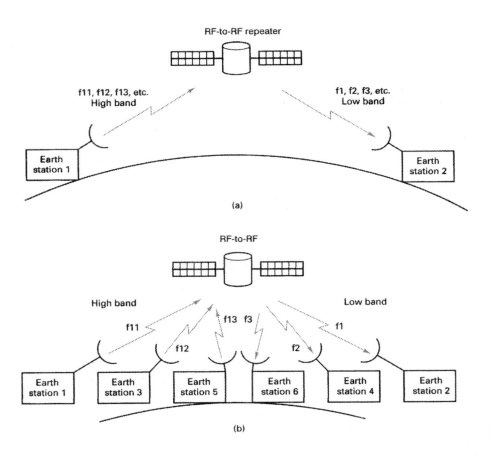

FIGURE 15-1 Fixed-frequency earth station satellite system: (a) single link; (b) multiple link

system through a common satellite transponder. Multiple accessing is sometimes called *multiple destination* because the transmissions from each earth station are received by all the other earth stations in the system. The voice-band channels between any two earth stations may be *preassigned* (*dedicated*) or *demand-assigned* (*switched*). When preassignment is used, a given number of the available voice-band channels from each earth station are assigned a dedicated destination. With demand assignment, voice-band channels are assigned on an as-needed basis. Demand assignment provides more versatility and more efficient use of the available frequency spectrum. On the other hand, demand assignment requires a control mechanism that is common to all the earth stations to keep track of channel routing and the availability of each voice-band channel.

Remember, in an FDM/FM satellite system, each RF channel requires a separate transponder. Also, with FDM/FM transmissions, it is impossible to differentiate (separate) multiple transmissions that occupy the same bandwidth. Fixed-frequency systems may be used in a multiple-access configuration by switching the RF carriers at the satellite, reconfiguring the baseband signals with multiplexing/demultiplexing equipment on board the satellite, or using multiple spot beam antennas (reuse). All three of these methods require relatively complicated, expensive, and heavy hardware on the spacecraft.

Communications satellites operating in the C-band are allocated a total bandwidth of 500 MHz symmetrical around the satellite's center frequency. This is often referred to as one satellite channel, which is further divided into radio channels. Most communications satellites carry 12 transponders (radio channel transmitter/receiver pairs), each with 36 MHz of bandwidth. The carriers of the 12 transponders are frequency-division multiplexed with a 4-MHz guard band between each of them and a 10-MHz guard band on both ends of the 500-MHz assigned frequency spectrum.

If adjacent transponders in the 500-MHz spectrum are fed from a quadrature-polarized antenna, the number of transponders (radio channels) available in one satellite channel can be doubled to 24. Twelve odd-numbered transponders transmit and receive with a vertically polarized antenna, and 12 even-numbered transponders transmit and receive on a horizontally polarized antenna. The carrier frequencies of the even channels are offset 20 MHz from the carrier frequencies of the odd-numbered transponders to reduce crosstalk between adjacent transponders. This method of assigning adjacent channels different electromagnetic polarizations is called *frequency reuse* and is possible by using orthogonal polarization and spacing adjacent channels 20 MHz apart. Frequency reuse is a technique for achieving better utilization of the available frequency spectrum.

15-2-1 Anik-E Communications Satellite

Anik is an Eskimo word meaning "little brother." The Anik-E communications satellites are Domsats (domestic satellites) operated by Telsat Canada. Figure 15-2 shows the frequency and polarization plan for the Anik-E satellite system. One group of 12 radio channels (group A) uses horizontal polarization, and one group of 12 radio channels (group B) uses vertical polarization for 24 total radio channels, each with 36 MHz of bandwidth. There is a 4-MHz bandwidth between adjacent radio channels and a 10-MHz bandwidth at each end of the spectrum for a total satellite channel bandwidth of 500 MHz. There are 12 primary radio channels and 12 spare or preemptible radio channels.

15-3 MULTIPLE ACCESSING

Satellite *multiple accessing* (sometimes called *multiple destination*) implies that more than one user has access to one or more radio channels (transponders) within a satellite communications channel. Transponders are typically leased by a company or a common carrier for the purpose of providing voice or data transmission to a multitude of users. The method by which a satellite transponder's bandwidth is used or accessed depends on the multiple-accessing method utilized.

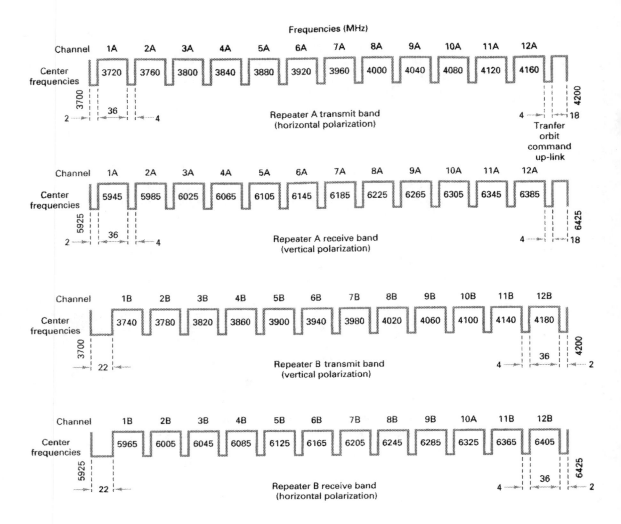

FIGURE 15-2   *Anik-E* frequency and polarization plan

Figure 15-3 illustrates the three most commonly used *multiple-accessing arrange-ments:* frequency-division multiple accessing (FDMA), time-division multiple accessing (TDMA), and code-division multiple accessing (CDMA). With FDMA, each earth station's transmissions are assigned specific uplink and downlink frequency bands within an allotted satellite bandwidth; they may be *preassigned* or *demand assigned.* Consequently, FDMA transmissions are separated in the frequency domain and, therefore, must share the total available transponder bandwidth as well as the total transponder power. With TDMA, each earth station transmits a short burst of information during a specific time slot (*epoch*) within a TDMA frame. The bursts must be synchronized so that each station's burst arrives at the satellite at a different time. Consequently, TDMA transmissions are separated in the time domain, and with TDMA the entire transponder bandwidth and power are used for each transmission but for only a prescribed interval of time. With CDMA, all earth stations transmit within the same frequency band and, for all practical purposes, have no limitations on when they may transmit or on which carrier frequency. Thus, with CDMA, the entire satellite transponder bandwidth is used by all stations on a continuous basis. Signal separation is accomplished with envelope encryption/decryption techniques.

FIGURE 15-3   Multiple-accessing arrangements: (a) FDMA;
(b) TDMA; (c) CDMA

15-3-1   Frequency-Division Multiple Access

Frequency-division multiple access (FDMA) is a method of multiple accessing where a given RF bandwidth is divided into smaller frequency bands called *subdivisions*. Each subdivision has its own IF carrier frequency. A control mechanism is used to ensure that two or more earth stations do not transmit in the same subdivision at the same time. Essentially, the control mechanism designates a receive station for each of the subdivisions. In demand-assignment systems, the control mechanism is also used to establish or terminate the voice-band links between the source and destination earth stations. Consequently, any of the subdivisions may be used by any of the participating earth stations at any given time. If each subdivision carries only one 4-kHz voice-band channel, this is known as a *single-channel per carrier* (SCPC) system. When several voice-band channels are frequency-division multiplexed together to form a composite baseband signal comprised of groups, supergroups, or even mastergroups, a wider subdivision is assigned. This is referred to as *multiple-channel per carrier* (MCPC).

Carrier frequencies and bandwidths for FDM/FM satellite systems using multiple-channel-per-carrier formats are generally assigned and remain fixed for a long period of time. This is referred to as *fixed-assignment, multiple access* (FDM/FM/FAMA). An alternate channel allocation scheme is *demand-assignment, multiple access* (DAMA). Demand assignment allows all users continuous and equal access of the entire transponder bandwidth by assigning carrier frequencies on a temporary basis using a statistical assignment process. The first FDMA demand-assignment system for satellites was developed by Comsat for use on the *Intelsat* series *IVA* and *V* satellites.

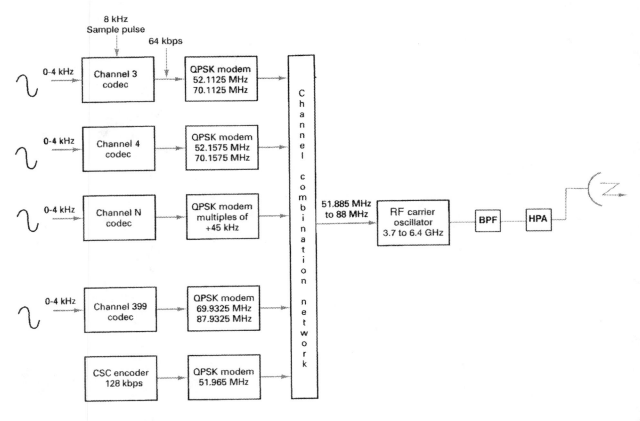

FIGURE 15-4   FDMA, SPADE earth station transmitter

15-3-1-1 SPADE DAMA satellite system. SPADE is an acronym for *s*ingle-channel-per-carrier *P*CM multiple-*a*ccess *d*emand-assignment *e*quipment. Figures 15-4 and 15-5 show the block diagram and IF frequency assignments, respectively, for SPADE.

With SPADE, 800 PCM-encoded voice-band channels separately QPSK modulate an IF carrier signal (hence the name *single-carrier per channel,* SCPC). Each 4-kHz voice-band channel is sampled at an 8-kHz rate and converted to an eight-bit PCM code. This produces a 64-kbps PCM code for each voice-band channel. The PCM code from each voice-band channel QPSK modulates a different IF carrier frequency. With QPSK, the minimum required bandwidth is equal to one-half the input bit rate. Consequently, the output of each QPSK modulator requires a minimum bandwidth of 32 kHz. Each channel is allocated a 45-kHz bandwidth, allowing for a 13-kHz guard band between pairs of frequency-division-multiplexed channels. The IF carrier frequencies begin at 52.0225 MHz (low-band channel 1) and increase in 45-kHz steps to 87.9775 MHz (high-band channel 400). The entire 36-MHz band (52 MHz to 88 MHz) is divided in half, producing two 400-channel bands (a low band and a high band). For full-duplex operation, 400 45-kHz channels are used for one direction of transmission, and 400 are used for the opposite direction. Also, channels 1, 2, and 400 from each band are left permanently vacant. This reduces the number of usable full-duplex voice-band channels to 397. The 6-GHz C-band extends from 5.725 GHz to 6.425 GHz (700 MHz). This allows for approximately 19 36-MHz RF channels per system. Each RF channel has a capacity of 397 full-duplex voice-band channels.

Each RF channel (Figure 15-5) has a 160-kHz *common signaling channel* (CSC). The CSC is a time-division-multiplexed transmission that is frequency-division multiplexed

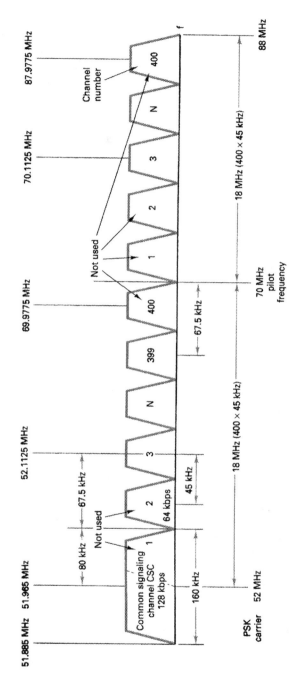

FIGURE 15-5 Carrier frequency assignments for the *Intelsat* single-channel-per-carrier PCM multiple-access demand-assignment equipment (SPADE)

Earth station 1 128 bits	Earth station 2 128 bits	Earth stations 3 – 49 128 bits each	Earth station 50 128 bits
← 1 ms →	← 1 ms →	← 47 ms →	← 1 ms →

← 50 ms →

128 bits/1ms × 1000 ms/1s ≈ 128 kbps or 6400 bits/frame × 1 frame/50 ms ≈ 128 kbps

FIGURE 15-6 FDMA, SPADE common signaling channel (CSC)

into the IF spectrum below the QPSK-encoded voice-band channels. Figure 15-6 shows the TDM frame structure for the CSC. The total frame time is 50 ms, which is subdivided into 50 1-ms epochs. Each earth station transmits on the CSC channel only during its preassigned 1-ms time slot. The CSC signal is a 128-bit binary code. To transmit a 128-bit code in 1 ms, a transmission rate of 128 kbps is required. The CSC code is used for establishing and disconnecting voice-band links between two earth station users when demand-assignment channel allocation is used.

The CSC channel occupies a 160-kHz bandwidth, which includes the 45 kHz for lowband channel 1. Consequently, the CSC channel extends from 51.885 MHz to 52.045 MHz. The 128-kbps CSC binary code QPSK modulates a 51.965-MHz carrier. The minimum bandwidth required for the CSC channel is 64 kHz; this results in a 48-kHz guard band on either side of the CSC signal.

With FDMA, each earth station may transmit simultaneously within the same 36-MHz RF spectrum but on different voice-band channels. Consequently, simultaneous transmissions of voice-band channels from all earth stations within the satellite network are interleaved in the frequency domain in the satellite transponder. Transmissions of CSC signals are interleaved in the time domain.

An obvious disadvantage of FDMA is that carriers from multiple earth stations may be present in a satellite transponder at the same time. This results in cross-modulation distortion between the various earth station transmissions. This is alleviated somewhat by shutting off the IF subcarriers on all unused 45-kHz voice-band channels. Because balanced modulators are used in the generation of QPSK, carrier suppression is inherent. This also reduces the power load on a system and increases its capacity by reducing the idle channel power.

15-3-2 Time-Division Multiple Access

Time-division multiple access (TDMA) is the predominant multiple-access method used today. It provides the most efficient method of transmitting digitally modulated carriers (PSK). TDMA is a method of time-division multiplexing digitally modulated carriers between participating earth stations within a satellite network through a common satellite transponder. With TDMA, each earth station transmits a short *burst* of a digitally modulated carrier during a precise time slot (epoch) within a TDMA frame. Each station's burst is synchronized so that it arrives at the satellite transponder at a different time. Consequently, only one earth station's carrier is present in the transponder at any given time, thus avoiding a collision with another station's carrier. The transponder is an RF-to-RF repeater that simply receives the earth station transmissions, amplifies them, and then retransmits them in a downlink beam that is received by all the participating earth stations. Each earth station receives the bursts from all other earth stations and must select from them the traffic destined only for itself.

Figure 15-7 shows a basic TDMA frame. Transmissions from all earth stations are synchronized to a *reference burst*. Figure 15-7 shows the reference burst as a separate transmission, but it may be the *preamble* that precedes a reference station's transmission of data. Also, there may be more than one synchronizing reference burst.

FIGURE 15-7 Basic time-division multiple-accessing (TDMA) frame

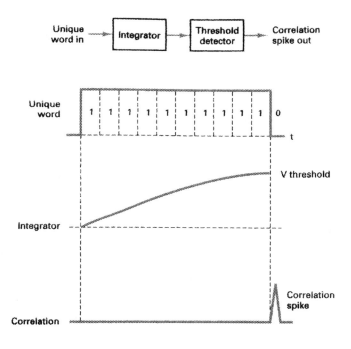

FIGURE 15-8 Unique word correlator

The reference burst contains a *carrier recovery sequence* (CRS), from which all receiving stations recover a frequency and phase coherent carrier for PSK demodulation. Also included in the reference burst is a binary sequence for *bit timing recovery* (BTR, i.e., clock recovery). At the end of each reference burst, a *unique word* (UW) is transmitted. The UW sequence is used to establish a precise time reference that each of the earth stations uses to synchronize the transmission of its burst. The UW is typically a string of 20 successive binary 1s terminated with a binary 0. Each earth station receiver demodulates and integrates the UW sequence. Figure 15-8 shows the result of the integration process. The integrator and threshold detector are designed so that the threshold voltage is reached

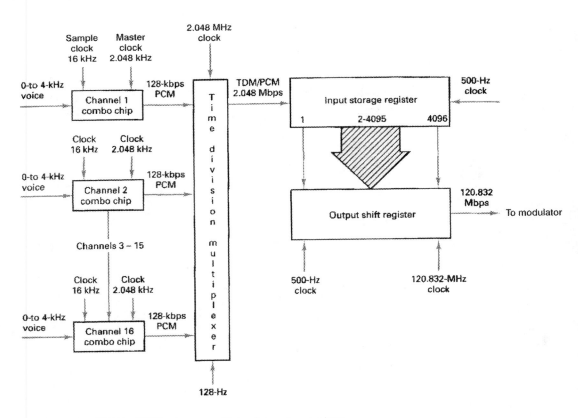

FIGURE 15-9 TDMA, CEPT primary multiplex frame transmitter

precisely when the last bit of the UW sequence is integrated. This generates a *correlation spike* at the output of the threshold detector at the exact time the UW sequence ends.

Each earth station synchronizes the transmission of its carrier to the occurrence of the UW correlation spike. Each station waits a different length of time before it begins transmitting. Consequently, no two stations will transmit the carrier at the same time. Note the *guard time* (GT) between transmissions from successive stations. This is analogous to a guard band in a frequency-division-multiplexed system. Each station precedes the transmission of data with a *preamble*. The preamble is logically equivalent to the reference burst. Because each station's transmissions must be received by all other earth stations, all stations must recover carrier and clocking information prior to demodulating the data. If demand assignment is used, a common signaling channel also must be included in the preamble.

15-3-2-1 CEPT primary multiplex frame. Figures 15-9 and 15-10 show the block diagram and timing sequence, respectively, for the CEPT primary multiplex frame. (CEPT is the Conference of European Postal and Telecommunications Administrations; the CEPT sets many of the European telecommunications standards.) This is a commonly used TDMA frame format for digital satellite systems.

Essentially, TDMA is a *store-and-forward* system. Earth stations can transmit only during their specified time slot, although the incoming voice-band signals are continuous. Consequently, it is necessary to sample and store the voice-band signals prior to transmission. The CEPT frame is made up of eight-bit PCM-encoded samples from 16 independent

FIGURE 15-10   TDMA, CEPT primary multiplex frame

voice-band channels. Each channel has a separate codec that samples the incoming voice signals at a 16-kHz rate and converts those samples to eight-bit binary codes. This results in 128 kbps transmitted at a 2.048-MHz rate from each voice channel codec. The 16 128-kbps transmissions are time-division multiplexed into a subframe that contains one eight-bit sample from each of the 16 channels (128 bits). It requires only 62.5 μs to accumulate the 128 bits (2.048-Mbps transmission rate). The CEPT multiplex format specifies a 2-ms frame time. Consequently, each earth station can transmit only once every 2 ms and, therefore, must store the PCM-encoded samples. The 128 bits accumulated during the first sample of each voice-band channel are stored in a holding register, while a second sample is taken from each channel and converted into another 128-bit *subframe*. This 128-bit sequence is stored in the holding register behind the first 128 bits. The process continues for 32 subframes (32×62.5 μs = 2 ms). After 2 ms, 32 eight-bit samples have been taken from each of 16 voice-band channels for a total of 4096 bits ($32 \times 8 \times 16 = 4096$). At this time, the 4096 bits are transferred to an output shift register for transmission. Because the total TDMA frame is 2 ms long and during this 2-ms period each of the participating earth stations must transmit at different times, the individual transmissions from each station must occur in a significantly shorter time period. In the CEPT frame, a transmission rate of 120.832 Mbps is used. This rate is the 59th multiple of 2.048 Mbps. Consequently, the actual transmission of the 4096 accumulated bits takes approximately 33.9 μs. At the earth station receivers, the 4096 bits are stored in a holding register and shifted at a 2.048-Mbps rate. Because all the clock rates (500 Hz, 16 kHz, 128 kHz, 2.048 MHz, and 120.832 MHz) are synchronized, the PCM codes are accumulated, stored, transmitted, received, and then decoded in perfect synchronization. To the users, the voice transmission appears to be a continuous process.

There are several advantages of TDMA over FDMA. The first, and probably the most significant, is that with TDMA only the carrier from one earth station is present in the satellite transponder at any given time, thus reducing intermodulation distortion. Second, with

FDMA, each earth station must be capable of transmitting and receiving on a multitude of carrier frequencies to achieve multiple-accessing capabilities. Third, TDMA is much better suited to the transmission of digital information than FDMA. Digital signals are more naturally acclimated to storage, rate conversions, and time-domain processing than their analog counterparts.

The primary disadvantage of TDMA as compared with FDMA is that in TDMA precise synchronization is required. Each earth station's transmissions must occur during an exact time slot. Also, bit and frame timing must be achieved and maintained with TDMA.

15-3-3 Code-Division Multiple Access

With FDMA, earth stations are limited to a specific bandwidth within a satellite channel or system but have no restriction on when they can transmit. With TDMA, an earth station's transmissions are restricted to a precise time slot but have no restriction on what frequency or bandwidth it may use within a specified satellite system or channel allocation. With *code-division multiple access* (CDMA), there are no restrictions on time or bandwidth. Each earth station transmitter may transmit whenever it wishes and can use any or all the bandwidth allocated a particular satellite system or channel. Because there is no limitation on the bandwidth, CDMA is sometimes referred to as *spread-spectrum multiple access;* transmissions can spread throughout the entire allocated bandwidth. Transmissions are separated through envelope encryption/decryption techniques. That is, each earth station's transmissions are encoded with a unique binary word called a *chip code.* Each station has a unique chip code. To receive a particular earth station's transmission, a receive station must know the chip code for that station.

Figure 15-11 shows the block diagram of a CDMA encoder and decoder. In the encoder (Figure 15-11a), the input data (which may be PCM-encoded voice-band signals or raw digital data) is multiplied by a unique chip code. The product code PSK modulates an IF carrier, which is up-converted to RF for transmission. At the receiver (Figure 15-11b), the RF is down-converted to IF. From the IF, a coherent PSK carrier is recovered. Also, the chip code is acquired and used to synchronize the receive station's code generator. Keep in mind, the receiving station knows the chip code but must generate a chip code that is synchronous in time with the receive code. The recovered synchronous chip code multiplies the recovered PSK carrier and generates a PSK-modulated signal that contains the PSK carrier plus the chip code. The received IF signal that contains the chip code, the PSK carrier, and the data information is compared with the received IF signal in the *correlator.* The function of the correlator is to compare the two signals and recover the original data. Essentially, the correlator subtracts the recovered PSK carrier + chip code from the received PSK carrier + chip code + data. The resultant is the data.

The correlation is accomplished on the analog signals. Figure 15-12 shows how the encoding and decoding is accomplished. Figure 15-12a shows the correlation of the correctly received chip code. A + 1 indicates an in-phase carrier, and a − 1 indicates an out-of-phase carrier. The chip code is multiplied by the data (either + 1 or − 1). The product is either an in-phase code or one that is 180° out of phase with the chip code. In the receiver, the recovered synchronous chip code is compared in the correlator with the received signaling elements. If the phases are the same, a + 1 is produced; if they are 180° out of phase, a − 1 is produced. It can be seen that if all the recovered chips correlate favorably with the incoming chip code, the output of the correlator will be a +6 (which is the case when a logic 1 is received). If all the code chips correlate 180° out of phase, a −6 is generated (which is the case when a logic 0 is received). The bit decision circuit is simply a threshold detector. Depending on whether a +6 or −6 is generated, the threshold detector will output a logic 1 or a logic 0, respectively.

As the name implies, the correlator looks for a correlation (similarity) between the incoming coded signal and the recovered chip code. When a correlation occurs, the bit decision circuit generates the corresponding logic condition.

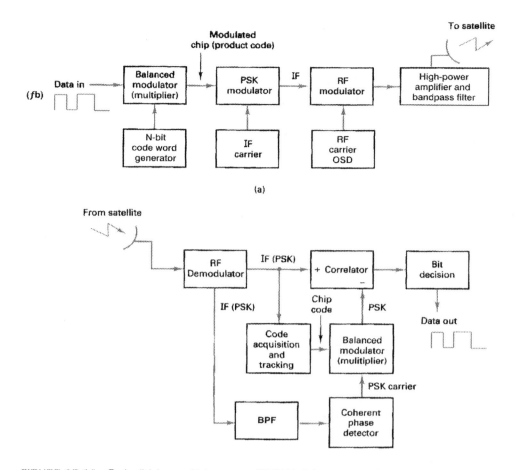

FIGURE 15-11 Code-division multiple access (CDMA): (a) encoder; (b) decoder

With CDMA, all earth stations within the system may transmit on the same frequency at the same time. Consequently, an earth station receiver may be receiving coded PSK signals simultaneously from more than one transmitter. When this is the case, the job of the correlator becomes considerably more difficult. The correlator must compare the recovered chip code with the entire received spectrum and separate from it only the chip code from the desired earth station transmitter. Consequently, the chip code from one earth station must not correlate with the chip codes from any of the other earth stations.

Figure 15-12b shows how such a coding scheme is achieved. If half the bits within a code were made the same and half were made exactly the opposite, the resultant would be zero cross correlation between chip codes. Such a code is called an *orthogonal code*. In Figure 15-12b, it can be seen that when the orthogonal code is compared with the original chip code, there is no correlation (i.e., the sum of the comparison is zero). Consequently, the orthogonal code, although received simultaneously with the desired chip code, had absolutely no effect on the correlation process. For this example, the orthogonal code is received in exact time synchronization with the desired chip code; this is not always the case. For systems that do not have time-synchronous transmissions, codes must be developed where there is no correlation between one station's code and any phase of another station's code.

The primary difference between spread-spectrum PSK transmitters and other types of PSK transmitters is the additional modulator where the code word is multiplied by the incoming data. Because of the pseudorandom nature of the code word, it is often referred

Chip time t_c | **Chip time t_c**

Data in	(Logic 1 = +1)						(Logic 0 = –1)					
x Chip code	1	1	–1	–1	1	1	1	1	–1	–1	1	1
Product code	1	1	–1	–1	1	1	–1	–1	1	1	–1	–1
Recovered chip code	1	1	–1	–1	1	1	1	1	–1	–1	1	1
Correlation	1	1	1	1	1	1	–1	–1	–1	–1	–1	–1
			+6 V						–6 V			

(Product code/Recovered chip code → Comparison)

(a)

Data in	(Logic 1 = +1)						(Logic 0 = –1)					
x Orthogonal code	1	1	–1	1	–1	–1	–1	–1	1	–1	1	1
Product code	1	1	–1	1	–1	–1	–1	–1	1	–1	1	1
Recovered chip code	1	1	–1	–1	1	1	1	1	–1	–1	1	1
Correlation	1	1	1	–1	–1	–1	–1	–1	–1	1	1	1
			0 V						0 V			

(Product code/Recovered chip code → Comparison)

(b)

FIGURE 15-12   CDMA code/data alignment: (a) correct code; (b) orthogonal code

to as *pseudorandom noise* (PRN). The PRN must have a high autocorrelation property with itself and a low correlation property with other transmitter's pseudorandom codes. The code word rate (R_{cw}) must exceed the incoming data rate (R_d) by several orders of magnitude. In addition, the code rate must be statistically independent of the data signal. When these two conditions are satisfied, the final output signal spectrum will be increased (spread) by a factor called the *processing gain*. Processing gain is expressed mathematically as

$$G = \frac{R_{cw}}{R_d} \tag{15-1}$$

where G is processing gain and $R_{cw} >> R_d$.

A spread-spectrum signal cannot be demodulated accurately if the receiver does not possess a despreading circuit that matches the code word generator in the transmitter. Three of the most popular techniques used to produce the spreading function are *direct sequence, frequency hopping,* and a combination of direct sequence and frequency hopping called *hybrid direct-sequence frequency hopping* (hybrid-DS/FH).

15-3-3-1 Direct sequence.   Direct-sequence spread spectrum (DS-SS) is produced when a bipolar data-modulated signal is linearly multiplied by the spreading signal in a special balanced modulator called a *spreading correlator*. The spreading code rate $R_{cw} = 1/T_c$, where T_c is the duration of a single bipolar pulse (i.e., the chip). Chip rates are 100 to 1000 times faster than the data message; therefore, chip times are 100 to 1000 times shorter in duration than the time of a single data bit. As a result, the transmitted output frequency spectrum using spread spectrum is 100 to 1000 times wider than the bandwidth of the initial PSK data-modulated signal. The block diagram for a direct-sequence spread-spectrum system is shown in Figure 15-13. As the figure shows, the data source directly modulates the carrier signal, which is then further modulated in the spreading correlator by the spreading code word.

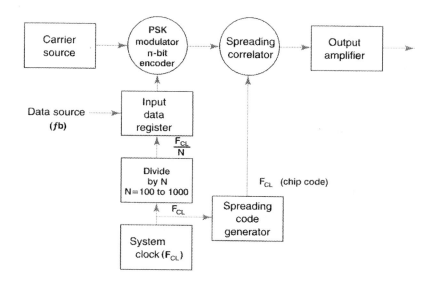

FIGURE 15-13 Simplified block diagram for a direct-sequence spread-spectrum transmitter

The spreading (chip) codes used in spread-spectrum systems are either *maximal-length sequence codes,* sometimes called *m-sequence codes* or *Gold codes.* Gold codes are combinations of maximal-length codes invented by Magnavox Corporation in 1967, especially for multiple-access CDMA applications. There is a relatively large set of Gold codes available with minimal correlation between chip codes. For a reasonable number of satellite users, it is impossible to achieve perfectly orthogonal codes. You can only design for a minimum cross correlation among chips.

One of the advantages of CDMA was that the entire bandwidth of a satellite channel or system may be used for each transmission from every earth station. For our example, the chip rate was six times the original bit rate. Consequently, the actual transmission rate of information was one-sixth of the PSK modulation rate, and the bandwidth required is six times that required to simply transmit the original data as binary. Because of the coding inefficiency resulting from transmitting chips for bits, the advantage of more bandwidth is partially offset and is, thus, less of an advantage. Also, if the transmission of chips from the various earth stations must be synchronized, precise timing is required for the system to work. Therefore, the disadvantage of requiring time synchronization in TDMA systems is also present with CDMA. In short, CDMA is not all that it is cracked up to be. The most significant advantage of CDMA is immunity to interference (jamming), which makes CDMA ideally suited for military applications.

15-3-3-2 Frequency-hopping spread spectrum. Frequency hopping is a form of CDMA where a digital code is used to continually change the frequency of the carrier. The carrier is first modulated by the data message and then up-converted using a frequency-synthesized local oscillator whose output frequency is determined by an *n*-bit pseudorandom noise code produced in a spreading code generator. The simplified block diagram for a frequency-hopping spread-spectrum transmitter is shown in Figure 15-14.

With frequency hopping, the total available bandwidth is partitioned into smaller frequency bands, and the total transmission time is subdivided into smaller time slots. The idea is to transmit within a limited frequency band for only a short time, then switch to another

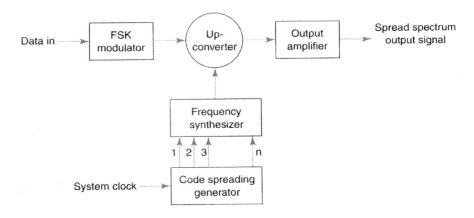

FIGURE 15-14   Simplified block diagram of a frequency-hopping spread-spectrum transmitter

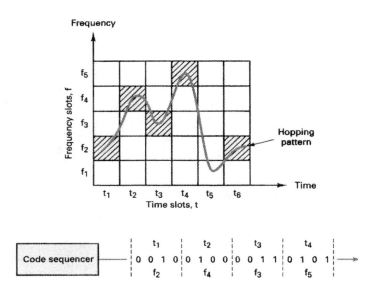

FIGURE 15-15   Frequency time-hopping matrix

frequency band and so on. This process continues indefinitely. The frequency-hopping pattern is determined by a binary spreading code. Each station uses a different code sequence. A typical hopping pattern (frequency-time matrix) is shown in Figure 15-15.

With frequency hopping, each earth station within a CDMA network is assigned a different frequency-hopping pattern. Each transmitter switches (hops) from one frequency band to the next according to their assigned pattern. With frequency hopping, each station uses the entire RF spectrum but never occupies more than a small portion of that spectrum at any one time.

FSK is the modulation scheme most commonly used with frequency hopping. When it is a given station's turn to transmit, it sends one of the two frequencies (either mark or space) for the particular band in which it is transmitting. The number of stations in a given frequency-hopping system is limited by the number of unique hopping patterns that can be generated.

Essentially, there are two methods used to interface terrestrial voice-band channels with satellite channels: digital noninterpolated interfaces (DNI) and digital speech interpolated interfaces (DSI).

15-4-1 Digital Noninterpolated Interfaces

A *digital noninterpolated interface* assigns an individual terrestrial channel (TC) to a particular satellite channel (SC) for the duration of the call. A DNI system can carry no more traffic than the number of satellite channels it has. Once a TC has been assigned an SC, the SC is unavailable to the other TCs for the duration of the call. DNI is a form of preassignment; each TC has a permanent dedicated SC.

15-4-2 Digital Speech Interpolated Interfaces

A *digital speech interpolated interface* assigns a terrestrial channel to a satellite channel only when speech energy is present on the TC. DSI interfaces have *speech detectors* that are similar to *echo suppressors;* they sense speech energy, then seize an SC. Whenever a speech detector senses energy on a TC, the TC is assigned to an SC. The SC assigned is randomly selected from the idle SCs. On a given TC, each time speech energy is detected, the TC could be assigned to a different SC. Therefore, a single TC can use several SCs for a single call. For demultiplexing purposes, the TC/SC assignment information must be conveyed to the receive terminal. This is done on a common signaling channel similar to the one used on the SPADE system. DSI is a form of demand assignment; SCs are randomly assigned on an as-needed basis.

With DSI it is apparent that there is a *channel compression;* there can be more TCs assigned than there are SCs. Generally, a TC:SC ratio of 2:1 is used. For a full-duplex (two-way simultaneous) communication circuit, there is speech in each direction 40% of the time, and for 20% of the time the circuit is idle in both directions. Therefore, a DSI gain of slightly more than 2 is realized. The DSI gain is affected by a phenomenon called *competitive clipping*. Competitive clipping is when speech energy is detected on a TC and there is no SC to assign it to. During the *wait* time, speech information is lost. Competitive clipping is not noticed by a subscriber if its duration is less than 50 ms.

To further enhance the channel capacity, a technique called *bit stealing* is used. With bit stealing, channels can be added to fully loaded systems by stealing bits from the in-use channels. Generally, an overload channel is generated by stealing the least-significant bit from seven other satellite channels. Bit stealing results in eight channels with seven-bit resolution for the time that the *overload channel* is in use. Consequently, bit stealing results in a lower SQR than normal.

15-4-3 Time-Assignment Speech Interpolation

Time-assignment speech interpolation (TASI) is a form of analog channel compression that has been used for suboceanic cables for many years. TASI is very similar to DSI except that the signals interpolated are analog rather than digital. TASI also uses a 2:1 compression ratio. TASI was also the first means used to scramble voice for military security. TASI is similar to a packet data network; the voice message is chopped up into smaller segments made of sounds or portions of sounds. The sounds are sent through the network as separate bundles of energy, then put back together at the receive end to reform the original voice message.

15-5 SATELLITE RADIO NAVIGATION

Navigation can be defined as the art or science of plotting, ascertaining, or directing the course of movements, in other words, *knowing where you are and being able to find your way around.* The most ancient and rudimentary method of navigation is *wandering.* Wandering is simply continuing to travel about until you reach your destination, assuming of course that you have one. My good friend and worldwide traveler, Todd Ferguson, once said, "True travel has no destination." Wandering is the popular navigation technique used by many students during their first week of classes at all colleges and universities. Probably the earliest effective or useful means of navigation is *celestial navigation*. With celestial navigation, direction and distance are determined from precisely timed sightings of celestial bodies, including the stars and moon. This is a primitive technique that dates back thousands of years. An obvious disadvantage of celestial navigation is that it works best at night, preferably with clear skies.

Another rather rudimentary method of navigation is *piloting*. Piloting is fixing a position and direction with respect to familiar, significant landmarks, such as railroad tracks, water towers, barns, mountain peaks, and bodies of water. Piloting derived its name from early aircraft pilots who used this method of navigation.

Dead (ded) *reckoning* is a navigation technique that determines position by extrapolating a series of measured velocity increments. The term *dead* is derived from the word "*ded*uced" and not necessarily from the fate of the people who used the technique. Dead reckoning was used quite successfully by Charles Lindbergh in 1927 during his historic 33-hour transatlantic journey and quite unsuccessfully by Amelia Earhart in 1937 during her attempt to make the first around-the-world flight.

Although each of the navigation methods described thus far had its place in time, undoubtedly the most accurate navigation technique to date is *radio* or *electronic navigation*. With radio navigation, position is determined by measuring the travel time of an electromagnetic wave as it moves from a transmitter to a receiver. There are approximately 100 different types of domestic radio navigation systems currently being used. Some use terrestrial (land-based) broadcast transmitters and others use satellite (space-based) broadcast transmitters. The most accurate and useful radio navigation systems include the following:

> Decca (terrestrial surface broadcast)
> Omega (terrestrial surface broadcast; provides global coverage)
> Loran (terrestrial surface broadcast)
> Navy Transit GPS (low-orbit satellite broadcast; provides global coverage)
> Navstar GPS (medium-orbit satellite broadcast; provides global coverage)

Loran and Navstar are the two most often used radio navigation systems today.

15-5-1 Loran Navigation

Until recently, *Loran* (*Long Ra*nge *N*avigation) was the most effective, reliable, and accurate means of radio navigation. Loran-A was developed during World War II, and the most recent version, Loran-C, surfaced in 1980. Today, Loran is used primarily for recreational aircraft and ships.

With Loran, receivers acquire specially coded signals from two pairs of high-powered, land-based transmitters whose locations are precisely known. The elapsed time between reception of the coded signals is precisely measured and converted in the receiver to distance using the propagation speed of electromagnetic waves. Using basic geometry and the relationship between distance (d), speed (v), and time (t) ($d = vt$), the location of the receiver can be determined with a high degree of accuracy. There is only one set of coordinates that possess a particular time (distance) relationship from four sources.

Loran is only as accurate as the preciseness of the transmission times of the coded signals. System errors are due primarily to propagation problems, such as the fact that Earth's surface is not smooth or perfectly round. Atmospheric conditions and multiple transmission paths can also adversely affect the performance of Loran. However, probably the most prominent disadvantage of Loran is the fact that it does not provide continuous worldwide coverage. Land-based transmitters can be located only where there is land, which is a relatively small proportion of Earth's surface. Consequently, there are locations where Loran signals simply cannot be received (dead spots). However good or bad Loran may have been or could be is unimportant because a newer, better technique of radio navigation called Navstar GPS has emerged that utilizes satellite-based transmitters.

15-5-2 Navstar GPS

Navstar is an acronym for *Nav*igation *S*ystem with *T*ime *A*nd *R*anging, and *GPS* is an abbreviation of Global Positioning System. Navstar GPS is the newest and most accurate system of radio navigation available. Navstar GPS is a satellite-based open navigation system, which simply means that it is available to anyone equipped with a GPS receiver. The United States Department of Defense (DoD) developed Navstar to provide continuous, highly precise position, velocity, and time information to land-, sea-, air-, and space-based users. In essence, Navstar GPS is a space-based navigation, three-dimensional positioning, and time-distribution system. The intent of the system is to use a combination of ground stations, orbiting satellites, and special receivers to provide navigation capabilities to virtually everyone, at any time, anywhere in the world, regardless of weather conditions. The Navstar Satellite System was completed in 1994 and is maintained by the United States Air Force.

15-5-3 GPS Services

GPS provides two levels of service or accuracy: standard positioning service and precise positioning service.

15-5-3-1 Standard positioning service. The *standard positioning service* (SPS) is a positioning and timing service that is available to all GPS users (military, private, and commercial) on a continuous, worldwide basis with no direct charge. SPS will provide a predictable positioning accuracy that 95% of the time is to within 100 m horizontally, 156 m vertically, and 185 m 3-D, with a time transfer accuracy to UTC (*Universal Transverse Mercator Grid*) within 340 nanoseconds. The accuracy of the SPS service can be downgraded during times of national emergencies. For security reasons, the accuracy of the SPS service is intentionally degraded by the DoD through the use of a technique called *selective availability*. Selective availability (SA) is accomplished by manipulating navigation message orbit data (epsilon) and/or the satellite clock frequency (dither).

15-5-3-2 Precise positioning service. The *precise positioning service* (PPS) is a highly accurate military positioning, velocity, and timing service that is available on a continuous, worldwide basis to users authorized by the DoD. PPS user equipment provides a predictable positioning accuracy 95% of the time of at least 22 m horizontally, 27.7 m vertically, and 35.4 m 3-D, and a time transfer accuracy to UTC within 200 nanoseconds. Only authorized users with cryptographic equipment and keys and specially equipped receivers can use the precise positioning service. PPS was designed primarily to be used by the U.S. and allied military, certain U.S. government agencies, and selected civil users specifically approved by the U.S. government.

15-5-4 Navstar Segments

Navstar GPS consists of three segments: a *space segment,* a *ground control segment,* and a *user segment.*

15-5-4-1 Satellite segment. The U.S. Air Force Space Command (AFSC) formally declared the Navstar GPS satellite system as being fully operational as of April 27, 1995. The satellite segment, sometimes called the *space segment,* consists of 24 operational satellites

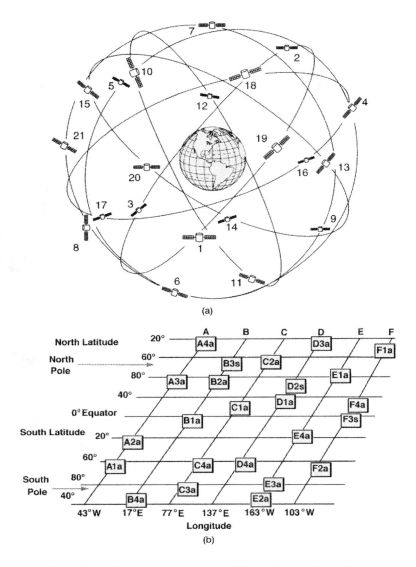

FIGURE 15-16   (a) Navstar constellation; (b) satellite relative positions

revolving around Earth in six orbital planes approximately 60° apart with four satellites in each plane. There are 21 working satellites and three satellites reserved as spaces. In the event of a satellite failure, one of the spare space vehicles can be moved into its place. (There are actually more than 24 satellites now, as some of the older space vehicles have been replaced with newer satellites with more modern propulsion and guidance systems.) Figure 15-16a shows orbital patterns for the 21 working satellites in the Navstar constellation, and Figure 15-16b shows the relative positions of the 24 satellites in respect to each other.

Navstar satellites are not geosynchronous. The satellites revolve around Earth in a circular pattern with an inclined orbit. The angle of elevation at the ascending node is 55° with respect to the equatorial plane. The average elevation of a Navstar satellite is 9476 statute miles (approximately 20,200 km) above Earth. Navstar satellites take approximately 12 hours to orbit Earth. Therefore, their position is approximately the same at the same sidereal time each day (the satellites actually appear 4 minutes earlier each day). Figure 15-17 shows the orbits of several Navstar satellites superimposed over a Mercator projection of

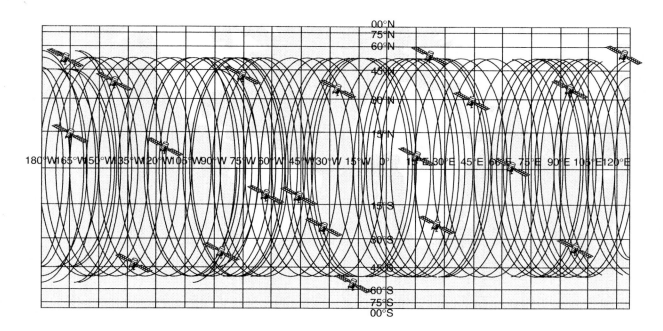

FIGURE 15-17   Mercator projection of Navstar satellite orbits

the world. As the figure shows, the satellites spiral around Earth in six planes virtually covering the surface of the entire globe.

The position of the Navstar satellites in orbit is arranged such that between five and eight satellites will be in view of any user at all times, thereby ensuring continuous worldwide coverage. Information from three satellites is needed to calculate a navigational unit's horizontal location on Earth's surface (*two-dimensional reporting*), but information from four satellites enables a receiver to also determine its altitude (*three-dimensional reporting*). Three-dimensional reporting is obviously more crucial on land because ground surfaces are not constant, whereas the surface of a large body of water is. Navstar satellites broadcast navigation and system data, atmospheric propagation correction data, and satellite clock bias information.

15-5-4-2 Navstar satellite groupings.   There have been three distinct groups plus one subgroup of Navstar satellites. The groups are designated as *blocks.* The 11 block I prototype satellites were intended to be used only for system testing. Block II satellites were the first fully functional satellites that included onboard *cesium atomic clocks* for producing highly accurate timing signals. Block II satellites are capable of detecting certain error conditions, then automatically transmitting a coded message indicating that it is out of service. Block II satellites can operate for approximately 3.5 days between receiving updates and corrections from the control segment of the system. Block IIa satellites are identical to the standard block II versions except they can operate continuously for 180 days between uploads from the ground. The latest satellites, block IIR versions, can operate for 180 days between uploads and possess autonomous navigation capabilities by generating their own navigation information. Thus, the accuracy of the system using block IIR satellites can be maintained longer between uploads.

15-5-4-3 Navstar satellite identification.   Each satellite has three identifying numbers. The first number is the Navstar number that identifies the specific satellite onboard hardware. The second number is the space vehicle (SV) number, which is assigned according to the order of the vehicle's launch. The third number is a *pseudorandom noise*

Satellite's code

Receiver's code

Time difference Δt

FIGURE 26-18 GPS pseudorandom timing code

(PRN) *code* number. This unique integer number is used to encrypt the signal from that satellite. Some GPS receivers identify the satellite from which they are receiving transmissions by the SV numbers; others use the PRN number.

Each Navstar satellite continually transmits a daily updated set of digitally coded *ephemeris data* that describes its precise orbit. *Ephemeris* is a term generally associated with a table showing the position of a heavenly body on a number of dates in a regular sequence, in essence, an astronomical almanac. Ephemeris data can also be computed for a satellite that specifies where on Earth the satellite is directly above at any given instant in terms of latitude and longitude coordinates.

15-5-4-4 Satellite ranging. The GPS system works by determining how long it takes a radio signal transmitted from a satellite to reach a land-based receiver and then using that time to calculate the distance between the satellite and the earth station receiver. Radio waves travel at approximately the speed of light, or 3×10^8 m/s. If a receiver can determine exactly when a satellite began sending a radio message and exactly when the message was received, then it can determine the propagation (delay) time. From the propagation time, the receiver can determine the distance between it and the satellite using the simple mathematical relationship

$$d = v \times t \tag{15-2}$$

where d = distance between satellite and receiver (meters)
v = velocity (3×10^8 m/s)
t = propagation time (seconds)

The trick, of course, is in determining exactly when the synchronizing signal left the satellite. To determine this, the satellite transmitter and earth station receiver produce identical synchronizing (pseudorandom) codes at exactly the same time, as shown in Figure 15-18. Each satellite continuously transmits its precise synchronizing code. After a synchronizing code is acquired, a receiver simply compares the received code with its own locally produced code to determine the propagation time. The time difference multiplied by the velocity of the radio signal gives the distance to the satellite.

Figure 15-19 illustrates how an aircraft can determine the range (distance) it is from four different satellites by simply measuring the propagation (delay) times and multiplying them by the speed of light. Again, simultaneous equations can be used to determine the aircraft's longitude and latitude.

For a receiver on Earth to determine its longitude and latitude, it must receive signals from three or more satellites identifying the satellite vehicle number or their pseudorandom timing code (PRN) and each satellite's location. The location of a satellite is described using a three-dimensional coordinate relative to Earth's center as shown in Figure 15-20. Earth's center is the reference point with coordinates 0, 0, 0. Thus, each satellite space vehicle has an X_s, Y_s, Z_s coordinate that pinpoints its location in respect to Earth's geocenter.

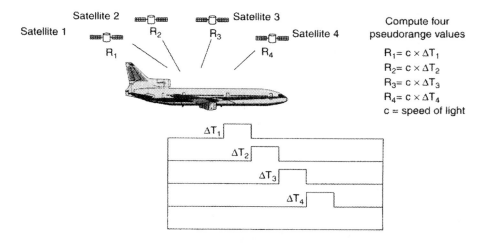

Time signals transmitted by satellites

FIGURE 15-19   GPS ranging solution

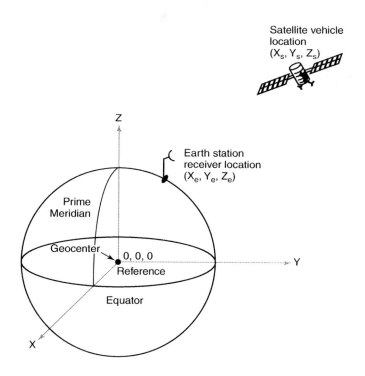

FIGURE 15-20   GPS satellite and earth station receiver coordinate system

The coordinates of the satellites, however, must be updated continually because they vary slightly as the satellite orbits Earth. The location of an earth station also has a three-dimensional coordinate, X_e, Y_e, Z_e, referenced to Earth's center as shown in Figure 15-20.

    If an earth station receiver knows the location of a single satellite and the distance the satellite is from the receiver, it knows that it must be located somewhere on an imaginary sphere centered on the satellite with a radius equal to the distance the satellite is from the receiver. This is shown in Figure 15-21a. If the receiver knows the location of two satellites

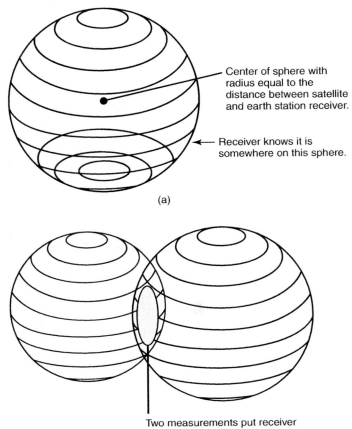

Center of sphere with radius equal to the distance between satellite and earth station receiver.

Receiver knows it is somewhere on this sphere.

(a)

Two measurements put receiver somewhere on this circle.

(b)

Three measurements puts receiver at one of two points.

(c)

FIGURE 15-21 Earth station receiver location relative to the distance from (a) one satellite, (b) two satellites, and (c) three satellites

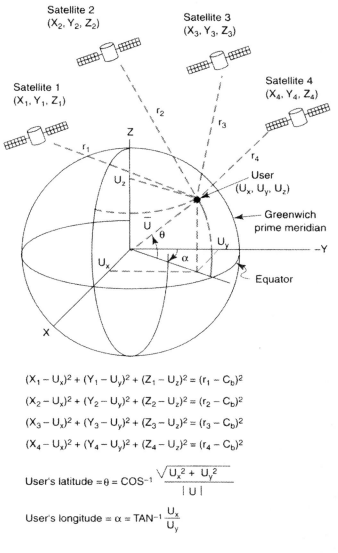

$$(X_1 - U_x)^2 + (Y_1 - U_y)^2 + (Z_1 - U_z)^2 = (r_1 - C_b)^2$$

$$(X_2 - U_x)^2 + (Y_2 - U_y)^2 + (Z_2 - U_z)^2 = (r_2 - C_b)^2$$

$$(X_3 - U_x)^2 + (Y_3 - U_y)^2 + (Z_3 - U_z)^2 = (r_3 - C_b)^2$$

$$(X_4 - U_x)^2 + (Y_4 - U_y)^2 + (Z_4 - U_z)^2 = (r_4 - C_b)^2$$

$$\text{User's latitude} = \theta = \text{COS}^{-1}\, \frac{\sqrt{U_x{}^2 + U_y{}^2}}{|U|}$$

$$\text{User's longitude} = \alpha = \text{TAN}^{-1}\, \frac{U_x}{U_y}$$

FIGURE 15-22 GPS satellite position calculations

and their distances from the receiver, it can narrow its location to somewhere on the circle formed where the two spheres intersect as shown in Figure 15-21b. If the location and distance to a third satellite is known, a receiver can pinpoint its location to one of two possible locations in space as shown in Figure 15-21c. The GPS receivers can usually determine which point is the correct location as one location is generally a ridiculous value. If the location and distance from a fourth satellite is known, the altitude of the earth station can also be determined.

Figure 15-22 shows there are three unknown position coordinates (*x, y,* and *z*). Therefore, three equations from three satellites are required to solve for the three unknown coordinates. A fourth unknown is the error in the receiver's clock, which affects the accuracy of the time-difference measurement. To eliminate the *clock bias error* (C_b), a fourth satellite is needed to produce the fourth equation necessary to solve for four unknowns using simultaneous equations. The solutions to the simultaneous equations for determining latitude and longitude are given in Figure 15-22.

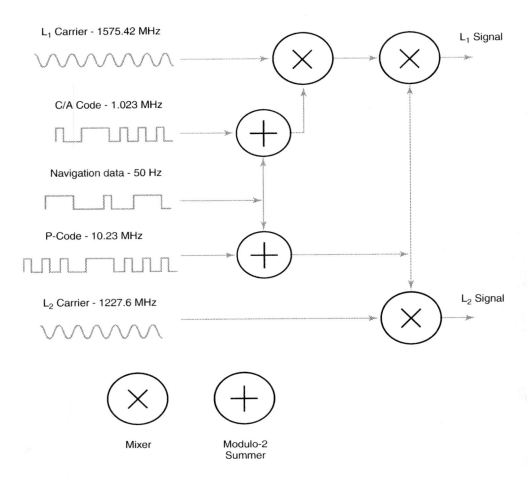

L$_1$ Carrier - 1575.42 MHz

L$_1$ Signal

C/A Code - 1.023 MHz

Navigation data - 50 Hz

P-Code - 10.23 MHz

L$_2$ Carrier - 1227.6 MHz

L$_2$ Signal

Mixer

Modulo-2
Summer

FIGURE 15-23 Simplified Navstar satellite CDMA transmitter

15-5-4-5 GPS satellite signals. All Navstar satellites transmit on the same two *L-band* microwave carrier frequencies: $L_1 = 1575.42$ MHz and $L_2 = 1227.6$ MHz. The L_1 signal carries the navigation message and the standard positioning service (SPS) code signals. The L_2 signal is used by the precise positioning service (PPS) equipped receivers to measure the ionospheric delay. GPS satellites use code division multiple accessing (CDMA spread *spectrum*), which allows all 24 satellites to transmit simultaneously on both carriers without interfering with each other. Three pseudorandom binary codes modulate the L_1 and L_2 carriers as shown in Figure 15-23.

1. The coarse/acquisition (C/A) code is a repeating pseudorandom noise (PRN) code with a 1.023-MHz chip rate and a period of 1 ms. This noiselike code modulates the L_1 carrier signal, spreading its spectrum over approximately a 1-MHz bandwidth. Each satellite vehicle has a different C/A PRN code which is used primarily to acquire the P-code. Satellites are often identified by their unique PRN number.

2. The precision (P) code has a 10.23-MHz rate, lasts a period of seven days, and contains the principle navigation ranging code. In the *antispoofing* (AS) mode, the P-code is encrypted into the Y-code which requires a classified AS module in each receiver channel and is used only by authorized users. The P(Y) code is the basis for the precision positioning system.

Subframe #	One subframe = 300 bits, 6 seconds			
1	TLM	HOW	Satellite vehicle correction data	
2	TLM	HOW	Satellite vehicle ephemeris data (I)	
3	TLM	HOW	Satellite vehicle ephemeris data (II)	30 seconds
4	TLM	HOW	other system data	
5	TLM	HOW	Almanac data for all satellites	

TLM - Telemetry word

8-bit Preamble	16 Data	6 Parity

HOW - Handover word

17-bit time of week	7 Data	6 Parity

FIGURE 15-24 Navigation data frame format

3. The Y-code is used in place of the P-code whenever the antispoofing (AS) mode of operation is activated. Antispoofing guards against fake transmissions of satellite data by encrypting the P-code to form the Y-code.

Because of the spread-spectrum characteristics of the modulated carriers, the Navstar system provides a large margin of resistance to interference. Each satellite transmits a navigation message containing its orbital elements, clock behavior, system time, and status messages. In addition, an almanac is provided which gives the approximate ephemeris data for each active satellite and, thus, allows the users to find all the satellites once the first one has been acquired.

The navigation message modulates the L_1-C/A code signal as shown in Figure 15-23. The navigation message is a 50-Hz signal made of data bits that describe the GPS satellite orbits, clock corrections, and other system parameters. The data format used for the navigation message is shown in Figure 15-24. The navigation data frame consists of 1500 data bits divided into five 300-bit subframes. A navigation frame is transmitted once every 30 s (6 s for each subframe) for a transmission rate of 50 bps. Each subframe is preceded by a telemetry word (TLM) and a handover word (HOW). The TLM contains an eight-bit preamble, 24 data bits, and six parity bits; the HOW contains a 17-bit code identifying the time of week, seven data bits, and six parity bits.

The first subframe contains satellite vehicle correction data and the second and third subframes contain ephemeris parameter data. The fourth and fifth subframes are used to transmit different pages of system data including almanac data for all systems. Twenty-five frames (125 subframes) constitute the complete navigation message that is sent over a 12.5-minute period.

15-5-4-6 Control segment. The Navstar control segment, called the *operational control system* (OCS), includes all the fixed-location ground-based *monitor stations* located throughout the world, a *Master Control Station* (MCS), and uplink transmitters. There are passive monitor stations located in California, Hawaii, Alaska, Ascencion Island (off West

Africa), Diego Garcia (Indian Ocean), and Kwajalein (Pacific Ocean), among others. The monitor stations are simply GPS receivers that track the satellites as they pass overhead and accumulate ranging and ephemeris (orbital) data from them. This information is relayed to the Master Control Station at Falcon Air Force Base, 12 miles east of Colorado Springs, Colorado, where it is processed and determined if the actual satellite position compares with the GPS-computed position. The Master Control Station is managed by the U.S. Air Force's 2nd Space Operations Squadron (2nd SOPS).

The MCS receives data from the monitor stations in real time, 24 hours a day, and uses that information to determine if any satellites are experiencing clock or ephemeris changes and to detect equipment malfunctions. New navigation and ephemeris information is calculated from the monitored signals and uploaded to the satellites once or twice per day. The information calculated by the MCS, along with routine maintenance commands, is relayed to the satellites by ground-based uplink antennas. The ground antennas are located at Ascencion Island, Diego Garcia, and Kwajalein. The antenna facilities transmit to the satellites via an *S-band* radio link. In addition to its main function, the MCS maintains a 24-hour computer bulletin board system with the latest system news and status.

15-5-4-7 User segment. The GPS user segment consists of all the GPS receivers and the user community. GPS receivers convert signals received from space vehicles into position, velocity, and time estimates. Four satellites are required to compute the four dimensions of *x, y, z* (position) and time. GPS receivers are used for navigation, positioning, time dissemination, mapping, guidance systems, surveying, photogrammetry, public safety, archaeology, geology, geophysics, wildlife, aviation, marine, and numerous other research applications. Navigation in three dimensions, however, is the primary function of GPS.

GPS navigation receivers are made for aircraft, ships, ground vehicles, and handheld units for individuals. GPS navigation precise positioning is possible using GPS receivers at reference locations providing corrections and relative positioning data for remote receivers. Surveying, geodetic control, and plate tectonic studies are examples. Time and frequency dissemination, based on the precise clocks on board the space vehicles and controlled by the monitor stations, is another use for GPS. Astronomical observatories, telecommunications facilities, and laboratory standards can be set to precise time signals or controlled to accurate frequencies by special-purpose GPS receivers.

15-5-5 Differential GPS

Differential GPS makes standard GPS even more accurate. Differential GPS works by canceling out most of the natural and man-made errors that creep into normal GPS measurements. Inaccuracies in GPS signals come from a variety of sources, such as satellite clock drift, imperfect orbits, and variations in Earth's atmosphere. These imperfections are variable and difficult if not impossible to predict. Therefore, what is needed is a means to measure the actual errors as they are occurring.

With differential GPS, a second receiver is placed in a location whose exact position is known. It calculates its position from the satellite data and then compares it with its known position. The difference between the calculated and known positions is the error in the GPS signal. Differential GPS is only practical in locations where you can leave a receiver permanently, such as near an airport.

Sources of errors in GPS are satellite clocks, selective availability, ephemeris, atmospheric delays, multipath, receiver clocks, and so on. Table 15-1 summarizes GPS error sources for both standard and differential GPS.

Table 15-1 Summary of GPS Error Sources

Per Satellite Accuracy	Standard GPS	Differential GPS
Satellite clocks	1.5	0
Orbit errors	2.5	0
Ionosphere	5.0	0.4
Troposphere	0.5	0.2
Receiver noise	0.3	0.3
Multipath reception	0.6	0.6
Selective availability	30	0
Typical position accuracy (meters)		
Horizontal	50	1.3
Vertical	78	2.0
3-D	93	2.4

QUESTIONS

15-1. Discuss the drawbacks of using FDM/FM modulation for satellite multiple-accessing systems.

15-2. Contrast *preassignment* and *demand assignment.*

15-3. What are the three most common multiple-accessing arrangements used with satellite systems?

15-4. Briefly describe the multiple-accessing arrangements listed in Question 15-3.

15-5. Briefly describe the operation of Comsat's SPADE system.

15-6. What is meant by *single carrier per channel?*

15-7. What is a common-signaling channel and how is it used?

15-8. Describe what a reference burst is for TDMA and explain the following terms: *preamble, carrier recovery sequence, bit timing recovery, unique word,* and *correlation spike.*

15-9. Describe guard time.

15-10. Briefly describe the operation of the CEPT primary multiplex frame.

15-11. What is a store-and-forward system?

15-12. What is the primary advantage of TDMA as compared with FDMA?

15-13. What is the primary advantage of FDMA as compared with TDMA?

15-14. Briefly describe the operation of a CDMA multiple-accessing system.

15-15. Describe a chip code.

15-16. Describe what is meant by an orthogonal code.

15-17. Describe cross correlation.

15-18. What are the advantages of CDMA as compared with TDMA and FDMA?

15-19. What are the disadvantages of CDMA?

15-20. What is a Gold code?

15-21. Describe frequency hopping.

15-22. What is a frequency-time matrix?

15-23. Describe digital noninterpolated interfaces.

15-24. Describe digital speech interpolated interfaces.

15-25. What is channel compression, and how is it accomplished with a DSI system?

15-26. Describe competitive clipping.

15-27. What is meant by *bit stealing?*

15-28. Describe time-assignment speech interpolation.

15-1. How many satellite transponders are required to interlink six earth stations with FDM/FM modulation?

15-2. For the SPADE system, what are the carrier frequencies for channel 7? What are the allocated passbands for channel 7? What are the actual passband frequencies (excluding guard bands) required?

15-3. If a 512-bit preamble precedes each CEPT station's transmission, what is the maximum number of earth stations that can be linked together with a single satellite transponder?

15-4. Determine an orthogonal code for the following chip code (101010). Prove that your selection will not produce any cross correlation for an in-phase comparison. Determine the cross correlation for each out-of-phase condition that is possible.

15-5. How many satellite transponders are required to interlink five earth stations with FDM/FM modulation?

15-6. For the SPADE system, what are the carrier frequencies for channel 9? What are the allocated passbands for channel 10? What are the actual passband frequencies for channel 12 (excluding the guard bands)?

15-7. If a 256-bit preamble precedes each CEPT station's transmission, what is the maximum number of earth stations that can be linked together with a single satellite transponder?

15-8. Determine an orthogonal code for the following chip code (010101). Prove that your selection will not produce any cross correlation for an in-phase comparison. Determine the cross correlation for each out-of-phase condition that is possible.

Answers to Selected Problems

CHAPTER 1

1-1. a. 869 nm, 8690 A°
    b. 828 nm, 8280 A°
    c. 935 nm, 9350 A°

1-3. 38.57°

1-5. 56°

1-7. a. RZ = 1 Mbps, NRZ = 500 kbps
    b. RZ = 50 kbps, NRZ = 25 kbps
    c. RZ = 250 kbps, NRZ = 125 kbps

1-9. a. 789 nm, 7890 A°
    b. 937 nm, 9370 A°
    c. 857 nm, 8570 A°

1-11. 42°

1-13. 36°

1-15. a. RZ = 357 kbps, NRZ = 179 kbps
    b. RZ = 2 Mbps, NRZ = 1 Mbps
    c. RZ = 250 kbps, NRZ = 125 kbps

CHAPTER 2

2-1. 16 kHz, 4000 baud

2-3. 22 kHz, 10 kbaud

2-5. 5 MHz, 5 Mbaud

2-7. I = 1, Q = 0

2-9.

Q	I	C	Phase
0	0	0	−22.5°
0	0	1	−67.5°
0	1	0	22.5°
0	1	1	67.5°
1	0	0	−157.5°
1	0	1	−112.5°
1	1	0	157.5°
1	1	1	112.5°

2-11.

Q	Q'	I	I'	Phase
0	0	0	0	−45°
1	1	1	1	135°
1	0	1	0	135°
0	1	0	1	−45°

2-13. Input 00110011010101
XNOR 101110111001100

2-15. 40 MHz

2-17.

Q	I	Phase
0	0	−135°
0	1	−45°
1	0	135°
1	1	45°

2-19. 3.33 MHz, 3.33 Mbaud

2-21. 2.5 MHz, 2.5 Mbaud

2-23. a. 2 bps/Hz

b. 3 bps/Hz

c. 4 bps/Hz

CHAPTER 3—NO PROBLEMS

CHAPTER 4

4-1. C = 0E, J = 1A, 4 = 0A, / = 17

4-3. C = C3, J = D1, 4 = F4, / = 61

4-5. 10100000 binary, A0 hex

4-7. 1000010010100000 binary, 84A0 hex

4-9. 4

4-11. Hamming bits = 0010 in positions 8, 6, 4, and 2

4-13. 8 V

CHAPTER 5

5-1. B8 hex

5-3. 4 inserted zeros

5-5. 8A hex

5-7. 65 hex

5-9. 4 deleted zeros

CHAPTER 6

6-1. a. 8 kHz

  b. 20 kHz

6-3. 10 kHz

6-5. 6 kHz

6-7. a. −2.12 V

  b. −0.12 V

  c. +0.04 V

  d. −2.12 V

  e. 0 V

6-9. 1200 or 30.8 dB

6-11. a. +0.01 to +0.03 V

  b. −0.01 to −0.03 V

  c. +20.47 to +20.49 V

  d. −20.47 to −20.49 V

  e. +5.13 to +5.15 V

  f. +13.63 to +13.65 V

6-13.
f_{in}	f_s
2 kHz	4 kHz
5 kHz	10 kHz
12 kHz	24 kHz
20 kHz	40 kHz

6-15.
f_{in}	f_s
2.5 kHz	1.25 kHz
4 kHz	2 kHz
9 kHz	4.5 kHz
11 kHz	5.5 kHz

6-17.
N	DR	db
7	63	6
8	127	12
12	2047	66
14	8191	78

6-19.
μ	gain
255	0.948
100	0.938
255	1.504

6-21. 50.8 dB, 50.8 dB, 60.34 dB, 36.82 dB

6-23.
V_{in}	12-bit	8-bit	12-bit	decoded V	% Error
−6.592	100110011100	11011001	100110011000	−6.528	0.98
+12.992	001100101100	01100010	001100101000	+12.929	0.495
−3.36	100011010010	11001010	100011010100	−3.392	0.94

6-25. 11001110, 00110000, 01011111, 00100000

CHAPTER 7

7-1. a. 1.521 Mbps

  b. 760.5 kHz

7-3. $\begin{matrix} +-\underline{0000}+-+0-\underline{00000}+-00+-+0 \\ 00- 00- \end{matrix}$

7-5.

channel	f(kHz)
1	108
2	104
3	100
4	96
5	92
6	88
7	84
8	80
9	76
10	72
11	68
12	64

7-7. a. 5 kHz

b. 1.61 Mbps

c. 805 kHz

7-11.

CH	GP	SG	MG
100–104	364–370	746–750	746–750
84–88	428–432	1924–1928	4320–4324
92–96	526–520	2132–2136	4112–4116
72–76	488–492	2904–2908	5940–5944

7-13.

GP	SG	MG	MG out (kHz)
3	13	2	5540–5598
5	25	3	6704–6752
1	15	1	1248–1296
2	17	2	4504–4552

CHAPTER 8—NO PROBLEMS

CHAPTER 9

9-1. a. 22-gauge wire with 44 mH inductance every 3000 feet

b. 19-gauge wire with 88 mH inductance every 6000 feet

c. 24-gauge wire with 44 mH inductance every 3000 feet

d. 16-gauge wire with 135 mH inductance every 3000 feet

9-3. a. −3 dBrnO

b. 18 dBrnc

c. 40 dBrnO

d. 47 dB

9-5. a. 51 dBrncO

b. −100 dBm

c. −1 dBmO

d. 36 dB

9-7. 2300 µs

CHAPTER 10—NO PROBLEMS

CHAPTER 11

11-1. 112 channels per cluster, 1344 total channel capacity

11-3. 8

11-5. a. 112
b. 448
c. 1792

CHAPTER 12—NO PROBLEMS

CHAPTER 13

13-1. -99.23 dBm
13-3. 28.9 dB
13-5. -85 dBm
13-7. 1.25 dB
13-9. 6.39 dB
13-11. 72.4 dB, 84.4 dB, 115.9 dB, 126.8 dBm, 138.8 dB, 137.5 dB
13-13. -94.3 dBm
13-15. 53 dB
13-17. $FM = 31.6$ dB, $A_t = A_r = 43.1$ dB, $L_p = 141.8$ dB, $L_b = 6$ dB, $L_f = 9.4$ dB, $N = -106$ dBm, $C_{min} = -78$ dBm, $P_t = 21.6$ dBm
13-19. -81 dBm

CHAPTER 14

14-1. Elevation angle = 51°, azimuth = 33°
14-3. a. 11.74 dB
b. 8.5 dB
14-5. $P_{rad} = 28$ dBW, EIRP = 68 dBW
14-7. -200.8 dBW
14-9. 26.18 dB
14-11. 19.77 dB
14-13. 12.5 dB
14-15. Elevation angle = 55°, azimuth = 15° west of south
14-17. a. $C/N = 10.2$ dB
b. $C/N = 8.4$ dB
14-19. 68.3 dBW
14-21. -199.6 dBj
14-23. $N_o = -202.5$ dBW, $E_b = -162$ dBj, $E_b/N_o = 40.5$ dB
14-25. 19 dB
14-27. 11.25 dB

CHAPTER 15

15-1. 15 transponders
15-3. 44 stations
15-5. 10 transponders

Spread Spectrum Techniques

Edited By
M.Tavakoli

Appendix

Spread Spectrum Techniques

A.1 Introduction

Spread spectrum techniques spread the spectrum of a message or a data signal over a wider bandwidth compared to the original bandwidth occupied by the data signal. Spread spectrum techniques, which have remained classified for a long time, entered the public domain with their recent applications in cellular communications. Spread spectrum techniques have gone beyond simple digital modulation techniques in handling the common communication problems. Even though their initial usage was restricted to military applications, features like multiple access and secure transmission have fostered their application in the field of wireless and cellular applications. PN codes along with other spreading codes are the backbone of spread spectrum techniques. This chapter provides a formal introduction to spread spectrum techniques in the field of digital communication and explores two most commonly used spread spectrum techniques: Direct-Sequence Spread Spectrum (DSSS), Frequency-Hopped Spread Spectrum (FHSS) and the generation and properties of spread spectrum codes.

A.2 Objectives

- Describe the basic concepts of spread spectrum techniques
- Evaluate the performance of spread spectrum systems
- Classify the different types of spread spectrum codes
- Explain the Direct-Sequence Spread Spectrum (DSSS) system, both the baseband and digital
- modulated system
- Explain advantages and disadvantages of spread spectrum techniques
- Explain the Frequency-Hopped Spread Spectrum (FHSS) system
- Explain Jamming and Low probability of interception (LPI) under spread spectrum techniques
- Describe the properties of PN codes
- Describe Gold and Kasami codes

A.3 History

Spread spectrum techniques were first used by Armstrong in the early 1920s using wide band FM. The spread spectrum techniques gained importance since their application in the development of military guidance and communication systems was realized. Spread spectrum techniques were used in World War II and later in the 1950s and 1960s for military applications. However, they were always kept secret. They were primarily used for RADAR anti-jam applications. Presently, these are used in the Global Positioning System (GPS), which is considered to be the largest spread spectrum system and has become an integral part of several wireless and cellular systems. Spread spectrum techniques were used commercially for the first time in the synchronous satellite transponders in the early 1980s.

A.4 Spectrum of a Signal

- Explain the concept of the spectrum of a signal.
- Explain the concept of spread spectrum.

Before moving ahead into the basics of spread spectrum techniques, it is essential to understand what a spectrum is and why the spread spectrum systems are known as such.

Any modulating system is defined by a single characteristic signature by which it can be identified. The signature includes the central frequency and the bandwidth of the signal when modulated. This signature is known as the spectrum of the signal and is the frequency domain representation of the signal.

Figures A.1(a), A.1(b), and A.1(c) show some of the most commonly used time domain signals and their corresponding frequency domain representations (spectra).

Figure A.1(a): Time Domain: Sinc; Frequency Domain: Rectangular

Figure A.1(b): Time Domain: Rectangular; Frequency Domain: Sinc

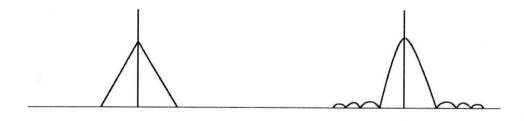

Figure A.1(c): Time Domain: Triangular; Frequency

A.5 Direct-Sequence Spread Spectrum Systems (DSSS)

In DSSS, the data signal is spread directly by a widespread code sequence. The main idea is to spread the spectrum of the modulated (modulation that can be baseband or digital) data signal a second time by using a wideband spreading signal. The wideband spreading signal is selected so as to make demodulation possible only by the intended receiver and to make demodulation impossible by an unintended receiver.

DSSS systems can be classified into:

- Baseband DSSS
- Modulated DSSS

The baseband DSSS system applies the DSSS technique directly to the baseband digital data. Similarly, the modulated DSSS applies the spread spectrum technique to the data that is already modulated by some digital modulation technique. Different types of modulation are used before the DSSS technique is applied. Most common are the BPSK and the QPSK modulation. The BPSK modulated DSSS system is discussed in the subtopic dealing with modulated DSSS.

A.5.1 Baseband DSSS System

The baseband DSSS system spreads the baseband digital signal using the wide-bandwidth spreading-code signal. The spreading is done to the baseband signal directly, without any digital modulation. The technique, and the system, is called baseband DSSS.

Figure A.2 shows a block diagram of a baseband DSSS system. The original data signal, which is of low bandwidth, is multiplied with the wide-bandwidth, direct sequence spreading code. This operation widens the bandwidth of the data signal. Figure A.3 shows an example of the original digital signal (NRZ bipolar +1, −1). The spectrum of the signal is shown in Figure A.4, bandwidth is very narrow. Figure A.5 shows an example of spreading code. Figure A.6 shows the result of multiplication the generation of DSSS output. Figure A.7 shows the spreading spectrum of the result. As you see in this figure the spectrum of the result is much wider than the spectrum of the data.

Despreading at the baseband DSSS receiver system is done by remultiplying the received signal with the same PN code used at the transmitter. The rate should be kept the same. Also, the despreading has to be perfectly synchronized for zero delay.

To synchronize the received signal with the PN code signal at the receiver, the transmitter would initially transmit a training sequence for a short period of time. No data is transmitted during this period. The training sequence is the PN code itself. The receiver has to become synchronized with the incoming signal using this PN code training sequence.

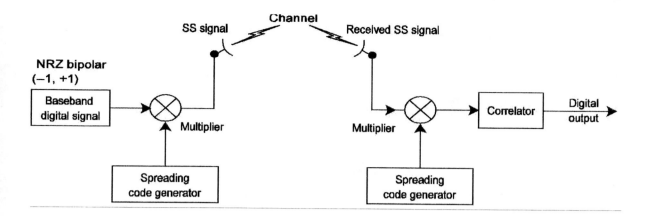

Figure A.2 : Block diagram of baseband DSSS baseband system

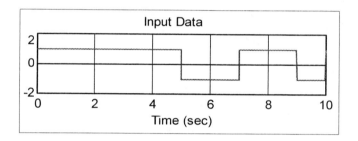

Figure A.3 Example of digital baseband signal

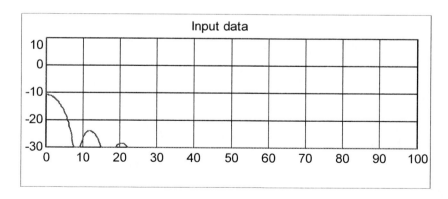

Figure A.4 Example of digital baseband signal spectrum

Figure A.5 Example of spreading code

Figure A.6 Spread spectrum digital output sequence

Figure A.7: Spread spectrum of the DSSS

A.5.2 Demodulation with Incorrect PN Code

Since all the users in a spread spectrum communication system share the same bandwidth for communication, it may appear as if the signals can be tapped by unintended users. The privacy and secrecy of the information signal lies within the uniqueness of the PN code used. With a wide range of PN codes and other spreading codes that can be generated, it is almost impossible to identify the PN code used at the transmitter for spreading.

A.6 BPSK DSSS System

In this section the following will be discussed

- Describe the BPSK DSSS system.
- Explain the effects of using an incorrect PN code for demodulation in a BPSK DSSS system.

Digital modulation techniques, due to their inherent advantages, are often employed to modulate the baseband digital signal before sending it onto the channel. There are two versions of the BPSK DSSS system:

In the first type, the digital signal is first BPSK-modulated using the BPSK carrier. The modulated signal is then spread across the wide bandwidth by means of the spreading code. At the receiver end, the signal is first despread by multiplication with the spreading code, and then it is BPSK-demodulated.

In the second type, the digital signal is first spread using the spreading code, just as in the baseband DSSS system. The resulting signal is then BPSK-modulated using the BPSK carrier. At the receiver, the signal is first BPSK demodulated, and then it is despread using the spreading code. Figure A.8 shows the block diagram of BPSK DSSS System.

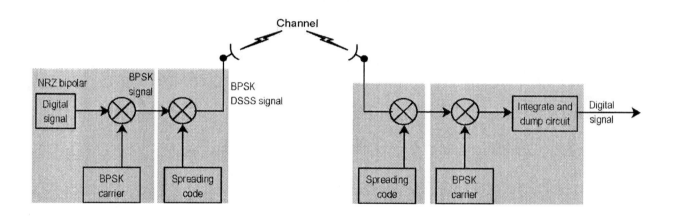

Figure A.8: BPSK DSSS System

A.7 Advantages and Limitations of DSSS Systems

Listed below are some of the advantages and limitations of the DSSS systems.

The advantages include:
- Best noise performance
- Very low probability of interception and most difficult to detect
- Low density power spectra for signal hiding
- Better anti-jam capability, especially for narrow-band jamming
- Multiple access capability
- Secure communication

- o High resolution ranging
- o Best possible discrimination in multipath environments.

The limitations are:
- o Long acquisition time due to the large code length
- o No performance improvement under AWGN
- o Fast code generator is required because the coding rate is much higher than the data rate
- o Requires high bandwidth compared to bandwidth of the signal. Bandwidth increase does not improve the performance under white noise.
- o Complex implementation

A.8   Frequency-Hopped Spread Spectrum System (FHSS)

The block diagram of the FHSS system is shown in Figure A.9. The FHSS technique is similar to Frequency Shift Keying (FSK) modulation. But here the selection of the frequency depends on the PN code rather than on the data.

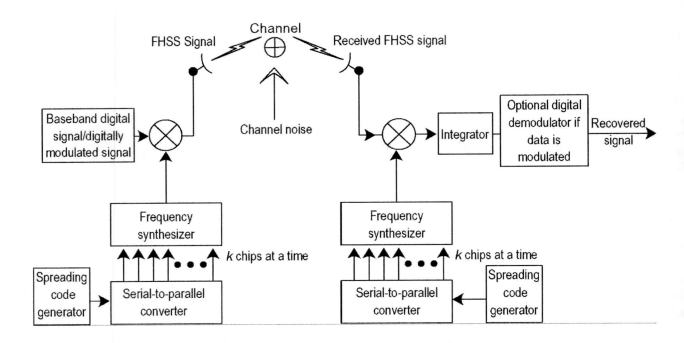

Figure A.9: FHSS Block Diagram

The PN code generator generates the PN code. At any instant, *k* bits from the PN code generator are taken in a cyclic fashion. These *k* bits determine the frequency that must be transmitted at any time instant. The baseband digital signal is then modulated (multiplied) with this frequency and transmitted. Any digital modulation can also be used to digitally modulate the signal before feeding to the spread spectrum system. In such a case, an additional digital modulator is present in the transmitting system, with corresponding demodulator equipment at the receiver side. The demodulation is done at the receiver end after despreading the spread spectrum signal. Also, the channel being assumed AWGN will add channel noise to the spread spectrum signal. At the receiver end, the same PN code is generated, and again the same k bits are taken in a cyclic fashion at the receiver to determine the frequency hops. The frequencies selected are multiplied with the received signal so as to despread the signal. The despread signal is given to the correlator and then to the decision circuit for recovering the digital signal.

A.8.1 Advantages and Limitations of FHSS Systems

Listed below are some of the advantages and limitations of the FHSS systems.

The advantages of the FHSS systems are:

- Can be programmed to be frequency selective to avoid some frequency regions that are otherwise licensed to other services.
- Relatively short acquisition time, as the code length is relatively smaller than that for the DSSS system
- Less affected by the near-far problem
- Greatest amount of spreading

Disadvantages of the FHSS systems are:

- Requires a very efficient frequency synthesizer that is very difficult to attain
- Cannot be used for ranging applications of the spread spectrum systems

A.9 Time-Hopped Spread Spectrum System

Time hopping, in its operation, is similar to pulse modulation in that the output of the transmitter is turned ON and OFF following some prescribed pattern. The PN code is used to determine the ON and OFF timings.

Time hopping is different from frequency hopping in the way the hops are made. In frequency hopping, the carrier frequency hops at the end of each chip time, which is determined by the k-bit duration of the PN code. However, in time hopping, the amplitude of the signal changes (ON and OFF) only at one/zero transitions. Now, the data is not ON for the whole length of time, but is keyed ON and OFF by the PN code. Since the PN code has almost a 50 percent run of ones and a 50 percent run of zeros along the code length, the duty cycle of the data signal would be as much as 50 percent of its original duration.

The fundamental limitation in the use of time-hopping systems is that, to avoid interference, very stringent timing requirements should be placed on the overall system to reduce the overlap of signal transmission between different transmitters. Also, due to the use of a single frequency, the system is vulnerable to jammer effects. A continuous jammer located at the central frequency of transmission can effectively limit the performance of the system. Time hopping may be used to reduce the interference between systems in time-division multiplexing. Due to the high vulnerability of the time-hop systems, they are not used directly in any of the commercial applications. Time-hopping techniques find some application when they are coupled with other spread spectrum techniques, especially with frequency hopping.

A.10 Spread Spectrum Process Gain

The process gain of a spread spectrum system is the ratio of the spread bandwidth to the information bandwidth. Processing gain is a measure of the difference between the system performance when using spread spectrum techniques and the system performance when not using spread spectrum techniques. It can be expressed as:

$$G_p = BW / R$$

Where, G_P = process gain; BW = bandwidth of the spread signal; and R = bandwidth of the digital information signal. Processing gain of a spread spectrum system is also known as the bandwidth expansion factor. This is because it gives the factor by which the bandwidth of the digital message signal is expanded.

A.11 Communication Problems with Traditional Digital Modulation Techniques

There are two common communication problems that cannot be solved using the existing digital modulation techniques. Spread spectrum technique solves these two problems.

Many of the modulation techniques, their corresponding demodulation techniques, and their performance study have been based on the assumption that the channel is AWGN. Under this assumption, the techniques offer efficient use of communication power and bandwidth with a minimum tolerable probability of bit error. The required bandwidth and energy per bit are readily available to provide a pre-specified bit error rate. Many of the real-world channels fit with the description of AWGN in nature. However, there are channels that cannot be assumed as AWGN in nature and doing so may lead to spurious and unprecedented results. A white Gaussian noise is a mathematical description of a channel with infinite power spread uniformly over all the frequencies. As a result, there is no localization of power over a finite fixed frequency or narrow band of frequencies. There are two examples of a real-world scenario where the channel cannot be modeled as AWGN.

Example A.1

In military communication systems, the transmission and reception systems might be jammed by an intentional, continuous tone jammer located in the vicinity of the central frequency in the spectrum. This causes a large amount of unwanted interference and affects all the communication taking place in that frequency zone. The interference caused cannot be modeled as stationary AWGN noise. The white Gaussian assumes the noise is spread uniformly across all the frequencies. (AWGN implies that the noise is additive. There are other types of noise where the noise is multiplicative).

In this case, intentional jamming creates the concentration of the jammer power at and around the central frequency. As a result, the power density is not uniform and, therefore, is not AWGN.

Example A.2

Another real-world scenario that does not fit the description of being an AWGN channel is when there is multipath between the transmitter and the receiver. Multipath or multiple propagation paths between the transmitter and the receiver cause a special kind of interference at the receiver due to the delayed replica of the original signal. This type of interference is very common in LOS digital microwave communication systems and urban cellular systems. In this scenario, the receiver actually receives a delayed replica of the original message signal. This delayed replica, which is treated as unwanted interference (noise), occupies the same spectrum as the original message signal and, as a result, has its power concentrated in fixed-frequency bands. Therefore, this also does not come under AWGN.

A.12 Jamming and Low Probability of Interception

Two communication problems that cannot be solved using the existing digital modulation techniques and require some advanced techniques are:

- o   Jamming
- o   Low Probability of Interception (LPI)

A.12.1   Jamming

Electromagnetic jamming is defined as the deliberate radiation, re-radiation, or reflection of electromagnetic energy to prevent or reduce the enemy's effective use of the electromagnetic spectrum. It is also used to degrade or neutralize the enemy's combat capability. Figure A.10 shows DSSS transmitter with the jamming signal added in the channel. Figure A.11 shows the rejection model for spread spectrum receiver.

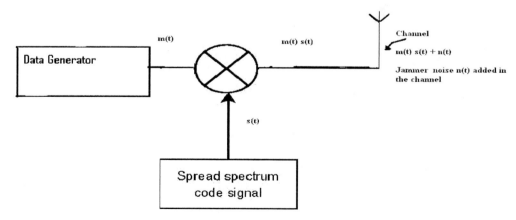

Figure A.10: DSSS transmitter with the jamming signal added in the channel.

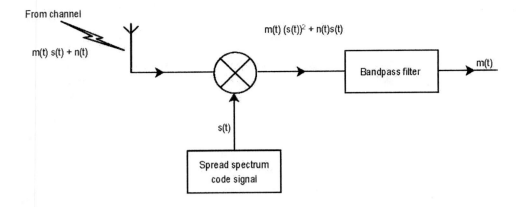

Figure A.11: Interference rejection model for spread spectrum receiver

Figure A.12(a) shows the desired signal spectrum overlapped with jammer's signal spectrum m(t)s(t)+ n(t).
Figure A.12(b) shows interference rejection signals after dispreading at the receiver

Figure A.12(a): Desired signal spectrum overlapped with jammer's signal spectrum

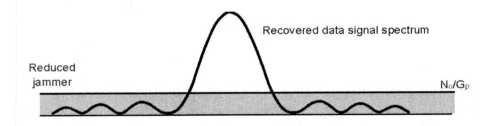

Figure A.12 (b): Interference Rejection Signals after despreading at receiver

Refer to appendix of the chapter to examine the simulation of a DSSS system under Jamming signal. In the case of pulse noise jammer, the spread spectrum decreases the noise power density of the jammer. Since the maximum probability of error is directly proportional to the noise power spectral density of the jammer, the effect of the jammer is highly reduced. This is because the process gain of the spread spectrum system is very high. The spread spectrum techniques reduce the bit error probability compared to the digital modulation techniques. Jamming is classified into different types based on the communication channels where it occurs. Examples of jamming are:

- Radio jamming
- RADAR jamming

A.12.2 Radio Jamming

Radio jamming is the intentional jamming caused near the central frequency of the receiver. This causes the receiver to receive the unwanted signal rather than the actual message signal. This is achieved by increasing the power of the jammer signal in the spectrum location of the message signal. The jammer signal is high-powered compared to the message signal. Therefore, the message signal is lost as noise and the receiver receives only the jammer signal. Radio jammers are classified on the level of perception at the receiver. The two types of radio jamming are *obvious* and *subtle jamming.*

> Obvious jamming is so named because the receiver can immediately detect the presence of a jammer. The obvious jammer sends out noise tones like stepped tones and random keying codes in the frequency range of operation of the receiver. The receiver can hear these sounds on its devices. This overrides the message signal, which is lost behind the high-powered jammer. Since this type of noise is detected, the receiver can take action to avoid the effects of the jammer. It may jump to another frequency band of operation to avoid the effects of the jammer. However, in military communication systems, the delay caused in avoiding the radio jamming while relaying urgent messages can be very damaging.
>
> Subtle Jamming remains undetected at the receiver. The receiver has no knowledge that the information-bearing signal is lost. The receiver does not recognize the problem and continues with its normal operation. This type of jamming is very dangerous as it is very difficult to detect and combat.

A.12.3 RADAR Jamming

RADAR jamming is the transmission of signals in the frequency band of operation of RADAR with the intention of either blocking the information or manipulating the information. There are two types of RADAR jammers:

> **Noise jammers**: The purpose of a noise jammer is to either delay the detection of the target or avoid it. This is achieved by transmitting a high-powered signal within the frequency band of the operation of the RADAR. This appears as thermal noise received by the RADAR, and the target goes undetected.
>
> **Deception jammers:** Deception jammers send out false information regarding the location, direction of travel, and velocity of the target to the RADAR. They do this by intercepting the original RADAR signal. They modify the information and retransmit the false information to the RADAR receiver

A.13 Low Probability of Interception (LPI)

In certain communication systems like military communications, it is required to encrypt the message to prevent interception by unintended receivers. Such communication systems are termed as Low Probability of Interception (LPI) systems. A very low transmitting power is used in these systems, and the transmitted signal is said to be "covert." This is achieved by using a signaling scheme other than the traditional modulation techniques. In LPI communication, the spread spectrum uses a secret code known as the *spreading code* to modulate the message signal. This code is only known to the intended receiver. When any other communication system tries to intercept the message signal, the message signal appears as noise to the listener. The energy reduction of the spreading signal compared to the message signal also helps the low probability of detection.

A.14 High Resolution Ranging

In finding the RADAR range, one-shot pulse is sent along the channel. After reflecting from the target, the pulse returns to the RADAR and is detected by the RADAR receiver. The time delay between the transmission and reception of the pulse provides the distance of the location of the target. One of the disadvantages of using single pulse for this purpose is that one-shot pulse is not reliable over a Gaussian channel.

Using spread spectrum techniques provides two advantages in this case. They are:

- The spread spectrum signal, due to its correlation properties, can be accurately detected even when it is buried deep in noise. This will increase the reliability of the target detection in RADAR applications.
- The time resolution of the pulses will be less, due to the high bandwidths used in spread spectrum techniques. Therefore, the distance of the location of the target can be found precisely with better resolution.

A.15 Multiple Accesses

Spread spectrum techniques also provide multiple accesses and are different from the other techniques for multiple accesses. This method is called Code Division Multiple access (CDMA). For example, in TDMA, the time is sliced between the different users, where each user can use the entire bandwidth during that time slice. In FDMA, each user is allocated a narrow bandwidth channel with low data rates, but continuous transmission all the time. In the case of spread spectrum techniques, all the users utilize the entire bandwidth all the time. Therefore, high data rates and high speed of data transmission is possible due to the availability of continuous transmission. However, there is a huge interference between the different user data. For example, in TDMA, the overlap in the frequencies is solved using the difference in time instants at which each user transmits. In FDMA, overlap in the time instants of transmission is solved using the different channels frequencies along which the users transmit. There is huge interference in the case of spread spectrum techniques due to the overlap in time instants and channel bandwidths used for transmission.

The solution to this problem is the use of different spreading codes for different users. The receiver can recover the intended signal from the overlapped combined signal using the spreading code. The high autocorrelation property of the spreading code helps receive the desired signal. The low cross correlation property of the spreading codes helps the user avoid the signals that are not intended for this reception. Therefore, multiple accesses are possible without any ambiguity and with high security in the spread spectrum communication. The generation of highly secure spreading codes is a very important aspect in spread spectrum multiple access communications. The generation of different spreading codes is discussed later in this chapter.

A.16 Spread Spectrum Code

Coding waveforms is one of the primary methods that has a bandwidth expansion factor greater than unity. Coding introduces useful redundancy that can be used at the receiver for efficient recovery of the message signal. These two properties of coding are similar to the requirements for a system to be considered a spread spectrum. Therefore, coding has an important role to play in spread spectrum communication systems.

The two required properties of the spreading codes are:

- The spreading codes must have a higher chip rate than the data rate.
- The codes must be completely random so that they cannot be easily cracked.

The different types of spreading codes used are:

- PN codes
- Gold codes
- Kasami codes
- Barker codes
- Walsh codes

A.17 PN Codes

In this section the following will be discussed

- Discuss the applications of PN codes.
- Explain the basics of polynomial arithmetic.
- Discuss the generation of PN codes using linear feedback shift registers.
- Describe the various properties of PN codes.

If the code is completely random, the receiver will not be able to decode it. If the receiver knows the method to decode, then the code is not completely random. These codes are known as PN codes because they are deterministic. Since these codes appear as noise to the unintended receiver, these codes are also called PN codes.

CDMA (Code Division Multiple Access) uses a PN code pattern to allow multiple users to use a common communication channel.

IS-95 is a digital mobile telephony standard based on CDMA technology. It defines the radio link or air interface between the mobile station and the base station in a CDMA network.

A.17.1 Polynomial Arithmetic

PN codes can be generated using polynomials known as primitive polynomials. When these primitive polynomials are used in a mechanized Linear Feedback Shift Register (LFSR), we can generate PN codes. A list of the primitive polynomials that can be used for PN code generation of order less than 6 are shown in Table A.1

Number of Stages in LFSR	Possible Primitive Polynomial
n = 1	$1 + X$
n = 2	$1 + X + X^2$
n = 3	$1 + X + X^3$ $1 + X^2 + X^3$
n = 4	$1 + X + X^4$ $1 + X^3 + X^4$
n = 5	$1 + X^2 + X^5$ $1 + X + X^2 + X^3 + x^5$ $1 + x^3 + X^5$ $1 + X + X^3 + X^4 + x^5$ $1 + X^2 + X^3 + X^4 + x^5$ $1 + X + X^2 + X^4 + x^5$

Table A.1: List of Primitive Polynomial

A.17.2 Linear Feedback Shift Register (LFSR)

A shift register is a series of registers placed next to each other. An LFSR is one in which a feedback path from the output to input is present. An LFSR can be used to generate PN codes when a primitive polynomial is used to determine the output. An example of LFSR is shown in Figure A.13.

With each clock, the value contained in each register is shifted to the adjacent register in a specific direction. The registers retain the values that are stored until the clock occurs. The feedback path connects the output of the last register on one end to the input of the register on the other end. Therefore, with clock frequency the shift register shows its contents as an output. After N clocks, where n is the number of registers in the LFSR, the pattern repeats itself. LFSR can be used to generate multiple PN codes.

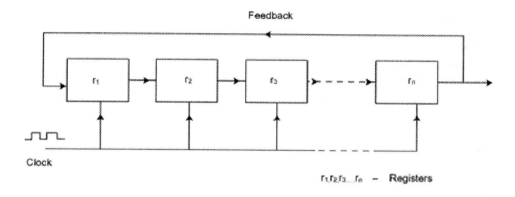

Figure A.13: An example of LFSR

A.17.3 PN Code Generation Using LFSR and Primitive Polynomial

Let the primitive polynomial be:

$$P(X) = 1 + c_1 X^1 + c_2 X^2 + c_3 X^3 \dots\dots c_{n-1} X^{n-1} + c_n X^n$$

The coefficients of the polynomial given by $c_1, c_2, c_3 \dots c_{n-1}$ and c_n act as switches. If a particular coefficient $c_i = 0$, then there is no tap connection to the modulo-2 adder (Ex-OR). See Figure A.12 and A.13. If $c_i = 1$, then that particular tap is connected to the modulo-2 adder.

For the different number of stages in LFSR, the two different LFSRs will yield two different types of PN codes. Also, the same PN code generated using the primitive polynomial $P(X)$ is also generated using a reciprocal polynomial $P'(X)$, which is given by:

$$P'(X) = X^n P(X^{-1})$$

Example A.3:

Referring to table A.1 for $n = 3$ the primitive polynomial is
$P(X) = 1 + X + X^3$. Find $P'(X)$

Solution:
$P'(X) = X^3 P(X^{-1}) = X^3 (1 + 1/X + 1/X^3) = X^3 + X^2 + 1$

This polynomial generates the same PN code as $P(X)$ as shown in table A.1 for $n = 3$.

Two different configurations of LFSRs used for generating PN codes are Simple Shift Register Generator (SSRG) and Modular Shift Register Generator (MSRG).

A.17.4 SSRG

Figure A.14 shows SSRG implementation of PN code generation.

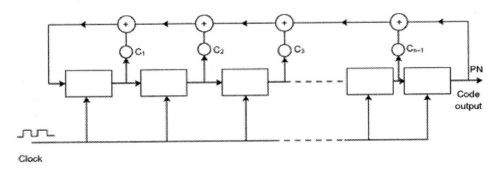

Figure A.14 SSRG generation of PN code

A SSRG uses the primitive polynomial coefficients to construct its structure. The output of the last stage is always fed into the first stage of the shift register. Every clock instant, the values in the selected registers are given to the modulo-2 adders present at the top. The selection of the registers is based on the values of the coefficients of the primitive polynomial c_i. Let n be the number of registers then the sequence repeats itself after N shifts where $N = 2^n - 1$.

A.17.5 MSRG

Figure A.15 shows MSRG implementation of PN code generation. The output of the last stage is always fed back to the first stage in the MSRG, as in the SSRG. The distinct feature of the MSRG is that the output of the last stage is always fed to the modulo-2 adders (Ex-OR) present just before each register. An MSRG is also known as Galois form LFSR. It also is sometimes referred to as Multiple Return Shift Register Generator (MRSRG).

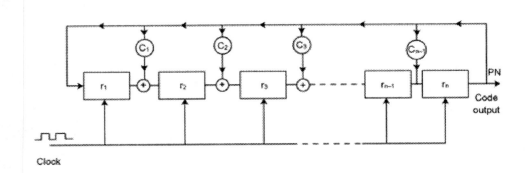

Figure A.15: MSRG generation of PN code

In this model, the shift register output is fed back to multiple inputs along the shift register. At each clock tick, this feedback output is modulo-2 summed with the previous register's value, and the sum value is shifted into the next register.

Example A.4

Draw the SSRG LFSR configuration for the given primitive polynomial $1 + X^2 + X^3$. Find the PN code generated by the primitive polynomial if the initial values in the registers are given by [1 1 1].

Solution

Comparing the primitive polynomial with the general form of the polynomial it is obtained that the values of the coefficients are $c_1 = 0$, $c_2 = 1$ and $c_3 = 1$. The SSRG configuration for the given primitive polynomial is shown in Figure A.16.

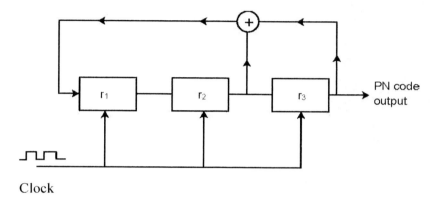

Clock

Figure A.16: SSRG configuration for primitive polynomial $1 + X^2 + X^3$

Given that the initial values in the registers are [1 1 1], the generation of the PN code is shown in Table A.2.

State	r1	r2	PN Code Output r3	r3 +r2 Mod.2 addition
Initial state	1	1	1	0
Clock #1	0	1	1	0
Clock #2	0	0	1	0
Clock #3	1	0	0	1
Clock #4	0	1	0	0
Clock #5	1	0	1	1
Clock #6	1	1	0	1
Clock #7	1	1	1	1
PN code output	110010 1			

Table A.2: Generation of PN code for the primitive polynomial $1 + X^2 + X^3$

Therefore the PN code output generated by the SSRG for the primitive polynomial $1 + X^2 + X^3$ is 1100101.

A.17.6 Maximum Length Sequence

PN code is also known as Maximal Length (ML) sequence. With the number of registered n the length of the code generated is equal to N = 2n - 1, which is the maximum code length. To generate ML codes, the polynomial used for generation should be primitive. The code word generated in ML sequences using a primitive polynomial is unique.

A.18 PN Code Properties

The properties of PN codes are very significant in their application in spread spectrum techniques and CDMA. A few important properties of PN codes are:

- Balance property
- Shift and add property
- Correlation property

These properties will be discussed in the following sections.

A.18.1 Balance Property

The balance property of the PN code specifies the balance of ones and zeros present in the generated code. The total number of ones in the PN code exceeds the number of zeros in the code by one. For an LFSR with n stages the length of the code is $N = 2^n - 1$. The output PN code will have $2^{n-1} = (N+1)/2$ ones. The corresponding number of zeroes will be one less than this value, that is $2^{n-1} = (N - 1)/2$

Example A.5

Verify that the PN code generated in Example A.4 satisfies the balance property.

Solution:

The PN code generated in Example A.4 is 1100101

The number of ones is equal to $2^{3-1} = 4$

The number of zeros is equal to $2^{3-1} - 1 = 3$

As you see the number of ones is one greater than the number of zeroes. Therefore, the PN code generated, satisfies the balance property

A.18.2 Shift-and-Add Property

According to the shift-and-add property of the PN codes, the modulo-2 addition of PN code with any phase-shifted version of the PN code will result in the same PN code, possibly with a different phase shift.

Example A.6

Verify that the PN code generated in Example A.4 satisfies the shift-and-add property.

Solution

The PN code generated in Example A.4 is 1100101. The shift-and-add property is verified in tabular form, as shown in Table A.3. Each least significant bit is circulated to the most significant bit by every shift. Then the shifted version added by modulo -2 sum operation to the original PN code. The result is one of the shifted versions of original code. For example modulo -2 addition of the original PN code 1100101 with the first shifted version 1110010 will result 1011100 which is the original code after five shifts.

	Right Circular Shift 1	Right Circular Shift 2	Right Circular Shift 3	Right Circular Shift 4	Right Circular Shift 5	Right Circular Shift 6
Original PN code	1100101	1100101	1100101	1100101	1100101	1100101
Shifted version	1110010	0111001	1011100	0101110	0010111	1001011
Shift and add sum	1011100 (shift 5)	1011100 (shift 3)	0111001 (shift 2)	1001011 (shift 6)	1110010 (shift 1)	0101110 (shift 4)

Table A.3: Shift-and-Add property

Since the entire shift-and-add sum results are equal to one of the phase-shifted versions of the PN code, the PN code generated satisfies the shift-and-add property.

A.18.3 Correlation Property

The communication channel is occupied with different transmitting signals propagating in several directions. When different transmitters transmit information signals, the chances of interference of one signal with another are very high. To capture the correct signal at the corresponding receiver, the signals should not interfere with one another. In spread spectrum modulation system, PN sequences are used to modulate the information signals to a higher level. The resultant signals are transmitted through the channel. The different transmitted spread spectrum signals occupy the same bandwidth in the channel. To study the chances of interference of these signals with another PN sequence transmitted with another information signal, it is necessary to study the relationship between the PN sequences. The correlation property establishes the relationship between different PN sequences. Correlation is the measure of how much a random signal varies compared to another without actually depending on it. Correlation between two data sequences describes the observed relation between two sequences. It provides an index of the degree to the two sequences covary in a linear fashion.

The two types of correlation are:

- Autocorrelation
- Cross correlation

A.18.3.1 Autocorrelation

Autocorrelation is the degree of correspondence between a PN sequence and a phase-shifted replica of itself. In other words, the autocorrelation function for a periodic PN sequence is defined as the number of agreements and the number of disagreements between two codes.

For zero delay, the chips in the PN sequence are matched exactly with the same PN sequence. In this case the number of agreements in one period of the PN sequence is N, and there are no disagreements. The value of autocorrelation is N. This is the maximum value of the correlator output. This value is divided by the length of the code while taking the normalized value, which gives unit value or 100% for perfect agreement.

Figure A.17 shows a typical PN code. Figure A.18 shows the correlation between two the same PN code. As you see in this case the autocorrelation is 100%.

Figure A.17 PN code used to show autocorrelation

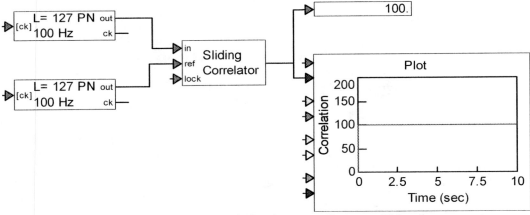

Figure A.18: Autocorrelation between the same PN codes

Example A.7

How is the autocorrelation property of the PN codes useful in a spread spectrum receiver?

Solution

Autocorrelation provides secure and reliable communication in noisy environments. First the signal is multiplied with the PN code. Multiplying it again with a synchronized copy of the same PN code results in the recovery of the original message signal. Recovery is possible with a synchronized copy of the PN code. Since the normalized autocorrelation value is unity, by multiplying it again, the required signal is recovered. As shown in Figure A.19 input data is multiplied with the spreading code and the result in receiver is multiplied with the same PN code and the data is recovered.

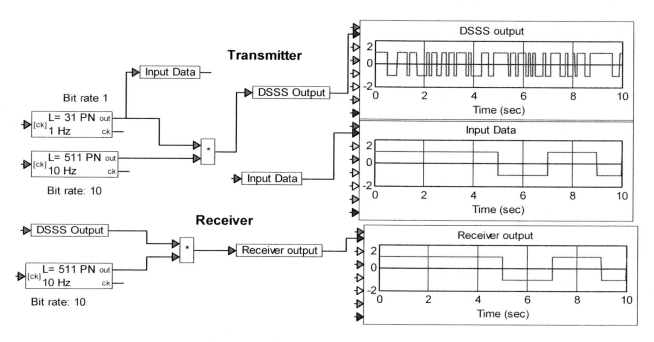

Figure A.19: Simple transmitter and receiver using PN code spread spectrum techniques

To achieve synchronization, the received signal may be time-shifted by chip periods. The corresponding correlation with the PN code at the receiver may be found. The occurrence of a peak means that the incoming data and the PN code at the receiver are synchronized. The receiver then starts demodulating the data from that instant onwards.

A.18.3.2 Cross Correlation

Cross correlation measures the level of agreement between two different PN sequences.
An example of two different PN code is shown in Figure A.20. The cross correlation between these two different PN code is shown in Figure A.21. The average of correlation is much less than 100%.

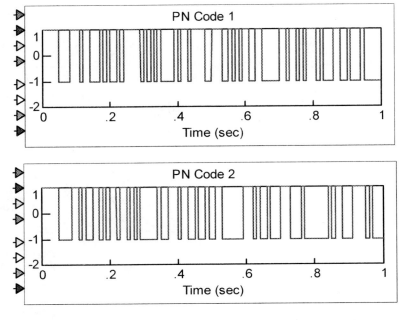

Figure A.20: Two Different PN Code

Figure A.21: An Example of Cross correlation between two different PN codes.

If the cross correlation output is zero, then the PN sequences are called orthogonal to each other. This is the critical property of the PN sequences to avoid interference. A PN sequence has good cross correlation property if the correlator output tends to zero for all the delays. It is not possible to have a perfect orthogonal PN sequence pair.

The orthogonal property of the PN codes makes the cross correlation between different PN codes almost negligible. This is why the data encrypted by one PN code appears as noise when encrypted by another PN code. Though the autocorrelation properties for the two sequences are very good, they are not orthogonal. This limitation restricts the performance of the communication system, and the chances of interference still exist. The average cross correlation outputs are smaller than the huge single 100% peak obtained in the case of perfect correlation. Due to this huge difference in magnitude for perfect correlation with the same PN code and the cross correlation with a different PN code, it can be unambiguously determined if there is a match or not.

Using example A.6, as shown in Figure A.22, if the result in receiver is not multiplied with the same PN code the input data is not recovered.

Figure A.22: Different PN code is used in the receiver

Example A.8

Verify that the PN code generated in Example A.4 satisfies the correlation property.

Solution

The PN code generated in Example A.4 is 1100101.
The PN codes are represented as NRZ bi-level sequences, where a 0 is represented as -1 and 1 represented by 1. Therefore, the present PN code will be represented as 1 1 -1 -1 1 -1 1. The autocorrelation property of the PN code is verified in Table A.4. In this case autocorrelation is calculated as number of disagreement minus number of agreement between each bit of the original PN code and the shifted version of that code.

The autocorrelation has a value of −1 for all except for when the exact PN code, without any phase shift, is applied to the correlator. In the case of a perfect match, the value of the correlator output is equal to the length of the code in this case 7 which mean that 100% agreement. Therefore, the PN code generated satisfies the autocorrelation property.

Original PN code	1 1 -1 -1 1 -1 1	Autocorrelation
Shift #1	1 1 1 -1 -1 1 -1	-1
Shift #2	-1 1 1 1 -1 -1 1	-1
Shift #3	1 -1 1 1 1 -1-1	-1
Shift #4	-1 1 -1 1 1 1 -1	-1
Shift #5	-1 -1 1 -1 1 1 1	-1
Shift #6	1 -1 -1 1 -1 1 1	-1
Shift #7	1 1 -1 -1 1 -1 1	7

Table A.4: Autocorrelation Property

A.18.4 Limitation of PN Codes

The PN code has the best autocorrelation properties. The autocorrelation of the PN code is two-valued. When there is some phase shift, the value is equal to −1. When there is an exact match the value of autocorrelation is equal to the length of the code. This is possible when the correlation is computed over a full period of PN sequence. In the practical spread spectrum systems, two-valued autocorrelation is not possible because they have very long code for data security.

In the IS-95 CDMA system, a mobile station searches through different PN codes sent from the nearest base station to lock with the strongest signal. Fifteen-stage PN code is used, which has 32,768 chips in a full PN sequence. It takes around 30 msecs delay to correlate an entire sequence to determine the success or failure of finding the correct PN sequence. This delay is called the *code acquisition time*.

Generally, partial correlation is used in situations where the code length is long. Partial correlation is very important in situations where the period of the PN sequences is much longer than the correlation time.

The limitation of the PN code is caused by its cross correlation value. Sometimes the value of the cross correlation of different PN codes is more than the threshold value. The threshold value is used to decide whether or not there is a perfect match. Therefore, when the cross correlation value is more than the threshold value, the cross correlation value is taken as a match, causing erroneous results. Several other codes are used to overcome these limitations.

A.19 Other Spreading Codes

Some other types of codes used for spread spectrum techniques are:

- Gold codes
- Kasami codes

A.19.1 Gold Codes

A set of PN code obtained by modulo -2 addition of two ML sequences is known as a Gold code. Gold code has a set of PN sequences of the same length. The period of ML sequence for n registers is N= $2^n - 1$. With a synchronous clocking, the two ML sequences are added chip-by-chip to get a new PN sequence. The two ML sequences maintain a same phase relationship because they are of same length. Therefore, the new generated sequence will have the same code length. A total of $2^n - 1$ new code can be generated from a pair of ML sequences. Along with the two base ML sequences, the total number of sequences in Gold code is $2^n + 1$. Figure A.23 shows a block diagram of gold code sequence generator.

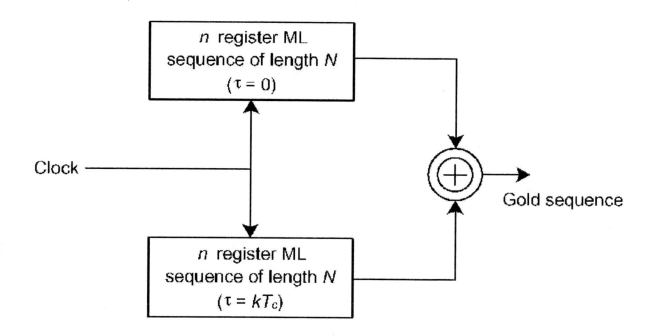

Figure A.23: Gold Sequence Generator

The resultant set of Gold codes is not of maximal length. The autocorrelation properties of the Gold code are poorer than that of maximum length PN sequences. $k\,T_c$ is the phase difference between two maximum length sequences. For different values of k, different codes are generated with the same length. Adding the two initial codes used for modulo -2 additions, 2n+1 code are generated. Figure A.21 shows the generation of Gold code using two PN sequence of different initial condition.

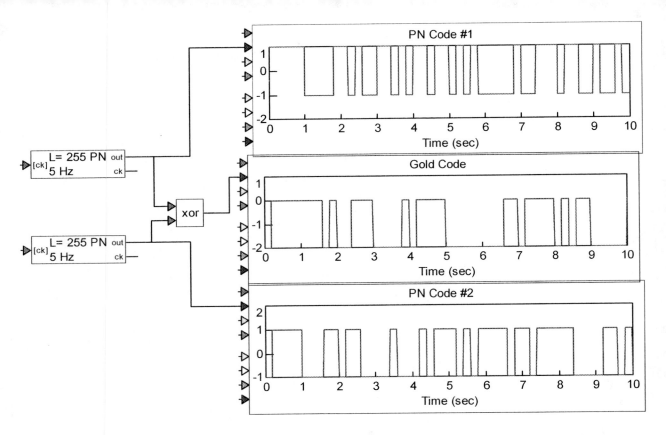

Figure A.24: Generation of Gold code using two PN sequence of different initial condition.

The autocorrelation of Gold code is not as good as ML sequence output. The cross correlation property of the Gold code is better than ML sequences. The improvement in the cross correlation properties of Gold code over ML code can be observed with careful selection of the Gold code.

Gold codes found in systems employing spread spectrum or code-division multiple access (CDMA) techniques. These systems are often used in communications equipment such as cellular telephones, global positioning systems (GPS).

Example A.9

How is the cross correlation property of the spreading codes useful in a spread spectrum receiver?

Solution

Cross correlation is the fundamental property on which the privacy of the message signal is maintained on a common channel in the spread spectrum signals. As seen table A.4 3 the values for cross correlation between different PN sequences are less compared to the values of autocorrelation. The received signal at a particular receiver is a combination of many message signals. If the combined signal has the desired signal, it can be recovered using the autocorrelation property of the spreading code. However, if an unintended receiver tried to tap the message signal using a different PN code, the corresponding despread data will appear as noise due to the very low cross correlation between the different spreading codes. The unintended receiver doesn't know the exact PN code used for the desired signal because of the huge volume of spreading codes available with variable lengths.

A.19.2 Kasami Codes

Kasami sequences are binary sequences of length 2^n where n is an even integer. Kasami sequences have good cross-correlation values. Kasami sequence generated by modulo-2 adding one ML code with a code obtained by decimating the ML code is known as Kasami Code.

Decimated code can be obtained as follows:

The process of generating a Kasami sequence starts by generating a maximum length sequence $N = 2^n - 1$ with n register. Maximum length sequences are periodic sequences that repeated periodically. Next we generate another sequence with the length $2^{n/2}+1$. This results the decimated sequence. Kasami sequences are formed by adding the modulo-2 addition of these two sequences. This set has $2^{n/2}$ different sequences. The number of sequences in Kasami code is less than the number of sequences in Gold code for a period of N.

Kasami codes have poor autocorrelation properties compared to maximum length sequences.

By comparing the cross correlations of the maximum length sequences, Gold codes, and Kasami codes, it is clear that the Kasami codes have good cross correlation properties. Although Kasami codes perform better than Gold codes, the number of Gold sequences for period N is more than the number of Kasami codes. This has limitation on Kasami codes if more sequences are required with fixed code length.

A.20 Examples of Spread Spectrum System

In this topic, you will look at one of the popular systems employing spread spectrum techniques. The Global Positioning System (GPS) uses spread spectrum techniques for finding the accurate position of the user's receiver specified by the latitude, longitude, and altitude of the user.

A.20.1 Global Positioning System

The Global Positioning System (GPS) [10] is a space-based global navigation satellite system (GNSS) that provides location and time information in all weather, anywhere on or near the Earth, where there is an unobstructed line of sight to four or more GPS satellites. It is maintained by the United States government and is freely accessible by anyone with a GPS receiver with some technical limitations which are only removed for military users. GPS was created by the U.S. Department of Defense (USDOD) and was originally run with 24 satellites. It became fully operational in 1994.

As of March 2008 there are 31 actively broadcasting satellites in the GPS constellation, and two older, retired from active service satellites kept in the constellation as orbital spares. The additional satellites improve the precision of GPS receiver calculations by providing redundant measurements. With the increased number of satellites, the constellation was changed to a non-uniform arrangement. Such arrangement improves reliability and availability of the system, relative to a uniform system, when multiple satellites fail. About nine satellites are visible from any point on the ground at any one time. Figure A.25 shows the orbital pattern of GPS satellite [13]. These satellites are in medium earth orbit approximately at altitude of 20,200 (12,600 mi) rotating in six orbit planes.

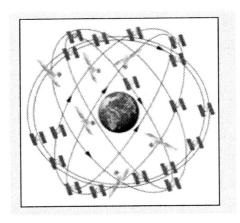

Figure A.25 Orbital pattern of GPS Satellite [13]

The GPS is a satellite-type spread spectrum system that makes use of a constellation of 31 satellites. Each of these satellites is in a 12-hour orbit.

The GPS system uses the direct-sequence spread spectrum technique for ranging. Spread spectrum systems can be used for high-resolution ranging by tracking the delay between the transmitter and the receiver. If the transmission delay is known, then the range from the transmitter to the receiver can be determined. In the GPS, the exact location of users can be determined by measuring their range from four GPS satellites whose positions are accurately known. Each satellite maintains a highly accurate clock, along with the data on the orbits of all satellites. All the satellite clocks are synchronized through a ground station in California. Each satellite knows the position of all the other GPS satellites at any time instant.

Figure A.26 shows GPS block diagram of the modulator configuration

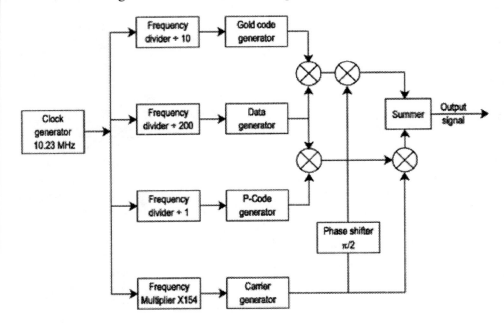

Figure A.26: GPS Block Diagram of Modulator Configuration

The modulator is a quadrature modulator. A master clock of 10.23 MHz is used to drive the system. The Gold code (short code of 1,023 chips) transmitted by each satellite is unique. The long P-code, however, is common to all the satellites. The Gold code is clocked at about 1.023 MHz and spreads the 50-bps data signal before being BPSK-modulated by the quadrature carrier at 1575 MHz. The other component is the data signal spread by the long P-code at a frequency of 10.23 MHz and then BPSK-modulated by the carrier signal. The final resulting signal is the summation of these two spread BPSK-modulated waveforms, resulting in QPSK modulation.

The central idea behind the working of the GPS is to transmit the spread spectrum signals, which allow range measurement, from a known satellite location. With knowledge of the satellite location and the distance to the satellite, the user location can be tracked on a sphere whose radius is the distance from the satellite. As the measurements from other satellites are taken into consideration, similar spheres will result, and finally the position of the user is determined from the intersections of all the spheres.

The position of the user can be determined based on the Gold code or the long P-code.
A long P-code makes a more accurate measurement, as the chip rate is higher. After synchronization, the user records the time delay between the transmission and reception of the Gold code. Therefore, the time of arrival for the Gold code from all four satellites is recorded. Based on the time of arrival, the pseudo-ranges of the receiver from all four satellites are calculated, and, when combined, these give the final latitude, longitude, and altitude information of the user.

There are other systems that employ spread spectrum techniques either in their entirety or in principle. Some of them are already operational, whereas others are still in the final stages of development. Since the use of spread spectrum techniques for some of these systems is highly classified, the information available is very limited. The different practical systems that employ spread spectrum techniques are:

- Tracking and Data Relay Satellite System (TDRSS)
- User transponder system
- Space shuttle spectrum despreader system
- Joint Tactical Information Distribution System (JTIDS)
- Avionics systems such as ARC-50 and Have Quick

With the advent of spread spectrum CDMA systems, the applications of spread spectrum have moved into commercial cellular communication as well.

A.21 Summary

- The frequency domain representation of a time domain signal is called the spectrum of the signal.
- Spread spectrum refers to bandwidth expansion of the narrow band data signal by a high bandwidth spreading code.
- The processing gain is the ratio of the spreading code chip rate to the digital signal data rate.
- The process gain of a spread spectrum system is the measure of the difference of performance with and without spread spectrum technique.
- Despreading is done at the baseband DSSS system by directly multiplying the received signal with the synchronized copy of the PN code used at the transmitter.
- Jamming and LPI are common communication problems that cannot be solved using traditional digital modulation techniques.
- Spread spectrum technique reduces the effect of jamming by spreading the jammer signal across the whole bandwidth of the spread spectrum signal.
- Spread spectrum systems have been primarily used for antijamming purposes in military applications.
- LPI systems are possible using spread spectrum techniques because the energy density of the data signal is reduced by spreading.
- Spread spectrum communication block is similar to a generic digital communication block, except for a spreading code generator.
- Spread spectrum technique offers high resolution ranging in RADAR applications. It does not offer any additional advantages when used in AWGN environments.
- PN code is so called due to its random and noise-like properties but is deterministic.
- Linear feedback shift registers are used for the generation of maximal length sequences.
- Correlation properties of the PN code are suitable to the code for spread spectrum applications.
- Autocorrelation of the PN code results in a single major peak whose amplitude is equal to the length of the code. This occurs for a perfect match without any phase shift in the code.
- Long delay times, poor partial autocorrelation properties, and high cross correlation make the PN code not suitable for practical applications.
- Gold and Kasami codes are also used as spreading code in spread spectrum systems.
- Gold codes are obtained by shifting and modulo-2 summing two maximal length sequences. Kasami codes are obtained by modulo-2 summing a maximal length sequence and its decimation code.

Homework Exercises

1. Why is the time hopping named as such?

2. What is the major limitation of the time-hopping spread spectrum techniques?

3. How do spread spectrum techniques provide energy density reduction?

4. Calculate the process gain of a spread spectrum system for which the data rate of the digital signal is 10 KHz, and the chip rate is 10 MHz. (Assume data bandwidth and spread spectrum bandwidth to be equal to the data rate and chip rate, respectively.)

5. How are multiple accesses possible with spread spectrum techniques if all the users use the same channel all the time?

6. Does expansion in bandwidth help reduce white noise for an AWGN channel? Why?

7. Design the SSRG LFSR PN code generator circuit for a primitive polynomial: $1 + X^3 + X^4$.

8. Compute the PN code that is generated by SSRG designed in question 7 if the initial values of the shift registers are [1 1 1 0].

9. Use the same primitive polynomial used for SSRG to design the MSRG.

10. Verify the shift-and-add property of the PN codes using the PN code generated in the previous two examples.

11. What property of PN code makes them suitable for use in spread spectrum communication?

12. Calculate the autocorrelation of the PN code: 1001011.

13. Calculate the cross correlation of the following two PN codes:
    PN1= 1001011   PN2= 1101001

14. Use the following PN codes to generate a Gold code sequence.
    PN1 = −1 −1 −1 1 1 1 −1 1 1 −1 −1 1 −1 1 −1   PN2 = −1 1 1 1 −1 −1 −1 −1 1 −1 1 1 −1 −1 1

15. Calculate the autocorrelation for the above Gold code.

References

1. Cooper, George R. and Clare D. Mcgillem. 1986. *Modern Communications and Spread Spectrum*. McGraw-Hill.
2. Dixon, Robert C. 1994. *Spread Spectrum with Commercial Applications*. John Wiley & Sons, Inc.
3. Lee, Jhong Sam and Leonard E. Miller. 1998. *CDMA Systems Engineering Handbook*. Boston: Artech House.
4. Proakis, John G. 2001. *Digital Communications*. Boston: McGraw-Hill.
5. Sklar, Bernard. 2001. *Digital Communications: Fundamentals and Applications*. Englewood Cliffs, NJ: Prentice Hall.
6. Wade, Graham. 2000. *Coding Techniques: An Introduction to Compression and Error Control*. Boston: Artech House.
7. Ziemer, Rodger E. and Roger L. Peterson. 2001. *Introduction to Digital Communication*. Prentice Hall.
8. Ziemer, Rodger E. and Roger L. Peterson. 1985. *Digital Communication and Spread Spectrum Systems*. New York: Macmillan.
9. http://www.sew-lexicon.com/gloss_e.htm
10. http://www.wikipedia.org/wiki/Jamming
11. http://www.sss-mag.com/shistory.html
12. http://www.newwaveinstruments.com/resources/glossary.htm
13. http://www.GPS.Gov/Multimedia/image

Appendix: Study of Jamming Signal on Spread Spectrum Techniques

In this simulation with VisSim a jamming signal is generated around the same spectrum of the input data. The jamming signal is added to the spread spectrum of the modulated signal. The sum is transmitted through the channel.
In the receiver the signal is demodulated with the same PN code. Through a decision process the data is recovered with no error.

Index

IF; *See* Intermediate frequency (IF)

ILD; *See* Injection laser diode (ILD)

Improved mobile telephone services (IMTS), 466–467, 468

Impulse noise, 422–423

IMTS; *See* Improved mobile telephone services (IMTS)

In-band signaling, 390

Index profile, 19–20

Information, 48

Information capacity, 49–50

Information density, 87

Information frame, 225–228

Information theory, 49

Infrared absorption, 25

Infrared light-emitting diode (LED), 7, 33–39
Burrus etched-well surface-emitting, 35
edge-emitting, 35
heterojunction, 34–35
homojunction, 34, **34**
and ILD, 35–39

Injection laser diode (ILD), 7

Institute of Electrical and Electronics Engineers (IEEE), 115–116; *See also* IEEE

Insufficient bandwidth, and ISI, 311–312

Integrated services digital network (ISDN), 244–251, 516
architecture, 246–247
broadband (BISDN), 249–251
conceptual view, 245
evolution of, 244–245
objectives, 246
principles of, 244
system connections and interface units, 247–249, 248

Intelsat I, 563

Interdigit time, 392

Interface parameters, 419

Interference, 473–476
adjacent-channel, 475–476
cochannel, 474–475

Interim Standard (IS); *See* IS-41 standard; IS-54 standard

International Standards Organization (ISO), 114

International Telecommunications Union (ITU), 114–115

Internet, 110

Internet Activities Board (IAB), 116

Internet Architecture Board, 116

Internet Engineering Task Force (IETF), 116

Internet layer, 143

Internet Research Task Force (IRTF), 117

Interoffice exchange system, **445**

Interoffice trunks, 445–447

Intersymbol interference (ISI), 310–312
degradation mathematical expression, 313
primary causes of, 311–312

Intranet, 110

Intraoffice call, 444, 445, **447**

Intraswitch call, 444

Ion resonance absorption, 25

Iridium satellite system, 520–523
frequency plan and modulation, 522–523
satellite constellation, 521–522
system layout, 521

IRTF; *See* Internet Research Task Force (IRTF)

IS-41 standard, 482

IS-54 standard, 501

IS-95 standard, 509–515
code-division multiple accessing (CDMA), 510–515

IS-136.2 standard, 501–504

ISDN; *See* Integrated services digital network (ISDN)

ISI; *See* Intersymbol interference (ISI)

ISO; *See* International Standards Organization (ISO)

ISO 3309, 235–236

ITU; *See* International Telecommunications Union (ITU)

ITU-T modems recommendations, 202–206
V.29, 202
V.32, 202
V.32 (V.fast), 206
V.32bis and V.32terbo, 202, 204–205
V.33, 205
V.34+, 206
V.42 and V.42bis, 206
V.90, 206
V.92, 206

ITU-T X series standards, **243**

Jett, E.K., 467

Kao, K.C., 3

Kapany, N.S., 2

Kepler's law, 564–565
mathematical expression for, 564–565

Key pulse (KP), 391

KP; *See* Key pulse (KP)

LAC; *See* Local exchange carriers (LAC)

Lamm, H., 2

LAPB; *See* Link Access Procedure Balanced (LAPB)

Laser, 3, 41–42
characteristics of, 42
construction of, 42, **43**
gas, 42
liquid, 42
semiconductor, 42
solid, 42
types of, 42

LATA; *See* Local Access and Transport Area (LATA)

Lateral displacement, 31

LCI; *See* Logical channel identifier (LCI)

LCU; *See* Line control unit (LCU)

Least significant bit, 283

LED; *See* Infrared light-emitting diode (LED)

Length field, 269

LEO; *See* Low earth orbit (LEO)

Level-at-a-time coding, 292

Light detectors, 39–41
characteristics of, 41
photoelectric effect, 39–40
PIN diodes, 39–40

Light intensity, 10

Light propagation, 9–18

Light sensitivity, 41

Light sources, 32–33

Limits of visibility, and satellite communication, 577

Linear bus, 136

Linear codes, 289

Linear PCM codes, 289–290
versus nonlinear, 290–291

Linear predictive coders, 304

Linear quantizer, 285

Line conditioning, 412
C-type, 412–417
D-type, 417–419

Line control unit (LCU), 170–180

Line discipline, 210–213
ENQ/ACK, 210–213, **212**
error control, 215–216
flow control, 214–215
poll/select, 211–213

Line speed
mathematical expression for, 304
pulse code modulation (PCM), 304–305

Line-of-sight path characteristics, 547–551

Link Access Procedure Balanced (LAPB), 240–241

Link budget, and satellite communication, 596–600

Link equations, satellite system, 595

Liquid lasers, 42

LLC; *See* Logical control link (LLC)

LNP; *See* Local number portability (LNP)

Loading coil, 404

Local Access and Transport Area (LATA), 459–460

Local area network (LAN), 137–138, 255–261
access control methodologies, 260–261
baseband transmission format, 259
broadband transmission format, 260
building backbone, 140
bus topology, 258–259
campus backbone, 141–142
carrier sense, multiple access with collision detect (CSMA/CD), 259, 260, 261
enterprise networks, 142
global area network (GAN), 140
metropolitan area network (MAN), 138–139
ring topology, 259
star topology, 257
system considerations, 257–259
token passing, 260, 261